Sidney V.
1965

By the Same Author

SUGAR IN THE AIR (1937)
ASLEEP IN THE AFTERNOON (1939)
DAWN IN ANDROMEDA (1956)

THE ADVANCE OF THE FUNGI

by

E. C. LARGE

DOVER PUBLICATIONS, INC.
NEW YORK

This new Dover edition, first published in 1962, is an unabridged and corrected republication of the work first published by Jonathan Cape Limited in 1940.

This edition is published by special arrangement with Jonathan Cape Limited and is for sale only in the United States, its dependencies and the Philippine Islands.

Manufactured in the United States of America

DOVER PUBLICATIONS, INC.
180 Varick Street
New York 14, N. Y.

CONTENTS

ACKNOWLEDGMENTS

IN the bibliography, which will be found at the end, I have included full particulars of some five hundred of the principal scientific papers, books, and other published writings of the past and present upon which this history is based. The titles of the various publications are indicative of the way in which a science has grown, and with this in mind I have arranged the references for each chapter in chronological order, noted translations into English of books and papers in other languages, and given the starting dates of some of the periodicals which have played a leading part in the story, with the recognized (World List) abbreviations for the names of them. Each of the historic illustrations of the fungi reproduced in the text is subscribed with the author's name and date of first publication. Where the word 'after' appears in the subscript it means that the figure is not a direct mechanical reproduction, but a line-copy that I have made with the assistance of a photograph. The figures without subscript are original.

I am indebted to those in charge of the libraries of the Royal Botanic Gardens at Kew, the Imperial Mycological Institute, the British Museum, the Science Museum, the Linnean, Chemical, and Royal Horticultural Societies, the Patent Office and the Ministry of Agriculture, for unfailing help in my search of the literature, and also to Dr. J. Caldwell, Dr. G. H. Pethybridge and Dr. R. N. Salaman, for the loan of numerous books and papers.

I thank my old friend Dr. E. S. Gyngell for the line drawings of oats in flower and of Wart Disease (Figs. 45 and 55); Dr. W. A. R. Dillon Weston for the original study of Apple Scab (Fig. 48); Dr. R. N. Salaman for permission to photograph the Blight-resistant potato plants (Plate VI); the Controller of H.M. Stationery Office for permission to reproduce the illustration of Potato Leaf Roll from the Ministry of Agriculture and Fisheries' Advisory Leaflet No. 278 (Plate V, *c*); and the Royal Dublin Society for permission to reproduce Figs. 53 and 54.

Finally I would express my warmest thanks to both Dr. G. H. Pethybridge, late Mycologist to the Ministry of Agriculture and Fisheries, and Dr. G. R. Bisby, formerly Professor of Plant Pathology at Manitoba University, for their very great kindness in reading the whole book in typescript and giving me their unstinted help in the work of correction before going to press.

September 1940 E. C. LARGE

Trace Science then, with Modesty thy guide;
First strip off all her equipage of Pride;
Deduct what is but Vanity, or Dress,
Or Learning's Luxury, or Idleness;
Or tricks to show the stretch of human brain,
Mere curious pleasure, or ingenious pain;
Expunge the whole, or lop th' excrescent parts
Of all our vices have created Arts;
Then see how little the remaining sum,
Which serv'd the past, and must the times to come!

POPE, *Essay on Man*, Epistle II, 1733

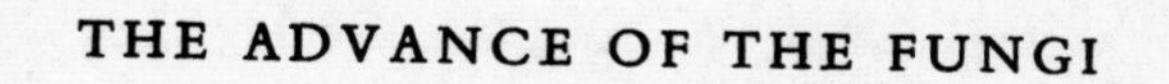
THE ADVANCE OF THE FUNGI

CHAPTER I

THE POTATO MURRAIN

'A FATAL malady has broken out amongst the potato crop. On all sides we hear of the destruction. In Belgium the fields are said to have been completely desolated. There is hardly a sound sample in Covent Garden Market.' So began the first warning of a calamity, in the editorial columns of *The Gardeners' Chronicle and Agricultural Gazette*, on August 23rd, 1845. The potatoes had suffered from diseases in the past: from 'Scab', from a malady called the 'Curl', from drought, and from too much rain in bad seasons, but nothing quite so destructive as this new murrain had ever been seen before. It struck down the growing plants like frost in summer. It spread faster than the cholera amongst men. *The Gardeners' Chronicle*, then under the very distinguished editorship of Dr. John Lindley, had published the first report of the appearance of the disease in England – a letter from Dr. Bell Salter in the Isle of Wight – the week before, and now Dr. Lindley was sounding the alarm. His editorial went on: '. . . the disease consists in a gradual decay of the leaves and stem, which become a putrid mass, and the tubers are affected by degrees in a similar way. The first obvious sign is the appearance on the edge of the leaf of a black spot which gradually spreads; the gangrene then attacks the haulms, and in a few days the latter are decayed, emitting a peculiar and rather offensive odour. When the attack is severe the tubers also decay.'

There was little optimism in Dr. Lindley's words; he saw that if this mysterious murrain continued to spread amongst the potatoes, an important part of the country's food supplies for the coming winter would be lost. And he said: 'As to cure for this distemper there is none. One of our correspondents is already angry with us for not telling the public how to stop it; but he ought to consider that Man has no power to arrest the dispensations of Providence. We are visited by a great calamity which we must bear.'

As the weeks went on, into September, the reports of the spread of the disease, from Poland, Germany, Belgium, France, and from all over England except a few districts in the north, proved that Dr. Lindley's fears were not exaggerated. Every kind of potato was attacked: the Black Scotch, the Bread Fruit, the Jersey Blues . . . When the potatoes were dug from the ground they were found marked with the dark patches, symptomatic of the disease. The colour of these patches was that of contused flesh, its tints were likened to those accompanying a black eye. Potatoes left on the floor of a barn for a week were found worse than when they were lifted. The disease was spreading amongst the potatoes in the ground and in store, and it was thought that every tuber, no matter how slightly affected, would be lost. A kind of mouldiness which the Rev. M. J. Berkeley had observed to appear on the diseased tubers would add greatly to the mischief by hastening decay.

It was apparent that the peculiar changes of weather which had occurred during the summer of 1845 had much to do with the outbreak and the spread of the Potato Murrain. The season had been very favourable for planting and hoeing, and the appearance of the crops was as promising as could be wished up to the beginning of July. The weather was then hot and dry, the temperature 1½ degrees to 4½ degrees above the average for the previous nineteen years. 'In short it was beautiful haymaking weather', wrote a Mr. F. J. Graham – in a prize essay on the history of the murrain, published in the *Journal of the Royal Agricultural Society* a little later – 'it then suddenly changed to the most extraordinary contrast that I ever witnessed in this fickle climate, the atmosphere being for upwards of three weeks one continued gloom, the sun scarcely ever visible during the time, with a succession of most chilling rains and some fog, and for six weeks the temperature was from 1½ degrees to 7 degrees *below* the average for the past nineteen years.'

Dr. Lindley's theory was that as a result of such changes in the weather the potato plants had become in some way overladen with water; they had been growing away fast and furiously during the good weather, then when the fogs and the rain came they absorbed moisture with avidity, and in the absence of sunshine transpiration was checked, the plants had been unable to get rid of the excess of water in their usual way, and so they had contracted a kind of dropsy and wet putrefaction had set in. The Rev. M. J. Berkeley, 'a gentleman eminent above all other naturalists of the United Kingdom in his knowledge of the habits of fungi', was of contrary opinion. He had at once connected the potato disease with the prevalence of a kind of mould on the affected tissues, but in Dr. Lindley's view, the eminent Mr. Berkeley, preoccupied with toadstools and mushrooms and moulds and mildews, all the greater and the lesser fungi, was attaching far too much importance to a little growth of mould on the diseased potato plants. It was only to be expected that 'as soon as living matter lost its force, as soon as diminishing vitality took the place of the customary vigour, all sorts of parasites would acquire power and contend for its destruction. It was so with all plants, and all animals, even man himself. First came feebleness, next incipient decay, then sprang up myriads of creatures whose life could only be maintained by the decomposing bodies of their neighbours. Cold and wet, acting upon the potato when it was enervated by excessive and sudden growth would cause a rapid diminution of vitality; portions would die and decay, and so prepare the field in which mouldiness could establish itself. And thus an evil, in itself too great, would be infinitely increased'.

The Rev. M. J. Berkeley agreed that there was much weight to John Lindley's argument; he advanced his own contrary views with a proper reservation of philosophic doubt, but in fact he had made up his mind and he was not a man to be shaken in his convictions. He not only insisted that the growth of mould on the potato plants was a highly significant phenomenon, but as soon as he had seen the diseased foliage himself, in his parish, near King's Cliffe in Northamptonshire, he put forward the revolutionary theory that the mould might be the cause and not the consequence of the Potato Murrain.

There was, in Paris, an old surgeon of Napoleon's armies, by name Dr. Montagne, with whom the Rev. M. J. Berkeley was in frequent correspondence. On his return from the wars, Dr. Montagne had decided to devote the rest of his life to the peaceful labour of searching out and describing the cryptogamic flora of France. From Dr. Montagne, Berkeley received specimens and sketches of the fungus found associated with the Potato Disease across the Channel. The fringes of mould on the leaves had exactly the same appearance, when examined under the microscope, as those on potato leaves from fields in Northamptonshire. There was the same mould on the diseased potatoes themselves, and though Berkeley had never seen this particular species of mould before, it did resemble in certain respects a mould that he had seen growing on onions and shallots. It also appeared to belong to the same natural order as the fungus which was associated with a very serious disease of silkworms in France and Lombardy. It was a lowly vegetable organism, a minute fungus of the genus Botrytis.

Berkeley had to admit that this particular species of Botrytis, now to be found on the stricken potatoes, was new to science, and it was difficult to see why it should suddenly make its appearance, throughout Europe, in the year 1845. All Berkeley could suggest was that now that the botanists knew what to look for, they would probably find that the same fungus had been flourishing for ages on potatoes in some part of the New World, where the weather conditions were normally the same as they had been in Europe during the unusual summer of 1845. The Potato Murrain, insisted the Rev. M. J. Berkeley, was due to the growth of this specific fungus, and no other, as a parasite on the potato plants. The humid, grey and wet weather, *might* have caused the living tissues of the plants to become charged with too much water, though such a thing did not appear to him very likely. It was much more probable that the weather simply favoured the spread of the moisture-loving fungus. In one respect only did the Rev. Mr. Berkeley agree with Dr. Lindley: as the development of the fungus depended entirely upon the weather, it would doubtless be impossible to find a remedy.

Thus began an argument between two learned men, each firm in his own conviction and with weight of reason to support it, on an issue that was in fact much deeper than that of attributing the Potato Murrain to its most probable cause. The issue was the establishment or the rejection of a new conception of the nature of Disease, not only in plants, but ultimately in all living things. A grand philosophical controversy was beginning, in which nearly every scientist or natural philosopher in the world would soon be taking sides. In advancing the hypothesis that a living parasitic organism on the potato foliage was the cause and not the consequence of the Potato Disease the Rev. M. J. Berkeley was anticipating the germ theory of Pasteur by nearly a quarter of a century.

There was something rousing about those intellectual passages at arms between Berkeley and John Lindley in the columns of *The Gardeners' Chronicle* of 1845 and 1846. John Lindley was not only a man of scientific attainment, professor of botany at University College in London; he was experienced in the practical and commercial cultivation of plants, and he was one of the best fighting journalists in the country. He knew how to give forceful expression to his own views and to defend them against all comers, but as an editor he held the scales fairly. He gave the fullest space and the weightiest consideration to every contribution from the pen of the Rev. M. J. Berkeley, and in addition he published a multitude of observations and speculations from other correspondents, anything and everything that might throw light on the cause and nature of the Potato Murrain. Some of the speculations then seemed sensible and some seemed wild. But they should stand recorded, for future workers to read, and to interpret for themselves in the light of later discoveries. John Lindley was not mistaken in his policy; amongst all the then unrelated facts, the gropings, shrewd guesses and confused notions, there were nearly all the clues.

It seemed a wild notion that a mere mould could be the cause of disease in a living plant. And in truth Berkeley could bring forward little enough of the evidence that would be required for rigorous proof of his contention. It was one thing to state that the mould caused the disease and quite another to show how it could do so. Even if it were established that the mould always accompanied the rotting and decay, it would be necessary to *demonstrate* which came first. Until that was done the 'fungal hypothesis' would be a mere notion, unsupported by proof. And which came first, the mould or the decay, the fungus or the disease, was not altogether unlike the ancient conundrum about the chicken and the egg. When it came to argument there was much to be said in favour of the precedence of debility or decay. Was it not common knowledge that the moulds and mildews, like their larger relatives the toadstools and the mushrooms, were generally to be found growing on decaying matter: on rotting horse manure, or dead wood, or stale bread, or the humus in the soil? They were part of Nature's provision for hastening the decomposition of dead organic matter, to render it available for use over again. And in all literature and fable the fungi were quite as much symbolic of pre-existent mortification, as of damp, dark, poison, and miscellaneous principles of evil. It was difficult to believe that they could establish themselves on a healthy green leaf, or on any host that was defended by its own internal forces of vigour and life.

The way in which moulds and mildews sprang up, as it were overnight, and the manner of their reproduction, was also highly mysterious. Although that ingenious Italian, Felice Fontana, had examined the Rust on the wheat under a microscope, as long ago as 1767, and recognized it as a minute vegetable with bodies resembling seeds; and although by 1807 Bénédict Prévost in France had actually seen the spores of the Bunt fungus on the wheat germinating like seeds in water, it was still commonly believed that small fungi could be produced in decaying matter by spontaneous generation. It seemed reasonable that such trifling growths could well be brought into being by the heat of putrefaction or the ambient atmosphere without the help of any seminal principle. Men of Dr. Lindley's intellectual calibre had long since rejected the notion of spontaneous generation in its cruder forms: they did not believe that mice could be produced by enclosing a piece of cheese and some old rags in a hat box, or that blow-flies were generated by bad meat; but they were perpetuating the idea, all unconsciously, in attributing the growth of living moulds so readily to fermentative processes of decay caused by pre-existent Disease. Since the time of Lavoisier fermentation had been regarded as a purely chemical process, the decomposition of unstable azotic — or nitrogenous — compounds in the organic material. If living fungi came into being as a result of purely chemical processes, that was spontaneous generation. All kinds of phenomena were being attributed to fermentation, or putrefaction, or decay, in cheerful ignorance of the fact that practically nothing was then known of the nature of fermentative processes themselves.

As Berkeley was very well aware, the Rust and Bunt of the wheat, which were certainly diseases of that plant, were already regarded by many of the greatest European botanists – Corda, Fries, Léveillé, De Candolle amongst others – simply as growths of small fungi. It was quite customary to speak, somewhat loosely, of these particular fungi as the *cause* of the Rust and the Bunt. The damage they did in no way resembled the new rotting away of the potato foliage and tubers. But if small fungi growing on the wheat could be said to cause diseases of the wheat, it was only putting two and two together, to say that another fungus found growing on the potato might be the cause of the new Potato Disease.

The fungal nature of the Rust and the Bunt was, however, by no means universally admitted, even by those few botanists who concerned themselves with the diseases of plants. Franz Unger of Vienna, another army surgeon, and one of the first to maintain a garden of plant diseases for his own instruction and pleasure, had published a very famous work called *Die Exantheme der Pflanzen*, in 1833. He contended that the growths which other botanists took to be small fungi on the leaves of plants were mere 'exanthemata', or outgrowths from the plants themselves, analagous to those found in eruptive diseases of animals. In consequence of some morbid condition, the plants came out in pustules, or grew fringes of unhealthy down on their leaves and began sporulating. As these outgrowths had organized vegetative forms, he did admit that they might have some individuality, but at most they were 'endophytes', little plants which had their origin *within* their hosts. Unger did not observe the spawn threads winding about among the leaf cells, or he might have been of a different opinion.

Unger's notions were current and influential even amongst the natural philosophers of 1845; while in the world at large the residues of even stranger beliefs were still extant. An old notion of the origin of mildew, prevalent in Shakespeare's time, was that, in damp localities, sticky or honey-like principles were exhaled from the surface of the earth, to be chilled at night, and to settle on plants as a kind of honey-dew. Hence one of the much-disputed derivations of the word 'mildew' by way of the German '*Mehltau*' or 'meal-dew' from the Gothic '*milip*' for honey, plus '*tau*' or 'dew'. The honey-dew on the plants was supposed to be congealed and corrupted by the subsequent heat of the sun, thus causing disease. As growths of mildew were very common in low-lying, damp localities, such as those in the neighbourhood of water-mills, the word was often written 'Mill-dew'.

In the tacit assumption that was being made by so many people, John Lindley included, that the little Botrytis fungus was growing on the potato plants only in consequence of some antecedent putrefaction, there was much that dated back to the ideas of that grand old early microscopist, Robert Hooke, in his *Micrographia* of 1667. Hooke was the first man ever to describe the appearance under the compound microscope of a fungus growth on leaves. With the newly invented and marvellous instrument, which he had made with his own hands, Hooke gazed in awe at many things in an undiscovered world. He described what he saw, and set down all his thoughts about his observations, whether others might think them valid, or dismiss them as wrong. He said: 'I have produced nothing here to bind the reader's understanding to an implicit consent.' He hazarded that 'the blue and white and several kinds of hairy spots, which are observable on different kinds of putrify'd bodies' (including decayed leaves of plants) 'are all of them nothing else but several kinds of small and variously-figured mushrooms, which from convenient materials in those putrefying bodies, are by the concurrent heat of the air, excited to a certain kind of vegetation'. He had been looking then at a blue mould on some old leather. But he also examined some Damask-rose leaves which were speckled with yellow stains, and on the underside of them he saw 'yellow hillocks of gummous substance marked with black spots'. Through his microscope he saw in those hillocks 'multitudes of black cases or bodies like seed cobs'. He saw what he took to be the growth of a minute vegetable, and he ascribed its generation to the action of some gummous or honey-like Mill-dew, which, coming upon the leaves, had caused them to putrefy. He supposed that under the influence of the putrefaction a living part of the rose leaves had gone to the making of the smaller plants he saw. 'So, though the seminal principles from which this minute plant on rose leaves did spring, were, before the corruption caused by the Mill-dew, a component part of the leaf on which it grew, and did serve as a coagent in the production of it, yet might it be so consummate, as to produce a seed which might have the power to propagating the same species.' In other words, leaf organs of the Damask rose had taken a creative initiative in the presence of decay and grown into little mushrooms. The ever-watchful and hard-worked Almighty had blessed this enterprise, and given seeds to the little mushrooms by which they might reproduce themselves, independently of the whim of the rose.

The doctrine of 'heterogenesis' did not take quite so picturesque a form in 1845, but it was inherent in the notions of those who thought that Berkeley's 'fungal hypothesis' was fantastic.

The speculations of natural philosophers about the cause of the Potato Murrain were highly interesting and important, but they sank to triviality before the practical necessity of saving all that could be saved of the year's potato crop, and of conserving seed for the coming season. Nothing was known of the course that the disease would take; the potatoes were rotting in the ground – not everywhere, but in a pestilence so universal why should any be spared? It was suggested that the rot might be caused by static electricity – generated in the atmosphere by the issuing puffs of smoke and steam from the hundreds of railway locomotives that had recently come into use, and for all that was surely known it might equally well be due, as others supposed, to mortiferous vapours or 'miasmas' rising from blind volcanoes in the interior of the earth. Should the potatoes be left in the soil, or dug up, or steeped in preservatives and dried, or exposed to the light, or kept in the dark? Nobody knew.

And then also, Disease was Disease. The Potato Murrain and the cholera were both diseases. To eat the blighted potatoes, however little sign they might show of infection, would perhaps cause cholera in man, and other distempers in beasts. Two thousand tons of potatoes shipped sound from Hull were rotten before they arrived in Belgium. At Erfurt in Germany an outbreak of dysentery was attributed to the bad potatoes. In Ghent market potatoes were seized by the authorities because of the danger of cholera. Poland was already threatened with famine, and there was a report – subsequently denied – that the Prussian army had been called upon to keep the starving people out of Prussian territory. The diseased potatoes might be as poisonous as ergoted rye; and the suffering *that* had caused amongst the peasants of Burgundy and Lorraine in 1816 was not forgotten. It was a fungus, *Claviceps purpurea*, which blackened and elongated the kernels of the rye in wet seasons; when hunger drove peasants to eat bread made from this bad rye, a terrible form of gangrene was the result. Ergot, through its constrictive action on blood vessels, not only caused abortion in women, it cut off the blood supply to the extremities of the body; hands and feet became devoid of sensation and then rotted most horribly away. In the progress of the ergot gangrene whole limbs fell off at the joints, before the shapeless trunk was released from its torments.

There was a certain heroism in the action of a Monsieur Bonjean of Chambéry, in undertaking to live for three whole days on potatoes blighted by the new murrain. He ate each day eight pounds of partially diseased potatoes and drank eight ounces of the water in which wholly putrid potatoes had been boiled. The smell of the infusion was abominable and the taste nauseous, but he suffered no ill effects, save indigestion and 'a disagreeable heat oppressing the chest'. The experiment of eating the blighted potatoes was made of necessity by the labouring classes, without any gratifying limelight for risks undertaken in the cause of science, and it was soon established that the undecayed portions of the blighted potatoes were wholesome enough. Measures were required to arrest the rot in the tubers or to utilize what was good of them in time. It was proposed that they should be pounded or grated to a pulp and washed with water to extract the grains of starch or potato flour, leaving the fibrous material and brown decayed residue for feeding to the pigs. The starch, or farina, could be baked into bread, and although its extraction was admittedly troublesome, the labouring classes would have a way of providing themselves, by their own industry, with adequate food for the lean time that was coming. In England, the Poor Law Institutions could be used as factories for extracting the potato starch; the labour involved was very suitable for the moral rehabilitation of paupers, and it would cost nothing.

On September 13th there was another dramatic paragraph in *The Gardeners' Chronicle*:

'We stop the Press, with very great regret, to announce that the Potato Murrain has unequivocally declared itself in Ireland. The crops about Dublin are suddenly perishing. The conversion of potatoes into flour, by the process described by Mr. Bodington in this issue becomes of the first national importance; for where will *Ireland* be, in the event of a universal potato rot?'

Where indeed? Although there was dire poverty in England, and the paupers in Andover workhouse had been reduced to eating the marrow and gristle of green horse-bones that they had been set to break up for manure; although the failure of the potato crop in England would bring gaunt enough distress, it was nevertheless true that the poorest labourer in England lived on oat gruel and bread as well as potatoes. The cereal crops had not failed. In Ireland the cottiers lived almost exclusively on potatoes. If the Potato Murrain spread through the small-holdings of Ireland there would be millions of men, women, and children, who would not merely suffer acute privation, but who would starve to death.

John Lindley had good reason to stop the press. The news would shock those readers who had any imagination or humanitarian feeling; but it was more serious than *that*. The Irish, despite their pappy diet of potatoes, had never been tame, and they could be expected to put up a certain fight before they died. There would be rebellions, lootings of landowners' property, even more assassinations, and a general disturbance of the very rickety peace. The interests of the prosperous English gentlefolk, who went in for luxury gardens and subscribed to *The Gardeners' Chronicle*, were involved. It was the wretched, potato-eating, cabin-dwellers of Ireland who paid most of the rent for that land, and dead men, even dead Irishmen in 1846, would pay no rent. The Potato Murrain in Ireland might well cause the gravest inconvenience and even loss to the land-owning classes: already there was a rumour that the shortage of food would give Sir Robert Peel the excuse he was seeking to repeal the Corn Laws. . . .

The literate public in England was well informed about The Condition of the People in Ireland, just before and during the outbreak of the Potato Murrain; there had been a searching inquiry by the Devon Commission in 1843, and it happened that Mr. Thomas Campbell Foster, special commissioner for *The Times* newspaper, was over there, in the summer of 1845, making a tour of the country. Mr. Foster was called to the Bar in the following year; he had a judicial mind and had recently perfected a new system of shorthand, very useful for the recording of facts. He wrote of the condition of the Irish people without fear or favour. Without favour for the Irish and without fear of the landlords. His style proclaimed him an upright and an honest man, who conceived it his vocation to tell the truth and to fear only God. He was disliked to a degree by both sides, and was ridiculed by Mr. Daniel O'Connor.

Foster's account of the people amongst whom the Potato Murrain descended, as plague and fire had once descended upon crowded London, was a story of parasitism, of a horrible rent-collecting system, whose hyphae and haustoria, or tentacles and suckers, reached down into every wretched cabin, and drained the substance of the people and the land. The owners of the estates in former times had kept open house, spent their days in hunting and shooting, and lived far beyond their incomes. They had used every means to raise money; incidentally, they had cut down most of the trees in Ireland, and sold the timber, so that the land was a treeless waste. Then they had granted long leases of their land to middlemen, for enhanced rents; thus evading all manorial or feudal responsibility for the welfare of their tenants, and handing the management of the land over to purely mercenary intermediaries, whose business it was to subdivide, and make their own profit, from letting the land retail. At every sub-division the rent went up, and the smallest farmers, forced to pay these increased rents, learnt the dodge from their superiors, and again sub-let their land, in roods of 'conacre' at a time to their labourers, or to the 'cottiers', who were the ultimate cells of this social organism. The cottiers lived in their miserable cabins, without chimneys and without windows, and on their quarter-acres of hired land they grew their 'lumpers' – their coarse but prolific potatoes – not in ridges but in so-called 'lazy beds': a primitive method of cultivation, which in fact required much hard work, but was often well adapted to the poorly drained land – especially in the west. On these potatoes they kept body and soul together, and except in the 'meal months' of July and August, the gap between the old potatoes and the new, they often tasted nothing but potatoes and pepper water from one month's end to another. Their stomachs were distended with from eight to fourteen pounds of potatoes per day.

To keep the bit of land on which the potatoes were grown was their desperate necessity. They had to pay the rent. The £10 or £12 per acre was remorselessly sucked up from them and divided between the landowners and the various middlemen. The wages for occasional labour on the estates and farms, and the pig, went to pay the rent. In the cabins there was always a pig; on the less poverty-stricken farms and on the estates, cattle were reared and corn was grown. The pigs, the cattle and the corn made up the wealth of the country, the marketable and exportable produce that went to pay the rents. The cottiers lived on the potatoes, on food inadequate for cattle but good enough for men. From the substance of the potato alone was built up the stuff of human bone, muscle, sperm, and milk for the young.

In one of Mr. Foster's articles in *The Times* of 1845 a typical *annual* budget was given for a labourer and his family in Ballinamore, where conditions were by no means so bad as in the extreme west. The man's wages were sixpence a day, and he had casual agricultural employment averaging six months in the year. The rent of his cottage was £2 10s. and of his rood of conacre another £2 10s. He kept a pig which he could sell for about £4. And on his rood of conacre he grew, according to Mr. Foster, some five tons of potatoes, giving a ration for himself and his family of thirty-two pounds of potatoes a day over the year. But here Mr. Foster was optimistic; it was almost unbelievable that the cottiers ever obtained anything like a crop of twenty tons of potatoes per acre, and on impoverished land. Apart from the potatoes, this was the annual budget:

	£	s.	d.
Wages	3	18	0
Value of Pig	4	0	0
	£7	18	0
Deduct Rent	5	0	0
Balance	£2	18	0

£2 18s. 0d., *per annum*, to buy meal, clothing, tools, candles, medicine, drink, and every other luxury or necessity for a human family. While the middlemen and the landowners took the man's pig and a quarter of his wages, it was not difficult to perceive that without the potatoes that family would starve.

The population of Ireland had grown from 4½ million in 1800 to over 8 million in 1845. The fertility of animals was said to rise with partial starvation, perhaps as a natural provision for the perpetuation of species in times of high mortality and danger; and this would seem to have been true of man in Ireland over that half century. But there were many factors favouring the increase. In the crowded cabins only elemental pleasures were free. The Catholic priests blessed the fecundity, for they themselves multiplied and grew the fatter the more souls they had to save. The 'squireens', the impecunious younger sons of the landowners, sought to create as many 'forty-shilling freeholders' as possible in order to barter their votes with politicians for jobs in the government. The infinite sub-division of the land, the very ease with which potatoes could be grown – everything favoured the increase of population.

Absentee landlords sometimes visited their Irish estates and were amazed at the hordes of haggard, dirty and wretched people that had, as it were, sprung up from nowhere. It was not their affair, but really the Government should do something for these unhappy people. Educate them, shake them out of their habits of idleness, encourage them to better themselves . . . If they would only adopt the new methods of agriculture, be a little more ambitious than to grow potatoes year after year on the same land, go in for the rotation of crops, work during the winter at improving their holdings and their dwellings instead of kippering themselves over their turf fires – how much better off they would be! It was true that any improvement they made was immediately followed by an increase in the rent. But they stood to profit just as much from improvements as did the landowners. How stupid it was of the lower orders to refuse to better themselves, merely because they would have to share their gains with their superiors!

It was impossible to do anything for the Irish. They whined about your being an 'absentee landlord', but if you did show yourself, at least anywhere near Tipperary, they were quite likely to hide behind bushes and shoot you in the back, while you were walking about the estate. They resisted every enlightened attempt to clear their cabins and potato plots away and to give them regular employment in the cultivation of decent-sized fields, and in mixed farming on properly-managed estates. They seemed to think that it would mean the loss of their independence, that their wages, though regular, would be reduced in value through dirty wangles by the dealers in food, and that they would be worse off than before. They had a fixed idea that the only object of the landowners and the 'authorities' was to bleed and cheat them in every possible way, and they held on to their 'lazy beds' and their potatoes, as though their lives depended upon it. That made it easy for the agents to squeeze a little more out of the property, which was sometimes a convenience, but it was sad that the Irish should resist every attempt to better their condition.

The natural improvidence of the Irish was, of course, the real cause of their misery. They never put any money by to meet their obligations. If the pig happened to die they couldn't pay the rent. And so they got into the hands of the Gombeen men. Usury was prohibited in Ireland, but with the Gombeen men it was different. There was nothing illegal about buying meal on credit and then immediately selling it back again, at a much reduced price to get a little ready money for the rent. The chain of transactions was something like this: the farmer, in return for an I.O.U. for £1 became the legal owner of a bag of meal worth 13s. Without moving the bag of meal, he then sold it back to the Gombeen man for 10s., and had that much ready cash. In three months' time the Gombeen man sued the farmer for the £1, but retired satisfied with 5s. or 6s. interest and another I.O.U. for £1, with which, in due course, the process was repeated. The plight of the farmer in the clutches of Gombeen men was miserable in the extreme, but the main thing was that by allowing the farmers to have resort to such help in times of trouble, the landowners *did* get their rent. The Irishman, for all his pride in driving a hard bargain with his neighbour, and his endless haggling over twopence, was a child in the understanding of money. When by some fluke a banknote came into his possession he would not infrequently *pawn* it to raise cash.

A 'parasite', by derivation, was 'one who supped at another's table'. In Ireland in 1845, the 'table' was the produce of the Irish soil, and the host was the population which raised that produce by its labour. The parasites were those who did nothing for their host but in their various ways supped on the rents, the votes, the rates, the profits, the usury, the taxes and the tithes. They constituted a complex and much ramified social organism growing within, and, in the case of absentee landlords, without, the body of Irish society. The juice, in its digested and fluid form, that this parasitic organism drew from the Irish population was money. In its undigested form it was the meat and the bread, the cattle, the pigs and the grain; while the share left for the host was the potatoes, a few rags and a little cheap whisky. No doubt the parasitic organism would have taken the potatoes also, were it not that something had to be left to keep the host alive. The various channels through which the parasitic social organism sucked the wealth of its host constituted collectively, its 'mycelium' or root-spawn. And it was quite apparent that if the impoverished Irish were now stricken by a natural calamity, the parasite would suffer also.

As news was received of the inexorable spreading of the Potato Murrain throughout the length and breadth of Ireland, and the cottiers, who had paid little attention to the blighted condition of the foliage, dug nervously in their plots and found the potatoes going rotten in the ground, the English authorities began also to take alarm. A commission of inquiry was appointed by Sir Robert Peel, and Doctors Lindley and Playfair went to Ireland where they were joined by Robert Kane. Kane had written a book on the industrial resources of Ireland, and Lyon Playfair, a minor chemist, was a great sitter-upon-commissions – he subsequently insinuated himself into the household of the Prince Consort, became a Baron and endeared himself for ever to connoisseurs of fatuity by announcing, when exhibiting the synthesis of water to Queen Victoria, that oxygen and hydrogen would *have the honour* of combining in her royal presence!

The commissioners certainly sent back news of the true extent of the disaster, but in reporting on the cause of it they played for time, with many pious references to the will of the Almighty. The pressing need, they said, was for them to examine the possible means of saving those potatoes that were not yet diseased. They should be spread out on the soil to harden and dry, for three days after lifting, if the weather was fine (in November); they should not be stored in pits, as was usual, but carefully laid out in dry peat ashes, two inches apart, and built up in layers of the ashes into a clamp which was to be neatly thatched, according to a diagram. Alternatively, hurdles might be placed over the tops of lime kilns, and the potatoes spread on bracken over the hurdles to dry. As for the potatoes that were partially diseased, probably the best that could be done with them was to smash them up with brickbats and wash out the potato flour. But John Lindley had to warn the public that potato starch was no substitute for the potato as food. Nor was he alone in speaking of 'what is not bread and satisfieth not'. Animals fed only on starch died of starvation nearly as soon as when totally deprived of food.

The learned commissioners came back home after a few weeks, and for the time being the Irish were left to their fate. The commission had done little more than to advise well-known methods for storing potatoes, which were, in the main too finnicky and laborious for the Irish peasant, accustomed to storing his lumpers in pits. Now, with the rot and the curse on them, they were left where they were in the ground. Which, except for the danger of damage from frost, was perhaps as good a measure as any, for the disease developed rapidly among the potatoes in the pits. Mr. Foster had been present in October, at the opening of a pit in which some sixty barrels of potatoes – five months' provision for a family – had been put down a few weeks before. On sorting the good from the bad less than a single barrel were found to be sound. It was this rotting of the tubers that baffled understanding; there was a 'Blight', a mysterious something unknown and indefinable, affecting the potatoes wherever they might be, and the popular belief was that no one could tell whether this Blight came from the heavens above, or the earth beneath, or the waters under the earth.

All kinds of proposals were put forward in November and December of 1845, for stopping the rot in the potatoes. Farmers, botanists, chemists, mere writers-of-letters-to-newspapers, all had ideas. The potatoes were to be dried in lime, or spread with salt; they were to be cut up in slices and desiccated in ovens; and cottagers were even to provide themselves with oil of vitriol, manganese dioxide and salt, and treat their potatoes with chlorine gas, which could be obtained by mixing these materials together. It was mentioned casually that the chlorine should not be inhaled, and once again it fell to John Lindley to warn the public – this time of the very real dangers in generating poison gas in the home. There was, moreover, no reliable evidence that chlorine gas would have any preservative effect.

Dr. Morren, of Brussels, who believed with Mr. Berkeley that a mould fungus 'having seeds finer than the dust motes in the atmosphere' was spreading amongst the potatoes and causing the rot, suggested that the seed tubers for the coming season should be steeped in a mixture which in fact contained an oxychloride of copper.[1] The incomparable Dr. Lyon Playfair, also mindful that seed potatoes would be scarce in 1846, respectfully suggested that the English gentlefolk should make a practice of having the eyes cut away from all potatoes used in their kitchens, and placed on one side, as they would do for sets which could be distributed judiciously, and at little cost, amongst the deserving poor.

His Grace the Duke of Northumberland, through the Royal Agricultural Society of England, of which he was Vice-President, offered a prize of fifty sovereigns, or plate to that value, for the best essay on a remedy for the

[1] 54 lb. lime, ¼ lb. copper sulphate and 7 lb. common salt in 25 gallons of water.

Potato Disease, and two prizes amounting together to another fifty sovereigns for other essays on the subject. The prize-winning essays, published in the Society's *Journal* during 1846, contained useful accounts of the symptoms of the disease and of the course it had taken in various localities, but when it came to a remedy the essayists' principal achievement was to call the disease by a new and rather grand name: *Gangroena vegetabilis*, or, simply 'vegetable gangrene'. There was much scoffing at the Rev. M. J. Berkeley's fungal hypothesis. It was said that he had taken little notice of the general health of the plant, whereas his fungus was magnified seven-hundred-and-eighty diameters. The prize-winning effort on the cause of the disease amounted to a statement that it was due to the unhealthiness of the plants.

Meanwhile, the systematic botanists of Europe, whose occupation it was to collect and study, classify and name, all the species of plants, including the fungi, which were to be found on earth, were seizing upon one salient fact. A small mould fungus was *always* to be found growing on the diseased parts of the potato plants. Some workers found a rich variety of different sorts of moulds, especially when their technique for incubating them was none too careful, but there was one species in particular that was clearly to be associated with the Potato Disease. It was the species of Botrytis described by Dr. Montagne, the botanists were soon in tolerably close agreement about *that*. Most of them supposed that the Botrytis was responsible only for a secondary stage of decay, but whether it was the consequence or the cause of disease the little fungus was certainly of very great interest. It was an addition to the known flora of Europe, and a part of the Creation that had not been catalogued before. That it might be instrumental in causing a most deplorable loss of human life, through famine, in Ireland and elsewhere, was a circumstance that gave added zest to its investigation, for even cryptogamic botanists were human; but the part that this microscopic and colourless plant was playing in human affairs was nominally outside the scope of 'pure' botanical science. The botanists were interested in the fungus for its own sake.

The first botanical worker to discover a plant previously unknown, whether it was as small as a mould or as large as a Sequoia tree, not only had all the thrills and satisfactions of discovery; he came in for a good deal of most gratifying renown among his fellow workers. Providing that he described his find adequately and accurately according to the botanical canons – in short, according to the rules – and published his description, he had the very great privilege of assigning a name to that which he had found. He was no less than Adam, in regard to his find, for whatsoever he called it, it was.

There were several rivals for this honour, over the fungus which grew on the blighted potato plants, and the names invented for it were sufficiently expressive of its destructiveness. Mlle. Libert, in Belgium, would have had it called *Botrytis vastatrix* Lib.; Desmazières, in France, *Botrytis fallax* Des.; but Dr. Montagne, who had described the fungus adequately at a session of the Société Philomathique in Paris on August 30th, 1845, was considered to have the priority by a few days, and despite a certain amount of disappointed snarling in some quarters, it was agreed that the fungus should be called *Botrytis infestans* Mont.

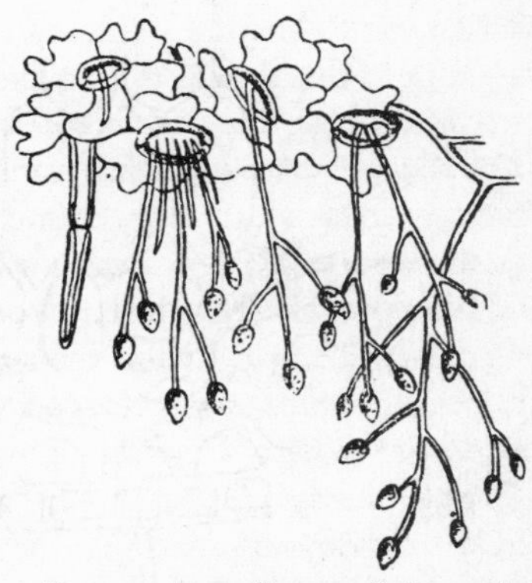

Fig. 1. A small part of the under surface of a potato leaf, magnified to about 100 times its natural size, showing the Potato Blight fungus, *Botrytis infestans* Mont., growing out of the stomata. Berkeley, 1846

Dr. Montagne sent his sketches and descriptions of *Botrytis infestans* to his friend the Rev. M. J. Berkeley in England, and they were formally published with Berkeley's 'Observations, Botanical and Physiological, on the Potato Murrain', in the first number of the *Journal of the Horticultural Society*, in January 1846. To make sure that the precise description of the fungus should be equally intelligible – or unintelligible – to scientific workers of all countries, and in all subsequent ages, it was written, as was customary for such new entries in the inventory of Nature, in Latin. Thus to the Vulgate, and in the vulgus, of Science, was appended the following inscription:

> *BOTRYTIS INFESTANS. Mont., coespitibus laxis erectis albis apice plus minus ramosis, ramis passim nodosis erecto-patentibus, sporis lateralibus terminalibusque solitarius ovoideo-ellipticis pro ratione magnis concoloribus subapiculatis, nucleo granuloso . . .*

And so on. The aerial parts of the fungus, when magnified sufficiently for details to be revealed, appeared somewhat as shown in Fig. 1. The growth of mould, visible to the naked eye as a white fringe of down, round the decayed areas and on the underside of blighted potato leaves, was made up of multitudes of exceedingly fine, semi-transparent, branching filaments, bearing colourless lemon-shaped spores. These spores broke away when mature and drifted in the air. They had all the appearance of fruits or seeds borne on the branches of the microscopic plant. Berkeley did not observe these spores in process of germination. Dr. Montagne was not at all sure, but it did seem to him that for all that these spores were so very minute, they were in reality spore-cases or 'sporangia' which, when ripe, contained smaller granular bodies which might be the true spores or 'seeds' of the fungus.

In another sketch, Fig. 2, Berkeley showed the 'root-strands' – constituting the mycelium or spawn of the fungus – as they were to be seen under the microscope in the interior of a potato leaf. The leaf-thickness was made up of several layers of cells: on the top there were the cells of the upper epidermis (which Berkeley did not trouble to show); beneath them came a tier

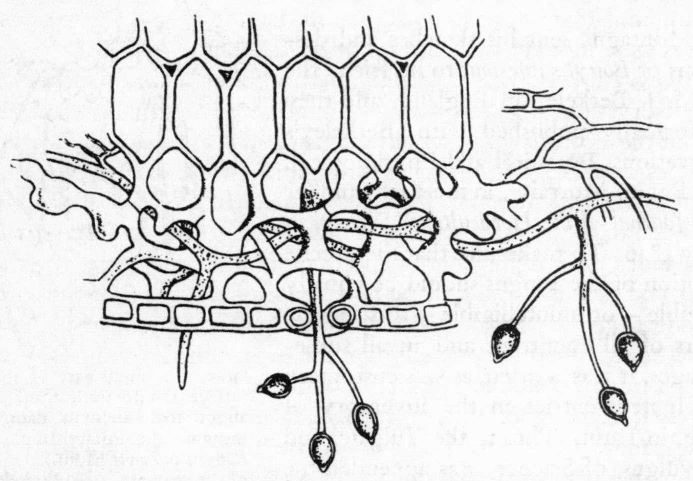

FIG. 2. Section of a potato leaf, greatly magnified showing the spawn-strands of the Potato Blight fungus creeping amongst the loose tissue of the underside, and sending out fertile shoots through the stomata. The mould is still young, one shoot not having yet formed any branches or fruit.

Berkeley, 1846

of vertical or 'palisade' cells, closely compacted, to which the leaf owed much of its rigidity and mechanical strength; while, under the palisade cells in their turn, the interior of the leaf was a kind of absorptive sponge, made up of thin-walled cells jumbled about, with air-spaces between them. The intercellular spaces communicated with the air outside the leaf by way of a multitude of minute pores – *stomata* from the Greek for 'mouths' – by which the lower epidermal cell-layer was perforated. The spore-threads of the fungus wound about in the air-spaces between the cells and took advantage of the stomata, as openings through which to put out their spore-bearing hyphae.

Normally, when no growth of the fungus was present, the moist and spongy tissue of the potato leaf manufactured food for the plant, and it had also a certain partial resemblance to a lung. It was bathed in air; with the help of sunlight it absorbed the gases which the plant needed from this air; and it gave off water vapour and other gaseous waste products of its living processes. It was evident that the spawn of the fungus, invading this tissue, would cause profound physiological disturbances. If a man could imagine his own plight, with growths of some weird and colourless seaweed issuing from his mouth and nostrils, from roots which were destroying and choking both his digestive system and his lungs, he would have a very crude and fabulous, but perhaps instructive idea of the condition of a potato plant when its leaves were mouldy with *Botrytis infestans* Mont.

The Rev. M. J. Berkeley certainly did not indulge in any such fancy, but in his observations on the Potato Murrain he made it quite clear that the spawn of the Botrytis grew within the tissue of the potato leaves and that it put out its spore-bearing branches through the stomata. That in some way the fungus drew its substance from the contents of the leaf-cells and thereby contributed to their decay was not in dispute. That the fungus might spread from plant to plant in the field by means of its air-borne spores was probable enough, and though it was difficult to see how a fungus growing on the leaves could affect the tubers underground, and even after they had been lifted and put into store, it was conceivable that the organism had some way of progressing through the underground stems of the plants so that the spawn of it was present in the tubers during growth. The point at issue was whether or not the fungus could attack *healthy* potato foliage. By January 1846 the prevailing belief was still that the fungus could establish itself only on foliage that was already languid or moribund through Disease. And if this were so, the detailed study of the fungus could not help much in solving the riddle of the Potato Murrain. It would still be necessary to find the cause of the *Disease*.

The mysterious principle, so glibly spoken of as 'Disease', was highly illusive. Most people seemed to regard it as an Absolute, linked without material agency to the Will of God. Even the natural philosophers, for the most part – the very botanists and chemists – were vying with one another in postulating intangible causes for invisible Disease preceding the fungal attack. Electricity was much discussed. Somebody had seen a lambent phosphorescent light playing over potato fields at night, somewhere in Ireland, where the disease was very bad. This phenomenon was about equally suggestive of a silent discharge of electricity or a personal appearance of the Evil One. Then again it was a well-known fact that some varieties of potatoes degenerated in cultivation, seeming to pine away and lose their productiveness when grown for some years running in particular localities. 'Degeneration' might be the cause of Disease. Others confidently proclaimed that the Disease was caused 'by simple eremacousis or excolation in consequence of a deficiency of vital energy in the plant'. 'Simple' eremacousis being a supposed burning or internal combustion of the weakened plant owing to the oxygen in the air having become too strong for it. It was noteworthy that in this controversy it was the Rev. M. J. Berkeley, a man accustomed by the exercise of his clerical profession to a certain amount of Christian protestation, who *rejected* all the nebulous, transcendental and spiritual explanations, while it was the more materialistically-minded scientists who most eagerly espoused them.

Berkeley was at one with Michael Faraday in his distaste for the postulation of unknown causes for natural phenomena, and in asserting straight out that the 'Disease' was non-existent, and that the growth of *Botrytis infestans* as a parasite on the potato plants was sufficient to explain all the phenomena of the Potato Murrain, his philosophy was that of his great namesake, author of the *Principles of Human Knowledge*. He rejected an unknown and unknowable *nuomen*: the 'Disease', and directed his attention to an observable *phenomenon*: the growth of a parasitic fungus on the plants. In his famous Observations of January 1846, Berkeley was able to sweep away a number, but not all, of the objections to his fungal hypothesis. For a start he was able to produce evidence that the Potato Murrain, and the particular species of fungus associated with it, had *not* appeared on earth for the first time during the previous year. A Dr. Bellingham had described an outbreak of precisely the same kind affecting potatoes in Canada in 1844, and one Joachim Acosta had transmitted information to the French Academy which then seemed to indicate that the malady had long been known in Bogota, where the Indians lived chiefly on potatoes. The creation of *Botrytis infestans* Mont. was probably coeval with that of the potato itself. Then, he was able to point to a number of other moulds which so far as he knew attacked *only* living and apparently healthy plants. However much you tried you could not get these moulds to grow on foliage that was dead or decaying. The Potato Blight fungus was not a 'saprophyte', it was not a plant that lived on the dead; it was a true parasite or vampire that supped on the juices of the living potato plants and thereby blighted and destroyed them.

No! said Dr. Lindley, the other members of the Government commission, and most of the botanists in Europe. The tissues of the plants were charged with water they could not eliminate, some degree of putrefaction or incipient decay set in, and *then* came the mildew. *Or* the long-observed tendency of potato varieties to degenerate in some way became universal and acute in an abnormal growing season, and so pre-disposed the plants to fungal attack. *Or* the unstable nitrogenous constituents of potato tubers and foliage were disturbed by electricity or corrupted by the wet. Something went wrong. They could not believe that the Botrytis could have established itself unless the plants were already debilitated and lacking in some power of resistance to agencies of decay.

CHAPTER II

FAMINE IN IRELAND

WHILE botanists wrangled and compared notes about their pretty fungi, it was winter in Ireland. As the small supplies of sound or only partially-blighted potatoes rapidly diminished some four-and-a-half million cottiers and poor farmers faced starvation. One or two of the landowners, who had managed to retain personal control of their estates, and were not themselves impecunious and on the verge of bankruptcy, forgave their tenants the payment of rent for a year, which meant that they could keep their corn for themselves and use it for food. Already, in October 1845, there were hills in Donegal ablaze with bonfires at night, marking local jubilation at such generosity on the part of Lord Kildare. But these humane concessions were very rare; the majority of the landowners, through their agents and collectors, pressed harder than ever for the rents, to make sure of them, while the getting was still good. The export of corn, and even of potatoes from some districts in Ireland was not stopped. There was food in the country, perhaps enough of pigs and cattle and grain to have nourished the whole population until the next harvest, but the people had no money wherewith to buy back what was taken from them in rent.

In England, the reports of the commission of inquiry had made it plain to Sir Robert Peel that the provision of some measure of relief during the approaching famine would be unavoidable. Peel, insolent and aloof in manner, an aristocrat of the rising industrial breed, whose wealth came from the Lancashire cotton mills, was not greatly concerned to alleviate human suffering. He exploited the situation with magnificent political opportunism. His pledge to his Tory supporters to pursue a vigorous policy of Protection had served its purpose and brought him into office and power. Now he was scheming to turn apostate and to use that power, in defiance of his party, for the advancement of the directly opposite policy of Free Trade. The Corn Laws, enacted in 1815 to prevent the price of wheat from slumping too far below the famine prices which had obtained during the Napoleonic wars, operated to the great advantage of the landowners, the old traditional aristocracy who drew their revenues from the farms. The Laws imposed heavy duties on imported grain and so 'protected' home agriculture. The Tory party was chiefly representative of the wealthy landowners, and Peel had made himself their darling. But there was one part of the Whig case for

Free Trade that was greatly to his mind. The Anti-Corn Law League, Cobden, Bright, and the rest, had been making out that Free Trade would bring the people the blessing of cheap bread. That was as might be. Those who had no bread could eat cake for all Peel cared; he was not a sentimentalist. But Free Trade would operate to the advantage of a caste then rising to effective power, towards which Peel belonged by birth and naturally gravitated. The English industrialists had a virtual monopoly of the world's machine manufactures. By the timely exploitation of this monopoly, with all the ports of the world open to them, and *laissez-faire* to trade as they pleased, the mill-owners and the iron-masters and the ship-builders, the brokers and the bankers would build for themselves an Empire the like of which had never been seen before. Theirs would be the Empire, the power and the glory. Theirs would be the name of England, and of that new might and richness he, Robert Peel, would be an architect; no more would he toady to the declining, land-owning oligarchy that in his heart he despised. The news of famine in Ireland was a godsend. Oh, what most excellent use could he not make of that!

On January 27th, 1846, Peel made his great speech in the House of Commons for the repeal of the Corn Laws. His heart bled for the suffering Irish; in England there was no grain to send them, for in England also the shortage of food was causing the gravest distress; the only thing that could be done, in the name of God and humanity, was to suspend the Corn Laws and admit foreign grain into the country. The Tories were aghast. For months the tremendous angered debates went on. Neither friends nor enemies were taken in, for Peel's humanitarianism reeked of guile. The Irish had been left to starve before, their present misery was being exaggerated, could not such epoch-making and dangerous measures be deferred until the real extent of the distress was seen? In histrionics Peel surpassed even himself. 'Good God', he cried, 'are you to sit in Cabinet and consider and calculate how much diarrhoea and bloody flux and dysentery a people can bear before it becomes necessary for you to provide them with food?'

While the debates continued Peel set up a relief commission, and a number of shiploads of maize were imported from America. The first issue of maize meal, from relief centres in Ireland, was made early in March. Maize was chosen, first because it was cheap and there was a large surplus available in America, and secondly because it was practically unknown in Ireland, and it could be distributed by the Government, at a low price, without too much opposition from the Irish dealers in grain. It was all important that the relief measures should not dislocate trade. And how could the corn merchants have sold their wheaten grain or flour, at prices which took proper advantage of the distress, with the Government in unfair competition with them? The choice of maize solved this difficulty, for no one in Ireland would buy maize meal if he could possibly afford to buy wheaten flour.

The maize meal was quite wholesome, and some of the gentry in Ireland themselves ate bread made with a proportion of it, to set an example, and to popularize the unfamiliar stuff amongst those it was destined to sustain. For all this, the ever-ungrateful Irish grumbled at the coarse yellow maize meal and called it 'Peel's Brimstone'. It was not easy for stomachs accustomed to distention by a bulky diet of potatoes to accommodate themselves at once to meagre rations of maize; but any inconveniences on this score were trifling when so many were dying of exhaustion by hunger, and the fever that followed in its train. In a short time the marvellously flexible digestive system of man accommodated itself to the maize, which for eighteen terrible months did sustain many hundreds of thousands who would then otherwise have joined the dead.

If the plight of the Irish was wretched in the spring of 1846, what had they to anticipate in 1847, if God ignored their prayers and sent just such another season as the last? If the Blight once again destroyed the potato crop? Already many of the fields were bare, for seed potatoes had been consumed, and there were many prophets of woe who said that the potatoes were lost for ever to Ireland, that they were not to be trusted again. Where was the use of planting them, of bending one's back to the spade? Many of the lazy-beds were empty, tillage was neglected.

Those who had hidden away and saved enough seed potatoes to plant their land had cause, as spring progressed into summer, to congratulate themselves on their faith in God's mercy. The plants were healthy! The murrain had passed over!

It was not a good summer, all over Europe the grain crops now were suffering, but the potatoes were spared. Or so it seemed, until about the end of July. Then the Blight appeared on the potatoes once again.

'On July 27th', wrote Father Matthew, 'I passed from Cork to Dublin, and this doomed plant bloomed in all the luxuriance of an abundant harvest. Returning on August 3rd I beheld with sorrow one wide waste of putrefying vegetation. In many places the wretched people were seated on the fences of their decaying gardens, wringing their hands and wailing bitterly at the destruction which had left them foodless.'

Funds were raised, much help came from America, the Society of Friends, as usual, were the first on the scene of disaster and the last to leave, but there were difficulties in the way of the main organization of relief. It was not so much the cost of the maize, for that would not greatly strain the resources of a nation that had recently effected great economies on the relief of pauperism at home, introduced the Income Tax, and returned a budget surplus of over five millions. The trouble was that the maize could not be *given* away: the demoralization of receiving rations of chickens' food without having to work for them would be worse for the Irish than being left to die. There was no precedent for such organized relief as that which now became necessary, no English Government had ever undertaken anything like it before, and there was great concern over the moral issues. The principle of Poor Law relief in England was that of 'offering the workhouse', and clearly there were no workhouses to offer half the population of Ireland. An expensive organization of relief works had to be set up which would make the whole of Ireland for the time being one vast emergency open-air workhouse. The only task that could be set everywhere was that of road-making; and it was extremely difficult to make the task-work on the roads less attractive than any form of employment normally available, in so miserable a part of the Kingdom as Ireland. The Committees did their best, but, even so, the people flocked to the roads and would not cultivate the land, and to the despair of the charitable there were some malingerers, who preferred the pretence of road-making to their habitual employment on farms and estates at sixpence or so a day. It was a shocking thing that some should try to get relief when they were not really starving, and in February 1847, a 'means test' was imposed. It was simple, and it effected a considerable economy. It was called 'the cooked food test'. Large iron boilers were installed at the relief centres, and the maize meal, sometimes mixed with a little rice or oatmeal, was boiled in water to make stir-about. In this way the one-pound portions of meal were made to swell into two or three pounds by absorption of water, and they were distributed thus – as a wet mash. The mash could not be stored, or it would ferment; it had no value on the market, it could not be sold or pawned; and as it was most unpalatable the Government could feel content that nobody would work on the roads for it who was not in a reasonably necessitous plight. The average cost of each ration was twopence, including the cost of the staff of the relief committees and all incidentals. As a further precaution many of the boilers were set up a mile or more away from the villages they served, so that those who were very sick or enfeebled would either die on the way or share the portions of those who could make a personal attendance to get them. One of the beauties of the cooked-food test was the pleasure it gave the righteous and the prosperous to reflect that the Government was not only providing food for the hungry, but even cooking it for them. Though indeed the only thing of which there was little shortage in Ireland was turf from the bog.

The local authorities and magistrates, representative of the landowners, shelved their responsibilities, and the burden of organizing the relief works throughout the country fell almost wholly upon the civil servants, the officers of the Board of Works in Dublin. Theirs was a story of devotion and often of heroism. They worked day and night to make the best of mean schemes; not a few of their number were assaulted or murdered by those who objected to the task system, many others died of the famine fever, which all had to brave. The sight of the haggard, half-naked, sick and emaciated people who dragged their aching bones for miles to perform their day's task on the roads was too much for some of the engineers who had to supervise such labour. Sometimes, when the weather was very bad, they held it sufficient if the folk made their appearance in the morning, and came back only if the weather improved later in the day. There was one who said that as an Engineer he was ashamed of allotting so little task work for a day's wages, while, as a man, he was ashamed of exacting so much.

A number of the landowners sought to divert funds and to get free 'relief labour' for the work of draining their particular estates; and speculators in Irish railway stock clamoured for the diversion of the labour to the piling up of railway embankments. But the Government, the landowners and the railway company promoters could not agree terms, and the construction of roads went on, many of them from nowhere to nowhere. In March 1847, 734,000 men, corresponding with their families to some three million people, were engaged on the relief works.

The Government did not assist emigration, contending that the proper criterion of fitness to emigrate was the possession by the applicant of the initiative, the means and the courage to do so. Any interference with this natural law would only flood the colonies with unwanted and undesirable people. There was mass emigration nevertheless, passage money was sent by relatives who had already escaped to the New World, and all over Ireland the lamentations of departure mingled with the keenings for the dead. In 1847, ninety thousand set out for Canada alone; and of this ninety thousand, two thousand died of fever before they reached Dublin or Kingstown, while thirteen thousand more died in Liverpool or during the passage, or at quarantine stations on the other side. Those who survived spread a trail of typhoid about them as they penetrated into the Canadian interior. Fever everywhere accompanied and followed the famine.

In 1847 the sadly reduced acreage under potatoes in Ireland escaped the Potato Blight — or, it should rather be said, the Blight attacks were local and relatively unimportant. There was good weather, brilliant sunshine, that year, from July to September. And over the whole of Europe the harvest, both of grain and potatoes, was abundant. The two worst years of famine were past. The relief works and the relief centres were gradually closed down as the new crop of potatoes became available, and the survivors were left to convalesce, as best they could, from the scourge that had fallen upon them. There was no decrease in the rents, and after the famine came all the horrors of the evictions. With the rent unpaid families were cast out of their homes, with their bundles and bits and sticks of furniture about them, to beseech shelter of heaven or crowd the few pestilent workhouses. The official relief measures, for a whole population, over a period of eighteen months, had cost Great Britain the unheard-of sum of £7,673,701. Nearly eight million pounds! Of course, a substantial part of this was to be repaid out of the Irish rates. It never *was* repaid in that form, but the debt was offset by the extension of the Income Tax to Ireland in 1853, so that the landowners there had to make some contribution after all. The poverty in Ireland, especially in the Congested Districts of the West, remained as a permanent sore. The Potato Blight was in Ireland for ever; it would become epidemic and ravage the crop again, whenever weather conditions favoured its development. In the years from 1845 to 1860 a million people died in Ireland alone as a direct consequence of the famine, and one and a half million emigrated. The part of the Potato Murrain in contributing to the sufferings during the 'Hungry Forties', in England and other parts of Europe, was a matter for the grimmest conjecture.

The Potato Blight fungus, *Botrytis infestans* Mont., had revealed itself as a new and formidable enemy of mankind. By destroying the stable food supply of a human society already very sick from economic causes, it brought about more of death and suffering than any other disaster since the Napoleonic Wars. It was an historic determinant of human affairs, for in 1846 it was the straw that turned the wavering inclination of British high political policy away from self-sufficiency and the protection of home agriculture to Free Trade and the unbounded expansion of commerce. The passage, on June 26th, 1846, of the Act which ultimately repealed the Corn Laws was perhaps the most significant single event in the history of the British Empire. The Duke of Wellington's comment was: 'Rotten potatoes have done it all; they put Peel in his damned fright'. That little fungus, only to be fairly seen in the strangely lighted field of the microscope, with its filamentous spawn and its translucent spores, not only brought famine to Ireland and unlocked the doors of England's Golden Age; it shed new light on the nature of Disease, awakened the natural philosophers to the significance of those living things that God created small, and called into being a new branch of applied science, second only in importance to medicine and human pathology – the science which was to have for its province the defence of the health of the crops. Very slowly that science took shape, and won its way out of Laocoön-like struggles with doubt and indifference, superstition and obscurity, after *Botrytis infestans* Mont. had written its name across the potato fields of Europe. Nearly a hundred years were destined to pass before the erasure of that signature would seem to be in sight, and historians could attempt to tell a half of the story.

It was said, in 1847, that all human power, experience and learning had proved vain and futile to discover any antidote to the Potato Blight when weather conditions favoured its spread. This was not quite true, for although even the fungal nature of the Blight was still very much in dispute, there were fragments of certain knowledge about its course, which pointed to some ways of mitigating the damage. It was observed and generally admitted that the Blight began on the *foliage* of the plants and later made its way to the tubers. There was one drastic measure that the potato growers could sometimes employ with advantage. They could *amputate*; they could cut down the potato haulms before the disease had reached the tubers. When this was done the potatoes might not be fully grown, but most of them would be sound. This measure was advocated by Dr. Morren in Belgium within a fortnight of the first outbreak of the Blight in 1845, and had it at once been adopted in Ireland, it would undoubtedly have saved much of the crop in the famine years.

Then it was noticed that the potatoes which grew nearer the surface of the ground were more often blighted than those which were more deeply-covered. It was thought that the upper tubers might be more tender or immature, and therefore more susceptible, but a good cover of earth over the potatoes might have a protective effect. An interesting fact, reported in *The Cambrian* newspaper, was that potatoes grown in the immediate vicinity of the copper smelting works at Swansea remained healthy and green, while those in Sketty, Llangyfelach, and the surrounding districts were universally diseased. It was difficult to see what the cause of this might be. John Lindley said it might be urged by the advocates of atmospheric contagion that one miasma had the power of repelling another from the potato fields. One correspondent wrote to *The Gardeners' Chronicle* and said: supposing the

Potato Murrain really *was* caused by a minute fungus, why had that fungus waited for over two hundred years after the introduction of the potato into Europe before manifesting itself? Was it possible that the fungus had recently migrated to Europe from South America, where the potato grew wild? He had looked up the weather records for 1845 and found that westerly winds had prevailed during all August and into September. Could the spores of the fungus have been blown over from the American continent owing to some singular changes in the winds? But if the living spores *had* been carried over some three thousand miles of ocean by wind it must have been years before 1845. Dr. Morren provided an account of the disease on potatoes in the vicinity of Lille in 1844, and said that it had first been observed at Liége in 1842.

John Lindley was less insistent on his theory, by 1848, that the plants were water-logged, and he had made some practical experiments arising out of the idea that the Potato Blight might be due to the degeneration of the potato through over-domestication. There was nothing nebulous or chimerical about this thought. Several kinds of wild potatoes had been sent to the Horticultural Society of London, at one time or another, from Chili, Mexico and Peru. These differed greatly from the domesticated potato, and it was very possible that some power of resistance to disease enjoyed by the potato in its wild state had been lost in centuries of domestication. Even if the Rev. M. J. Berkeley was right in thinking that the Blight Fungus could attack healthy plants, it still took two things to account for the devastation: the aggressiveness of the fungus and the weakness of the potatoes. If the Blight was an instance of the parasitism of one species of plant by another then a better understanding of the Blight was to be sought in two ways (*a*) through the study of the parasite and (*b*) through that of its host. With all due respect to Mr. Berkeley, John Lindley was of the opinion that the latter approach was just as important as the former. 'Amongst the many speculations that have been entertained concerning the Potato Disease', wrote Lindley in 1848, 'one consisted in the belief that in order to be secure against its future ravages it was only necessary to bring the plant once more from its native country and to begin over again the process of domesticating it.'

To test this possibility it was necessary to determine whether or not the wild potatoes were susceptible to the Blight when grown in Britain. In 1846 and '47, Lindley collected as many sorts of Central or South American potatoes as he could obtain, and had them grown in the Horticultural Society's gardens at Chiswick for purposes of observation. There were New Granada potatoes and Golden Potatoes from Peru; but amongst all the different sorts perhaps the most interesting were those of which tubers had been received on July 25th, 1846, from a German gentleman, one Herr Uhde, who was then residing or exploring in Mexico. The packet was marked only: 'Native Mexican potatoes from an elevation of 8000 feet.' The tubers of these wild potatoes were very small, it would have been hard to make a meal off them, even if they were good to eat. Some of them gave rise to very tall and weedy plants, which were thought to be the same as the *Solanum Maglia*, described by Molina and others, and found growing wild in Chile, in the latitude of Valparaiso. They also belonged, perhaps, to the same species which Darwin had seen on the Chonos Archipelago off the coast of Patagonia, during his voyage on the *Beagle*. Other tubers, from Herr Uhde's packet, produced plants of a particularly dwarf sort, bearing flowers very close to the ground and having 'potato-apples' or berries, which were about as large as black currants. The plants sometimes put out branches and blossomed again, at a maximum height of twelve to fifteen inches. The flowers were nearly an inch across and bright violet. Very few tubers were formed, many of the stems had none, and where they did occur they were small, flattened, somewhat kidney-shaped, and of white colour, with white, crisp, semi-transparent flesh. It seemed that this member of the Solanaceae – the potato, tomato, egg-plant and Deadly Nightshade family – had never been described before. John Lindley considered it a distinct species, and in his 'Notes on the Wild Potato', in 1848, he recorded its characteristics in Latin and gave it the name of *Solanum demissum*. '*Demissum*', because it was a dwarf.

Very interesting, this dwarf wild potato, which grew in Mexico, worth noting certainly – but what good was it? Its tubers were few and diminutive, and it was just as severely attacked by the Blight as the other potatoes in the gardens. A promising idea seemed to have come to nothing. But had he not said all along that owing to abnormally wet seasons the potato plants became surcharged with water and then wet putrefaction set in? It did not matter whether the potatoes were wild or domesticated, they rotted just the same.

It was the wet, the everlasting wet. Andrew Murray, in *The Book of the Royal Horticultural Society*, later recorded some happenings during those years of the Potato Famine, which must have impressed the *wetness* of the summers, indelibly upon Dr. John Lindley's imagination. He was the Secretary of the Horticultural Society, and in this capacity he had other things to do besides arranging scientific experiments in the Chiswick gardens. Those gardens were in the main a pleasure resort for the fashionable, and the wet 'caused inconvenience to great assemblages of people drawn together for enjoyment in the open air'.[1] At one of the 'breakfast-fêtes', which helped to make the gardens pay, tickets were sold, as usual, by exclusive lady-patronesses, at two guineas per head. In the marquees, 'gorgeous plate, fine china and sparkling crystal combined with the most delicate viands and high-priced wines to charm the eye and tempt the palate'. Then it rained – no less in Chiswick than it did in Ireland. Carriage after carriage deposited its fair and gaily dressed freight at the gates, and the cavalry lent their cloaks to the ladies – at two shillings and sixpence a time – to protect them during their passage from the carriages to the tents. The military bands played bravely to keep everyone in good cheer, the supply of champagne was liberal, the cold and the wet were almost forgotten. Then Dr. Lindley observed that the pillars supporting the tents were slowly but surely giving way in the wet. Disaster was imminent. He sent out into the streets, the pot-houses, the barns and smithies of Chiswick to hire men at any price to hold up the tents while the unsuspecting guests revelled within. The situation was saved. The fête even terminated with dancing on the wet and splashy grass, and it was said that a whole bushel of wet shoes and stockings were picked up in the gardens and neighbourhood next day, which had been thrown out of carriage windows as the owners drove off. Indeed it did rain, during the Hungry Forties.

[1] For illustration see Cruikshank's *Comic Almanac*, 1846.

CHAPTER III

OIDIUM ON THE VINES

On November 27th, 1847, the Rev. M. J. Berkeley had occasion to comment on the wisdom of encouraging a higher order of education amongst gardeners. It so happened that in Margate there was a clergyman so deeply imbued with a love of natural history and science that he had set up a literary and scientific institute to encourage the talent for inquiry which he found existent in no small degree amongst his parishioners. Already, one of these persons, of station so humble that it was almost unmentionable without apology in polite society, to wit 'a mere dispenser of the produce of the milky mothers of the herd' – or milkman, had written an essay on the lack of sanitation in Margate, which had startled the whole scientific world. And now another most meritorious piece of work came from the pen of a parishioner who was a mere working gardener.

The grape vines near Margate had been attacked since 1845 by a peculiar malady, never observed before. Every vine, whether in the open borders or in the houses, was affected. The disease appeared on the young shoots, tendrils and leaves, like a dusting of white and pulverulent meal; it spread rapidly on to the grapes themselves, withering the bunches when they were small and green, or causing the grapes to crack and expose their seeds when they were attacked later. The disease was accompanied by an unpleasant mouldy smell, and it ended in the total decay of the fruit. But one Mr. Tucker, gardener to J. Slater, Esq., of Margate, had not stood by, wringing his hands and saying that it was the will of the Almighty that the murrain on the potatoes should now spread to the vines. On the contrary, and in the exercise of an initiative most exemplary in a labouring man, he had obtained access to a powerful microscope and examined the afflicted foliage. He saw that a powdery mildew was growing on it, and then, without waiting for the fungus to be identified, and untroubled by any philosophic doubts as to whether it was the cause or the consequence of the disease, he looked about him for a practical way of stopping it. For once, in the history of plant pathology, the announcement of the outbreak of a new disease was coincident with the publication of an effective remedy for it.

Mr. Tucker was accustomed to using sulphur as a specific against mildew on peach trees, and he now tried sulphur for this new trouble on the grape vines. He made up a mixture of flowers of sulphur and lime in cold water and applied it to the leaves with a sponge. The treatment worked admirably: the mildew was killed on the affected shoots, its spread was prevented, and the rest of the grapes and the foliage grew away unharmed. In the end there was a good crop in the houses under Mr. Tucker's care, while in some of the other vineries in the locality there was not a single sound bunch of grapes to be seen.

Mr. Tucker, signing himself 'Progressionist', published a humble account of his observations in a letter of September 22nd, 1847, to the popular *Gardeners' Journal*, and the Rev. M. J. Berkeley, in the more influential *Gardeners' Chronicle*, pronounced that the causal fungus was a species of 'Oidium' not previously reported. He therefore translated 'Tucker' into Latin and named the parasite: *Oidium Tuckeri*. Mr. Tucker's name was destined not only for immortalization in the dusty records of cryptogamic botany, but for immediate, widespread and mournful celebrity.

The new disease of the grapes broke out in France. According to Dr. Montagne it was first observed, in 1848, on vines by the stoves at Versailles; whence it spread to the outdoor trellises and so to the neighbouring vineyards. By 1851 it had swept over the whole of France, south into Portugal, and along the whole length of Italy from the coast of Liguria to Naples; then, in the late summer of that year, it seemed to take a northerly course, through the Tyrol, overrunning Switzerland, and penetrating into the vine-growing districts of south Germany. Everywhere it caused consternation and panic among the vine-growers; it threatened their industry with ruin. The dread Oidium ravaged the finest of the vines. The Frankenthal, the table grapes cultivated by the stoves, were its first nurse; then the Chasselas, the Muscats, the Malvoisie, the White Grapes, the Tressaux, all the Hungarian strains, the Hermitage. . . . It was most destructive of those grapes which had the finest and most delicate skin and the most succulent fruit. The varieties which offered resistance were those which were least esteemed: the grapes of North America, the Gourneys, the Cots of Touraine. . . . By 1852 the choice vines of Madeira had been so ravaged that it seemed the cultivation of grapes would have to be abandoned on the island and orange trees planted instead.

There was less resistance this time to the theory that the fungus might be the cause of the disease, for it appeared first on those vines which the peasants called '*gaillarde*'. There were village mystics, and witch-like old women who said that the brave and joyous vines, which challenged the Gods with the greatest apparent vigour and health, would naturally be the first to suffer –

that they were in some occult way predisposed to disease. Some of the botanists also had theories about a 'plethora', or mysterious and unhealthy repletion, as a possible cause of the observable growth of mildew. But practical men were not disposed to believe that a plant could be diseased for the very reason that it was in too excellent a state of health. No! said Dr. Montagne, and Bethola, and Bouchardet, and Cuppari, and Gaddi, and Keller, and Hugo von Mohl, and Payen, and Savi, and Tulasne, and the members of the Venice commission of inquiry. This time we have caught the rat with the flour on its nose; it is the mildew, the powdery growth of *Oidium Tuckeri*, that is exhausting and killing the leaves, starving and splitting the grapes! Now Berkeley had the majority of the European botanists on his side. If the mildew flourished and spread most rapidly on the finest vines, growing on the best soil, it was because those had the sweetest sap, and sweet sap was food for the mildew as well as for the grapes.

But in his eagerness to demonstrate that the *Oidium Tuckeri* grew as a parasite on the vine foliage, Berkeley made an error of observation that for a time seriously weakened his case. In his first published sketch of the fungus he showed it growing *within* the tissues of the leaves, and sending its spore-bearing threads out through the stomata as did the Blight fungus on the potatoes. How could the fungus be anything but a parasite when its spawn was within the leaf, tapping the substance of the living cells? Mr. Tucker made the same mistake. Influenced by Berkeley's picture of the Potato Blight fungus, and too readily assuming that *that* was how *any* parasitic fungus on a leaf would grow, he had contrived to see, through his powerful microscope, something he expected to see, but that was not in fact there. 'Mycelium' under the leaf-cuticle, among the cellular tissue, ramifying and crossing in every direction. There were many pitfalls in Nature for those too quick to see what they wanted to see.

It happened that one of those who did *not* accept the 'fungal hypothesis' was J-H. Léveillé, doctor of medicine in Paris. And Léveillé, for all that he had only a modest and unremunerative practice, never knew how to get on in the world, and never wore even the red ribbon of the *Légion d'honneur*, was one of the greatest cryptogamic botanists in France. He made mistakes of interpretation, but very rarely of observation, and in 1851 he published a methodical classification of the many species of fungi composing the genus to which the Oidium belonged, decades in advance of his time. When describing the Oidium before the Société Philomathique in Paris and writing about it in the *Revue Horticole*, he pointed out that it was one of the commonest kinds of fungal growth found on the foliage of plants, it closely resembled the Powdery Mildews of the rose, peach, wheat, pea and hop, and its habit of growth was very different indeed from that of the Potato Blight fungus.

The spore-bearing 'stalks' of the Oidium did not arise from spawn within the leaf, but from a closely-interwoven web of glistening threads which crept over the leaf-surface. There were no spawn strands of the fungus to be found within the leaf at all. Straight stems arose from the superficial mycelium, bearing three, four or five oval, glass-like or 'hyaline' spores, joined end to end like beads of a necklace. These spores germinated when they had fallen on to a fresh part of the leaf-surface, putting out threads which were the beginning of a new tangle of mycelium. Léveillé was no artist, but a beautiful drawing of such a fungus, as seen under the microscope, agreeing with Léveillé's description, was provided a little later by Charles Tulasne.

Léveillé made a-much of the point that the Oidium had, apparently, no 'roots' penetrating the leaf. Without roots it could not very well be a parasite. It was an entirely superficial growth, which could be wiped off the leaves between finger and thumb, so that at most it was a 'false parasite', like ivy on a tree. As for the source of its nourishment – was it not easily conceivable that there might be some moist exudation, from leaves sickly from some internal cause, on which the mould could feed? Moulds would grow on the merest film of moribund juice. The areas under the patches of mould were always paler than the surrounding parts of the leaf, and no one could say which came first – the mould or the pallor. Léveillé's view was that the fungus did not propagate the malady, but that it was due to a 'primitive derangement of the tissues' to which the vines had always been subject, but which had become serious and destructive because of a succession of '*douce*' seasons. It was not easy to account for the universal presence of the fungus in association with the sickliness, and Léveillé had to resort to the already half-discredited theory of spontaneous generation. The morbid changes in the leaf tissue, he said, brought the living fungus into existence.

Berkeley still had to defend his 'fungal hypothesis', and when commenting on Léveillé's paper in 1851, he said:

'Where the mind can be brought to adopt notions of spontaneous or equivocal generation there is little difficulty in these matters, or at least the difficulty is thrown aside, but all patient investigation is against such notions, we must be content to treat the propagation of even such minute bodies as *Oidium Tuckeri* as we do those of the flowering plants. When a large crop of white clover makes its appearance on land recovered from the sea, it is an easy solution of the difficulty to say that the plants have been generated spontaneously from the soil. It may not be easy to account for their presence, but yet the lover of truth will not readily solve the difficulty by so unwarrantable a conclusion. In the case of the Potato Disease and the Grape Mildew, it appears that the parasites were not previously known. The conclusion is, as Morren well remarked about the Potato Blight, that they must have been

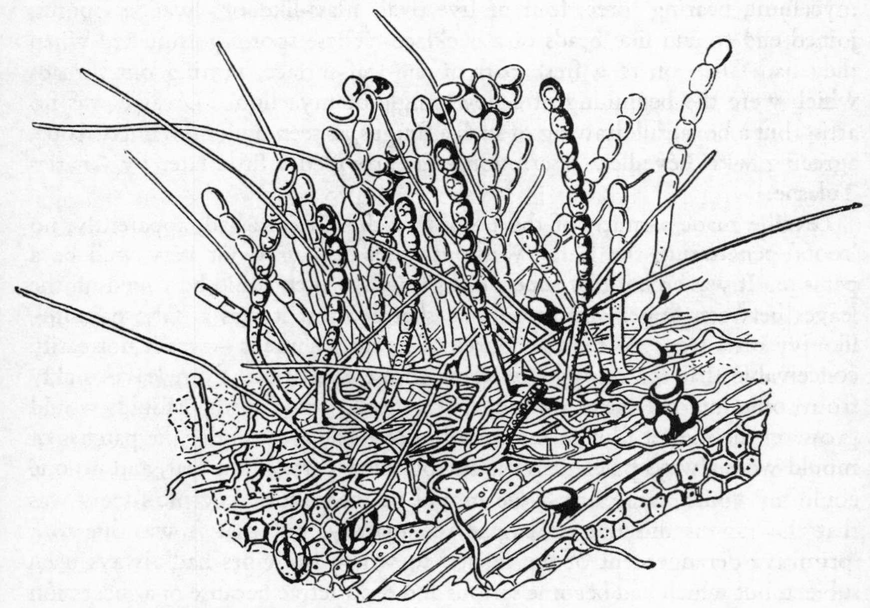

FIG. 3. The Oidium or Powdery Mildew of the Rose. The appearance of the Oidium of the Vine is similar except that the rigid branching hairs are absent. A germinating spore is shown in the foreground. (× 175)
After Tulasne, 1861

imported, and there is no more difficulty in this notion, or indeed so much, as in that of the introduction of such a quantity of white clover seed into the tracts recovered from the sea. . . . The Almighty produces effects of great magnitude and importance which are at first view altogether incommensurate with the causes from which they were derived.'

But it was Dr. Zanardini in Venice who provided the almost melodramatic evidence against *Oidium Tuckeri*. Several workers, including Léveillé, had noticed certain little brown spots on the vine leaves after the fungus had been wiped off, and in 1851 Zanardini showed that these were marks left where the fungus had been feeding, vampire-like, on the life-blood or sap of the leaves. On the undersides of those spawn strands which Léveillé imagined to creep harmlessly over the surface, he found multitudes of little suckers which penetrated the outer leaf-cells and served not only as mouths for the fungus, but as points of attachment. He called these little processes on the spawn strands 'fulcra', but later on the botanists preferred to call them 'haustoria' [*vide* Plate I, 4, 5 and 6]. The discovery of these suckers did not prove that the fungus was a parasite, as the suckers might still only be able to penetrate moribund cells, but it made a great impression on the minds of the botanists, and more and more of them were converted to the view that *Oidium Tuckeri* was a parasite caught in the act, and the veritable cause of the Vine Disease.

Once the fungus had been imported into Europe, its rapid spread through the vine-growing countries, over a period of years during which the weather favoured its growth, was understandable enough. Every square inch of mildewed leaf produced some two million spores, individually invisible to the naked eye. Most of these would settle on the ground and perish, but enough would be wafted about by the wind, carried on produce, or conveyed by insects or animals, to ensure their rapid dissemination. The fungus would spread wherever it found the climate congenial and the vines to its taste. *Oidium Tuckeri* and the Potato Blight fungus were both almost certainly indigenous in the New World, the former on some one or other of the many species of American grapes – Schweinitz had described it on *Vitis Labrusca* in 1834 – the latter on the wild potatoes of Chile and Peru. How was it that they had only so recently made their way to Europe? This question arose again and again.

But had not the Rev. M. J. Berkeley himself been receiving large parcels of botanical specimens, mostly fungi, from explorers in every part of the world, since about 1833? Certainly he received consignments from North America, Australasia, Ceylon, Batavia, the Philippines, the Congo and Peru. It was he who named and catalogued all the fungi brought back by Darwin from the voyage of the *Beagle* in 1836. During Berkeley's lifetime, more than ten thousand species of fungi passed through his hands, many hundreds of which he described for the first time. *Oidium Tuckeri* and *Botrytis infestans* were only two, out of a multitude of species previously unrecorded; for Berkeley and the rest were working on a part of the earth's flora that had so far been all too scantily explored. Importation by way of museum specimens was one channel of introduction for highly undesirable alien mildews.

Another was the stocking of botanical gardens, all over Europe, with acquisitions from overseas, and the field experiments which were being made in every country on the acclimatization of foreign economic plants. Then, in those first glorious years of Queen Victoria's reign, there was a great increase in mercantile traffic. There were some who thought that the Potato Blight was brought to Europe by the early steamships, the fungus on imported potatoes surviving the shorter time at sea. But it was only in 1840 that the first Cunarders crossed the Atlantic under paddle and sail, and they were often out-distanced by the clipper ships. The *Great Eastern* was not launched until 1858. It was very doubtful whether the steamships really had the historical distinction of bringing the Potato Blight and the Vine Mildew to Europe from the New World. But that they came with some imported produce or other was more probable than that their spores were carried over the ocean by any singular accident of the winds.

Again, with the beginning of England's great era of commercial prosperity horticulture was in great vogue. The nobility and gentry, and especially the *nouveaux riches* who made their money out of the mines and the mills, indulged greatly in hothouses, winter gardens and conservatories, which they crammed with all kinds of exotic plants, from palms to aspidistras. These heavily luxurious hothouses of the prosperous were as characteristic of the period as the undrained streets and the overcrowded hovels in the industrial towns, where the infant mortality reached sixty per cent and typhus ran with the rats and crawled with the lice. Paxton's design for a 'Crystal Palace' to house the Great Exhibition of 1851 was not chosen only for its intrinsic beauty, or because the light construction of glass and iron was then about the cheapest way of covering the desired space. It glorified the hothouse as the best-available symbol of the Wealth, Culture, Art, Enlightenment, Prosperity, and self-improving Industry of England. There were hothouses everywhere, and the nurserymen's businesses were flourishing. In these hothouses, both the foreign plants and the pests and fungi brought over on them were given the very best chance to make themselves at home. The hardier plants were naturally tried out in the open, and those species of fungi which could stand the climate spread and multiplied faster than rabbits in Australia.

Nobody would ever know by what particular route the Oidium of the Vine was introduced; it might indeed have been present in Europe for decades before it was first observed on the vines at Margate in 1845; it might have come from the East – from the vines of Asia. At any rate by about 1850 it was ravaging the Grand Vines of France, and, with that other small fungus, the *Botrytis Bassiana* which caused the Muscardine disease of silkworms, it was plundering the wealth of Lombardy.

Professor Duchartre, of the Institut Agronomique at Versailles, was among the first to try Mr. Tucker's sulphur remedy on the vines in France. He stirred up flowers of sulphur in water and dashed the mixture over the foliage with a garden syringe. The treatment was effective, a means was available of keeping the Oidium in check, but sulphuring the vines over hundreds of hectares of open hillside was a very different matter from spraying a few vines on the trellises or sponging down individual plants in the vineries at Margate. It meant going up and down the rows, mile after mile, with a garden syringe and a bucket of sulphur and water that had for everlastingly to be refilled. Many labour-saving variants of the process were tried. One of them was to wet the foliage with plain water first, and then blow on dry sulphur dust with a pair of specially-constructed bellows. Count Duchâtel had this done on some twelve hundred acres of his vines, and the treatment was quite effective, but it was very soon found that the preliminary wetting of the vines could be dispensed with, if the sulphur dust was applied when they were moist with dew. Often enough a perfunctory dusting of the vines with sulphur, irrespective of whether they were moist with dew or bone-dry in the heat of the day, was all that the peasants could be persuaded to undertake, and then the results were sometimes disappointing. When the sulphur came in contact with the patches of mildew it caused them to dry up, and thus checked the spread of the disease. But the sulphur was washed off the leaves by rain, and the vines were growing all the time: a week after the sulphuring there would be new foliage without a particle of sulphur on it, and tender for invasion. The mildew preferred the young shoots. The vinegrowers, with their syringes and sulphur boxes, had to contend with an organism that charged the very atmosphere with its spores.

The French chemists sought for improvements on the sulphur remedy. When solid sulphur and lime were simply boiled together in a saucepan with water, the two substances entered into chemical combination one with the other, and produced an amber-coloured fluid having a very strong odour of bad eggs. This lime-sulphur, or sulphuret of calcium as it was then called, was suitably diluted in water and then applied to the vines with a syringe. It sometimes scorched the leaves a little, but it was even more deadly to the Oidium than pure flowers of sulphur. The evil smell of the compound gave those who were using it a satisfying feeling that they were applying something very potent, and in fact the vapour of sulphuretted hydrogen was very toxic to the fungus – while it lasted. Once applied to foliage, however, the bad smell soon passed off, and a fine deposit of sulphur mixed with carbonate of lime remained. The ultimate effect was much the same as applying flowers of sulphur, but there was something to be said for boiling the sulphur up with lime first as the fluid was easy to apply with a syringe, the sulphuret of calcium as such, had an immediate destructive effect on the fungus, and after the fluid was decomposed by atmospheric oxidation it left sulphur deposited, wherever the solution had wetted the foliage, in a film that was not easily washed off by the rain. Before 1855, Becquerel had gone one better even than this lime-suphur. Having made his solution of sulphur by boiling it with an alkali – potash or lime – he then threw the sulphur out of solution again by adding an acid. The point of this apparently roundabout procedure being that the sulphur, precipitated from solution, was in the form of such minute particles that it made a kind of milk in water. It was the white 'milk' or magisterium of sulphur; a precipitate of sulphur so impalpably fine that it entered every crevice of the foliage *that was wetted by the spray*.

Both chemists and vinegrowers, however, soon found in practice that everything watered does not get wet. The young grapes, for example, with their waxy surface, could be dipped bodily into water, or into these sulphur solutions, and they would come out as dry as ever. One way of wetting a duck's back was to put the bird in soapy water. So a number of experimenters tried mixing soap with their sulphur solutions to make them wet the young grapes. The soap was curdled by the lime in the solutions and the curds at once choked up the holes in the syringe. Some of the other pioneers in the making of chemical spray fluids were more lucky, for they added skimmed milk to their sulphur solutions, and thanks to the casein in the skimmed milk, which was an excellent 'spreader' unaffected by lime, the grapes were well wetted and the holes in the syringe remained unobstructed. The preparation of mixtures for spraying the vines threatened to become a trifle complicated, but a good lime-sulphur *bouillie*, even with the addition of skimmed milk, was still much easier to make than a good *minestrone* or Irish Stew. The great practical difficulty was in the application of liquid specifics in the open vineyards with the little squirts and syringes that were then available. It was fortunate that the simpler methods worked reasonably well; in the vineyards fine dry sulphur was dusted on to the foliage, and in the greenhouses sulphur was painted on to the hot pipes, where it volatilized and gave off sulphur fumes.

The Oidium caused the greatest havoc during the early fifties, before the peasant vine-grower had been brought to realize that the troublesome sulphuring was the only alternative to ruin. After that the fungus was held in check, and although it still caused great losses in bad seasons, the vintages were no longer at its mercy. At first, when the mildew had not yet obtained a footing everywhere, and there were only a limited number of sites from which it was sending forth its spores, one timely application of sulphur would sometimes have an almost magical effect; but later, when the invader had settled down to stay, and every terrace was copiously provided with it in its overwintering stages, more and more applications became necessary, and it was popularly supposed that the mildew was getting used to the poison, that the sulphur was losing its effect. In the course of long years, when the practice of sulphuring the vines had become traditional, it was found that three applications of sulphur were usually necessary: the first in the spring, when the young shoots of the vines were only from two to four inches long; the second about the time of flowering; and the third about two weeks before the 'turn' or *veraison* when the grapes from being green and hard began to take on the sweetness and colour of maturity.

While the vinegrowers on the Continent were contending with *Oidium Tuckeri*, one of its near relatives, another of the Powdery Mildews, was causing consternation among the hop growers of Worcester and Kent. The Hop Mould was no newcomer, it had been known in the hop gardens for generations, but it first became a serious plague during those 'Blight years' of the late forties, which so greatly favoured the increase of all kinds of fungal parasites on the crops. Like the Vine Mildew, from which it was almost indistinguishable in its summer stage, the Hop Mould grew on the *surface* of the leaves, where it was apparent to the naked eye as white mouldy patches. When it grew on the leaves it weakened the hop plants as a whole by putting a greater or lesser part of their food manufacturing or assimilatory apparatus out of action, but the irreparable damage was done when the mould grew over the 'burrs', the female inflorescence or 'flowers' of the plants, which after wind-pollination developed into the seed-cones or 'hops' of the brewers. When the Mould spread over the burrs they did not develop into mouldy hops – they did not develop at all. They shrivelled into small hard balls, covered with the fungus and there were no 'hops' either to pick or to sell.

The hop growers, in the main, held the rooted conviction that the growth of the Mould was due to some unhealthy condition of the sap of the hop plants, attributable to the weather, but they were eager enough to try the sulphur treatments which were proving successful on the vines. And here again the various treatments, if applied in time, worked very well. Fine dry sulphur was puffed on to the hop bines, and here and there the farm pump was used to spray them with lime-sulphur.

By 1855, the majority of the hop growers were saving their hops by means of sulphur, only to run into a new trouble. The hop factors, the middlemen of the Borough, who sold the hops to the brewers, issued a manifesto. The brewers, they said, objected to 'the incorporation of sulphur in the hop plant', the slightest trace of sulphur would spoil the beer, and involve the whole brewing industry in great financial loss, if not ultimate ruin. John Lindley, in *The Gardeners' Chronicle*, had one or two trenchant things to say about this precious Manifesto. He began by reminding the brewers that it was customary to burn a little sulphur under the hops when they were drying in the oast houses, to preserve them and give them a good colour. It was late in the day to discover that a trace of sulphur spoilt the beer, and if the brewers were really suffering any loss, well, he had heard of their use of picric or carbazotic acid, an intensely bitter but deleterious substance, in place of hops, and perhaps it was the picric acid that spoiled the beer, and not the good produce of the Kentish hop gardens, sulphured or otherwise. The brewers discreetly withdrew their objections, before John Lindley went into further details, and the sulphuring of the hops continued.

Sulphur was the remedy for the Powdery Mildews on the vines and the hops — why should it not also be effective against the Potato Blight? Farmers, in the main, knew nothing of the distinctions between different species of fungi; if there was a 'Blight' in the air it seemed natural to them that all sorts of crops should be affected; and if in a 'Blight' season there was an outbreak of cholera, or an unusual number of dead fish were washed up in the Humber, those happenings were probably due to the same cause. By 1855 there was still no remedy for the Potato Blight, and with the idea that sulphur might be a panacea for all kinds of plant disease, it was certainly tried on the potatoes. But it had little effect, and the thoughtful were left wondering why sulphur should kill mildews on some plants but not on others. One of the reasons was already apparent to those who studied the habits of growth of the mildews concerned. The powdery mildews on the Vines and the Hops grew on the surface of the leaves with all their spawn strands exposed, so that fumes from particles of sulphur dusted upon them, or traces of sulphur acids, could readily destroy them. The spawn of the Potato Blight fungus however was buried and protected within the leaf tissue, where no chemical could destroy it without at the same time destroying the leaf itself. It seemed, moreover, that sulphur was less toxic to the Blight fungus than to the Powdery Mildews, and though it could certainly injure the exposed spore-bearing parts of the fungus, which grew out from the breathing pores, and thus had some immediate effect, what was the use of *that*, when the unharmed root-spawn could send out a new growth in a few hours?

The sulphur which saved the vines was no remedy for the Potato Blight, and that disease continued to ravage the potato crops, to a greater or lesser extent, according to the weather, entirely unchecked. Seasons of partial famine in Ireland, attributable to it, ceased to be news. The eviction of impecunious tenants continued, the landlords 'consolidated their position', and the practice of agriculture in Ireland was to some extent improved, as it had already been improved in England, by farming in larger units at the expense of the dispossessed. There was a search for plants that might serve as substitutes for the potato, and in 1854, Decaisne, of the Jardin des Plantes in Paris, was experimenting in the acclimatization of the Chinese Yam. Sets were sent to England and tried in many localities. This particular Yam, *Dioscorea Batatas*, proved hardy both in France and in the British Isles. Its roots were pure white, very rich in starch, and when steamed or roasted they tasted very much like the best of potatoes. They even had advantages from the culinary point of view, as they took only half the time to cook. The yield of edible roots per rod, or per acre, was also promising, but unfortunately the roots penetrated very deeply into the ground – they would go down three feet or more – and cultivation to that depth was difficult where it was not impossible. Nature had, moreover, modelled these roots upon a most inconsiderate plan. They were rather like long misshapen parsnips the wrong way up, smaller at the top than at the bottom, so that there was no pulling them from the ground, and each one had to be carefully and laboriously *excavated*. The trials were not continued to the point of discovering from what soft-rots and other maladies these roots would suffer if they were grown, for example in the deep black soil of the Fens, but it was felt that the Yam, even the Chinese Yam, could never be a substitute for the prolific and easily-cultivated potato, provider of one-fifth of England's food supplies.

CHAPTER IV

FRUITS OF THE FUNGI

THE Oidium had not been overrunning the vines and the hops for very long before another, and a very different kind of fungal growth was noticed on the leaves of the hops. There was not only the white Hop Mould, there was also

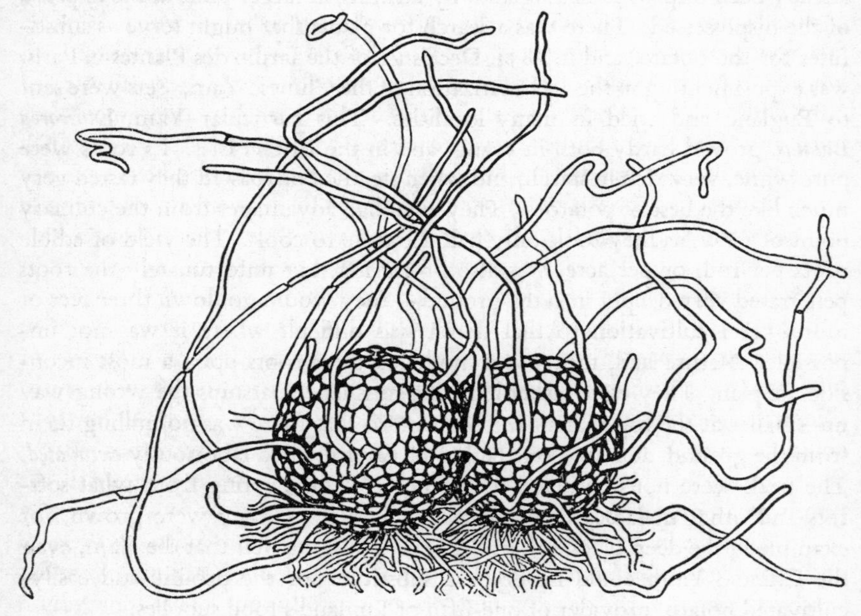

FIG. 4. The over-wintering 'fruits', or perithecia, of the Hop Mould. (× 300)
After Tulasne, 1861

the Red, or Brown Mould, which came later. When this Red Mould was examined under the microscope it did not present a spectacle of beautifully poised, glistening and transparent spores in vertical chains. There were, instead, a number of dark-coloured, and comparatively large sperical objects, sitting snug on the silken felt of spawn strands which had grown over the leaf surface, and furnished with long, tendril-like appendages. These objects had a certain resemblance to a clustered mass of exceedingly tiny spiders, except that they did not move, they were completely spherical, and each of them had more appendages than any spider had legs.

A number of small fungi were known which grew in this way, and as they were often of a reddish colour, they were called Erysiphe, from the Greek for 'red' – or, more strictly, 'rust' – as in 'Erysipelas'. No two kinds of fungi could look more different from each other than did the Oidium and the Erysiphe on the hop leaves. Both had a spawn of fine filaments which crept over the leaf-surface and drew nourishment from the outer leaf-cells by means of tiny suckers; but the spores of the Oidium which grew up in poised chains from the spawn, were *naked*, while the spores of the Erysiphe were enclosed and protected within the dark-coloured spheres, which were in fact, spore-cases, or perithecia. The delicate spores of the Oidium drifted off, when ripe, in any breath of wind, but the spores of the Erysiphe were released only after a long period of rest, when the hard rind of their spore-case burst and they emerged, yet further enclosed within a delicate sac – which was rather like the skin within the shell of an egg. The Erysiphe was one of a very numerous group of fungi, which Berkeley for convenience of reference had called the 'sac-fungi', or, as he would have it in Greek, the 'Ascomycetes'. The Erysiphe, said Berkeley at first, had nothing to do with the Oidium, it was a different fungus altogether.

But it was a singular fact that the Erysiphe should make its appearance on just those parts of the hop leaves where the Oidium had been growing, or was even yet erecting its chains of spores. Of course, the growth of the Oidium *might* produce some half-decay of the foliage on which the Erysiphe could flourish, so that the one parasite naturally followed the other. But if that were so – where were the 'seeds' of the Erysiphe lurking, until the Oidium had prepared the way for them?

Dr. Léveillé in Paris was convinced that the Oidium with its exposed chains of vegetative spores, and the Erysiphe with its spherical fruits, were but successive stages in the development of one single fungus. That the Oidium was merely the Erysiphe when young. It was hard for Berkeley to admit the possibility of such a thing: he was the most industrious of taxonomists, and the existence of polymorphism – state of having more than one form – among the lower fungi would profoundly disturb the whole beautiful system of classification that was being worked out for them. What would happen to the taxonomists' noblest labours if half the minute fungi then recognized as distinct species were to be regarded as mere stages in the development of some of the rest? When so much scholarly work had been done in articulating names for thousands of species of fungi from resurrected fragments of

Latin and Greek, and they had all been arranged in a neat and natural order, the least that Nature could do was to keep her multitudinous inventions tidy in the pigeon holes provided for them. No! Oidium was Oidium, and Erysiphe was Erysiphe, and so they should remain, separate and distinct *in saecula saeculorum*. But Berkeley was not the only cryptogamic botanist with a passion for taxonomy, and certainly, so far as the Erysiphaceae were concerned, Léveillé was a far better taxonomist than Berkeley. He extracted a great deal of pure taxonomical pleasure out of the Powdery Mildews, which Berkeley, because of his obstinacy, missed altogether. The different Oidiums on the vine, hop, strawberry, rose, barberry, hawthorn, oak, peach, maple and other plants, were so much alike in appearance that it was difficult to distinguish them one from another. They had few of those exquisite but characteristic differences in the shapes of their parts which the taxonomists loved. When the Oidiums, however, were related to the forms of Erysiphe which followed them, then the case was very different. The spherical conceptacles or spore-cases of the Erysiphaceae, with their appendages, might have been designed by nature for the express purpose of giving the taxonomists a special and particular joy.

The Erysiphe found on the hops, for example, had long thread-like appendages, plain at the ends; while the one on the barberry had appendages which were splayed out at the ends in a most ornamental and characteristic fashion [Plate I, 1a.]. Other species had appendages terminating in processes shaped like little cog-wheels, or like bits of bent-iron work on fancy gates, and these shapes were so constant and unmistakable that they served as the veritable signatures or fingerprints of the different species. On the basis of these appendages and of some characteristics of the conceptacles themselves, Léveillé, by 1851, had sorted the whole of the Erysiphaceae into a number of genera or families, which he called, after their most representative members, Uncinula, Sphaerotheca, and so on. Generations later, Léveillé's classification was substantially adopted, with envy and admiration, by all botanists. The Powdery Mildew on the vine was called *Uncinula necator*, and that on the hops, *Sphaerotheca humuli*. But at the time little attention was paid to these distinctions, and the botanists continued to refer, with less precision, to the Oidium and Erysiphe on the hops and the Oidium on the vines. One practical significance of Léveillé's taxonomical labours was that they showed very clearly that the various Powdery Mildews were caused by distinct and different fungi; the one on the vines did not grow on the hops, and the one on the roses did not grow on the barberry. The importance of this fact, to farmers and gardeners, was evident, and it was a contribution towards one of the key realizations in plant pathology: that specific plant diseases were caused by specific pathogens. The Powdery Mildews on different plants were certainly not all manifestations, as some supposed, of one common or garden Erysiphe.

With Léveillé's classical monograph, the idea that the spherical bodies with their appendages, which distinguished the Erysiphe, might simply be the fruits of the Oidium, or that the Oidium was just a young and budding stage of the Erysiphe, had already made much progress, and the 'polymorphists' were able to put forward a very plausible account of the function and purpose of the two stages in the life-history of a typical Oidium-Erysiphe mildew. In the spring and early summer, the White Mould of the Hops grew on the young foliage, each patch a microscopic forest whose 'trees' were chains of short-lived and unprotected spores. These spores spread the mould through the hop gardens, each new patch to which they gave rise producing its millions of spores in turn. But the delicate summer spores, which died in a few days if they did not come to rest on moist and young hop foliage, were not the true 'seeds' of the fungus. They more closely resembled buds, which when detached from their parent spawn would promptly strike elsewhere. They were 'bud-spores', to be called, variously, gemmae, gonidia, and finally conidia. They were not protected, as seed-spores would have to be, for lying dormant over the winter on decaying leaves or in the soil. They could not carry the fungus over, alive, from one year to another. The true 'seed-spores' of the Oidium had still to be found, and in what more likely place should they be sought than within such hard spore-cases as those of the Erysiphe, which were so well adapted for preserving their small sac-fuls of spores against decay in the winter, and for discharging them in the spring when there was new foliage on which they could grow? The conceptacles of the Erysiphe, with their long tendrils for anchorage or dispersal, were simply what they appeared to be – the perfect fruits of the Hop Mould.

But probability was not *proof*, and for proof it was necessary to demonstrate that some part of the supposed early growth of the fungus, the Oidium, actually developed into the fruits of the Erysiphe. And here, once again, several botanists managed to see exactly what they expected to see. At the Great Exhibition of 1851, a certain Dr. Plomley hung up a drawing of the Hop Mould which showed conceptacles developing half-way up the spore chains of the Oidium. The suggestion being that two immature summer spores in the chain, next to each other, co-operated in some sexual way and grew into one winter fruit. In 1852, Professor Giovanni Battista Amici, of the Royal Academy of Georgofili in Florence, described similar growths in the spore chains of the Oidium of the Vine. And the brothers Tulasne in Paris made a great feature of such organs in their magnificent drawings from nature of several species of Erysiphe gathered near Versailles in 1853 [Plate I, 3]. Opinions differed as to what these intermediate sporangia might be. Some said they were the conceptacles of the Erysiphe in an early stage of development, and pointed to this as the desired proof that the Oidium and the Erysiphe were indeed successive stages of the same fungus. But Baron Cesati of Lombardy took them to be parts of a different fungus altogether, which Ehrenberg called *Cicinnobolus Florentinus*, growing on or among the Oidium and confused with it. The brothers Tulasne called the bodies 'pycnidia' and regarded them as a third kind of fruit, belonging to the Erysiphe-Oidium fungi, but different from both their chain spores and their conceptacles.

If there were not more of humanity in one brave error than in ten tame accuracies, the mistake of the brothers Tulasne in claiming pycnidia for the Erysiphaceae would be a poor introduction to their revealing and beautiful works. But as it happened the mistake could serve only to throw into prominence the grace and meaning of the whole. The brothers were devout Catholics, and their work of adoration, no less than of science, was to reveal in what great diversity and abundance God had given fruits to the very least of his creation, even to the most minute of the cryptogamic plants. Their researches were dedicated to the glory of God, and if from excess of zeal they sometimes saw fruits of the fungi which did not exist, that was as nothing to the great wealth of fruits which they did truly find, or to the liberation of scientific thought which followed their refusal to accept too narrow a view of the metamorphoses through which lower forms of life might pass.

The brothers Tulasne were born, and at last came to die, within a year of each other. In their botanical labours, as in their life, they were so closely associated that the name 'Tulasne' was often taken to refer to a single individual, and later workers reproducing their drawings of the fungi, the finest ever made, rarely attributed them to Charles or to Louis, but always to one, indisseverable 'Tulasne'. The close association of the brothers, their fusion, as it were, of two individualities into one being, and to one end, was reflected in the nature of their discoveries. It was their achievement to establish that the red and the black Rusts on the wheat were two stages in the development of a single organism, and that the Oidium and the Erysiphe were equally members of each other.

Louis Tulasne at first studied for the Law, a vocation for which his retiring disposition and pellucid, natural honesty rendered him entirely unfitted; but

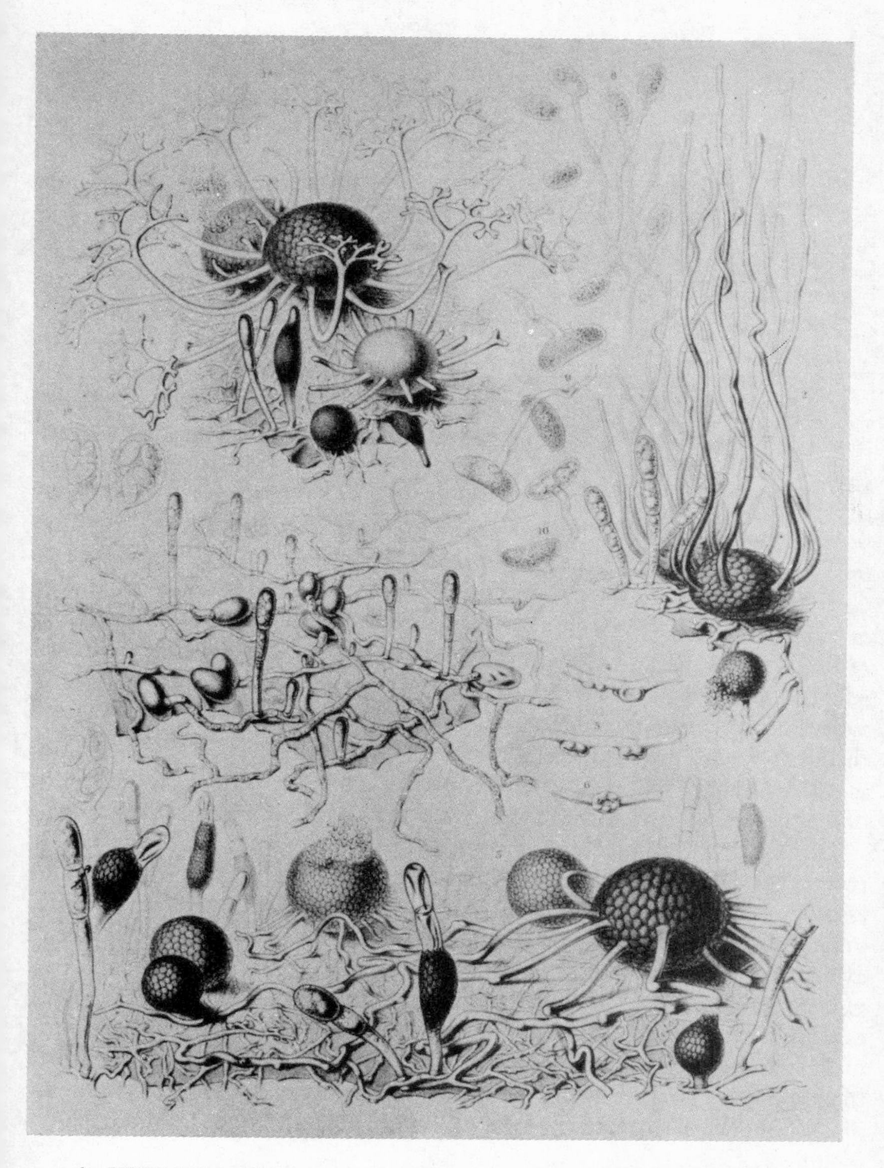

1 ab ERYSIPHE Berberidis DC. 2. E. Astragali DC. 3—6. E. communis (Hypericearum) Fr.
7 ab E. Pisi DC. 8. E. tortilis Fr. 9—10. E. pannosa (Rosæ) Fr.

PLATE I. Some species of Erysiphe: a page from the Selecta Fungorum Carpologia
(*Reduced*)
L. R. & C. Tulasne, 1861

by 1842 he had found his place, and was working as an assistant naturalist at the Jardin des Plantes. Charles Tulasne practised medicine, also in Paris, and found scope for his artistic talents and his taste for botanical pursuits in making the drawings to illustrate his brother's scientific papers. They published several great memoirs in the *Annales des Sciences naturelles*, especially those concerning the Rust and Smut fungi afflicting cereals, but their masterpiece, and joint labour over some fifteen years, was the *Selecta Fungorum Carpologia*, 'exhibiting especially those facts and illustrations which go to prove that various kinds of fruits and seeds are produced either simultaneously or in succession by the same fungus'.[1] The work was to have been very comprehensive, covering all the principal families of the fungi, but Louis's health failed him in 1864, and when the brothers retired to Hyères in the south of France, to spend the rest of their days in the service of the Church, they left behind them three perfect volumes only, which were printed in Paris by command of the Emperor, between 1861 and 1865. The text, by Louis, was in Latin throughout, which was perhaps a pity, for the matter was such that the beauties and exactitudes of the French language would have been quite adequate for its original raiment, but the drawings, by Charles, had an unearthly beauty, and were works of art that far transcended mere illustrations. The microscope in the hands of the brothers Tulasne was a lamp lifted in the darkness of a sub-world, amongst the strange orchards of the cryptogams. The third volume bore the inscription: '*Non nobis, Domine, non nobis, sed nomini tuo da gloriam.*'

The first volume of the *Carpologia* was exclusively devoted to the Erysiphaceae, for which the brothers claimed no less than five different kinds of fruits or spores. There were the bud-spores of the Oidium stage, in chains; the 'pycnidia' which developed half-way up those chains and which burst, releasing charges of so-called 'stylospores' when ripe; and there were the indisputable spherical conceptacles of the Erysiphe from which membraneous sacs each containing usually eight sac- or 'asco-' spores were released after a period of rest. The principal evidence which the brothers could offer in support of their conviction that all these fruits did indeed belong to a single fungus, was that they all appeared to arise from the same mother-spawn [Plate I]. The evidence was strong, but it did *not* amount to rigorous proof, for there remained the possibility that, in the confused tangle of spawn-strands on the leaves, spawn belonging to more than one species of fungus might be present. The affinity even of the Oidium to the Erysiphe was still not formally proven. But the effect of the brothers' work

[1] Grove's translation, 1931, *vide* pages 383 and 453, herein.

as a whole was persuasive and philosophical, it established the 'polymorphism' of the lower fungi on grounds of probability, and it set other workers searching amongst the successive fruits of different species of fungi for the 'perfect' fruits, the overwintering conceptacles or other protected organs in which the true seed-spores were carried. Botanists could no longer believe that the Oidium, with its mere vegetative bud-spores, was the whole of a living organism; it needed the overwintering fruits of the Erysiphe to complete it. The homage paid by naturalists of later generations to the work of adoration of the brothers Tulasne was to be found in a common agreement to regard all fungi of which the winter fruits were unknown as 'imperfect' – the *Fungi Imperfecti*.

The next theme of inquiry in these fundamental botanical researches which were revealing the nature of the enemies with which the practical farmer had to contend, could be conceived as arising out of the realization that parasitic fungi had fruits and true seed-spores – they were not mere growths of 'mould'. If there were fruits and seed-spores – where were the equivalents of the 'flowers'? Or where did fertilization take place? Where, in the life-histories of the Vine Mildew and the Hop Mould, were the sexual conjugations almost universally to be found in nature before the formation of fertile seeds or eggs?

No one knew why sex was necessary. It was not necessary for reproduction, as parthenogenesis was common enough, especially as an alternative mode of generation, amongst many of the smaller species of living things. But Nature, or her husband, the Almighty, had not devised such a wonderful variety of highly ingenious mechanisms for copulation or pollination, and fitted them to everything from polar bears to periwinkles, merely for fun. Many of the *consequences* of sexual reproduction, even in 1855, could be perceived clearly enough: the sharing of the qualities of two parents amongst their offspring, the division of labour, the advantages – and disadvantages – of cross-breeding. These were apparent, not only to botanists and stock-breeders, but to every old woman who said the new baby had its father's eyebrows and its mother's nose. By 1939, a great deal more was known about the consequences of sexual reproduction, and of its mechanisms, but the wisest had still to admit that they had not the slightest inkling of the dispositions in the ultimate structure of matter, in the nature of Life, or in the will of God, which made sex necessary or inevitable. It was still only possible to observe the how and when of its occurrence, and the limit of human philosophy was to justify it from its consequences, and to say *because* it does so and so, *therefore* it *is*.

It was discovered in the time of the brothers Tulasne that sea-weed laid eggs – or oospores – and that these eggs were fertilized by spermatazoids. The observation of the sexual processes, fairly complete for the flowering plants, had not then been extended to all the 'lower' plants which were propagated by means of spores. They had been dubbed 'Cryptogamia', by Linneaus in the eighteenth century, for the very reason that their reproductive processes were mysterious and obscure. Amongst the minute fungi sexual conjugation had not yet been observed, but arguing by analogy, from the sexuality of the sea-weeds and other algae, to which the fungi appeared to be closely related, it was in the highest degree probable that sexual reproduction *did* take place amongst them, as amongst nearly all living things. Argument by analogy had been the bane of science since the Dark Ages; it was never to be trusted, but it indicated directions of search.

Sexual conjugation very generally occurred when an organism had to pass through a dormant, gestatory, or resting stage in its life-history: before the formation of a seed that had to lie dormant over the winter; or of an embryo that had to live through a long period of gestation in a womb, or of incubation within the shell of an egg. It was as though the dual contribution from male and female gave the embryo strength to survive the strain of hibernation, or pre-natal development. When the organism had not to pass through such a stage, sexual reproduction did not always occur. A cutting from a plant would take root and grow, reproducing that from which it was taken, without any sexual process. The Canadian pond-weed could spread from end to end of a river, by detachment of parts, without ever breaking into flower, for its growth was continuous and it had no resting stage.

Once the mould on the hops was recognized as a living plant – not a product of fermentation, or of spontaneous generation, or a morbid outgrowth from the cells of its host, but a plant propagated by the equivalents of buds and seeds, and even bearing fruits in which those seeds were protected during the winter – then it was reasonable to study its growth for evidences of sexual conjugation. And there was a pointer to the stage at which that process might occur – not preceding the putting-forth of the bud-spores or conidia, but just before the formation of the overwintering fruits.

It was Anton de Bary, small, nervously-eager young professor of botany then making his reputation at Freiburg, who explored the sexuality of the fungi and penetrated beyond the beautiful appearances seen by the brothers Tulasne to the life-processes at work. In 1853, at the age of twenty-two, de

Bary took a medical Degree, and in that same year his first and famous little book, *Die Brandpilze*, was published by Müller in Berlin. It concerned the fungi which caused the Rusting and Smutting of the wheat, the oats, the barley and the rye. With this book de Bary staked his pitch in mycology, but for some years afterwards he devoted himself to the study of the algae. He could scarcely do otherwise, for the great botanical questions of the day were then centring round the development of the algae, and the works of Thuret and Bornet, Hofmeister and Pringsheim were at the leading edge of the search into the nature of life on earth. It was to be de Bary's part to extend the work on the morphology and physiology of the algae to those other spore-bearing plants which were called the fungi. The difference in mentality between the young de Bary – after he had been to school with the algologists – and his seniors, the brothers Tulasne on the other side of the Rhine, was illustrated by the differences in their drawings. Those of Tulasne were full, three-dimensional, emotional; those of de Bary were plain, two-dimensional, diagrammatic, stripped of every inessential detail, concentrated upon a single particular, and made with the mechanical assistance of the camera lucida. They were the product of an acute and searching intelligence, inspired not by instincts of reverence, but by desire for exact knowledge. And this knowledge was sought, not by the examination of organisms in their mature complexity, but by tracing out their development from generation to generation, from spore to spore. It was a pregnant and a new method in science; something of its sociological counterpart could be seen in the contemporary works of Karl Marx; it was the historical method applied to botanical research.

The tracking down of the sexual processes of moulds and mildews, and the subsequent phases of their development, might seem a pursuit remote from the concerns of everyday life; but when it was realized that the surest and deadliest way of extirpating any living species was to prevent its natural reproduction, then the researches into the sexuality of crop-destroying fungi, were seen to be of the very greatest practical significance.

Nature was often very gracious to human investigators who desired to probe her secrets. She left some clues amongst the simpler organisms to those that were more complex. The Erysiphaceae, the Powdery Mildews, were one of her gifts to the mycologists; they had *some* things in common with all the mildews causing diseases of plants, their life-histories were not very complicated; many of them were easy to find in *all* the stages of their growth, and their parts were exposed on the *surface* of leaves, where Man could watch them at his ease, once he had made for himself the necessary aids to vision. Anton de Bary took advantage of this invitation, and finding a typical Powdery Mildew, *Erysiphe Cichoracearum* D.C., growing on dandelions, which apparently suited it very well, he set himself to correct and amplify some of the observations that had been made on the fungi of the family Erysiphaceae. What was true for one of them *might* be true of them all – others could look into *that* later on – meanwhile it was of more value to science to have a thorough knowledge of *one* species in the family than a partial knowledge of dozens of them, and the Mildew, growing on his officinal dandelions was handy.

He waited until the autumn, when the winter fruits, the perithecia, of the Mildew were developing, and then pryed about with his microscope over the surface of small pieces of the dandelion leaves, to discover exactly how the formation of the fruits began. One of the suggestions of the brothers Tulasne had been that their 'pycnidia' – the fruiting bodies half-way up the spore chains – produced tiny 'male' sperm-spores which found their way on to some corresponding 'female' organs of the minute plant, thus starting the growth of its fertile and perfect fruits. De Bary did not find this happening at all. In fact he was sceptical about the very existence of those 'pycnidia' of the brothers Tulasne, and he showed ultimately that they did *not* belong to the Oidium-Erysiphe Mildews. They were growths of another fungus parasitic upon them. Little fleas had smaller fleas . . . The Erysiphes parasitized the hops and the vines, and this other fungus, to which he gave the name of *Cicinnobolus Cesatii*, parasitized the Oidium stage of the Erysiphe. Its spawn traversed the chains of bud-spores, and the swellings, the alleged 'pycnidia', were its fruiting bodies. This point was settled, with as much finality as could be expected, by one of de Bary's Contributions to the Morphologie and Physiology of the Fungi, published at Frankfort in 1870. *Cicinnobolus Cesatii* was a wonderful name for the beneficent parasite that attacked the Oidium; it rumbled round the roof of the mouth, it honoured Baron Cesati, and it was sufficiently suggestive of the bulbous and bolster-

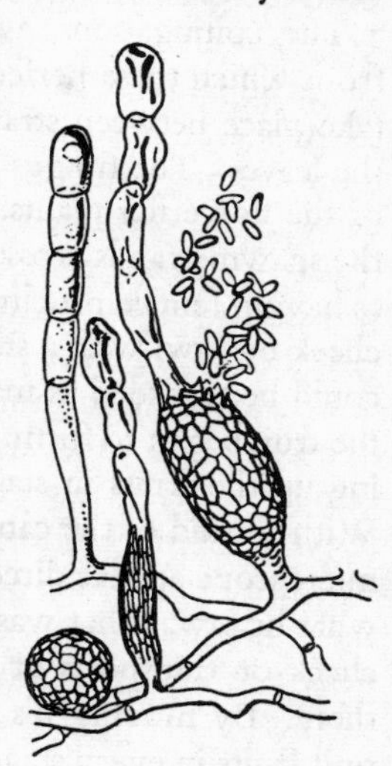

FIG. 5. One parasitic fungus grows upon another. The fruits regarded by Tulasne as pycnidia and stylospores of Erysiphe, found by de Bary to be parts of *Cicinnobolus Cesatii* parasitic upon it (1869). (× 300) After Tulasne, 1861

like growths. John Lindley was a spoil-sport, and it was just downright nasty of him to say that the progress of botany as a science was more impeded in England by the repulsive appearance of the names it employed than by any other cause whatever. The Cicinnobolus was very interesting, most appropriate and onomatopoeic, and it was a great advantage to have it cleared out of the way, leaving the Erysiphe fungi with only the summer bud-spores, or conidia, in chains, and the perfect overwintering fruits.

The conjugations, which looked suspiciously like sexual conjugations, from which these perfect fruits really developed, were found by de Bary to take place between strands of the root-spawn, creeping over the surface of the leaves. The fungus had no parts corresponding to the pollen and stigma of the flowering plants. Conjugation occurred at some of the places where the spawn-strands crossed. The underlying strand, which could be regarded as having female proclivities, bulged out a small protuberance, which pressed cheek by jowl with a similar protuberance from the overlying strand, which could be regarded as male. After the osculation of these two protuberances, the fruit began to form. The two original cells divided and multiplied, building up the fruits in stages, by a wonderful process of cellular architecture. With the aid of the camera lucida, which made the magnified images in the microscope appear directly over his paper, de Bary had only to draw round what he saw. That was not so easy as it might sound, but it imposed a stern check on transports of enthusiasm and the drawing of things that were not there. By moving his pieces of dandelion-leaf about, de Bary was able to find fruits in every stage of development and so trace out the whole process.

With such evidence available, there was little doubt about the way in which the overwintering fruits of the Powdery Mildews developed from conjugations between the spawn strands. But de Bary, a man of great caution and intellectual integrity, was the severest critic of his own researches. He pointed out that though the fruits *appeared* to arise from a sexual process he had still not yet *proved* that that was indeed so. He had seen the two first cells pressed together, but he had *not* been able to detect any transference of substance from the one to the other. It was not until thirty-three years later, when the significance of the nuclei within cells was better understood, when machines had been invented for cutting successive sections of plant organs only one or two thousandths of a millimetre in thickness, and dyes had been found that would reveal even something of the structure of the nucleus, by staining its parts different colours — it was only after great advances had been made in technique and in the understanding of the intimate mechanism of the sexual process in terms of the nuclei, that de Bary's discovery could be confirmed. Harper, in 1896, was able to show the fusion of 'male' and 'female' nuclei from the two parent cells.

De Bary was not mistaken, and with his observations, in 1863, the complete life-cycle of a typical Powdery Mildew, for example the Hop Mould, could be traced in outline. An ascospore from one of the sacs in an over-wintering fruit germinated on a hop leaf, and gave rise to a gossamer

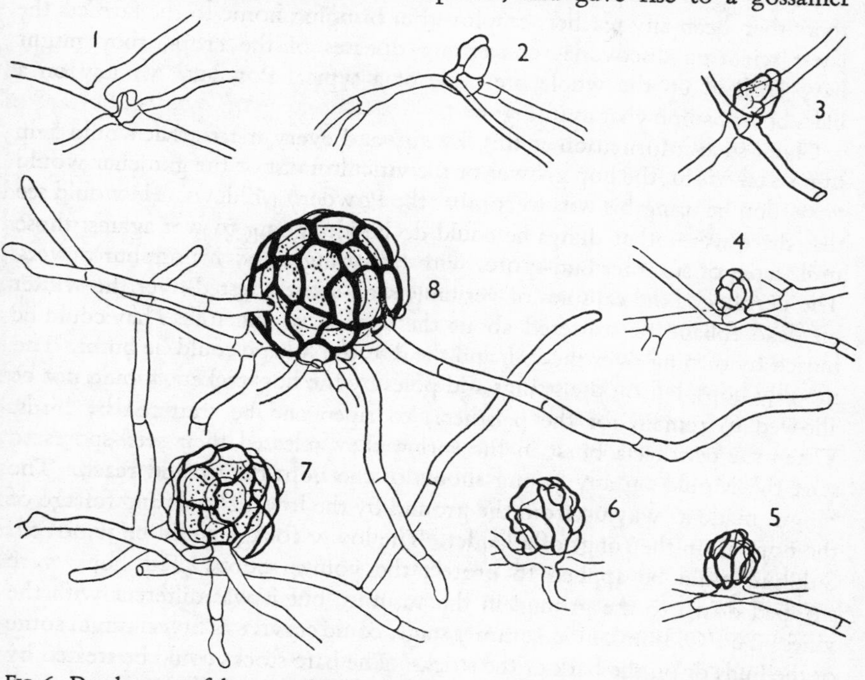

FIG. 6. Development of the over-wintering fruits of a typical Erysiphe or Powdery Mildew, from conjugations between the spawn strands. (× 300)
After de Bary, 1863

growth of spawn or mycelium over its surface. From the mycelium there arose chains of vegetative bud-spores. Later, as winter approached, sexual conjugations took place between the mycelial strands, and from these developed the only true fruits of the fungus — the perithecia. These fruits rested on dead leaves or on the soil during the winter, and in the spring liberated their charges of ascospores to start the cycle over again. That was all — except for one small addendum, that was of the very greatest practical importance: some species of Erysiphe, in localities where the winter was mild, or in sheltered places, could also survive from one season to the next, in their summer or Oidium stage, and they could do this either on wild or on cultivated plants. Of the dread Erysiphe on the vines, for example, only the Oidium stage was known, and it was not until 1892 that Couderc found the perfect overwintering fruits on the European vines. The perfect stages of some of the species of Erysiphe had not yet been found by 1863, but the Erysiphe or Powdery Mildews as a class had given up their mystery. Had there then been any teachers employed in bringing home to the farmers the latest scientific discoveries concerning diseases of the crops, they might have chalked up the whole life-cycle of a typical Powdery Mildew on a blackboard, somewhat as in Figure 7.

Given such information as this, by any and every means that would help him to take it in, the hop grower or the viticulturalist or the gardener would very soon be using his wits to combat the Powdery Mildews. He would see that there were other things he could do besides going to war against those multitudes of summer bud-spores with his syringes and his sulphur dusters. The perithecia, the capsules of veritable seed-spores, rested over the winter on dead foliage or scattered about the surface of the soil. They could be buried by turning over the soil, and the diseased foliage could be burnt. The mouldy hops, left on the strings and poles by the hop-pickers, would not be allowed to remain for the perithecia to ripen and be scattered by birds. When the perithecia burst in the spring they released their seed-spores to start the Mould on any young shoots of the hops they could reach. The fungus made its way up from the ground by the lower shoots and foliage of the hops as up the rungs of a ladder. The lower foliage could be removed. Sulphur could be applied to protect the young shoots. The hops were stripped down to the ground in the autumn, but it was different with the vines. The 'Oidium', in its summer stage, could survive as mycelium in some of the buds or on the bark of the stocks. The bare stocks could be treated by pruning or washing with fungicidal solutions. Taken all the year round, there were many ways of attacking a parasitic fungus, *once its life-cycle was known*. For the Powdery Mildews the life-cycle *was* known by 1863. But by whom? By a small company of learned botanists who had the advantage of being able to read French, German, English, and Latin with a sprinkling of Greek. A part of the knowledge was shared by well-educated gardeners, or employers of gardeners, who read the Rev. M. J. Berkeley's articles in *The Gardeners' Chronicle*. The numerous viticultural societies and provincial academies of learning in France and Italy disseminated information about the Oidium of the vines. Pamphleteers and journalists got hold of a part of the story, often to confuse it with misleading notions of their own. There was no responsible service, in England or in any other country, for giving the farmers reliable information, in plain language, on the subject of plant diseases. The botanists, and the cultured, orchid-fancying kind of gardeners, did not really care to have their botany vulgarized, robbed of its scholasticism, and deflated for the benefit of the general public.

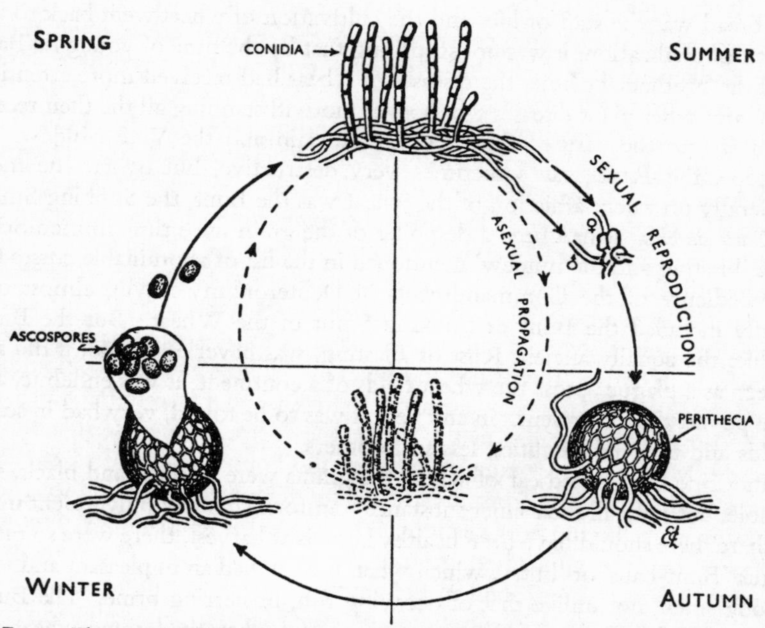

FIG. 7. The complete life-cycle of a typical Powdery Mildew – represented diagrammatically.

Known by 1863

[The Hop Mould is not known to over-winter in its conidial stage in England. The 'Oidium' of the vines in France over-winters in *both* ways.]

So the farmers dismissed the learned discourses of the botanists, when they happened to overhear any of them, as the mere jabber of highfalutin scholars who couldn't grow a marrow on a manure heap, let alone manage a farm. They applied their good empirical remedy – the sulphur – usually at the right time, but often when it was too late, and persisted in such beliefs as that the Mould grew on the hops because the plants were unhealthy; that it was caused by the weather, or that it was attributable to some mysterious and indefinable 'blight' in the air.

CHAPTER V

THE BUNT OF THE WHEAT

As bread was the staff of life, and the cultivation of wheat went back to the dawn of civilization, it was not surprising that by the time of young de Bary and the brothers Tulasne, the diseases of wheat had received more attention than any other plant diseases whatsoever, notwithstanding all the then recent inquiry into the nature of the Potato Murrain and the Vine Mildew. In Europe, the Rust was sometimes very destructive, but by far the most generally prevalent affliction of the wheat was the Bunt, the Stinking Smut, *la Carie de blés*. It had been a despoiler of the grain since time immemorial. The 'blasting and the mildew' mentioned in the list of abominable curses for disobedience of the Commandments in Deuteronomy XXVIII, almost certainly included the Bunt or Stinking Smut of the Wheat. But the Bunt, unlike the equally ancient Rust or Blasting, was never epidemic; it did not sweep as a plague across the wheat fields of a continent; it was endemic, and like poverty, ever-present. In any year it was to be found, very bad in some fields and in some localities, less so in others.

In a ripe but bunted ear of wheat the grains were swollen and black, still whole, but with all their inner substance transformed into a pulverulent mass. Where there should have been healthy kernels at harvest, there were so many black 'Bunt-balls' or 'butts', which when broken had an unpleasant and very strong smell, not unlike that of decaying fish, or herring brine. The Bunt-balls ripened at the same time as the grain, and when the bunted wheat was put to the flail, or threshed in the threshing machine, many of these Bunt-balls burst, and the black powder which they contained contaminated the clean grain. To pick out the bad ears was impracticable, the bunted wheat was reaped and threshed with the good. The flour, in consequence, was discoloured and of unpleasant odour and taste. The bread made from it was not poisonous and it was eaten by the poor. It was not known to cause any such disease as did the ergoted rye, but where there was much Bunt in the wheat it would fetch only a very low price and much of it had to be fed to animals on the farm. In England, bunted wheat was commonly bought up by the gingerbread makers, who disguised both the bad colour and the taste with their ginger and treacle, and no doubt gilded the product on occasion.

The Bunt was common enough but, already in 1855, the appearance of more than an occasional bunted ear in a wheat field was rather a sign of negligence on the part of the farmer than an unavoidable calamity, for simple means of preventing the disease had been found, and had long since been adopted in farm practice. For the story of how these means were discovered it was even then necessary to look back over a hundred years, and to appreciate the work of two men, experimenters of rare genius, who between them anticipated half the 'technique' of modern plant pathology.

The first was Mathieu Tillet, sometime Master of the Mint at Troyes. Tillet was only a farmer in a small way, he had no systematic training in the botany of his time, nor in what were then regarded as the enlightened principles of agriculture. But he chose to devote his leisure to experiments on the crops, and to writing dissertations upon them, by way of developing the powers of his mind. When, in the year 1750, the Academy of Arts and Sciences at Bordeaux, of which Tillet was a member, offered a prize for the best dissertation on the cause and cure of the blackening of the wheat, which was then sorely troubling the farmers in the locality, Tillet responded eagerly to the invitation. He was fascinated by a notion that making practical experiments might be of material help in solving difficult problems of natural philosophy. The problem proposed by the Academy provided him with something on which to try out his idea, and when it came to publishing his dissertation he apologized with great tact and humility for placing before those more learned than himself certain conclusions which were based on mere observation and experiment, and not on reasoning from accepted philosophical tenets. He remarked that 'the experiments a man himself conceives and performs have something to their advantage. They are valuable to him who performs them, hence he follows them closely, and as they become familiar, so they strike him in different ways, and by increasingly stimulating his curiosity cause him to multiply his observations'. And, of course, they enabled a man to see with his own eyes those things which he was talking about.

Tillet's '*Dissertation sur la cause qui corrumpt et noircit les grains de bled dans les épis, et sur les moyens de prevenir ces accidens*' was awarded the Academy's prize – of which the humble provincial experimenter was immensely proud.

It was then variously supposed that the corruption of the wheat in the ear was due to sunstroke – the sun shining too brightly on ears heavy with water after rain; to morbid and sporadic effects of pestilential mists; to poor drainage of the soil; to unpropitious influences of the moon or the weather at the time of sowing; to the attacks of insects; to the use of sheep manure;

or to a principle, at once ethereal and honey-like, called *Enmiéture*, which was supposed to fall out of the sky even in good weather and corrupt the young kernels. Over the Channel, the Englishman, Jethro Tull, had been strongly of opinion that the disease was due to some decay of the seed in wet ground, and he advocated a preservative for the seed which some people claimed to be of magical efficacy and others declared completely useless. The alleged preservative was discovered by the accident of planting seed which had been salvaged from a shipwreck, and it consisted in sprinkling the seed grain with a solution of sea-salt and then drying it with lime. There were a great many theories at offer as to the cause of the corruption, and most of the agricultural writers of the time 'quoted the opinion of the younger Pliny, who said nothing decisive on the point at issue'.

Tillet succeeded in putting practically every one of the theories to the test of direct experiment. He began with the sunstroke and wet-ground theories, planting the same seed in pots which he (*a*) kept normally watered and well-drained, and (*b*) flooded with water four times daily over the whole growing period. There was no difference in the number of bunted ears. Nor did the exposure of the 'water-logged' plants to the brightest sun produce any sign of the Bunt where it was not already apparent. So much for that. The insect theory at first seemed to him more plausible, for when pulling apart the chaff of bunted ears in the field, he several times observed small black insects running out. Indeed it seemed hardly necessary to seek further – black insects, blackened grain. But it was necessary to be sure; and he had also noticed that seed, dirtied with the dust from the Bunt-balls, seemed to give rise to plants with more bunted ears than there were amongst those which had arisen from clean seed. He was convinced that the black insects were the real culprits – but he would be thorough, he would put all the rest of the possibilities to the test of experiment just the same.

He had a piece of land, five hundred and forty feet long by twenty-four feet wide, in the middle of a large field on which wheat was grown by several of his neighbours. He began by dividing his piece of land *crosswise* into five equal parts. The first of these he manured with pigeon droppings, the second with sheep manure, the third with night-soil, the fourth with horse and mule manure, and the fifth he left without any manure at all, as a check, or, as it would be called in the important-sounding jargon of the twentieth century, a 'control'. He next divided his piece of land *lengthwise* into four strips, each five feet wide, using the four feet of width which he had over for paths between the strips. The four strips he reserved for seed treated in four different ways. The first for seed deliberately blackened with dust from the

Bunt-balls; the second for seed treated with sea-salt and lime, the fourth for seed treated with lime only or with lime and nitre, and the third and last, once again the 'control' for apparently clean seed that received no treatment of any kind. His piece of ground was thus divided into twenty equal smaller plots, and, of these, plots which had received each of the five different manurial treatments were reserved for each of the four differently-treated sorts of seed. He had one of his twenty plots for untreated seed manured with pigeon droppings, another for deliberately 'bunted' seed manured with night-soil, and so on. The ingenious, plait-like lay-out of the plots made it possible for him to compare the effects of all the several combinations of seed and manurial treatment, simultaneously.

But he went further even than this, for he next subdivided each of his twenty plots into six equal strips, which he sowed on different days to test the effect of different weather conditions at the time of sowing. In the end he had therefore one hundred and twenty small plots, each eighteen feet by five feet, on one of which he had limed and salted seed, on unmanured soil, planted on a wet day; on another, deliberately bunted seed, manured with pigeon droppings, planted on a fine, dry day, and, once again, so on. A hundred and twenty combinations of the three variables, differing amongst themselves by only one variable at a time. It was all winter wheat, and the plots were duly sown, in accordance with the plan, on October 16th, 22nd and 27th, and November 3rd, 10th and 22nd, 1751.

Tillet watched and pondered over his plots as the wheat came up and as it grew. He made notes. In the spring and summer of 1752 he was about the plots every day, giving his whole mind to them, and finding, in attempts to account for the differences they presented, all the intellectual perplexities and satisfactions of a grand checker-game with Nature. *He* had ruled out the board, and the pieces were the healthy and the blackened ears of wheat. It was no ordinary kind of checker-game, for *Nature* disposed the pieces, and it was for him to worry out the rules, from the position of the pieces on the board.

The solution was simpler than Tillet had any reason to expect. *All* the plots which had been sown with seed deliberately contaminated with dust from the Bunt-balls showed a predominance of bunted ears. *All* the plots sown with good but untreated seed showed a few bunted ears. All the plots sown with seed which had been treated with lime, lime and salt, or lime and nitre, were practically free from bunted ears. The riddle was solved then, and for all time: the Bunt, *la Carie de blés*, was caused by the infection of the seed-grain by the black dust from the Bunt-balls when they broke under the flail. The kind of manure applied to the land, and the weather at the time of sowing made no appreciable difference to the number of bunted ears. The black insects had nothing to do with the Bunt, nor had the cold mists in the summer, for they had chilled both good and bad ears alike. The treatments with lime and salt, or nitre, were effective, but they did not act by preserving the seed in the wet soil – they removed or counteracted some infective or mortiferous principle in the Bunt dust which adhered to the seed.

It was a magnificent piece of experimental work for 1752, or indeed for any time, and during the next two seasons, Tillet not only repeated his trials and confirmed his first results, but amplified them with much subtlety. If the seed was contaminated by the Bunt dust, why not the straw? Might not the bunted straw, which found its way back in farmyard manure to the soil, contaminate the seed after it had been sown? Tillet had an old Spanish horse, which he now made an unwilling participant in his experiments. The horse had to eat only bunted wheat and it was littered with bunted straw. A pile of 'suspected' manure was thus accumulated and kept apart. The horse was then fed on clean wheat and littered with clean straw, so that a supply of 'clean' manure was obtained for comparison. Straw blackened with Bunt dust was also chopped up and added to each of the other kinds of manure. Tillet thus found, again by direct experiment, that clean seed sown in plots treated with manures which contained infected straw, gave rise to slightly more bunted ears, than in those plots where straw had been absent from the manure, or free from Bunt dust. He next provided himself with a bag of Bunt dust and sprinkled it along the drill at the time of sowing or broadcast it over the soil. Again when the wheat came up there was an abnormally high proportion of bunted ears.

Near Tillet's plot of ground there was a field belonging to the Carthusian Fathers, and he watched the labourers at work there, sowing wheat. One evening, when they had gone away, he trespassed on the good Fathers' land and carefully sprinkled a square patch of it with Bunt dust which he had to spare from his legitimate experiments. The next summer there was a conspicuous square patch in that wheat in which an extraordinarily large proportion of the ears were bunted. Tillet strolled over, with his hands in his pockets, and asked Father Portier what he thought might be the cause of the phenomenon. He replied without hesitation that it was due to an evil wind in the mist. 'Och aye,' said Mathieu Tillet, or words to that effect.

Having proved beyond all doubt that the Bunt of the wheat was a seed-borne disease, Tillet sought for the most economical means of preventing it. He treated his seed with various lyes – alkaline solutions obtained from the ashes of plants; and he also tried ammonia, obtained in the old Roman way, by leaving tanks of bovine or human urine to putrefy. He found that the lye solutions gave the best results, but they cost money – two or three sous per bushel of seed treated. Even that would be too much for most of the farmers, and he recommended the use of the putrid urine, which was almost as good, and which cost nothing whatever. Tillet desired that his neighbours should profit by his work, which was for the community and not merely for the Academy, but he was wise enough not to lecture the farmers. He contrived that they should make experiments for themselves, so that it seemed to them that the discovery of the cause and cure of the Bunt was their own. He was as good a psychologist as an experimentalist, for he said: 'When one knows the characteristics of the farmers, their sometimes poorly comprehended economies, their predilection for their own practices, and their hesitancy to receive anything not conceived by someone in their midst, one feels that it would be necessary, if he would assure himself of their tractableness, to put them to no expense in acquiring something of value to them, to avoid requiring their departure from a certain round of operations to which they are committed, and to trick them, so to speak, in abandoning them, to look into scarcely any difference between the precautions one counsels them to observe and those which they have always been constrained to practice.'[1]

Tillet's discoveries solved one riddle, only to posit another. How was it that a little dust from the Bunt-balls on the wheat seed caused the ears to be bunted in the following year? The wheat plants showed no sign of disease until the ears began to fill out, and even then the only abnormality was in the ears, which grew somewhat stumpy, with grains which were at first soft and bluish, and later blackened and swollen, till at harvest they were filled with the Dead Sea dust. What was the connection between the Bunt dust on the seed and the production of bunted ears? What *was* the Bunt dust? And *how* did it corrupt the wheat plants? These were questions that Tillet could not answer. He examined the dust under his (eighteenth-century) microscope and found it to be composed of innumerable, minute, spherical bodies, very uniform in size. He did not clearly recognize them as fungus spores, although he was very near the mark. 'Possibly', he said, 'we shall conclude by considering them as the result of some hidden internal contamination, differing little from that which is to be observed in Lycoperdon or the Puff Ball, the intact envelope of which encloses a black powder, which when viewed under the microscope also presents an infinitude of round and coequal particles.'

[1] Humphrey's translation, 1937.

In 1760 the wheat gave meagre crops in France, bread was very dear; there was widespread misery and privation. The savants everywhere solicited the authorities to inquire into the evil, and thus the Agricultural Society of Paris came into being. It was found that *la Carie* was the most redoubtable cause of the failure of the wheat crops; often it was responsible for the direct loss of a quarter to a half of the grain, and all the rest was more or less tainted by this Stinking Smut. To the newly formed Society belonged the credit of introducing into French agricultural practice the steeping of seed wheat. The knowledge which Mathieu Tillet sought to share with his neighbours was carried into every province of France. After Tillet came the Abbé Tessier, who, by about 1783, had tried everything he could think of, from brandy and *crême de menthe* downwards, for the prevention of *la Carie*. It was Tessier's great contribution to stress the importance of lime. In whatever solution the wheat was steeped, it was always advisable to dry it afterwards with lime. The English lime and sea-salt was preferred, but even washing in plain water would do much good, if it was followed by lime. Whether the lime was used in the steep, or as a drying agent, it was the essential ingredient in all the most effective treatments, and after Tessier the whole operation of treating the seed wheat, no matter what materials were actually used, became known in France as *le chaulage*. With the progress of *le chaulage* the great losses from the Bunt gradually diminished over the whole country, for not only was the grain saved but there was cleaner seed.

In 1807, Bénédict Prévost, Academician and Professor of Sciences at Montauban, announced two further discoveries. They directly concerned the Bunt of the wheat, but they were of fundamental significance in the whole art and science of preventing diseases of the crops. He found, in fact, two keys; one to the nature of many plant diseases, and the other to their control. But it was not for over seventy years, until after 1880, that the keys of Bénédict Prévost were really turned in their locks.

Prévost's apparatus included a microscope – which confused the appearance of the objects observed with all the colours of the rainbow – a drinking glass, a copper alembic, a thermometer and an old copper pannier covered with verdigris. He began by shaking some of the dust particles from Bunt-balls into the drinking glass, and soaking them in a little water to find out what action water had upon them. He took out drops from time to time and peered at them through the microscope. The particles *grew*. They had life. They developed into queer microscopic organisms, half vegetable, half animal, in appearance. They were little spores or seeds. When they had been in the water for about three days, a short stumpy transparent tube grew out from them, which was surmounted by a tuft of small shoots, star-like, at the top. As they continued to grow, these shoots – the rays of the star – lengthened into a plume, so that the tiny plant had some resemblance in form to a lily or an onion, with a 'bulb' at the bottom, a straight 'stem', and then long narrow leaves splayed out. The colourless, lily-form threads seemed to reach out and sway in the water, so that after a while they looked less like the leaves of a plant than the tentacles of a polyp, or of one of those small transparent hydra which hunted water-fleas. In the end, these 'leaves', or filaments, or tentacles – whatever they were – appeared to mat together into a limp wick, and to put forth small buds or fruits.

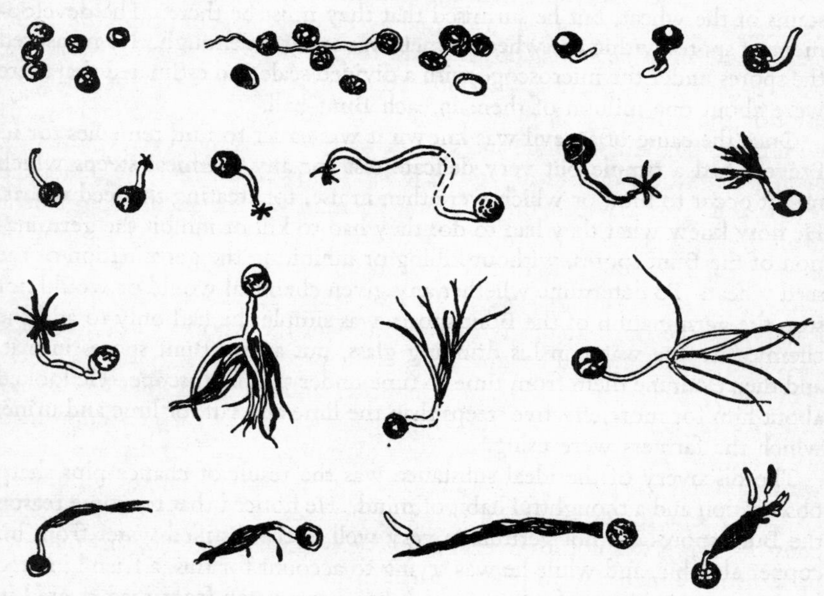

FIG. 8. The germination of Bunt spores in water. (× 200) (original scale).
After Bénédict Prévost, 1807

Prévost recognized and plainly asserted that the minute reticulated spherical bodies which composed the Bunt dust were the 'seeds' or spores of a microscopic plant, and it was this living plant – and no mysterious virus or poison – which caused the disease of the grain. This realization, reached forty years before Berkeley put forward his fungal hypothesis to account for the Potato Blight, was the first of the keys of Bénédict Prévost.

And Prévost saw, too, how the Bunt fungus, or *hydre végétale* as he called it, might attack the seedlings of the wheat plant. The Bunt spores, which, as Tillet had discovered, retained their vitality for many years when kept dry, germinated in the moisture surrounding the wheat seed in the soil, much as they germinated in his drinking glass. They would give rise to the same tiny, colourless plants, the tendrils of which would obtain entry into the seedlings, probably before they reached the surface of the soil. The parasite would then thread its way up the culm of the wheat as it grew, until the grain was forming in the ear, when it would fructify within the skins of the grains, utilizing their substance for the formation of its own dusty spores. Prévost was unable to discern any mycelial threads of the fungus actually traversing the stems of the wheat, but he surmised that they must be there. The development of spores within the wheat kernels was apparent enough. He measured the spores under the microscope with a divided scale and estimated that there were about one million of them in each Bunt-ball.

Once the cause of an evil was known it was easier to find remedies for it. Prévost had a simple but very delicate test for any chemical steeps which might occur to him, or which were then in use, for treating the seed wheat. He now knew what they had to do: they had to kill or inhibit the germination of the Bunt spores, without killing or inhibiting the germination of the seed wheat. To determine whether any given chemical would or would not stop the germination of the Bunt spores was simple; he had only to add the chemical to the water in his drinking glass, put a few Bunt spores into it, and then examine them from time to time under the microscope. He looked about him for more effective steeps than the lime and salt, or lime and urine, which the farmers were using.

The discovery of the ideal substance was the result of chance plus sharp observation and a thoughtful habit of mind. He noticed that for some reason the Bunt spores did not germinate very well in the distilled water from his copper alembic, and while he was trying to account for this, a friend invited him to inspect a crop of wheat, which had been raised from seed treated in a way usual in the district, but which was quite remarkably free from bunted ears. When strolling through the farmyard, Prévost noticed an old copper pannier, and his friend told him that it was handy for use in *le chaulage*. It was his custom to put the seed wheat into it, and then dip the whole into the pot containing sheep's urine and milk of lime.

Copper alembic, copper pannier . . . It seemed a fantastic idea – but was it possible that water, by mere contact with copper metal, could acquire some property which made it poisonous to Bunt spores? It was unlikely indeed, but it could be put to the test. Prévost returned to his experiments, and this time he put a small square of polished copper metal into the water in which the spores normally germinated very well. The spores still germinated, but the subsequent growth of the microscopic plants was arrested at an early stage. Their fine threads wilted and died. He repeated the experiment with pieces of copper covered with verdigris, and the effect was much more pronounced. The Bunt spores were sensitive to minute traces of copper in the water.

It at once occurred to him to try copper acetate, which could be made by dissolving verdigris in vinegar, and copper sulphate, the commonest and cheapest soluble salt of copper. He found that as little as one part of copper sulphate in two hundred and eighty thousand of water sufficed to prevent the germination of the Bunt spores. Even a dosage of one part in a million of the copper salt – corresponding to one part in four million of copper metal in solution – was sufficient if the seed was steeped for a few hours. The copper acetate was about equally effective. Other experimenters had tried dangerous poisons for the treatment of the wheat: arsenic and bichloride of mercury. Prévost had discovered that the element copper, so little poisonous to man and other animals that pumps and saucepans were made of it, was deadly to the spores of the Bunt fungus at one part in four million of water. This discovery of the unique effect of copper on fungus spores was the second of the keys of Bénédict Prévost.

At the beginning of the nineteenth century there were one or two of the great agricultural reformers still left in England, who made it their business to watch for all important discoveries on the Continent. This scouting was sadly neglected later, but Sir John Sinclair, Sir Joseph Banks and Arthur Young did not miss much. A copy of Prévost's memoir, with its three engravings tinted in water colour, was among Sir Joseph Banks's most treasured possessions, later preserved for the nation in the library of the British Museum.[1] Not only was the copper sulphate steep soon made known in England, but Sir John Sinclair, in one of his journeys to pick up hints from farm practice in the Netherlands, even came across one of the anticipations of Prévost's discovery. There was nothing new under the sun. A Mr. Vandoorslair, in the district called the Pays de Waes, between Ghent and Antwerp, informed him of a preparation sold to the peasants for many years by the druggists of Malmes for the prevention of diseases of the wheat. This remedy, which was very little known in the surrounding districts, and not at all to the philosophic world, turned out to be nothing other than acetate of copper in powder. One half of an English pound of it, for six bushels of

[1] Fig. 8, herein, is drawn from that copy.

wheat, was mixed with as much human urine as would enable the light bunted grains to be floated off. The remaining seed was then steeped in the mixture for three hours and subsequently dried, with or without lime. Thanks to the watchfulness of Banks and Sinclair, the copper treatment was even adopted in England long before it became common in France or Germany. According to the Rev. M. J. Berkeley, writing in 1856, its use was preferred and had become traditional among the English farmers, while on the Continent it was used only here and there, until the treatment was revived and further investigated by Julius Kühn.

In practice the farmers used much more copper sulphate than was just sufficient to prevent the germination of the Bunt spores. They used a pound in ten gallons of water, but as the 'bluestone' cost only a few pence a pound, the cost of material for the treatment was trifling. The serious objection to it was that the bluestone solution, left to dry on the seed before sowing, caused considerable injury, particularly to those grains which had been cut or bruised in any way during the threshing. This disadvantage was largely overcome by steeping the grain in baskets for a carefully limited time, and then pitching it on to the floor of the barn and shovelling it over with dry slaked lime. The lime served the triple purpose of 'neutralizing' the excess of copper sulphate, encrusting the grain with an insoluble cupric deposit which tended to preserve it in the soil, and of drying the grain in readiness for the sowing.

If the first use of copper sulphate for the prevention of a fungus disease of the crops was of the very greatest historical interest, so also was the use of copper sulphate *in conjunction with lime*. In France, there was another very effective treatment for the wheat, which depended upon the use of lime, but which required no copper. It was called 'The Absolute Preservative of Mathieu de Dombasle'.

Mathieu de Dombasle, who was born in 1777 and died in 1843, did much to improve the practice of agriculture in France. Of which Arthur Young had said: 'My God, give me patience to see so fine a country, so favoured by heaven, treated so badly by men.' During the Napoleonic wars Dombasle started the French sugar-beet industry, and when the price of sugar fell, after 1815, he turned his hand to the improvement of agricultural implements, invented the Dombasle plough, and was associated with the introduction of threshing machines. He founded a famous college of practical agriculture at Roville, a village on the Moselle between Nancy and Epinal, and he wrote many books and pamphlets on the political economy of the land. In his *Calendrier du Bon Cultivateur*, he described the operations, the year round, for the good cultivation of the crops of France, setting forth in a very cogent and straightforward way the best agricultural practice of his time. His philosophy was summed up in one sentence: '*La charrue est dans tous les lieux la première base de la richesse publique.*' But it was folly when improving the tillage of the land to neglect any measures that could be taken to prevent the wastage of crops by disease. There was still far too much of the Stinking Smut in the wheat. He improved upon the sea-salt and lime of Jethro Tull by substituting Glauber salts (sodium sulphate) for the sea-salt. The grain, placed in heaps on a stone floor, was watered with an eight per cent solution of the salts and then dried with lime. The treatment caused less injury to the grain than did that with copper sulphate. No doubt the Glauber salts, *per se*, had *some* effect on the germinating Bunt spores, but once again it was necessary to remember the lime, which did more than dry the grain. When sodium sulphate and lime were brought together in a moist state, they did not remain sodium sulphate and lime. The sodium and the calcium changed partners, and, presto, there was a magma of gypsum and caustic soda. The Glauber salts were relatively innocuous, but the caustic soda was as caustic as its name implied. Untreated seed wheat, in one of Mathieu de Dombasle's instructive experiments, gave rise to a crop with 486 black and carious ears per thousand. Seed from the same source, after treatment, gave only 2 bunted ears per 1000. A saving of half the crop. *Le chaulage* was unquestionably one of the most important operations in the cultivation of wheat.

By 1847, when the Potato Blight was still a mystery, and systematic investigations in the whole field of plant pathology had yet to begin, there was the inspiring example of *one* serious disease of the crops, of which much was already known, and for which a number of remedies had not only been found, but adopted in practice. At the expense of a small proportion of the seed which always failed to come up after the chemical treatments, the Bunt of the wheat could be almost entirely suppressed by human agency.

But the Bunt of the wheat was only one of a very numerous group of fungus diseases which afflicted the cereal crops. It was one of the smutting, charring, burning or blasting diseases which were sometimes referred to, collectively, by an old name, common to both English and German – the 'Brand' diseases of cereals. Hence the title of Anton de Bary's *Die Brandpilze* of 1853. Although so dependent on moisture for their development, the Brand diseases had always been likened – with some stretching of the imagination – to the results of burning or fire. They fell into two fairly distinct categories: the Smuts or Dust-Brands, which, according to their kind, either converted the substance of the grain alone into black dust or reduced whole ears to charred skeletons; and the Rusts, or Rust-Brands, which streaked the straw and leaf-blades of the plants with dusty pustules which had the colours of charcoal or flame, and which, by exhausting the plants and depriving the ears of their alimentary chyle, caused shrivelling of the grain. The Smut fungi, which went by the Latin name of *Ustilago*, and the Rust fungi, typified by the *Uredo*, were almost inextricably confused together by the botanists before the eighteen-forties, when first the good doctor Léveillé, and then the brothers Tulasne, entered upon the mighty labour of sorting them out. Many species, or bits of species, of both Ustilago and Uredo were known under a bewildering multiplicity of scientific and popular names. The brothers Tulasne sought to discover which 'fruits' or kinds of spores belonged to which, and, by careful comparative studies, to confirm Léveillé's separation of the two families. The next important advance in knowledge of the Bunt fungus was made in connection with these studies, which were published in the *Annales des Sciences naturelles* in 1847 and 1854.

The brothers began by confirming the difference, long since appreciated by the farmers, between the Bunt or *Carie* of the wheat, and its black sister, the *Charbon*, or (Loose) Smut. Where the Bunt-balls remained intact until threshing time, the spores of the Smut were ripe when the wheat was in flower, they were blown about the field as a black dust by the wind, the chaff came away, and only the bare and blackened rachis of the smutted ear remained at harvest. The Smut fungus was not the same as the Bunt fungus, and to make it quite clear which they were talking about, the brothers named the Bunt fungus *Tilletia caries*, after Mathieu Tillet, and reserved the generic name 'Ustilago' for the Loose Smuts. Fortunately the Loose Smut – on the wheat – was not nearly so serious as the Bunt. Berkeley mentioned in 1856 that the English farmers took little notice of it, and even had a superstitious belief that a little Smut in a wheatfield augured well for the crop in other respects. They said *that*, much as they said that when the moon was on its back it was filled with rain. Sometimes, when the moon tipped its contents, and the Smut was unusually bad, there would be 'black rain'. Clouds of spores, lifted by the wind, were washed down again. But black rain was rare enough for it to be regarded as a supernatural occurrence. Usually there was not much Smut and it did little harm. It had not the unpleasant fishy smell of the Bunt, and as the spores were blown away before the wheat was harvested they did not contaminate the whole run of the grain. There was only the direct loss of the smutted ears.

The Loose Smut was much more serious on the oats and barley than on the wheat, and it was a terrible plague of maize. There were a number of Loose Smuts, caused by different species of Ustilago, affecting the many different species of wild grasses and cultivated cereals. They could not be combated by the seed treatments then in use for the Bunt of the wheat, for the reason that they infected the seed in an entirely different way. And this was not discovered until much later in the nineteenth century. There was no remedy for the Loose Smut diseases until certain of the sterilization processes arising out of the researches of Pasteur were adapted for use against them. Meanwhile that obliging guinea pig of the mycologists, *Tilletia caries*, cause of the Bunt of the wheat, was made to betray a few more of its secrets.

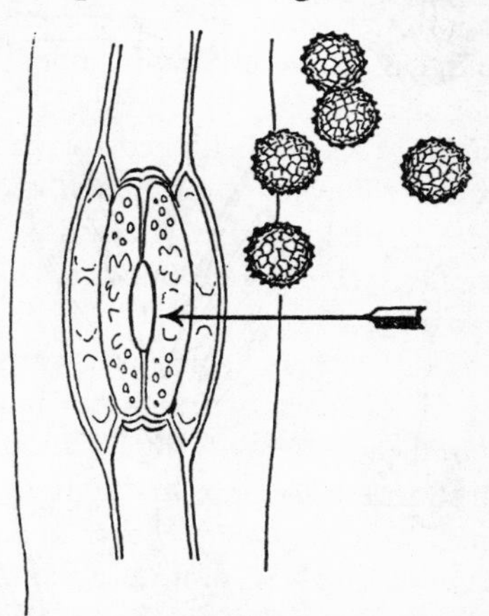

FIG. 9. One of the first stomata[1] of a wheat seedling, with Bunt spores to the same scale (× 300). How does the Bunt obtain entry?

With a very much better microscope than had been available in the time of Prévost, the brothers Tulasne re-examined the germination of the Bunt spores. The outstanding question was: how did the Bunt fungus obtain entry into the wheat plant? The only openings in the young stems of the wheat were the stomata or 'breathing-pores', and they were smaller than the Bunt spores, which could not therefore pass directly into the interior. In this form the question was naive, and Prévost had shown that it would probably be the threads from the spore after germination which penetrated the seedling, but this part of Prévost's work was scarcely understood in his time, and in 1847 there were still many who believed that the spores contained granules small enough to *sift* through the stomata, as grains of pepper might be introduced into a pepper pot through the holes in the top.

When the Bunt spores germinated the stumpy tube which they first pushed out was quite small enough in diameter to enter the stomata, but the actual development of the microscopic Bunt-plants before any parts of them penetrated the wheat was much more remarkable than *that*. The star-like sprouting of threads at the end of the stump and their growth into a kind of plume or aigrette were as pictured by Prévost. But when the plume was

[1] The stoma (of the coleoptile) is here sketched from a figure by John Percival in *The Wheat Plant*, Duckworth, 1921.

examined in greater detail something very curious was to be noted about its threads. They were linked together in pairs by small cross-pieces, so that each pair was like an elongated letter H. Why? Anton de Bary suggested, a little later, that the linkages represented sexual conjugation, and that the threads, alternatively male and female, paired off together while yet on their parent stump. However this might be, when all the plasm in the original

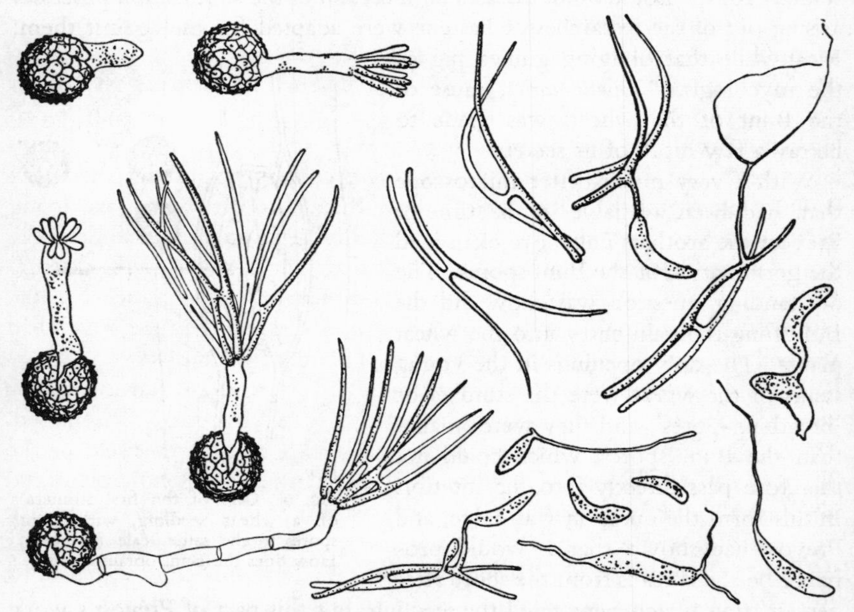

FIG. 10. The Germination of Bunt Spores in water. (× 460) (original scale). After Tulasne, 1854

spore, swollen by absorption of water, had been squeezed along the stumpy tube into these paired threads, they broke away and began to undergo further developments on their own. They put out finer tubes in turn and squeezed their plasm into fruit-like bodies, sporidia, or secondary spores. These mere bits of plasm-in-a-membrane, after detachment, continued to grow, putting out more groping threads and even tertiary spores. The H-shaped elements on their mother-stumps, and the various detached bits of plasm in all their extrusive metamorphoses, were endowed with movement. They swayed and humped and pushed themselves about in the water. Louis and Charles Tulasne had been very sceptical about the reference to this movement in

Prévost's *Mémoire*; they did not altogether believe in vegetable hydras. But there it was – the movement was apparent enough with the high magnification provided by their excellent microscope, and their eyes did not deceive them.

It was now possible to visualize, even more graphically than did Prévost, the way in which the Bunt fungus could enter the wheat seedlings, when the Bunt spores and the wheat seed were germinating alongside each other in the soil moisture. Once within the tissues of the seedling, the vegetative part of the fungus would consist of fine mycelial tubes traversing or winding about among the cells. Léveillé had observed such intercellular mycelium belonging to other kinds of Brand fungi. The origin of the anticipated mycelium could be seen by watching the Bunt spores germinating in drops of water. The oddly-shaped sporidia were constantly pushing their thin enveloping membranes into new hollow threads, down which the living plasm passed to form new growth. It was only necessary for these fine tubes on the sporidia to be insinuated into the stomata, or to push straight through the soft cell-walls of the young seedling, and then the plasm in the bulb-like part of the sporidium, outside, would be squeezed along the tube which had pricked an entry, to lengthen into a mycelial filament within.

All this, however, was even yet surmise, and when at last it was actually seen to happen, a turning-point in the history of mycology was passed. When the germ-tube of a fungus spore was first seen in the field of the microscope stabbing its way through the epidermis of its host plant and originating mycelium within, then the parasitism of that fungus was proven at the bar of science. The first endophytic fungus ever observed in the act of penetration was neither *Tilletia Caries* nor the Potato Blight fungus, but a little *Pythium* which attacked fresh-water algae. The crucial observation was made by Ferdinand Cohn, in 1854. And by 1858, Julius Kühn, in Silesia, had seen the collar of the wheat plant penetrated by the Bunt fungus itself, and the copious growth of its mycelium through the soft tissues of the stem.

CHAPTER VI

'VEGETABLE PATHOLOGY'

WHEN the Royal Agricultural Society of England was incorporated in 1840, the coming necessity for the establishment of a branch of agricultural science, to be concerned especially with the diseases of the crops, was clearly foreseen. There were two ways of increasing the produce of the land; the first was to increase the obtainable yield by good cultivation, selection of stocks and herds, drainage, rotation, and the skilled use of manures and fertilizers; the second was to decrease the wastage of produce due to pests and diseases. Both endeavours had equally to be encouraged if the landowners and the farmers were to prosper and the rapidly-increasing population of the country was to be fed. By way of preface to the first number of the Society's *Journal*, published in January 1840, there was a responsible survey, by Philip Pusey, M.P., of the state of agricultural science in England in 1839. As an example of the national gain which might result from the Society's work for the advancement of agriculture, under the banner of 'Science with Practice', he mentioned that the average yield of wheat in England was then 26 bushels per acre. If this average could be increased by only one bushel per acre,[1] the gain, with wheat at its then current price, would be £1,200,000 yearly, equivalent to a capital sum of £24,000,000.

'But', he went on, 'we have to look at least as much to the prevention of loss as to increase of profit . . . Little does the sanguine calculator upon paper know of the farmers' real anxieties and frequent disappointments – of the blights and the rusts and the mildews; the insects and the fungi, which, falling as if in an unseen cloud on his fields, impair, if not destroy, the vegetative power which he has so carefully and expensively endeavoured to nurture. There is no department of agriculture in which minute inquiry is more needed than this: first to examine accurately the various diseases of plants and to note the habits of the animals which prey upon them; then to ascertain if possible the remedies that may be applied; and the followers of kindred sciences may be fairly invited to aid us in the formation of this branch of knowledge, which may be called agricultural pathology.'

[1] When the Society celebrated its centenary in 1939, the ten-year-average yield for wheat in England and Wales was about 32 bushels per acre. A part of this increase was, however, due to the fact that the cultivation of wheat was then in the main restricted to the very best of the former wheat land.

The words were well spoken, but for many years little was done; no real start was made. And, indeed, it never fell to the Royal Agricultural Society to take the lead in the promotion of this branch of agricultural science. A number of John Curtis's very valuable papers on 'Farm Insects', notably on those affecting the turnip crops, were published in the early issues of the Society's *Journal*; but the contributions on the *diseases* of the crops were very few and far between, and they contained little that was new. All the scientific enthusiasm in agriculture was going to the other side of the programme: the increase of the fertility of the soil.

In the early forties, the dodge of obtaining 'super' phosphates by treating bones with sulphuric acid was being exploited, supplies of Peruvian guano and Chilean nitrate began to arrive in quantity, and the famous manurial experiments at Rothamsted were started by J. B. Lawes (1841). The so-called Chemical Revolution of Lavoisiér and his school, which marked the close of the eighteenth century, had led to an illuminating realization of one of the first principles of soil science – really a consequence of the general principle of conservation of mass. The chemists, and notably Justus von Liebig in Germany, had worked out methods of chemical analysis which revealed the amounts of the several elements which various crops took from the soil, and, when this information was available, it was not unreasonable to conclude that the input of the several elements to the soil-bed had to be equal to the out-take for any particular level of productiveness to be maintained. Also, there was reason to suppose that if the soil was enriched with those elements taken by a particular crop, the level of productiveness in respect to that crop could be *raised*. There were many ways, besides the application of the new imported nitrates and the manufactured 'super' phosphates by which the input and output budget of the elements necessary for plant growth could be raised and balanced at a higher level. The plentiful work which these problems provided, leading as it did to most gratifying and sometimes spectacular increases, was more attractive than the doctor's job of preventing the wastage caused by blights and mildews. A penny saved was never a penny gained, unless the process of saving the penny happened to be as pleasurable, to the human being concerned, as that of gaining it. To dose crops with magical new fertilizers, and then to weigh the produce and determine the gain, was exceedingly good fun, and if, like John Lawes, you happened to have shares in a company selling the fertilizers, there was a good healthy profit motive behind your researches. But the number of people who found delight in the thankless and unremunerative job of wading through all the multilingual prolixities of the cryptogamic botanists, in search of information pointing to the rational principles that were to be followed in treating plant diseases – the number of such persons, on earth, was very, very, small.

The outbreak of the Potato Blight in 1845, the famine in Ireland, the spread of the Oidium over the hops and the vines, and the abnormal severity of all the native blights and mildews, during the late forties, provided the grimmest of reminders that the diseases of the crops were not to be neglected. These pestilences were capable of destroying more produce in a couple of bad seasons than could be gained in a decade by the help of the new fertilizers. Indeed, the use of some of these fertilizers, particularly of the imported nitrates, which were then unbalanced by potash, was a disturbing factor, no doubt having something to do with the increase in the prevalence of disease. Excessive nitrogen caused a lush, soft growth of foliage, on which, as it was discovered later, fungal parasites flourished. The total failure to find any remedy for the Potato Blight pointed to the need for some synthesis of the information scattered in the world's scientific literature about plant diseases, and the extraction from it of guiding principles. Knowledge available of one disease might throw light upon another. Berkeley recognized this when he turned back to the half-forgotten work of Prévost, and adduced observations that had been made on the propagation of the Bunt of the wheat, in support of his hypothesis that the Potato Murrain was of fungal origin. But mere searching of the past and contemporary literature was not enough; Berkeley and John Lindley worked hard enough to collect and sift every scrap of information they could find on the Potato Murrain – their writings in *The Gardeners' Chronicle* and the *Journal of the Horticultural Society* were enduring evidence of *that* – but for the understanding of such plagues which could sweep over the crops of whole continents and make their way from the New World to the Old, or from the Old World to the New, properly organized and far-flung investigations would have to be set up. The job was too big for even the most industrious of professors of botany, or clerical-fungologists, or doctors of medicine on the Continent, to cope with as a mere side-line. Berkeley was indeed writing as a Father of Plant Pathology, when in September 1845 he said: 'There must be a continued series of observations conducted both by practical and scientific men, embracing every possible point and extending to remote districts, with the power of comparing the different phases the disease exhibits and the varying circumstances in which it appears. This alone can lead to anything satisfactory. The expense doubtless would be considerable, but the utility, whether immediate or more remote, would be fully commensurable with the expenditure.'

But after the repeal of the Corn Laws – which no more ruined the English farmers than it lowered the cost of bread, since the cost of bringing foreign grain to England made it as expensive as the home-grown – agriculture was prospering as well as the manufacturing industries. Everybody who had any capital in England was making money hand over fist. Free Trade and a virtual monopoly of machine manufacture was increasing the wealth of the country at such a rate that very much attention to the Blight on the potatoes or the Smut on the corn was hardly to be expected. There was *laissez faire* for the merchants and the industrialists. There was *laissez faire* also for the fungi on the crops, and the typhoid in the Poor Law institutions. There was *laissez faire* for the landowners; and the land-enclosure, which was still going on, had reduced the agricultural labourers to pauperism or driven them to the mills. But the progress of appropriation from the powerless had led to vast technical improvements in the practice of English agriculture in the course of a century: the large farms were well-cultivated, and now with better drainage and increasing scientific manuring, agricultural production, like the promotion of railway companies, was pushing ahead.

The English soil was producing three-quarters of the wheat consumed in the country, and keeping pace with the increasing demand. In 1845 the price of wheat was 50s. 9d. per quarter, in 1847 69s. 5d., in 1855, 74s. 9d (*vide* Fig. 25, page 145). New sources of wealth were opening up every year. Over the period from 1850 to 1860 a hundred and ten million pounds worth of gold was found in Australia; the Bessemer process cut the cost of steel-making by one half; the first aniline dye was discovered by W. H. Perkin, and the synthetic dye industry began with his factory at Greenford in Middlesex; India was annexed to the Crown, and the bulk of its spinning and weaving industry was appropriated for Lancashire, along with its produce of raw cotton – indeed it was the Golden Age. The English traders were as free as the Thelemites, and, in their own estimation, twice as virtuous.

The grand moral, or amoral, principle behind all this prosperity was *Fais ce que vouldras*, Free Competition, or *Laissez faire*. In 1859 it found its poet, not in Matthew Arnold or Macaulay, but in Charles Darwin, for he gave it a new name, 'the survival of the fittest', and proclaimed that it was operative as a natural law from the beginning unto the end of creation. What more was needed to convince those worthy Victorians of the absolute rectitude of their ways? Before Darwin, it was acknowledged with a reluctant piety that the ways of the Almighty might be superior, in certain moral respects, to those of even the most virtuous of men. The Almighty, for example, had a care for every sparrow that fell to the ground. Now that this nonsense was exploded, and it was revealed as God's will, or a law of nature, that some smug cat or wily rodent should at once devour the helpless bird, the exploiter of child labour in the mills, or the Irish landlord busy with evictions, need no longer feel bowed in excess of humility before *any* superior power. On the contrary, he could feel something of the fallen aureole of the Almighty glowing about his ears.

It was not until the fat period was over, and the leaner years of stringent commercial competition with other nations began, that any organized endeavours were made in England to combat the diseases of the crops. After 1847, it was not until 1873, at the beginning of the Great Depression, that the Royal Agricultural Society of England encouraged any further investigation of the Potato Blight. And it was not until years later still, when English agriculture was faced with ruin, that any effective measures to defend the health of the crops were promoted by Government action. By then the lead had passed to other countries; but in plant pathology, as in so many other branches of applied science – instance the synthetic dye industry – it was an English pioneer who made the start which was followed up elsewhere.

In 1854, the Rev. M. J. Berkeley began his famous work on 'Vegetable Pathology' in *The Gardeners' Chronicle*. The idea that there should be a recognized branch of science concerned with the diseases of plants, and to be called 'Vegetable Pathology', as the study of disease in man was called 'Human Pathology', had been simmering in his mind since the publication of his first paper on the Potato Blight in 1846. As nobody seemed inclined to take up the idea, he at last decided to make a start himself, and his Articles, published in serial form, week by week in *The Gardeners' Chronicle*, over a period of nearly three years, were the result. His plan was 'to place before his readers, in a compendious and easily accessible form, all that was well ascertained upon the subject. The papers to comprise everything really valuable, both in theory and practice, which could be at all supposed to come within the scope of an intelligent cultivator'.

He began with forty-three Articles on plants in a state of health, and went on systematically to consider what constituted disease in plants, the causes of disease, the classification of diseases, and, lastly, remedial measures. There was one thing about this scheme for which later workers hardly gave him sufficient credit. It had been objected that over the Potato Blight he paid little attention to the general health of the plants, while 'magnifying the fungus seven-hundred-and-eighty diameters'. In the twentieth century, when men of science had outgrown their first enthusiasm for the germ theory of disease, precisely the same objection was raised: the plant pathologists were said to pay too much attention to the parasitic fungi and other pathogens, and too little to the conditions necessary for the growth of healthy plants – to the environmental factors of earth, air, light, warmth and moisture. But Berkeley could hardly be said to have neglected these factors, when he devoted forty-three of the Articles to them, before he even began to consider what was meant by disease! His Articles on the nutrition and general physiology of plants in health, were not perhaps the best part of his work, for those were not his subjects, but in putting them first he laid down a good plan for the new science which he sought to define.

When it came to the classification of the abnormalities which he regarded as diseases of plants, Berkeley at first tried to use the same categories which the physicians were then employing for the diseases of man. Internal or constitutional disorders, functional and organic; external or accidental disorders, and so on. The limitations of these several categories were exceedingly vague, for no two physicians agreed in what they meant by them, and their attempts at definition constituted, for the most part, a scholastic war of words. It was inevitable that this should be so, while the proximate causes of so many diseases were wholly unknown. Berkeley floundered about with 'constitutional' and 'organic' for some while and then his ruling demon took charge. He was a taxonomist, instinctively given to sorting things into genera and species, to which he could assign Latin, or preferably Greek, names. He probably divided all the venial and mortal sins into genera and species on Sunday mornings, and he managed to divide the 'diseases' of plants, on week-days, into forty-two genera, including: *Sterilitas*, or unproductiveness; *Sphrigosis*, or rankness; *Betchomania*, or multiplication of petals; *Senectis*, or old age; *Exostasis*, or warts; *Heliosis*, or sunstroke; and finally *Parasitae*, or [effects of] external parasites. On all these subjects Berkeley had something interesting to say; his papers contained a wealth of curious and practical information to delight the gardener; his rhetoric was all very philosophical, and rich as Christmas pudding with choice instances of *Betchomania* or *Sphrigosis*, but the best of the articles were those on the *Parasitae*, the relatively few disorders of plants which could then be attributed to vegetable parasites. These articles were the forerunners of the leaflets and monographs on plant diseases which would be issued by every Department or Ministry of Agriculture in the world, half a century later. He gave brief descriptions, intelligible to the gardener, of the fungi which caused the disorders, lingered over the derivation of their names, mentioned the host plants on which each species had been found, paid attention to the weather conditions which seemed to favour their spread, referred to the principal experiments which had been made in checking their ravages, discussed the opinions of his contemporaries about them, and freely added any other facts or conjectures which seemed to him pertinent. He went on writing articles on the *Parasitae*, long after he had brought his 'Vegetable Pathology' to a close, and these addenda contained some of his most valuable contributions. Again and again he put his finger surely on the fungus which was causing a disease, and only the whole history of plant pathology through the nineteenth century would show the great part he had in it. When he came to conclude his scheme of Vegetable Pathology in 1857, with 'Remedial Measures', he was perhaps getting a little tired, for the articles under this head were few, and not particularly searching.

The Rev. M. J. Berkeley was one of the great Victorians, and he was above all else a *worker*. A prodigiously hard worker. He was of commanding presence and robust physique. Educated: Rugby and Cambridge. As perpetual curate of Apethorpe and Wood Norton, he had a very small stipend on which to maintain a large family. He was obliged to take in private pupils. He was active in his parochial work. He was a good classical scholar, and he read all the proof-sheets of Bentham and Hooker's *Genera Plantarum* as linguistic critic. From 1836 to 1870 he was the universal referee for anybody in England who wanted information about fungi. His herbarium of fungi, ultimately acquired by Kew, contained ten thousand species, and the new species he described were not far short of six thousand. In 1857, as though his labours on 'Vegetable Pathology' had not been enough for him, he published his important *Introduction to Cryptogamic Botany*, a book of six hundred pages, 'with 127 illustrations on wood, drawn by the author'.

In later generations many a mycologist, chancing to look at the portrait in oils of Miles Joseph Berkeley, massive beside his brass microscope, on a wall of the conference room of the Linnean society in London, would be tempted to exclaim: Ah, there indeed was the Father of British Plant Pathology! But saying this they would be somewhat carried away: there never was any such thing as *British* Plant Pathology, only Plant Pathology, and that was the child of a thousand minds, of the inquiring genius of many nations. Berkeley happened to christen it and give it a name, but it had earlier Fathers in Mathieu Tillet and Fontana, and Bénédict Prévost. True, it was a science born of social need, but as necessity was only the *mother* of invention, and *she* was there all the time, it was indeed the Fathers of the science that mattered. Some of these men had a real and often conscious desire to serve humanity, to prevent wastage, hunger and suffering. Some loved the growing corn, and the deep enmauved green of potato fields in flower. Some loved the strange beauties of the fungi which the microscope revealed, and dedicated their works to the glory of God. Many found their chief satisfaction in getting the better of other botanists. Many worked to quench a curiosity. Some eyed mundane rewards, others eternal fame. Not a few found in the laboratory an escape from their wives, or from the anxieties of stupid wars, or from the tedium of their ways of earning a living. And, in the last analysis of human motivation, no doubt there were many who found in the prevention of disease all the pleasures of power – of successful interference with courses of events.

One circumstance which provided Berkeley with a limited but much-interested public in England for his writings about microscopic fungi, was that microscopes were then about as popular among the educated classes as the better kinds of miniature cameras were to be by 1939. Everybody who *was* anybody would be sure to have somebody in the family who owned a tall brass microscope, often with polarizing prisms and other expensive extras, through which to observe the artistic and instructive spectacles provided by the poor animalcules and lowly diatoms at the other end of the scale of life. *The Micrographic Dictionary* of Dr. Griffith and Mr. Henfrey, a fat scientific encyclopaedia of things-to-look-at-under-the-microscope, was almost a popular work. The fungi provided an additional wealth of things-to-look-at, and indeed Berkeley himself saw to it that they were adequately dealt with in a later edition of that work. No genteel home, furnished with the proper evidences of interest in the Sciences as well as the Arts, could afford to be without sources of information about ascospores, pycnidia and the like.

Four years after Berkeley began his articles on 'Vegetable Pathology' in England, Julius Kühn's text-book on 'The diseases of cultivated plants, their cause and prevention' was published in Germany. Kühn had no classical education, he detested taxonomy, and he had no time for luxury gardeners. He served his apprenticeship as a youth in farm and estate management, and at twenty-three he became responsible for the efficient farming of a large Crown domain in Silesia. He tried out commercial fertilizers, the sowing of grain in drills, tile-drainage and so on, and became much interested in a disease of Rape, which he studied on his own. He found the causal fungus and gave it a name which was accepted by the scientific world, thus acquiring some reputation as an original investigator. At the age of thirty, in 1855, he left the farm-management job to study, for the shortest time that would serve his purpose, at the Agricultural Academy of Poppelsdorf. He went through the scientific papers of De Bary, Tulasne and earlier workers, in a thoroughly business-like way, to extract what there was in them that seemed to him to be of practical importance to farmers, threw in one or two small but sound pieces of research of his own, and prepared a thesis about plant diseases for which he obtained his doctorate at Leipzig in 1856. He then returned to farm management. His first and only book on plant diseases was the celebrated *Krankheiten der Kulturgewächse*, etc., based on the thesis, and published in 1858. Three-quarters of a century or so later, when Plant Pathology had become a recognized subject for university courses, this book was greatly admired by the lecturers, and when the students were asked who was the Father of Plant Pathology, those who answered 'Julius Kühn' obtained full marks.

The book was chiefly remarkable for what it left out — all the philosophic doubts, historical matter, elaborate detail, and argument about and about. It had the cut-and-dried air of the classroom, and it was severely practical. The drawings with which it was illustrated were wooden, and devoid of any merely artistic graces. It was 'a model of concision and accuracy': it anatomized the body of the subject-matter under two heads, the first being general observations on plant diseases, and the second, special researches on particular diseases. It ended with a short section on the utility of the microscope to the practical farmer. In the first part it dealt with predisposing causes of plant disease, unfavourable soil and climatic conditions, *und so weiter*, and then with what might be called proximate causes: insect attack producing galls, etc., parasitism by other flowering plants, such as the dodder, and, finally, attack by fungus parasites. In the second section there were valuable and plainly written chapters on the Smut, Rust, and Ergot diseases of cereals; on the Mildew, Sooty Mould, Honey Dew, and Leaf-Blights affecting various agricultural plants; on the disease of Rape seed, and on the diseases of root crops, including potatoes. That the several fungi were the cause and not the consequence of these diseases was treated throughout as an established fact, and the emphasis was on the study of the diseases for the sole object of preventing them. Apart from the presentation of existing knowledge with this end in view, the chapters included some original matter: Kühn's own observations of the disease of the Rape, on the mycelium of the Bunt fungus within the wheat plant, and on improved methods of treating the seed wheat with Prévost's copper sulphate.

Kühn's book was never translated into English, and Berkeley's articles were never even collected into book form, let alone translated into German; but, by 1860, the idea of 'Vegetable Pathology' as a new branch of applied science was at least in existence, and there were two works indicative of its scope and of its relationship respectively to agriculture and to horticulture.

CHAPTER VII

OOSPORES AND ZOOSPORES

MEANWHILE, the emigration from Ireland was continuing. In the fifteen years since the Famine, the population had been sadly reduced, and with the evictions there had been some improvement in agricultural practice, but the peasantry was still mostly dependent for food upon the potato and there was local famine or more acute misery whenever the potato crop was diminished in a 'Blight' year. Some political and religious concessions had been made to the Irish, but the system of land-tenure was unchanged, and the country was still drained of almost the whole of its exportable produce. In Ireland the Potato Blight was a recurring tragedy, and it was by far the most serious plant disease throughout the British Isles. Every farmer, English, Scottish, Welsh or Irish, suffered loss because of it – sometimes nearly the whole of his crop, more usually a tenth to a third of it, rarely, in a dry district, or in a good season, only a few potatoes here and there. It was the same in many other European countries: Belgium, Holland, Germany. The Potato Blight was a permanent, if intermittent, scourge, a spectre of greedy waste that waited only upon the dew and the rain to strike down the green haulms.

It seemed that there had been but little increase in knowledge about the Potato Blight fungus since it was first described by the old surgeon of Napoleon's armies, Dr. Montagne, in 1845. There had been a veritable revolution in thought about its relation to the Potato Disease, but only a little more had been discovered about the fungus itself. That little, however, was quite important. First of all the fungus had been given a new generic name, *Peronospora infestans* instead of *Botrytis infestans*, following the recognition by the botanist Caspary, in 1852, that it resembled the fungi for which Corda had proposed the name *Peronospora* more closely than it did those for which the botanists preferred to reserve the name *Botrytis*. The distinction turned upon some small but clear differences in the morphology of the two kinds of fungi, and more than this was implicit in the change of name. It came to be realized, much later, that the common habit of the Botrytis fungi was to live on decayed leaves, or to kill the leaf-tissue first and then live on its dead substance. They were 'facultative' parasites. The Peronospora fungi, on the other hand, grew in the living leaf-tissue, and their spawn died in it as it decayed. They appeared to be 'obligate' parasites, dependent upon the living substance of their hosts. It was significant that the fringe of visible downy mildew round the decayed areas on the underside of blighted potato leaves was always on the green edge that had not yet succumbed, never remaining for long on the decayed tissue which it left behind in its progress. This was, when one came to think of it, a fairly clear indication that the Potato Blight fungus was not one of the many small fungi which commonly lived on decaying matter, but a true parasite of the potato plant.

Then, in 1857, Speerschneider of Blankenburg, somewhere in the forests of Thuringia, had published his observations on a most interesting series of experiments. In the autumn of 1855 he noticed by chance that there were some germinating spores of the Potato Blight fungus clinging to the surface of potatoes when he dug them from the ground. Or, rather, these spores seemed to be the same as those of the fungus which caused the destruction of the leaves. Following up this clue, he placed blighted leaves in flower pots, laid sound tubers upon them, and then filled up the pots with damp earth which he took pains to obtain from two feet below the surface of a field where no potatoes were grown. He also potted up a number of sound tubers in the same way without diseased leaves. He kept the earth in the pots moist for ten days, and then knocked it out to see what had happened. He found that young or immature tubers, and also old ones from which he had removed a part of the skin, had become blighted where they had been in contact with the diseased leaves, while those which had been put in pots without diseased leaves remained perfectly sound. He examined the tissues of the diseased tubers and found them invaded by copious growths of mycelium. From these experiments he concluded that the Blight of the tubers was directly connected with that of the haulms – a point which was then still in dispute – and he said that spores of the fungus from the haulms germinated on the surface of the potatoes in the soil, penetrating the skin by means of their germ-tubes, and so giving rise to the mycelium within, which was the cause and not the consequence of disease. But he did not describe the act of penetration, and his observations were confined to the tubers.

About 1860 the fundamental botanical investigations of Anton de Bary were extended to this Potato Blight fungus, which was now known as *Peronospora infestans*, and he approached the study of it by two different routes. He sought first to trace the germination of its familiar summer spores and to observe them in the act of infecting healthy potato leaves, and he then looked about for the perfect, over-wintering fruits of the fungus, à la Tulasne. The results of his labours were recorded in a very famous pamphlet, in German, 'On the now-prevailing Disease of the Potato, its cause and its prevention', published at Leipzig in 1861, and in an equally celebrated memoir, in French, 'On the development of some parasitic fungi', which appeared in the *Annales des Sciences naturelles* for 1863.

The careful observation of the Blight spores in process of germination led to a discovery which interested the whole scientific world. De Bary's method was to 'plant' the Blight spores (shown here in Figs. 1 and 2, Chapter 1) not only in drops of water on glass slides, but also in drops of water *on the leaves of healthy potato plants*, and then to watch what happened, very attentively, through the microscope. Sometimes the spores germinated, as did those of the Oidium of the Vine, by pushing out a single delicate rootlet or germ-tube (Fig. 11). But quite often, as he was astonished to discover, the spores would first swell up, as shown in Fig. 12 (a), and divide the protoplasm they contained into a number of smaller portions, which presently broke away, and swam about in the water as a swarm of tinier spores (b) and (c). Each of these little naked spores was furnished with two propulsive hairs, and they jostled and dispersed when their mother-spore opened, much more like so many little unicellular animals let out of a bag, than anything one might expect to find belonging to the vegetable kingdom.

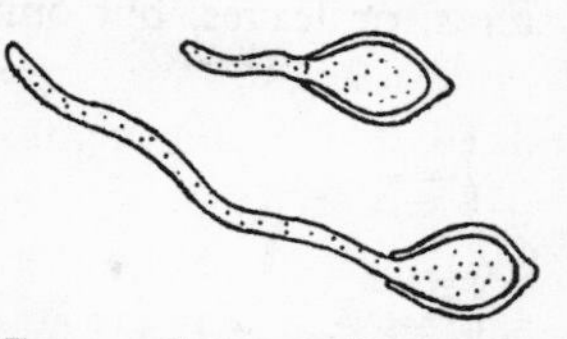

FIG. 11. A spore of the Potato Blight fungus germinating as a whole, by putting out a single germ-tube. (× 390)
After de Bary, 1863

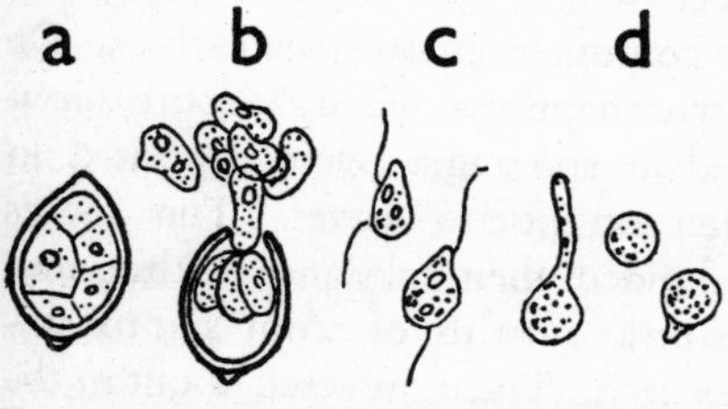

FIG. 12. A spore of the Potato Blight fungus functioning as a sporangium and releasing a swarm of smaller 'zoospores'. (× 390)
After de Bary, 1861

De Bary was less surprised by this phenomenon than he might have been if he had not spent several years observing the development of those pond-scums and seaweeds — the fresh and salt water algae. In several species of the algae the production of such animal-like, motile spores, appropriately called 'zoospores', was common enough, and they served the life-purposes of those interesting plants in various ways. Sometimes they were spermatozoids which took the male part in sexual reproduction, and sometimes they were asexual or vegetative spores which could be likened to fragments of the plant broken away, to go on growing elsewhere. When they were spermatozoids their propulsive hairs enabled them to swim about and find the female organs they had to fertilize. When they were vegetative spores their motility assisted their dispersion in the water and the spreading of the plant colonies. The fungi and the algae were considered to be very closely related, they both belonged to the same large tribe of cryptogamic plants, great and small, which the botanists called the *Thallophytes*: the plants which had no true roots, stems, or leaves, but only an undifferentiated *thallus*, such as the tangle of seaweed, or the spawn and spore-bearing strands of the microscopic Potato Blight fungus. The fundamental difference between the algae and the fungi was that the algae were provided with chlorophyll, with which to elaborate their own food from the gases of the atmosphere, while the fungi had none and were thus compelled to live as scavengers or parasites. If some of the algae had zoospores, it was not really remarkable that some of the fungi should have them also.

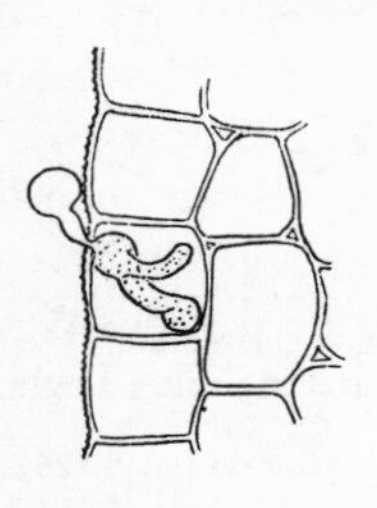

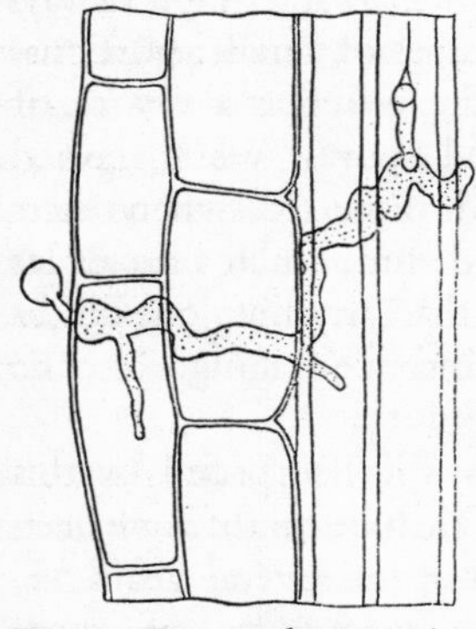

FIG. 13. Entry and penetration of the Potato Blight fungus, by means of its zoospores, into the cells of a potato leaf. (× 390) After de Bary, 1863

The main question now was how the swarms of little zoospores helped the Potato Blight fungus in its evil work of parasitizing the potato plants. They did not have any sexual function, for when they were liberated no female organs of the fungus were to be seen which they could fertilize, and they did not conjugate among themselves. De Bary studied what happened when the spores, now to be regarded as sporangia, were deposited in drops of water on potato leaves. The spores swelled up, divided their substance within, and released their little swarms of from six to sixteen zoospores each. These quivered about in the water for a while, and then, when they had settled down on the leaf-surface, they pushed out small germ-tubes, Fig. 12 (d), pressed them hard against the wall of the leaf-cell beneath them, and then either shoved or dissolved their way through. Having thus made a small hole for entry, they squeezed their protoplasm through it, leaving the empty skin of the spore behind. Once within a cell of the leaf-epidermis the bladder-like intrusions began to absorb the cell-juices rapidly, so swelling somewhat and elongating until they reached the next cell-wall, which they in turn passed, finding their way to the air-spaces between the cells, where they lengthened, branched, and slithered forward at ease, only putting out a small sucker into a leaf-cell now and then, for nourishment. The fungus was thus established within the leaf – the leaf-tissue was soon enmeshed with its spawn filaments – and when this spawn had gathered enough of substance and strength, it put out aerial filaments, through the stomata, to bear a new crop of spores.

Sometimes each spore would germinate as a whole, to penetrate the leaf with a single germ-tube, and sometimes it would break up into swarms of smaller zoospores which did the same thing, but at six to sixteen times as many points of entry. Here then was the function of the zoospores, and, incidentally, the clearest experimental proof that the Blight fungus *did* parasitize the potato plant. De Bary watched the process from generation to generation of the asexual, summer spores. It remained to be demonstrated that the fungus could invade healthy plants and that it caused 'The Potato Disease'.

To this end, De Bary selected a number of potato plants, grown in pots, and as far as any man could say, perfectly healthy. He divided them into two lots, one of which he left alone, but carefully protected from adventitious infection, and the other of which he deliberately 'inoculated' by placing spores of the Blight fungus on the moistened leaves. In a few days the inoculated plants exhibited the decayed spots which were the first symptom of Blight in the field, and their foliage then passed through all the stages of the Potato Disease until it was completely destroyed. The other lot of plants, which had not been infected, continued to flourish and showed no sign whatever of disease.

From the rapidity with which a single spore of the Blight fungus could germinate on a potato leaf, obtain entry, and produce a new crop of spores, the amazing rapidity with which the Blight could spread in a potato field or across a countryside, was no longer difficult to understand. The fungus grew rapidly around each point in the leaves where it obtained entry, leaving exhausted tissues to decay and blacken behind it, and marking its centrifugal progress with the characteristic fringe of down, on which hung myriads of new spores. These spores were detached and borne off when ripe by the slightest movement of the air, washed down by the rain, or carried about by insects. The majority would fall to the ground, but a very large number would reach the foliage of other potato plants, where, subject to there being sufficient moisture for their germination, they would obtain entry and within three days be releasing the next generation of spores. A single blighted potato plant in a field was capable of releasing several million spores. And, as though this were insufficient, each of these mother spores could in turn release a numerous swarm of eager, motile zoospores.

The spread of the Blight on potato *foliage*, in humid weather, was now adequately explained; but it was not the Blight on the foliage that troubled the farmers so much – it was the Blight on the tubers. By stopping the growth of the plants too soon the Blight on the foliage naturally reduced the crops – sometimes by three or four tons an acre – but when in addition to this it was found that half the tubers were blighted and going rotten in the ground, there would be very little left of the crop. It remained to be discovered how the fungus growing on the leaves could reach the potatoes in the soil below. Except at lifting-time there was little opportunity for the tubers to come into direct contact with partially-blighted green leaves, as in the experiments of Speerschneider.

De Bary buried some healthy potatoes in soil, and then shook the spores off some blighted potato leaves on to the soil surface, afterwards gently watering them with a rose in imitation of rain. The spores were washed down through the soil to the potatoes, and when these were dug up again after a while, several of them were blighted. The fungus mycelium in them was the same as in the blighted potato foliage, and when they were cut and left under a bell-glass, or stored whole in a cellar, a profuse growth of the characteristic downy mildew appeared on them. This, then, was one way, and perhaps the most likely way, in which the Blight travelled from the foliage to the tubers. The spores were washed down by rain. There might be another way, the reverse of what happened with the Bunt on the wheat; the mycelium of the fungus might creep from the blighted leaves, down within the leaf-stalks, inside the haulms, and so to the tubers on the underground stems. But the growth of the fungus was localized on the leaves and haulms, and De Bary could find no evidence whatever of mycelium traversing the plants from leaves to tubers.

The next, the really vexed problem about the Potato Blight fungus, was how it managed to survive from one season to another. Its mycelium died and rotted with the tissues of its host; its summer spores or zoosporangia were delicate, they retained their vitality only for a week or two; they could not possibly survive the winter in the soil. It was true there was living mycelium in the blighted potatoes, and if these were kept over the winter and planted the next year for 'seed', the still-living fungus might make its way up with the first shoots, produce summer spores on them, and so start the vegetative reproduction of the fungus again in the potato fields. Against this there was the fact that even conspicuously blighted sets often gave rise to perfectly healthy plants, and the Blight did not usually become evident to the farmer until July. Even if the fungus could survive from year to year in this way, it would be by asexual propagation or mere continuity of growth. Where did the sexual process occur in the life-history of the fungus, and where were its perfect, over-wintering fruits?

De Bary was unable to find the perfect fruits of the Potato Blight fungus, but by tracking down the development of certain other fungi, apparently closely related to it, he obtained a clue to where they might ultimately be found, and to the way in which they would almost certainly be formed. The brothers Tulasne had found the perfect fruits of some other species of Peronospora, but the formation of such kinds of fruit was more easily to be observed on a fungus which caused the 'White Rust' of cabbages, lettuces, mustard plants and Shepherd's Purse: the *Cystopus candidus* of Dr. Léveillé. The general habit of growth of this fungus was very similar to that of *Peronospora infestans*, except that its white, summer fructifications were formed under the cuticle of the cabbage or mustard leaves, which was torn as they reached maturity, with the result that the plants were marked with the white, rusty pustules from which the disease took its popular name. The observations which had been made on this fungus, and which De Bary confirmed, showed him that the formation of the perfect fruits was started by sexual conjugations between the strands of root-spawn. But where *was* that root-spawn? Not exposed on the surface of the leaves, like that of the Hop Mould, but buried within the leaf-tissue. The perfect fruits of Cystopus were to be found *within* the leaves of its host plants.

The copulation of *Cystopus candidus* Lév. was a curious and somewhat eerie process, down in the green half-light among the leaf-cells. The end of one of the spawn threads, nosing through the intercellular spaces, would stop in its progress and swell out into a small globular body. Then another spawn-thread, pursuing a different path through the maze would make contact with this globular body, and itself swell up, to a lesser degree, alongside it. These two victims of the life-urge – which together would easily go through the smallest perforation in a cigarette paper that could be made with the extreme tip of a very fine needle – continued to grow and later effected a transference of substance, the smaller to the larger, by means of an exceedingly minute communicating tube, Fig. 14 (a). The smaller partner, evidently the male, then dwindled and ultimately perished, while the female developed into a fruit – a tiny capsule containing a fertile egg-spore, or 'oospore', trimly protected by a hard rind to resist surrounding decay (b). In cross-section the oospore was as shown at (c) in the Figure, the contents being granular living protoplasm.

De Bary took some of the mustard leaves, in which the fungus had formed fruits, and left them to rot for months in damp earth. The oospores ripened as the leaves decayed and were plainly to be seen under the microscope as small, amber-coloured, warty bodies. As spring came round they underwent further developments. The granular plasm which they contained began to swell, and soon burst through the warty rind (d). As it increased in volume so the plasm divided into a number of small oval portions which were held for a

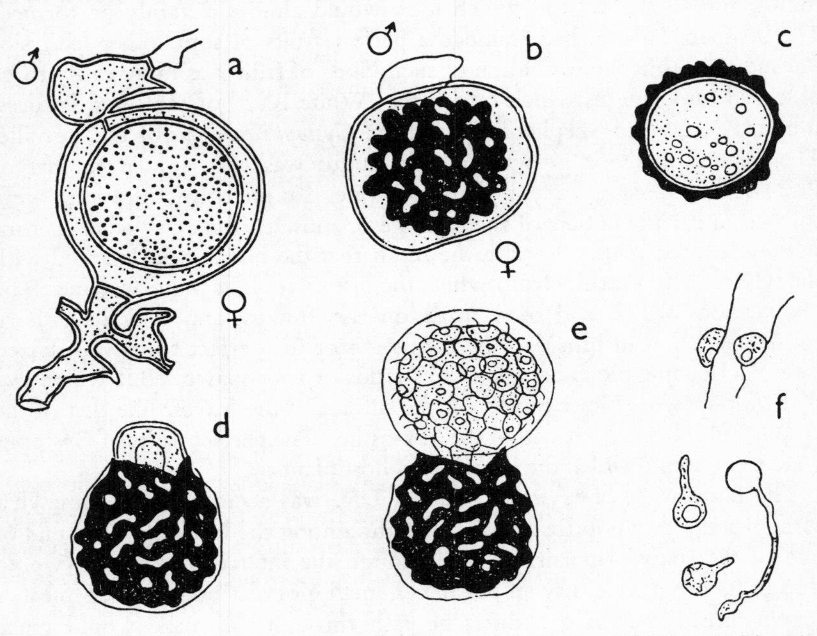

FIG. 14. Fertilization and development of the overwintering fruits of *Cystopus candidus* Lév., the fungus causing the 'White Rust' of cabbages, mustard, etc. ♂ male organ, or antheridium. ♀ female organ or oogonium. (× 390) After de Bary, 1863

while in a thin membraneous sac (e). The oval bits of naked plasm, as they grew, each put out two tiny cilia or hairs – they were zoospores. When their enveloping membrane burst they swam forth (f), seeking the first leaves of some cruciferous plant on which to germinate and establish the White Rust fungus for another year. The oospores of the fungus in decayed leaves lay in wait for the seedlings of the plants when they pushed through the soil in the spring.

With these observations, the life-cycle of the White Rust fungus stood revealed. Its development had been traced, stage by stage, through summer and winter, round the year. There was no longer any mystery about the way it survived through the dark cold months during which there was no green foliage on which it could grow: its living 'seeds' were snug in the stuff of rotting leaves on the ground. Did the Potato Blight fungus survive the winter in the same way? That was the question.

De Bary now knew where to look for the over-wintering fruits of the Blight fungus: they would probably be found where the root-spawn of the fungus was, or among its remains. Which was to say in either of two places: in the dead leaves and haulms of potato plants, or in the blighted tubers themselves. He sought for the missing fruits of the fungus in both places, but they were not there. In thousands of sections cut and macerations made from the tissues of blighted plants, they could not very well have escaped his detection, with the magnification he employed. Such fruits were never particularly small as microscopic objects went. The perfect fruits of the Potato Blight fungus simply were not there. They eluded discovery, and the way in which the fungus managed to survive the winter, and to reappear, as it were from nowhere, in July, remained a mystery.

'What did we tell you,' said those who still gave credence to the old theories of heterogenesis and spontaneous generation, 'the potato plants themselves produce the germs of your Peronospora: it comes from decay'. But Anton de Bary knew better than that: like begat like, and every living thing came from an egg. 'How do you know,' went on the heterogeneticists, 'why should it be true for the Blight fungus, when you can't find its eggs?' Some day they will be found, said Anton de Bary, unless perchance the fungus is perennial, and having lost the capacity to produce perfect fruits, it goes on growing continuously in its summer form, somewhere, all through the year.

'Where does the Blight go in the winter-time?' became one of the unsolved riddles of science.

CHAPTER VIII

ENTER LOUIS PASTEUR

IN 1861, Albert, Prince Consort of England, died of typhoid fever.[1] There was then no knowledge of the real nature or cause of typhoid fever, and, *a fortiori*, no knowledge of the hygienic or prophylactic measures by which his regrettably early decease from this cause might have been prevented. If anyone had suggested that the good Prince died because of the multiplication in his intestinal tract of a microscopic fission-fungus, nourished by the royal juices and brewing virulent poisons in them, that person would have been considered mad. A very great deal more was known about the Potato Blight by 1861 than about typhoid fever. The fungal organism that caused the Potato Blight was known, at least in part; the bacillus of typhoid was not even identified until 1884.

That typhoid was an infectious disease was apparent to everybody; in epidemics it spread among men almost as fast as the Blight spread in the potato fields, but the agency by which it was communicated from one person to another was a mystery. There might be pernicious 'miasmas' or the Disease itself might have 'germs' – much as one might speak of the germs of an idea. The 'germs' might even have a material existence, for all kinds of notions of germs had been playthings of the philosophers for about as long as there had been any philosophers in the world. But in 1861 the notions about germs were even more nebulous than those about 'atoms' before Dalton. Nobody seriously imagined that the germs of typhoid fever would ever be seen, measured, counted, and cultivated in dishes and test-tubes.

One very good reason why knowledge of the bacteria – a few species of which were subsequently found to cause infectious diseases of man – lagged so far behind that of the micro-organisms associated with the principal diseases of plants was that the bacteria were of a second order of smallness, and of deceptively insignificant appearance when seen with even the highest powers of the microscopes available. One introduction to what Pasteur called 'the world of the infinitesimally small', for those accustomed to think in terms of visual imagery, might have been provided by some such diagram as Fig. 15, herein. The spore-bearing hyphae of the Potato Blight fungus, the summer and winter fruits of the common Powdery Mildew of the Rose, the germinating spores of the Bunt fungus on the wheat – they all appeared

[1] *Ency. Brit.*, 14th ed. I, 522.

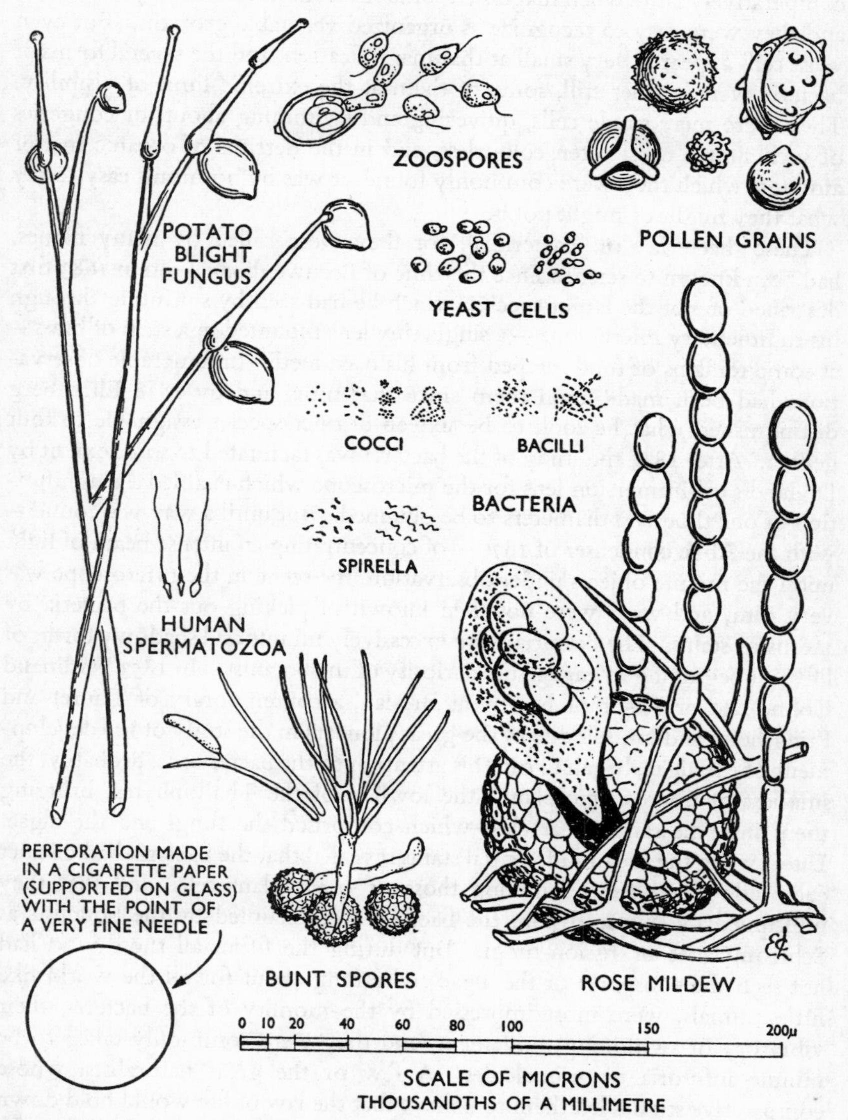

FIG. 15. A study in comparative size: some bacteria, yeast-cells, pollen grains, microscopic fungi, etc., drawn to the same scale. (× 350)

comparatively large when magnified some three hundred and fifty diameters, and they were easy to recognize as organized vegetable growths. But even yeast cells appeared very small at that magnification, and the several forms of bacteria were smaller still, some of them at the extreme limit of visibility. They were mere single cells, quivering and swimming about, or congeries of such simple cells, often colourless, and in the detritus of organic matter amongst which they were commonly found, it was by no means easy to say what they might or might not be.

These 'bacteria', or 'bacteridia', for they were called by many names, had been known to science since the time of Leeuwenhoek, who in 1683 first described one of the larger species, which he had seen by squinting through his rudimentary microscope – a single tiny lens mounted in a strip of brass – at some remains of food scraped from his own teeth. Innumerable observations had been made upon them since that time, and by 1838 Ehrenberg distinguished what he took to be sixteen distinct species assignable to four genera. After 1844 the study of the bacteria was facilitated to some extent by Dolland's oil-immersion lens for the microscope which enabled a magnification of one thousand diameters to be obtained. But until a way was found – with the Abbe condenser of 1870 – of concentrating an intense beam of light upon the minute objects under observation, the scene in the microscope was very dim, and ways were not then known of picking out the bacteria by means of stains. The bacteria were excessively minute and shadowy forms of life, just beginning to engage the curiosity of the botanists. In 1853 Ferdinand Cohn, late professor of botany at Breslau, a contemporary of Thuret and Pringsheim and himself one of the great pioneers in the study of the development of the algae, began to turn his attention to the bacteria, as, probably, the smallest of microscopic plants, the lowliest of the Thallophytes; bringing them into the same great class which comprised the fungi and the algae. Later, when the use of differential stains revealed that the bacteria had distinct cell-walls somewhat resembling those of other plant cells, and that they multiplied by simple fission, the bacteria were claimed by the botanists as Schizomycetes or fission-fungi. But during the fifties all those who had not seen the zoospores of the algae swimming about for all the world like little animals, were most impressed by the motility of the bacteria, their vibratory or swimming movement, and they were commonly taken to be minute infusoria or animalcules. A few of the great naturalists, whose comparative studies led them to believe that the law of life would hold down to its lowest manifestations, were convinced, as Spallanzani had been in the eighteenth century, that the swarms of bacteria found in infusions of decaying organic matter had their origin in living spores which drifted in the air. That like all other living things they grew from 'seeds' or 'eggs'. For the rest of the world, however, it seemed very plausible that such minute bodies could well be animated by little sparks of life set at liberty when the stuff of larger organisms died – the theory of 'heterogenesis'; or that the processes of fermentation and putrefaction, then regarded as purely chemical, could originate such trifling living things by the way – and this was 'spontaneous generation'. By 1861, resort to the ancient theories of heterogenesis or spontaneous generation to account for the appearance of parasitic fungi on the crops had been thoroughly discredited, but for the smaller organisms, the bacteria, such notions still held sway, and the idea, put forward from time to time, that there might be as many distinct species of bacteria as there were flowers of the field was regarded as an extravagant pleasantry or a precious piece of nonsense.

As the microscope was improved, and as the botanists paid more and more attention to the smallest things in their weird gardens, the fission-fungi might have been admitted quietly into the vegetable kingdom, in the course of twenty years or so, and most people might have taken their biogenesis for granted, but for one historic circumstance – in 1859 Darwin's *Origin of Species* was published. Darwin's cautious hypothesis, that some species were evolved from others in the course of time, was thoroughly respectable, it was an illuminating idea, by no means new, and it was of profound and special interest to the botanists and zoologists, as it provided them with a better basis for the classification of living things than they had ever had before. It introduced a fourth dimension – Time – into taxonomy, as into morphology, and it enabled the naturalists to make most interesting museum arrangements illustrative of a hypothetical Tree of Life, out of their bundle of sticks. Nobody minded all this, and even when the evolutionists began sketching in the probable descent of the worthy English bourgeoisie, even of the most vociferous bishops of the Church, it was considered in bad taste only by those who could not appreciate the relatively high moral virtues of the apes. No! in the Grand Darwinian Theory – which went far beyond anything Darwin ever said – there was something much less innocent than all this. The break-away from the dogma of original creation had its roots in a long-repressed desire on the part of some people to spit in the eye of the Church. The political significance of a heresy which threatened to weaken the influence and temporal power of the Church was real enough, but equally real and very deep philosophical issues were also raised. The ultimate clash was between vitalism and materialism; it divided the scientific world into two camps; started, as it were, two great and opposing tidal waves of passionate thought which irrigated with violence every province of the biological sciences. The wealth of eagerness and hard-thinking that went into attempts to establish the theory of evolution did much for the advancement of knowledge; but the determination on the part of those of another mind that the theory of evolution should *not* be pushed to the absurdity of its logical conclusion, led to advances which were perhaps of even greater practical moment. And especially was this so in the field of pathology.

It could easily be seen why the resurrection of a dwindling belief in the possibility of spontaneous generation was regarded as a philosophic necessity by those who sought to explain away the Creation by wild extrapolations and extensions of Darwin's hypotheses. So long as it was possible to regard the production of living organisms of *any* kind, no matter how small, as a result of purely chemical and physical processes, it was (just) possible to imagine the evolution or elaboration of life-forms, stage by stage, through successive geological epochs, all the way up from a unicellular organism to a blessed Queen Victoria herself, or even a Thomas Henry Huxley. It required an elastic imagination, not to be deterred by a wholesale absence of confirmatory evidence, but still, it was very much to the taste of some devotees of material progress, who could not bear to acknowledge that there was anything in heaven or earth undreamed-of in their philosophy. For the thorough-going, out-and-out materialist, a belief in physico-chemico-genesis was an absolute necessity; for if the smallest living cell could still be brought into being only through the reproduction of its kind, by the passing on of life from like to like, the farthest-flung train of Evolutionary speculation brought no ultimate balm. There would be no ha'p'orth of reason to suppose that the first amoeba could ever have crawled spontaneously out of the primordial slime. If it was still necessary to imagine some super-natural occurrence or act of Divine intervention to account for the first animalcule, one might just as well believe that God created Adam in his own likeness, and leave it at that. It would seem a divine enterprise even more worthy of admiration, if one happened to be a man and not an animalcule. 'Materialism' and 'vitalism' were dull, Latin words. What did they mean? Just this: the materialists put Dirt before Life; it pleased them to think of all Life as born of the inanimate Dirt. The vitalists, on the other hand, men for whom Christianity was a faith essentially humane, along with most of the men of science who studied living things, *alive*, instinctively put Life *before* Dirt: a living God before the first dawn on earth, biology before chemistry, and human desires and passions before Gold.

Enthusiasm for the Grand Darwinian Theory was conspicuously lacking in France, where evolutionary ideas made slower progress than in any other country, and it was by no manner of accident, unrelated to the civilization of France as a whole, that Louis Pasteur, in 1861, was attacking the doctrine of spontaneous generation. He was digging the supposedly fecund Dirt away from the very base of the evolutionists' precious Tree of Life, and leaving that Tree suspended as an eternal mystery in the Divine air. That was what Pasteur was really doing at that time; he was not seeking for germs of diseases, and he had scarcely begun to dream that the logical course of his researches would ultimately put the medical profession upon the track of the pathogenic fission-fungi, one species of which had caused the death of the good Prince Albert, encourager of the industrial arts. Pasteur's investigations into the disease of Silkworms in the south of France were not begun until 1865, he did not turn his attention to Anthrax in sheep until 1877, and it was 1885 before the first child was inoculated against hydrophobia. In 1861, Louis Pasteur, too good a Catholic, and much too good a chemist, to tolerate materialistic doctrines against the evidence of his senses, was attacking the 'philosophic necessity' of spontaneous generation.

In 1840, Mr. Philip Pusey, outlining a programme for the Royal Agricultural Society of England, had said: 'The followers of kindred sciences may fairly be invited to aid us in the formation of this branch of knowledge, which may be called agricultural pathology.' Pasteur was one of the men, who in the course of the years, and by a route of his own, did come to the aid of the new branch of science. His discoveries, his conceptions, his experimental methods, all had a vital and formative part in the makings of plant pathology, no less than of animal and human pathology. But his findings did not tack on, in any neat sequence, to the work of the cryptogamic botanists; he was a chemist, and his approach was different; he was a man of original genius ploughing neighbouring ground, and it would be for historians to walk in *his* furrow, noting what he had turned up, and pondering on the significance thereof.

As a young man, in 1848, when he was only twenty-six, Pasteur made his first, brilliant scientific discovery, and happily it received immediate and full recognition by the greatest *savants* in France. This success fired in him a consuming passion for research, and started him on his course with an unbroken youthful ambition. His maiden discovery meant so much more than an addition to knowledge of the properties of tartaric acid. A minute difference, which he was the first to perceive, among the crystals of the acid, the right and left handedness of certain of the crystal facets, was associated with the power of their solutions to turn polarized light to the right or to the left. What did it mean? It meant that some at least of the molecules of which the whole universe was composed had the power of assembling in two ways, one of which was the mirror image of the other. It was a discovery of cosmic significance, and for a while Pasteur was intoxicated, as any young man might be, with the splendour of it. He found that yeast – one of the sugar-*fungi* – would fement a mixture of the ammonium salts of his right and left handed acids. It decomposed the right-handed one, and left the other untouched – though the two acids were *chemically* identical. Later he found that one of the common bread-moulds, *Penicillium glaucum*, would also grow on a solution of the mixed salts, again breaking down the right-handed one for its nourishment and leaving the other behind. The solution, when he started, was optically inactive, the right-handed and the left-handed molecules having equal and opposite effects on the beam of polarized light. As the mould grew, the solutions turned the light more and more to the left. The preference of the living fungus for the molecules with the right-handed twist was so definite that the cultivation of the mould in the mixed solution was one of the very few practical ways of separating one optically active compound from an optically inactive mixture of the two. Was not this discovery of profound interest to those studying the fungi causing diseases of the crops? Did it not provide a remarkable piece of information about the food requirements of the fungi? Did it not suggest experiments to determine whether *Peronospora infestans* had the same queer preference as *Penicillium glaucum*? But this was by the way; the point that Pasteur seized upon was that a living organism, the bread-mould, made a selection between the right and left handed molecules. *Molecular dissymmetry was intimately connected with the life-process.*

In his imagination, Pasteur saw life and the universe, then, as one grand exhibition of molecular dissymmetry. 'Life', he said, 'is dominated by dissymmetrical actions. I can foresee that all living species are primordially, in their structure, in their external forms, functions of cosmic dissymmetry'. He grew plants on rotating tables, and even proposed to grow them in rays of sunlight reversed by systems of mirrors with the idea that he might thereby cause the molecules in the plants, and the plants themselves, to twist the other way round; to reverse the very atomic clockwork of nature and grow plants that would be the mirror images of their normal selves. Later generations would come to think of Pasteur, as he was when he was sixty, half-paralysed, bearded and grave, and too easily they would forget that he was ever a young man, whose genius it was to perceive in the minute the signature of the universal. Behind his finely disciplined intellect, and the beautiful exactitude of his researches, there was an imagination very youthful, very daring, very light and free.

While the crystals of tartaric acid were still sparkling for Pasteur, with all the magical brilliance of first discovery, he had not only travelled about Europe collecting specimens of tartar from many sources, poking about in the dregs of the wine vats where the argol or tartar was found, he had also sought for the 'Pasteur' phenomenon of optical dissymmetry in other substances, and one of these, which like tartaric acid itself, existed in more than one optical form, was amyl alcohol. A product of fermentation. Pasteur was happy when his teaching appointment at Lille in 1854 took him into a district where there were many distilleries. He would have to prepare lectures on the chemistry of fermentation for the apprentices and technical workers of the district, but, alongside his teaching work, he would be able to continue his researches and perhaps find some more dissymmetrical substances. The distillers' vats were good places in which to look for them.

He had not been studying fermentation for very long before he began watching the yeast cells in the fermenting worts and liquors, with a very particular attention. Under the microscope, they appeared, normally, as small globules, often with a smaller globule budding out at the side, like a 'dolly' on a potato. They multiplied in this way, by budding. In fermentations that went well and gave good brews, the cells were all of this kind; but in those that went wrong, and produced sour wine or inferior beer there were present cells of a different shape, not globular, but elongated or sausage-like. Could that small abnormality make all the difference to the brew? Molecular dissymmetry receded into the background and Pasteur had now a new enthusiasm – to discover the part of yeast cells in fermentation.

The numerous group of simple unicellular fungi associated with various fermentative processes – of which ordinary yeast in alcoholic fermentation was only one – thus began to receive the attention of an exceedingly astute observer. Pasteur's thought, from the very first, was that the yeast globules, and smaller, elongated bodies were the cells of living organisms, *and as they had life so they would require food.* Every child knew that a living cat needed food, and that it got it from somewhere; but it was of the essence of genius to recognize equally clearly that the smallest microscopic cell, so long as it was alive and growing, was under the same imperative necessity of obtaining food, and that the food could come only from its surroundings. Not only were the cells of yeast and other simple organisms taking their nourishment from the solutions of sugar and other substances in which they lived – they were also, of necessity, transforming it. They were using part of it to build up their own substance and rejecting the rest. Hence the chemical changes which took place in fermentation.

This realization led Pasteur to a number of discoveries of great industrial value, which seemed little short of magical to those for whom the life-processes of microscopic organisms had no reality. He discovered that the process of making vinegar from wine depended on the growth of a particular kind of fungus—'the vinegar plant'—on the beech-wood chippings over which the wine was allowed to flow. Where the wine would not 'turn' to vinegar, he put in a little of the living fungus and the vinegar-makers' trouble was at an end. He showed that a souring, a so-called 'disease', of wine was due to the growth of an undesirable organism in it after it had been bottled, and he showed the wine-makers how to overcome the trouble, very simply, by heating the wine, to kill the cells of the organism, before it was bottled. An early instance of 'pasteurization', although, indeed, the Romans had been familiar with this dodge for preserving wine. He studied the souring of milk, or lactic fermentation, showed that it was due to the growth of yet another kind of organism in the milk, and tracked down the fermentation of grape-juice to which no yeast was added as such to a wild yeast which was to be found on the skins of the grapes.

The significance of all this in plant pathology? Well, when the potatoes were rotting in Ireland in 1846, the incomparable Dr. Lyon Playfair had announced with confidence that the rotting was due to some purely chemical action, analogous to that which caused the familiar and well-known souring of milk. Now the souring of milk itself was shown to be due to a living organism, and there were many besides Dr. Playfair who would have to eat their words.

After he had left Lille, and taken up his post as director of scientific studies at the École Normale in Paris, in 1857, Pasteur produced abundant evidence that the various fermentations, sourings and putrefactions of milk, beer, wine, urine, were brought about by living organisms in the liquids, and that when the organisms were absent or killed the chemical changes did not take place. But the very idea that fermentation was brought about by any life-process was rank heresy for the chemists at that time. Pasteur had dared to put Life before Dirt, and at once he had the great Berzelius and Justus von Liebig against him.

The chemists had but recently overthrown the old belief that 'organic' substances could be built up from their elements *only* under the influence of a mysterious principle called the *Vis vitalis*, or, more simply, of 'Life'. When

Wöhler, in 1832, synthesized a very typical 'organic' substance, namely urea, from nothing more animated than potassium cyanide, ammonia and red lead, the *Vis vitalis* theory had begun to totter, and with the subsequent synthesis of a considerable number of other organic compounds in the laboratory, it was regarded as dead and buried. Although, in fact, the chemists had succeeded in making only a few of the *waste products* of life, they were nevertheless persuaded that there was no philosophic reason why every kind of stuff found occurring in living organisms should not ultimately be made from dead material in the laboratory. This was an expression of the chemists' necessary faith in their own powers. Now Pasteur, himself a brilliant chemist, seemed to be prostrating himself before the old *Vis vitalis* once again, and he was scornfully accused of attempting to put back the clock of up-to-date nineteenth century progress.

Liebig pronounced that yeast died when it was put in beer-wort or sugar solution, or that enough of it died to give off some unstable chemical substance, containing ammonia, which involved the sugar in its own decomposition, splitting it up into carbon-dioxide gas and alcohol. If some of the yeast happened to live in the wort, that was quite immaterial – it was only the substances in dead yeast that mattered. In short, the Dirt. Pasteur found that far from giving off ammonia, yeast absorbed it to build up its own living cells, and he offered Liebig a kilogramme of pure yeast, which he had obtained by planting as much living yeast as would cover a pin's head in a solution of sugar and ammonium salts. He could not very well magnify a single yeast cell into something about the size of a cow, lead it along to Liebig, feed it before his eyes on beer wort or sugar solution, and then milk it, in his presence, of alcohol and the other products of fermentation. But short of that he did his best.

Pasteur's researches on 'so-called spontaneous generation', which continued from 1859 to 1865, arose directly out of his work on fermentation. He had discovered that fermentation and putrefaction were dependent upon the growth of living organisms. Where did those organisms come from? Yeast was deliberately added in some fermentative processes, but all infusions of organic matter, left about, would start to ferment with apparent spontaneity, and even when they had been boiled to kill everything in them, they would soon be found teeming with living cells, of yeasts, of moulds, and of bacteria. Pasteur, who had read all about the experiments of the Abbé Spallanzani, and Needham and Buffon, and Schwann and von Helmholtz, knew the answer before he began. The organisms came from the air, in which their imponderable 'spores' were always floating about, as the grosser seeds of some of the flowering plants drifted in the wind. But the apparently spontaneous appearance of minute organisms in infusions of fermenting or decaying material was the very 'fact' upon which the last belief in spontaneous generation now depended. Pasteur set himself to prove experimentally what he knew beforehand must be true. As the truth would be most unwelcome, and he would be challenged at every step of the way, he had to contrive a series of experiments which would give unambiguous results, and yet be of such simplicity that no one could pretend to misunderstand them. Pasteur undoubtedly found something highly attractive in this undertaking; he was not without his share of original sin, and he had an impatient, ready and scathing tongue with which he was well able to defend himself in the conclaves of science. The very full-stops in the accounts of his researches on spontaneous generation were emphatic. They did something more than close the sentences, they said 'this blasts your error, get round it if you can!'

He did not succeed in routing the materialists' belief in the possibility of spontaneous generation. It was, in truth, impossible to prove that it never occurred in nature. Or that it never had occurred in the past. Even in his own experiments, the very things he did to make sure there were no living organisms in his infusions at the start, the heating and the filtration, could equally well destroy the delicately constituted, but inanimate molecules from which life might be supposed to start. And so long as smaller and smaller living organisms continued to be discovered or suspected, about which there was sufficient lack of knowledge, so long would it be possible for those of wishful mind to say: here, at least, we have a living thing which *may* have been produced by physico-chemico-genesis; here, possibly, is the missing link between inanimate matter and life.[1] But Pasteur *did* show that the postulation of spontaneous generation was wholly unnecessary to account for anything that happened in the course of his experiments, and as his experiments were expressly designed to cover all the instances in which the phenomenon was supposed to occur, he left his opponents with nothing to put forward but unverified suppositions. The best of them took to leaving an abhorred blank for the origin of life on their evolutionary charts, but it was not so much the ultimate philosophical aim of Pasteur's researches that mattered, as the many incidental discoveries to which they gave rise by the

[1] In 1939 the filter-passing viruses were sometimes sneakingly indicated as possible physico-chemical ancestors of life. And the possible synthesis of carbohydrates by the action of sunlight on carbonic acid in the waters of sterile primordial seas was here and there regarded as highly significant. It was only necessary to imagine molecules of foodstuff twittering over into elementary organisms capable of consuming it, as cheese was once supposed to turn into mice, and the story would be complete.

way – aseptic surgery for example, and the clarification of the principles upon which the whole of a vast food-canning industry would later come to depend.

Pasteur made up a number of broths and infusions of organic matter that very quickly fermented or went bad when left exposed to the air: sugar solutions, yeast water, milk, urine, meat juices, and infusions of hay. As Spallanzani had done before him, he put the infusions into small glass flasks, heated them to destroy any spores or cells of living organisms, either in the liquids or in the air within the flasks, and then sealed the flasks. But this time he sealed them *positively* — by drawing out the narrow necks and fusing the glass with a blowlamp. The infusions kept clear and 'good' indefinitely. There was a partial vacuum within the flasks owing to the condensation of steam in them after they had been sealed. When he broke the seal, thus permitting a few cubic centimetres of air to rush in, the preparations promptly went bad, and in a few days they were teeming with living organisms, all of which had arisen from the multiplication and growth of the few microscopic cells and spores let in with the air. He repeated the experiments, sterilizing the air before admission by passing it through a red-hot platinum tube. There was then no growth of organisms in the preparations and they kept good. The preservation was not due to the exclusion of oxygen, as Gay-Lussac had supposed, and it was not due to the vacuum in the flasks, but simply to the exclusion of the germs of living organisms with which the air was charged. The success of the preserve-maker, d'Appert, in heating his tightly-sealed jars of fruit-stuff, was thus explained.

To show that the air did contain the germs of living organisms it would be instructive to catch some of them directly from the air and to present them for observation under the microscope. To do this Pasteur stuck a tube out of his window and drew in air from the street through a filter-plug of guncotton. He dissolved the guncotton with solvents and examined the organisms left behind. There was a rich variety: spores of common moulds, yeast globules, and the smaller cells of bacteria or infusoria. All these organisms were killed by the process of dissolving the guncotton. In other experiments he took small portions of the filter-plugs direct from his tube, containing dust and live germs caught from the air, and placed them in flasks of sterile nutrient solutions (sugared yeast-water) which had kept good and clear. The various organisms grew rapidly in the solutions and he was able to examine their progeny.

There were, first of all, the common moulds, *Mucor* and *Penicillium*, the one bearing its spores in spherical spore-capsules, the other in long flails.

On January 23rd, 1860, Pasteur introduced one of his dust-laden plugs into the neck of a flask of nutrient solution which was laid horizontally. He then sealed up the flask. By the next day the spores of the two moulds in the plug had germinated and pushed out filaments in all directions; on the 25th they had fructified and were producing a new crop of spores, while on the 27th the growth was stationary, as the fungi had by then used up all the available nutriment or oxygen. But there were the two moulds, mycelium and spore-capsules or flails, cultivated on the neck of the flask moistened with nutrient solution, from spores caught from the air, as surely as one might cultivate mustard and cress by planting the seeds on damp flannel. The two species of mould which Pasteur cultivated in that experiment were not parasitic on living plants, they grew on stale bread, old boots and damp walls, but they were of the same order of size and complexity of vegetative form as the Potato Blight fungus or the Oidium of the vine. Had Pasteur drawn his air, not from a street in Paris, but from a vineyard or potato field in the summer, he would have trapped spores of *Oidium Tuckeri* or *Peronospora infestans.* They might not have grown in his particular nutrient solution, but they would have been among his catch. It was not long before those studying the parasitic fungi on the crops began to use spore-traps of various kinds, and to cultivate their fungi also in nutrient solutions; these dodges became a most useful part of their investigational technique; and they owed them to Louis Pasteur.

But the organisms with which Pasteur was primarily concerned were not the larger moulds with their tangles of spawn strands and relatively elaborate fructifications, but the unicellular yeast-fungi which increased by simple budding, and the bacteria which increased by fission of their single cells into two. Of these simpler organisms the air yielded many kinds, and with his little sealed vacuum flasks of nutrient solution Pasteur had a ready means of sampling the microflora of the air in different localities. He had only to break the narrow necks of the flasks, where the sample was to be taken, to let a little of the air go in with a rush, so collecting and trapping any organisms there might be in it. He then sealed the necks of the flasks with a blowpipe again and left the organisms to grow.

He made hundreds of flasks, opened them in the streets before and after the fall of rain, in the town and in the country, in cellars and on roof-tops, and had some interesting adventures with them on the Mer de Glace, to which he climbed in preference to going up in a balloon. The organisms collected varied according to the place in which the air was sampled. In a few instances, especially up on the Mer de Glace, there happened to be no organisms in the small quantity of air taken, and the fermentable material kept good despite its admission. In one series of experiments he opened a large number of flasks, on a terrace in the open air, to make a kind of general survey of the

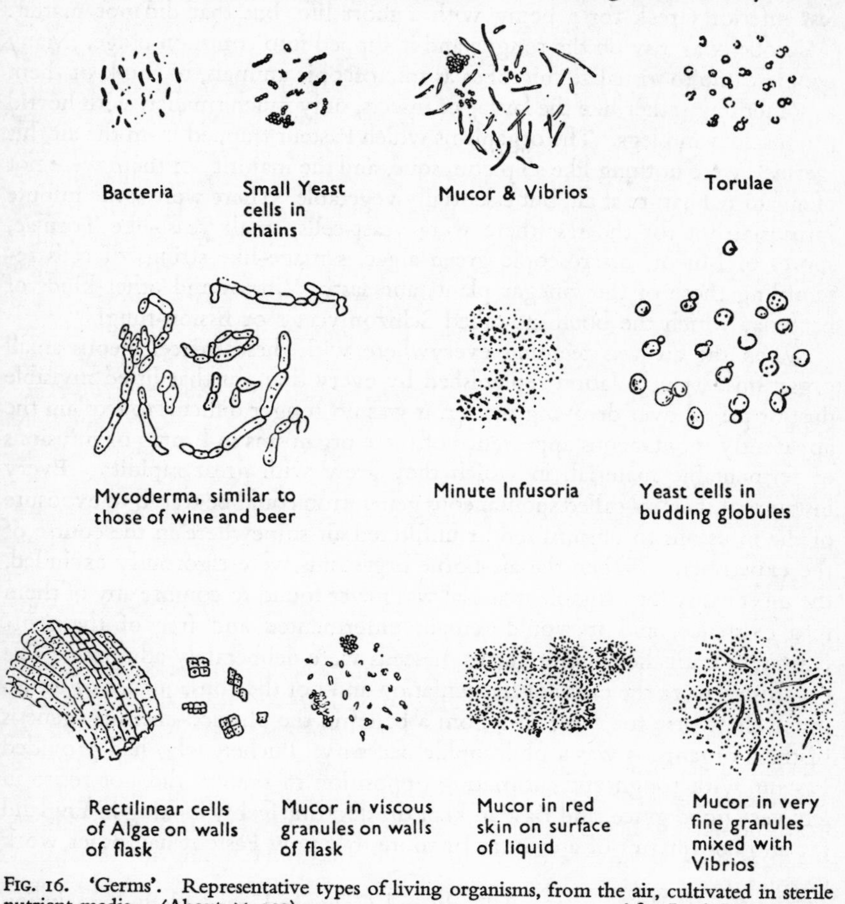

FIG. 16. 'Germs'. Representative types of living organisms, from the air, cultivated in sterile nutrient media. (About × 350) After Louis Pasteur, 1862

variety of organisms the air commonly contained, and then made drawings of the different sorts as they were to be seen under the microscope (Fig. 16).

Later on, in 1878, when talk about these organisms in the air was on everybody's lips, a new popular name was coined for them by Dr. Sédillot. Playing the good old word-taking and word-making game of the nursery, with

Greek roots, he shunted 'micro' (small) on to 'bios' (life), trimmed the result, and obtained 'microbe', which he hoped might mean a microscopic being. Some friendly classical scholars advised him that 'microbe' would be rather less inferior Greek for a being with a short life, but that did not matter. 'Microbe' was easy on the tongue and it slipped into common usage. Many people came to visualize microbes as microscopic animals, to think of them as something rather like the larvae of insects, only much smaller, with horrid proboscides and legs. The organisms which Pasteur trapped from the air, his 'germs', were nothing like so picturesque, and the majority of them were not of an animal nature at all, but essentially vegetable. There were some minute infusoria, but for the rest there were yeast-cells, small yeast-like Torulae, spores of Mucor, microscopic green algae, sausage-like strings of cells resembling those of the vinegar plant, and lastly Vibrios and other kinds of bacteria, which the botanists called Schizomycetes or fission-fungi.

When the air was teeming everywhere with these miscellaneous small organisms, its population replenished by every draught that lifted invisible dust or passed over decaying matter, it was no longer difficult to explain the apparently spontaneous appearance of these organisms in broths or infusions of fermentable material, in which they grew with great rapidity. Every instance of their so-called spontaneous generation could be traced to exposure of the infusions to unsterilized or unfiltered air somewhere in the course of the experiment. When the air-borne organisms were rigorously excluded, the most easily fermentable material was never found to conjure any of them into existence, and it would remain unfermented and free of them indefinitely until their living germs or seeds were deliberately admitted. The organisms were the cause of fermentation and not the consequence of it. So much the worse for those to whom a belief in the physico-chemico-genesis of these organisms was a philosophic necessity. Puchet, who had provided Pasteur with tough and infuriating opposition in France, did not retire in any very good grace, and Bastian kept the doctrine feebly kicking in England for another quarter of a century or more, but now Pasteur had other work to do.

By 1863, both Pasteur and Ferdinand Cohn had reached the conclusion that *putrefaction* of organic matter was a process of the same nature as fermentation, also consequent upon the growth of living organisms. The suppuration of surgical wounds was regarded as an instance of putrefaction, and by 1865, Dr. Lister in England was excluding air-borne germs from wounds with filter-pads of cotton wool, and killing the germs which settled on the skin, on instruments, and on exposed tissues during operations, with carbolic acid as an antiseptic. Davaine and Rayer, moreover, had made an observation which might be of the most profound significance in connection with the infectious diseases, the fevers and the plagues of all animals, including mankind. They had found that a living rod-shaped bacteridium was present in great numbers in the spleen of sheep stricken with the Splenic fever, or Anthrax. The organism was not present in healthy sheep. Of course, the organism might in some way invade the tissues of pre-diseased sheep as other germs invaded wounds. But was it not possible that this fission-fungus, this bacteridium of Davaine's, had the same relationship to Anthrax in sheep that *Peronospora infestans* had to the Potato Blight? Might it not be the *cause* of the disease? With this discovery of Davaine's a vast field for speculation was opened up.

The plant doctors were concerned with these new developments no less than the medical profession. When plant tissue was cut or wounded or broken down through the action of the larger parasitic fungi, hosts of smaller organisms, yeasts and bacteria, would get in from the air or the soil and complete the work of decay. They could, for example, rot blighted potatoes in the ground, reducing them to skinfuls of slime. Although so far there was only a doubtful possibility that bacteria could be causal agents of disease, either in plants or animals, they were certainly secondary agents of putrefaction and decay. The principal attackers of the crops were among the larger species of the microflora, but the smaller lay always in wait. The 'vegetable pathologists' would now have to study not only the moulds and mildews, but the yeasts, the myxomycetes and the bacteria.

The province of search was extended; but what should be said for that other lead given by Pasteur? His approach to the study of micro-organisms by way of their *chemical* effects on the fluids in which they lived? Unfortunately Pasteur never directly concerned himself with any plant disease. But suppose the study of the Potato Blight had followed his chemical route: what considerations would have come uppermost? The Blight fungus would have been more clearly seen as an organism living on the substance of the potato leaves, growing at its expense, absorbing it, but using of necessity only a part of it to build up its own different body, and rejecting the rest. The waste products of the fungal metabolism might have a highly toxic effect on the tissues of its host. They might cause much more damage than the mere leeching by the fungus of some of the plant sap, or the partial obstruction of the air spaces between the cells with the threads of its gossamer mycelium. The weight of a *million* spores of the Blight fungus was only about four milligrams; the loss of that amount of substance would seem trifling to a whole potato leaf. Again, from the chemical viewpoint, the Blight fungus was very particular about its food. It would grow only on a few plants confined to the Solanaceae: potatoes, egg-plants, tomatoes. Clearly there was something specific in the sap of these plants indispensable for its growth. If a variety of potato could be found, bred, or otherwise produced, without this chemical principle in its sap, or with some other principle noxious to the very fastidious Blight fungus, then *there* would be a disease-resistant variety of potato.

Assuredly, those early researches of Louis Pasteur left the plant pathologists with much to brood over, and their suggestiveness had not been exhausted by 1939.

CHAPTER IX

THE BARBERRY AND THE WHEAT

In the great controversy over spontaneous generation, Anton de Bary supported Pasteur. Pasteur, in effect, said: 'Gentlemen, I regret the necessities of your detestable philosophy, but spontaneous generation of small organisms does *not* occur in my flasks.' Anton de Bary, with his monumental paper in the *Annales des Sciences naturelles* for 1863, here already referred to in Chapter VII, said: 'Gentlemen, I have the honour to advise you that it does not occur among my little fungi either, and as this would seem to cover the whole of your present ground, we may now adjourn. *Omne vivum e vivo*. Good day!' Only one thing now was lacking for the complete discredit of the doctrine, and that was its rejection by leading evolutionists themselves. In 1870, Thomas Henry Huxley, great zoologist and veritable protagonist of Evolution, delivered the blow. He coined a new name, 'abiogenesis', for the doctrine, only the more conveniently to refute it. He would sooner the whole theory of evolution fell to the ground than base it upon what was in his considered judgment an error. He acknowledged that it was impossible to point to any authentic instance of a known living thing being produced without parents. The most he could say was that protoplasm might, in the remote past, have been built up in successive steps from non-living matter, and that it might be so built up again, even in the laboratory. But this was all 'might' and 'maybe': legitimate speculation, and a proper reservation of philosophic doubt; it was no basis for a truly scientific theory. It had been easy for the materialists to claim a physico-chemical origin for microscopic organisms about whose development sufficiently little was known. Both de Bary and Pasteur had been provoked to dispel some of that ignorance, in sheer defence of the underlying faith by which they lived. One of the by-products of Pasteur's researches was the hereinbefore-mentioned introduction of aseptic surgery. One of the by-products of de Bary's was the solution of the ancient riddle of the Barberry and the Rust of the Wheat. This riddle was set in antiquity, guessed in 1809, and solved in 1865.

It was a custom among the Romans, certainly during the first century B.C., to hold a feast on a day corresponding to April 25th each year, in honour of Robigus, the Corn God. The festivities included a ceremonial procession to the sacred grove of the Deity, five miles out of Rome along the Claudian way. Wine was poured over the altar and one of the most important sacrifices was that of a red dog. The red Rust of the wheat usually made its appearance about April 25th, when the dog star was thought to be exerting some malign influence. The sacrifice of the red dog at that time was therefore very cunning, according to all the best prevailing religious, astrological and magical principles. If the ceremony was impressive enough Robigus would be bribed and bamboozled into accepting a cheap red substitute for the destructive Rust on the corn; the taste of singed dog would remind him to chain up the dog star; the wheat would be saved, and his faithful mortal constituency would not go hungry below.

Whether the potent defensive magic of the Rubigalia had any effect upon the wheat was thought in later times to be somewhat doubtful, but the records of the ancient ceremonies provided certain evidence that the Romans were impressed by the *redness* of the Rust. The symptoms of the disease were probably unchanged with the passing of the centuries. In the spring and early summer the leaf-blades and stems of the young wheat would be somewhat wizened, and marked with small red or orange streaks, which gave to the field in the mass an appearance suggestive of attack by fire. Later, the coloration would sometimes spread to the chaff of the ears, and the effect of the apparent 'burning' was always to dry up the plants, so that the grain was shrivelled to a greater or lesser degree. When the attack was severe the very soil would be red with the dust which escaped from the streaks or pustules on the plants, and sometimes it would blow about in a reddish cloud. At the time of the harvest the dust was often observed to have turned black, or dark brown, as though it were the residue of spent 'fire'.

This disease, here consistently referred to by its modern name, the 'Rust', to distinguish it clearly from the Smut diseases that cause blackening and corruption of the grain in the ear, was ever the most serious *epidemic* disease of wild and cultivated grasses. In some seasons and in some localities its attacks would be slight, but all too often it would blast the grain-fields over vast areas. Statistical records of the losses it caused were few and imperfect until the twentieth century, but then in 1904 and again in 1916, it was to destroy two hundred million bushels of wheat in the United States of America alone, and one hundred million in Canada. In different countries, and in earlier times, the Rust was called by many different names. It was the Red Rust and the dreaded Black Stem Rust of the American prairies; in France it was *la Rouille*, in Germany *Der Rostbrand*, in the time of Moses 'the Blasting', in England, 'the Mildew', the 'Red Rag', the 'Red Robin', the 'Red Gum'. The scientific names given to the fungus associated with the disease, or to successive stages of it, recalled the Rubigalia, and were variously compounded from *Uredo*, because of the burning, *Puccinia*, because of the affection that Micheli, who named it in 1729, had for a certain Physician and Teacher of Florence, and *Rubigo*, because of the redness and the old God of the Corn.

Throughout the seventeenth, eighteenth and into the nineteenth centuries, the old magical beliefs concerning the Rust lingered on, at least as popular superstitions and farmers' tales. It was unlucky for a red dog to run among the corn, and a barberry bush in the hedge, because of its often rusty appearance, its yellow flowers, yellow wood and red berries, was believed capable of communicating some evil yellow-red contagion to the corn near by. Because of its intense yellow colour an infusion from the bark of the barberry was long esteemed as a 'simple', according to the old doctrine of Signatures, for the cure of jaundice and other affections of the liver. And just as the barberry infusion had, in truth, some medicinal effect, so there were more than superstitious grounds for the belief in a relationship between the barberry and the Rust of the wheat. Often enough it was noticed that barberries bloomed and hung forth their red berries in the hedges of wheat-fields where no trace of Rust developed. Perhaps the wheat in those particular fields had been sown when the stars were propitious, for careful observers again and again reported more Rust on the wheat in the neighbourhood of barberry bushes than elsewhere.

The first preventive measure ever adopted against the Rust of the wheat was, in fact, the destruction of barberry bushes. The measure was half-logical and half-magical in its rationale, but it was enforced by law, in several localities, during the seventeenth and eighteenth centuries. As early as 1660, a Barberry Eradication law was passed at Rouen, and in 1755, when Massachusetts was still a Crown colony, the legislative assembly of that province enacted that: 'Whereas it has been found by experience that the Blasting of Wheat and other English grain is often occasioned by Barberry bushes, to the great loss and damage of the inhabitants of this province . . . whoever, whether community or private person, hath any Barberry bushes growing in his or their land, within any of the Towns in this Province, he or they shall cause the same to be extirpated or destroyed on or before the thirteenth day of June, Anno Domini One Thousand Seven Hundred and Sixty.'

Although in England the destruction of the barberry was never enforced by law, the unlucky shrub was certainly under suspicion during the eighteenth century, and undoubtedly many bushes were destroyed. After an inquiry made by the English 'Board of Agriculture', under the Presidency of Sir John Sinclair in 1807, into the causes of disease among the grain crops, no general recommendation to destroy barberry bushes was made. So beautiful a shrub as the barberry – whose berries were esteemed for making comfits and barberry wine – was not to be destroyed wholesale on mere suspicion of its harmfulness to the wheat. No reasonable man could advocate such a step, when no one had the slightest inkling of any natural way in which the barberry could possibly cause the alleged harm. It would be as sensible to set about destroying the Blackthorn and the Spindleberry, the Dog Rose and the Travellers' Joy.

In 1841, that great English teacher of botany, Professor Henslow, reporting to the Royal Agricultural Society on the diseases of wheat, said: 'A notion has long prevailed, not only in England but on the Continent, that the barberry-bush is in some way or other connected with the Mildew (Rust). Sensible observers, many of them practical agriculturalists, have persuaded themselves that this is really the case; and they have asserted that their conviction of the truth of this hypothesis rests upon effects which they have themselves witnessed. I should consider such testimony of far greater value if I found it opposed only by the contradictory convictions of scientific inquirers; for however unlikely it may seem to the latter, there are too many mysteries in the works of nature hitherto unravelled, not to induce us to pause before we decide a thing to be impossible merely because we have no reason for considering it at all probable.'

This particular mystery in the works of nature came to be unravelled at last, but it took all the adoring search of the brothers Tulasne for the fruits of the fungi, a thousand contributions from contemporary and earlier botanists, something of the experimental methods of Pasteur, and of the great algologists, to build up the body of knowledge and technique by which the problem was eventually solved. The discovery of the true relationship of the Barberry to the Rust on the wheat was all but the last step in the uncovering of the life-history of the Black Rust fungus, one of the strangest and most versatile masqueraders in the whole cryptogamic underworld. When this, and other of the Rust fungi, had been revealed and followed through all their successive stages, mycology as a whole had grown. It was no longer the study of many thousands of species and half-species of fungi, partially classified and imperfectly related to each other. It had become a systematic and comparative science, concerned with one of the great branches in the tree of life, which with the rise of evolutionary thought, could already be seen in something more than shadowy outline as a whole, and in its true relationship with the other great branches of life-forms exhibited by the ferns and the algae above, and the bacteria and yeast cells below.

By 1767, the Italian naturalist, Felice Fontana, had examined the Rust streaks on the stalks and leaf-blades of wheat, with his microscope, and had reached the conclusion that they were caused by the growth of 'small parasitical plants'. The dust in the streaks, he said, was composed of two sorts of small bodies, one resembling 'eggs' almost all of the same size and of the colour of rusty iron or cinnamon; the others rather long, perfectly black and 'in some sort bearing the appearance of small fungi or common nails'. The wheat was 'affected with two sorts of mildew'. 'Both the red and the black sorts were sown in long streaks upon the leaves and stalks of the corn, preserving a parallel direction with the fibres of the plants but never crossways.' As the nail-shaped bodies grew upon stalks he was early persuaded that they were indeed parasitical plants, but the red 'eggs' puzzled him at first as they seemed to be without stems or roots. It was some time before he detected one 'egg' on 'a most perfect stem', but after that he found many others similarly provided. The growth of the two parasitical plants, the red and the black, in great numbers, caused the streaks visible to the naked

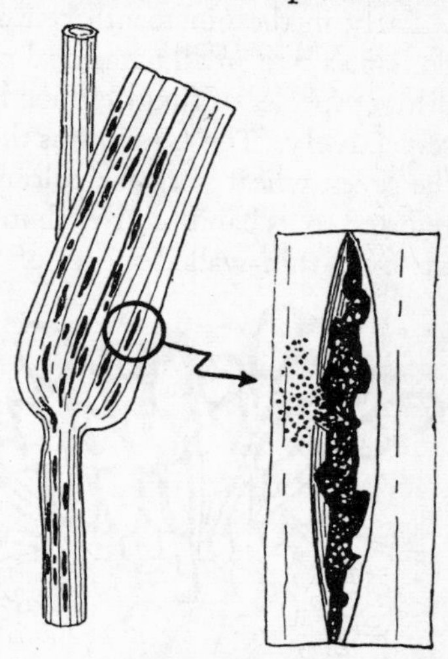

FIG. 17. Rust streaks on the stem and leaves of wheat, about natural size, with a single streak enlarged to show torn edges of the ruptured leaf-cuticle. Diagrammatic.

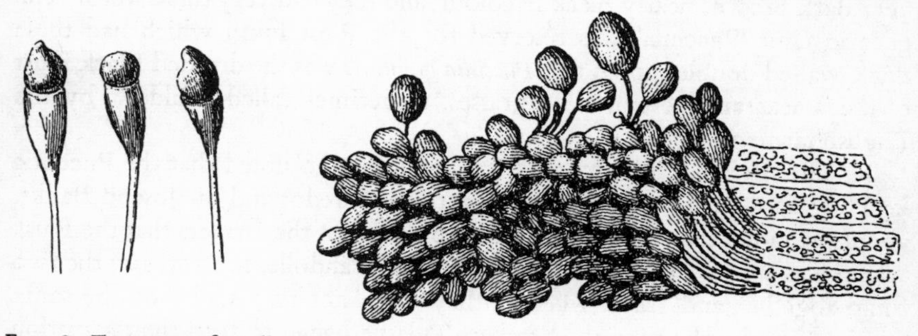

FIG. 18. Two sorts of small vegetable bodies (spores) observed in the streaks of Rust on the wheat. Left, black and nail-shaped. Right, red and egg-like. Fontana, 1767

eye, and robbed the corn of its vital alimentary sap. Fontana's paper was by no means overlooked in his time: a faithful English translation of it, for example, complete with the several figures, was published in Young's *Annals of Agriculture* in 1792.

Early in the nineteenth century, Persoon was among those who studied Fontana's two small parasitical plants more closely. He took them to be two distinct species of fungi, which he named *Uredo linearis* and *Puccinia graminis*, respectively. The Uredo was the one with the reddish spores, which touched the green wheat with the colours of 'burning' or fire, and the epithet *linearis*, referred to its habit of growth in linear pustules. Fontana's 'eggs' were simply the oval, thin-walled spores of the fungus, growing close together, each on a short stalk or pedicel, which broke through the skin of the leaves and stems as they developed, and broke away when ripe as a fine reddish dust. There were several species of Uredo to be found growing on various grasses and other plants; this one on the wheat was the red Rust, the evil that the sacrifice of a red dog was once supposed to keep away.

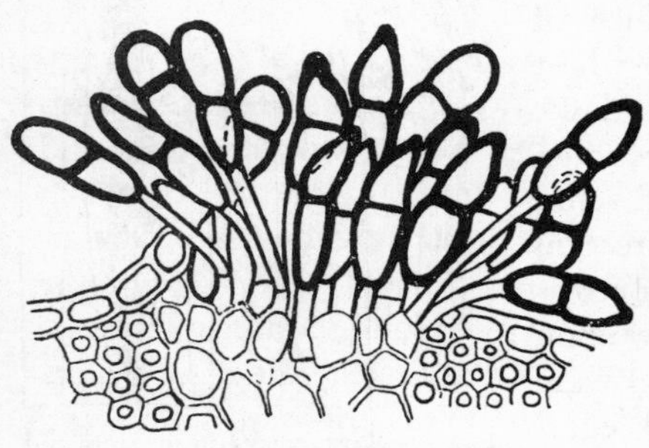

FIG. 19. Teleutospores of *Puccinia graminis*. (× 250) After de Bary, 1865

The *Puccinia graminis* was the fungus with the black, two-celled spores, growing in the same way on the wheat as the Uredo, often in the same pustules, but usually later in the summer. Fontana had truly noted its characteristic feature: the double spores. These were, in fact, only a little different in shape from Fontana's 'nails', they were very dark brown, nearly black in colour, and they had very thick walls. The generic name 'Puccinia' was reserved for the Rust fungi which had these thick-walled double spores, and *Puccinia graminis* was the dreaded Black Rust of the wheat and certain wild grasses, sometimes called 'Mildew' by the English farmers.

Bénédict Prévost, in 1807, was one of those who noted that the Puccinia kept suspiciously frequent company with the Uredo; and Sir Joseph Banks, about the same time, referred to a current belief of the farmers that the Rust which was at first red, turned black later. De Candolle, in 1815, saw the two fungi together and asked whether they were not two stages of the same species. But by the time the brothers Tulasne began to turn their attention to the Rust fungi, about 1845, hundreds of such fungi, growing on various plants, had been found, and as the only conspicuous way in which they differed from one another was in the shape, colour, and grouping of their spores, such differences had been made the basis of an all-too-rigid system of classification. Each species of fungus had one and only one kind of spore – by their spores should ye name them! The red Uredo could no more turn into the black Puccinia than a tabby cat could turn into or give birth to a black pig.

Corda and Fries thought that such fungi as the Puccinia might be parasites upon the Uredos. Unger, who rather put back the clock by regarding such fungi as mere exanthemata or outgrowths from their host plants, recognized some seven or eight kinds of Puccinia, usually accompanied by Uredos, but he believed them independent. He coined the good word 'endophytes' for these microscopic vegetable growths, which, as he believed, had their origin *within* the tissues of the green plants on which they were found. And Dr. Léveillé, who did not share this belief, borrowed the convenient term and spoke of 'endophytic fungi'. It covered all the small fungi, some of which would later be regarded as 'Rust fungi' and some of which would not, which had their mycelium within the tissues of leaves and broke through the leaf-surface in various ways to liberate their fruiting bodies or spores. Léveillé sorted these endophytic fungi, more or less neatly, into eight genera or categories to which he affixed the labels: Uredo, Trichobasis, Uromyces, Coleosporium, Lecythea, Podosporium, Physonema, and Cystopus. Other botanists were not altogether satisfied with the categories or with the names, and they changed some of them back, or altered them, to Puccinia, Phragmidium, Melampsora, Aecidium. In fact each supposedly different species of fungus had on the average half a dozen different names, given to it at different times by different workers; and the 'genera' under which the species were card-indexed were also variously named and variously assembled. The ever-changing nomenclature was indicative of the gropings for the true bases of a science, but sometimes the taxonomical superstructure became so important for its own sake that the *savants* paid insufficient attention to simple relationships directly apparent to the illiterate farmer.

The brothers Tulasne, inspired from the first by the happy idea of seeking for successive fruits of the fungi, went back to nature, threw all the so-called species and genera of what were approximately the Rust fungi into one big heap, and started again.

They found that there were five, and only five, main kinds of fruits or spores, to be found among all the different species; and sometimes in the course of its development a single endophytic fungus would put out two three, or even four of the different kinds of fruits in succession. Further search might well show that some of them really put out all five.

In the particular instance of the Black Stem Rust on the wheat, the farmers were nearly, but not quite, right. The Red Rust did not turn into the Black but it was followed by it, the Uredo and the Puccinia were not two different parasitic fungi, but successive stages in the fructification of one and the same. This was well established by the brothers Tulasne, by 1854, and later confirmed by their good friend,' the young mycologist of Freiberg', Anton de Bary, who joined in these researches in 1853, with his book on *Die Brandpilze*. De Bary left a drawing which would help to make the point quite clear: he showed the two kinds of spores growing from the same mycelium (Fig. 20).

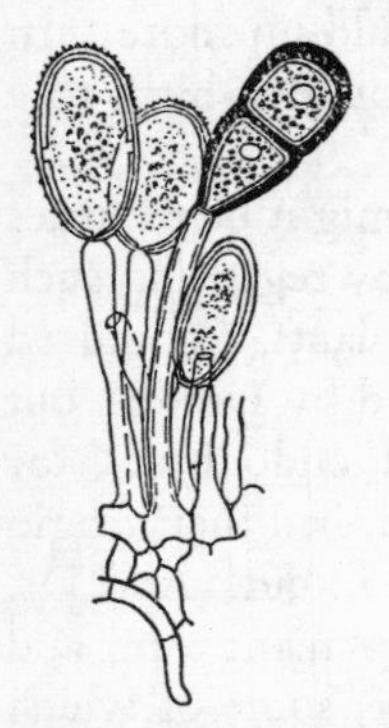

FIG. 20. The red and black spores of the Black Stem Rust fungus on the wheat, rising from the same mycelium. *Uredo linearis* is a stage of *Puccinia graminis*. (× 300) After de Bary, 1865

Uredo linearis had now to be deleted from the mycologists' inventory of species, for it was only an early stage of *Puccinia graminis*. Once this dualism or dimorphism was appreciated it was easy to see how the two kinds of spores helped the Rust fungus to survive and multiply. The red 'uredo' or summer spores of the fungus were comparatively delicate, they had a short life, germinated fully in eight to ten hours, began growing at once when they came in contact with moisture on the green wheat plants, and thus they served to spread the Rust during the spring and summer. The thick-walled, double-celled spores, which came later, did not break loose and blow about so readily, they germinated only after a considerable delay, they remained attached to the straw in the autumn, and evidently they were winter spores, by means of which the fungus survived when its summer growth was dead.

So far so good — and so much the worse for the wheat. Here were two of the sorts of fruits belonging to the Rust fungi. What of the others? The next were highly

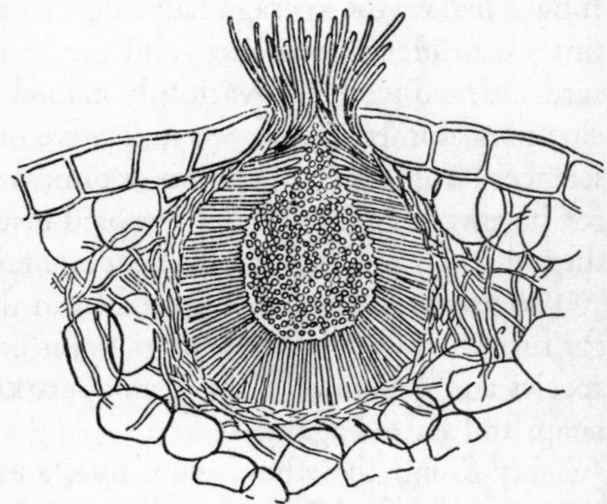

FIG. 21. Spermogonium of a Rust fungus, *Uromyces appendiculatus* Lév. (× 200) After de Bary, 1863

mysterious: SPERMOGONIA *rara, sparsa, epi- et hypophylla, singula e* peridiolo *immerso, ostiolato, et in ore longe ciliato, pallido, aurantiaco v. fusco,* sterigmatibus *linearibus, diametro uniformibus,* spermatiisque *acrogenis, ovatis ellipticisve, aureis v. fuscis, muco hyalino immersis et cirrhose eructatis.* Often, among the Uredo-Puccinia fungi, and very commonly with their near relatives that were called Æcidium, there were to be found little organs, apparent to the naked eye as mere dots in the leaves where the fungi grew, which on examination under the microscope appeared rather like those Spanish wine-flasks made of goat-skin with all the hair left on and turned inside. The walls of these small flask-shaped receptacles were made of the spawn strands of the fungus, interwoven and felted together, and the fine hairs which densely lined the interior carried exceedingly tiny spores, or spermatia, at their tips. The flasks were filled with a viscous mucilage, sometimes of fragrant odour, which exuded through the narrow neck on to the leaf-surface, bringing the spermatia with it. Neither the brothers Tulasne nor Anton de Bary could get these spores to germinate: they had not the seed-like propensities of the red or the black Rust spores, and the best guess that could be made about their function, was that they served the Æcidium as its sperm: that they were the male elements in a so-far undiscovered sexual process. Once again, such spermatia were known to take part in the sexual reproduction of certain species of seaweeds – but with the seaweeds there were corresponding female organs and egg-cells for the sperm to fertilize, among the Rust fungi there were, apparently, none. Later on, when much theorizing in terms of evolution had encouraged the bad habit of regarding as 'vestigial' any and every kind of organ of which the function was unknown it was sometimes said that the Rust fungi or their ancestors must have had both sperm and egg-cells in some previous geological epoch, and that the male parts alone had survived – because of some 'male precocity' of the organism – long after they had ceased to serve any useful purpose. The brothers Tulasne and Anton de Bary, however, noted that the fragrant and sticky mucus in which the sperm spores were exuded would no doubt be attractive to insects, which would thus carry the sperm about, but for the rest they contented themselves with describing the spermogonia very carefully, and leaving the question of their function open – a very pretty problem for the investigators of the future. Whether the 'spermatia' were of sexual significance or not, they could certainly be counted as spores, and with the 'uredospores', and the thick-walled, double-celled winter spores – for which de Bary later coined the name 'teleutospores' – that made three kinds, all very different from each other.

The fourth kind of spore made its appearance when the black teleutospores germinated in the spring. The forms into which these double-celled winter spores extruded their plasm on germination were not quite so remarkable as the hydra-like growths put out by the Bunt spores (*vide* Fig. 10, p. 84), but they were peculiar enough. Each compartment of the spore put out a relatively stout transparent tube, or promycelium, along which all the protoplasm in the half-spore was forced, leaving an empty spore-shell and later an empty tube behind. The growing end of the tube branched after a while into four spicules, as it were under pressure from the plasm within, and the ends of the spicules in turn swelled up, to produce four small and bulb-like 'sporidia'. These broke away from the spicules when ripe, and continued to grow, elongating into mycelial threads at once, or first protruding yet other, or secondary, sporidia. The function of these small naked sporidia was evidently to penetrate into the tissues of the green host plant in the spring.

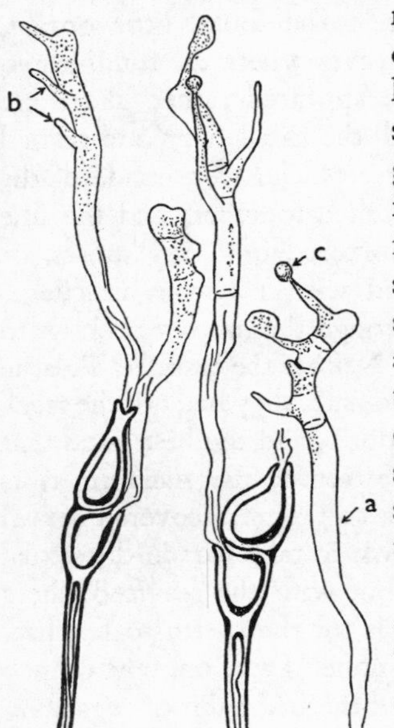

FIG. 22. Germination of the teleutospores of *Puccinia graminis* (*a*) promycelium, (*b*) spicules, (*c*) sporidia. (× 300)
After Tulasne, 1854

The 'sporidia' were the fourth and last kind of spores definitely associated by the brothers Tulasne with the Rust fungi on grasses and cereals. But there were a great many other species of Rust fungi to be found on other plants, and in grouping them all together for comparative study both the brothers Tulasne and de Bary cast their nets wide. It was significant that they drew in the 'Cluster Cup' fungi, botanically known as Æcidium, one fine species of which was to be found on gooseberry bushes and another on the common barberry. These Cluster Cup fungi had only two kinds of spores: spermatia, borne on tiny hairs within small flasks of nectar (Fig. 21), and round, yellow, vegetative spores, formed in parallel chains and contained in vast numbers within the cluster cups. Because these cluster cups – bedded in the leaf tissues – were completely enclosed within a membrane, and more or less globular before they burst and released their charges, many botanists had been grouping them, not with the Rust fungi at all, but with the Puff Balls, the Bird's Nest Fungi and the False Truffles. The cluster cups, or æcidia, were commonly yellow, rather less than a tenth of an inch in diameter, growing just under the skin of leaves, which they tore through when they were ripe. The differences between these cluster cups and the streak-shaped pustules which contained the uredospores of the Rust fungi, seemed to the brothers Tulasne to be less significant than the similarities, and in treating the two supposedly very different genera of fungi together, as near relatives, they found the fifth fruits of the Rust fungi and drew close to the solution of

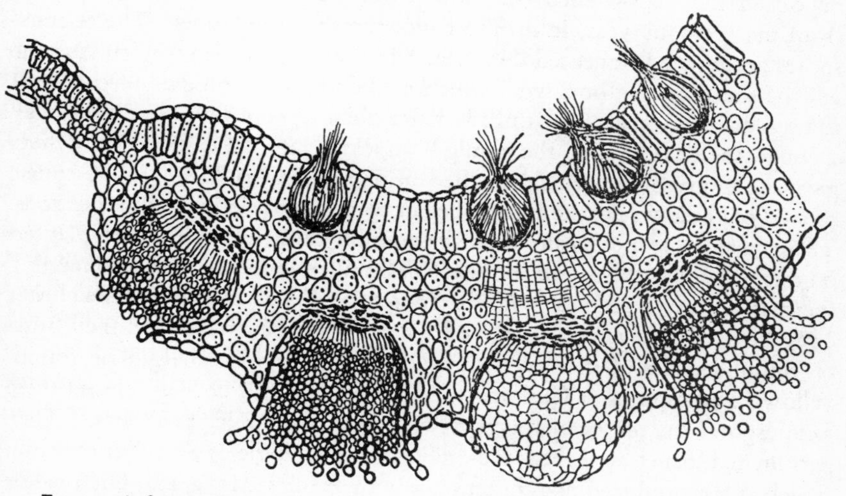

FIG. 23. A famous illustration, the Mona Lisa of plant pathology, copied once again. Cross-section of a rusted barberry leaf showing the Cluster Cup stage of *Puccinia graminis*. The normal thickness of the leaf is indicated to the left. Spermogonia breaking through upper leaf-surface; æcidia in various stages of development below. (Magnification not stated on original. About × 60). After Sachs, 1868

the ancient riddle of the Barberry and the Wheat. But even yet they did not guess the answer.

It was Anton de Bary who put the pieces of the jigsaw together, and — but for the true function of the mysterious spermogonia, which was not discovered until 1927 — traced out the complete life-cycle of *Puccinia graminis*, between the years 1860 and 1865. Louis Pasteur was then deliberately growing bacteria in nutrient solutions; and de Bary was growing parasitic fungi — not in nutrient solutions but in living media: the leaves of the host plants in which they had their natural habitat. He was making experimental inoculations of leaves with the spores of parasitic fungi, in order to trace the development of those fungi from spore to spore, as one might plant an acorn and then watch the seedling grow inch by inch into an oak tree with acorns of its own.

The Rust fungi which de Bary first cultivated did not include the *Puccinia graminis* of the wheat, but certain other species which parasitized beans and peas. The *Uromyces Phaseolorum* of Tulasne, for example, and *Uromyces appendiculatus* Lév. He raised the young host plants which were to be the subject of this 'vegetable experimentation' under bell-glasses, and carefully deposited the thick-walled teleutospores of the fungi, which he had kept from the previous year, in drops of moisture on their leaves. The teleutospores germinated, squeezed their plasm into little sporidia on spicules at the end of the promycelium, very much as did the teleutospores of the Rust fungus of the wheat, and threads from these sporidia pressed their way through the epidermis of the young bean leaves into the tissues. They there gave rise to mycelium which ramified among the leaf-cells, and in the course of two or three weeks the fungus began to put forth its first fructifications. These were not spores by any means resembling those which had been planted on the leaves, but the mysterious little flasks filled with nectar and containing spermatia, always *associated with the Cluster Cup fungi*. In a short time cluster cups themselves began to form, and when at last they were ripe, they burst on the undersides of the leaves, liberating their copious charges of round, yellow 'æcidiospores'. This was very interesting, and de Bary sowed these æcidiospores on the bean leaves to see what would happen next. They germinated, penetrated the leaves, gave rise to a tangle of mycelium within, which at last produced not cluster cups with æcidiospores again, but oval or egg-shaped uredospores; and nor was this the end, for following the uredospores came teleutospores at last; the perfect end-spores or true over-wintering seed-spores of the fungus, with which the whole cycle had started. With these de Bary had his 'acorns' back again. He had made the very remarkable discovery that the cluster cups represented a stage in the development of the Rust fungus that parasitized the beans and peas, and he had obtained all five fruits of the fungus in succession, starting with the winter or teleutospores.

He tried the same experiment with *Puccinia graminis*, the Rust fungus which grew on the wheat. But this time the little sporidia put out by the winter spores when they germinated did *not* penetrate the wheat leaves. He tried again and again, but in no circumstances could he obtain any growth of the Rust fungus on the wheat plants by inoculating them with the teleutospores. It was very strange; in nature those spores undoubtedly germinated and struck somewhere, or the fungus would not survive from year to year. What was the explanation? Was it conceivable that the spores grew and established the fungus on some plant other than the wheat? That the fungus required *two* host plants in order to complete the full cycle of its development? This was quite an hypothesis but – supposing it were valid, what could the other plant be? A common weed? Some kind of sedge? Another agricultural plant? A shrub perhaps, of the hedgerow? A shrub? *Donnerwetter!* Why not the barberry? The Cluster Cup fungus on the barberry, the *Æcidium berberidis* of Persoon, was common enough, and for centuries the farmers had believed in some connection between barberry bushes and the Rust of the wheat. Perhaps, indeed, this might be it.

De Bary put forward the idea in his 'Memoir to serve as a supplement to works on the question of so-called spontaneous generation', in the *Annales des Sciences naturelles* for 1863, and two years later he published an account of his further researches, by which the riddle was solved. He took the dark-brown, double-celled teleutospores of the Rust of the wheat and sowed them upon the leaves of the barberry. They germinated, their sporidial threads penetrated readily, and a fine crop of cluster cups followed. *Æcidium berberidis* could now also be struck off the register: it was only one of the stages of *Puccinia graminis*. The round yellow spores from the cluster cups would be carried by the breeze from barberry bushes to the wheat, starting the Rust on the wheat in the spring. Sir Joseph Banks, who in 1809 had hazarded the guess that the spores of the parasitic fungus on the barberry might blow over on to the wheat, had been perfectly right.

Unfortunately, de Bary was unable to obtain rigorous confirmation of this last step in the cycle by experimental inoculation of wheat plants with the æcidiospores from the barberry. As it happened he did not strike quite the right conditions, but that in nature the spores did establish the Rust on the wheat was a legitimate inference, supported by countless observations on the prevalence of Rust near barberry bushes, and the life-cycle of the Rust fungus was at last revealed.

In describing this cycle, de Bary coined a few new terms which would make the stages of it easier to refer to, and to think about. The thick-walled, winter spores of the fungus (1) which preserved their vitality on the straw of cereals or hay of wild grasses from the autumn to the spring, and which could in fact be put away in a box and kept like seeds, he called by the name here already used for them, 'Teleutospores', because they marked the perfect end and the point of beginning again in an eternal cycle of life. They were like the aces in a pack of cards – that could be either 'high' or 'low'. The Greek root '*teleuto-*' expressed this idea, and its reintroduction was a positive enrichment of the currency of language; it had power to stir the imagination anew. The tiny naked bulbs of plasm, which were the fruits of the Teleutospores (1) on germination in water, and whose function was to penetrate the defences of the barberry leaves, remained 'Sporidia' (2). The round yellow spores produced in long chains within the Cluster Cups, or Æcidia, on the

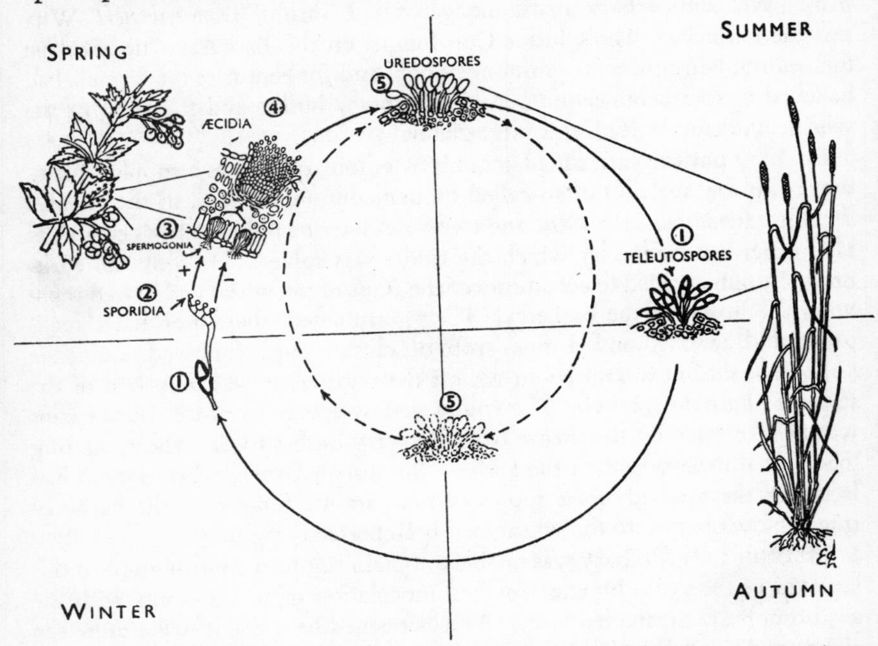

FIG. 24. The Life-cycle and Five Fruits of the Black Stem Rust fungus, *Puccinia graminis*, on the Barberry and the Wheat. The dotted inner loop indicates a possible alternative way of survival by summer growth persisting through the winter in favourable circumstances.

Known 1865[1]

barberry, after some mysterious sexual process in which the 'Spermatia' (3) probably took part, were 'Æcidiospores' – '*æcidio-*' being merely a borrowing from the Greek for a goblet or vessel. The function of the Æcidiospores (4) was to carry the fungus from the barberry to the wheat or other kind of grass on which it could grow, and there give rise to the red stage of the Rust, the old Uredo, with its crops of 'Uredospores' (5). These spores spread the Rust through the wheatfields from the relatively few plants infected from

[1] Except for the division of the life-line, + and –, between (1) and (4), which was discovered by Craigie, 1927.

the barberries in the spring; they were vegetative summer bud-spores with much the same function as those of the Potato Blight fungus or the Oidium of the Hops and the Vines. The spawn within the wheat leaves which gave rise to these Uredospores, subsequently put forth its overwintering fruits – the Teleutospores – and so the cycle went on from year to year.

To distinguish between such species of Rust fungi as those on the beans and peas, which completed their life-cycle on one host plant, and others like that on the wheat and the barberry, which required a second host-plant for some part of their development, de Bary coined the adjectives 'autoecious' and 'heteroecious'. They were forged and synthetic terms which went with fair English or plain German about as well as lumps of concrete in a meadow; they made a simple idea sound difficult, but in flinging them into the scientific literature, de Bary gave the verbose something to proliferate about. Perhaps, after all, it was not a bad idea to erect HETEROECISM, as it were upon a pole, marking the advance that had been made in knowledge of the Rust on the wheat. It was a warning to all those seeking the causal organisms of disease to be on the look-out for alternative hosts.

Who knew but that the missing fruits and the over-wintering stage of the Potato Blight fungus might not be found on some other plant? Many instances of 'heteroecism' were found, or were later to be found, in nature. The liver-fluke of sheep passed through a part of its life-cycle within the bodies of water-snails. And was not the malaria parasite ultimately found to pass through brood after brood of asexual generations in the blood of man while having its sexual stage in the stomach of the female mosquito?

None of the discoveries by de Bary and the brothers Tulasne concerning the Rust of the wheat led to any immediate advance in methods of combating the disease. In England de Bary's discovery of the true part of the barberry in spreading the Rust, was neglected and all too often pooh-poohed for nearly a quarter of a century.[1] The most that even the Rev. M. J. Berkeley had to say was: 'We must listen patiently, however our preconceived notions may militate against a matter which at the first glance seems visionary'. It was for workers of succeeding generations to look hard at that life-cycle of *Puccinia graminis*, which had been revealed by 1865; to seek out the stages at which the organism was vulnerable, the points at which its thread of life could be cut by practicable means. Obviously, the destruction of barberry bushes was one method; but it was only one. Thought and further search would reveal others. The fungus might be able to survive even after the destruction of the barberry bushes, if there were some other plant on which the cluster cups

[1] *Vide* W. G. Smith's *Diseases of Field and Garden Crops*, 1884.

could develop, or if the uredospores could survive on stubble and wild grasses in warm localities through the winter. Better than destroying the barberry bushes, it might be possible to breed or select varieties of wheat with foliage so tough that the germ threads of the sporidia could not penetrate it, or with juices so uncongenial that having penetrated they could not grow. It might be possible to attack the fungus in its red stage on the wheat, with sulphur, as the vinegrowers attacked the Oidium on the vines. It might be sufficient to spray barberry bushes instead of destroying them. By the ploughing-in of stubble and the burning of wild grasses on which the fungus grew the winter spores might be destroyed. The contribution from pure botanical science was not a plan of attack, but a magnificent piece of reconnaissance, a chart of the enemy's positions.

CHAPTER X

SCHOOL FOR PLANT DOCTORS

IN 1866, Anton de Bary's *Morphology and Physiology of the Fungi*, or, rather, his *Morphologie und Physiologie der Pilze, Flechten und Myxomyceten*, was published as Part II of Hofmeister's *Handbuch der physiologischen Botanik*. It was a text-book of fundamental importance, marking the end of a revolution in thought concerning the origin of crop-destroying fungi. While it was a work of pure botany, devoted to the fungi in general, beneficent as well as destructive, saprophytic as well as parasitic, and while it was by no means a treatise on plant diseases, it nevertheless drew together systematically the knowledge which had by then been won of the parasitic species, the successive stages in their development, their life-forms and processes, their means of reproduction, and their ways of invading and living at the expense of their host-plants. With the publication of this work, the 'young mycologist of Freiburg' was soon established as the world's leading authority on the fungi. He achieved an ambition then dear to every German professor, a 'school' began to gather about him, students from many countries sought the privilege of working under him in his laboratory, and among these men were many who were to be the crop-doctors of the future. He migrated, with steadily increasing and fairly-earned renown, to the University of Halle in 1867, and to Strasbourg in 1872. He became known as 'The Master Mycologist'.

Like Julius Sachs' *Lehrbuch der Botanik* of 1868, another part of the foundations of the 'new botany', de Bary's text-book was a basic and even an exciting work, for it could almost be said that Science *meant* botany and zoology in those days, as in the twentieth century it would seem to mean, for so many people, chiefly astronomy and mathematical physics. The discoveries about the algae, the fungi, the bacteria, and other lowly plants, so significant in pure science, in industry, in agriculture, in medicine, and in the story of evolution, were about as startling to the thoughtful public then, as the curvature of space and the splitting of the atom would be to a later generation.

Pasteur's name was to become in the course of time a household word, everybody would know that his work had something to do with 'germs' and with the conquest of disease. But, by a strange trick of fame, Anton de

Bary's name would be remembered only by a few, and his contributions would be all too rarely mentioned except in purely scientific writings. In fact, by 1866, de Bary had reached a point in the understanding of the causation of diseases, albeit in plants, that was far ahead of the medical profession. He had established or confirmed that many of the most serious diseases of plants were caused by living pathogens, and he was studying those pathogens by deliberately inoculating plants with them, nearly twenty years before the same realizations were reached and the same methods were employed in human pathology. The veil was lifted from the parasitic fungi first, and then, by a natural step, it was the turn of the smaller pathogenic bacteria. It was that way round.

By 1865, Louis Pasteur had drawn his researches on 'spontaneous generation' to a close, and, following his star, he had gone to Lyons to investigate the *Pébrine* of the silkworms. He was to discover that it was caused by living bacteria. It was the first disease of any animal, great or small, to be attributed beyond question to the parasitism of these so-called 'fission-fungi', and it was the fate of the silkworms, rather than the observation of the 'bacteridia' of Anthrax by Davaine and Rayer (1859–63), that was to lead Pasteur on to the study of the bacterial diseases of cattle, fowls, and ultimately of man.

By 1865, the brothers Tulasne had retired to the south of France; John Lindley, the great editor of *The Gardeners' Chronicle*, was dead; the Rev. M. J. Berkeley was to write on 'Vegetable Pathology' for some years yet, before he passed over his collection of ten thousand species of fungi to Kew, and drew a very small and well-earned pension from the Civil List. A new generation of mycologists and plant-doctors was rising now, and among these young men, yet licking their pencils at school, or working for their first degrees at Universities, were Harry Marshall Ward in England, Pierre Marie Alexis Millardet in France, and Michael Stephanovitch Woronin in Russia. Germany was the home of the 'new botany' as perhaps Sweden with Linnaeus and Elias Fries, had been of the 'old'. In Germany there were now not only doughty professors specializing in every department of plant physiology, including that of the fungi and the bacteria, but other workers and other works devoted to the applied science of plant pathology soon followed in the wake of Julius Kühn. There was Ernst Hallier's tentative *Phytopathologie* in 1868, and in the early seventies a beginning of massive compilations by Paul Sorauer. His first *Handbuch der Pflanzenkrankheiten* appeared in 1874, and thereafter it was added to, volume by volume, re-written and revised for edition after edition, until it became the most comprehensive work on the subject in existence. An offshoot of Sorauer's labours was the first, and for a long time the most important German periodical devoted to plant diseases, the *Zeitschrift für Pflanzenkrankheiten und Pflanzenschutz*, which began in 1890. In 1874 there was a great book by Robert Hartig on the diseases of forest trees.

Meanwhile, in America, the Civil War was over, it was the unsettled period of reconstruction, and the Department of Agriculture, inaugurated in 1862 during the presidency of Abraham Lincoln, was just beginning to assemble its forces. In a few of the States small experimental farms and agricultural laboratories were already in being. Their first work was on the analysis of fertilizers, the distribution of seeds, and the introduction and trial of plants for acclimatization. One or two of the States, notably Massachusetts, Missouri and the State of New York, had already appointed official entomologists whose duty it was to report on insect pests, and in 1871 Thomas Taylor became Microscopist to the Department and was responsible for its first series of original publications on plant diseases caused by microscopic fungi. Besides Taylor, there were many workers throughout the States who were now studying the books and papers of Berkeley, Tulasne and de Bary, and beginning to explore for themselves the fungal diseases of plants on the American continent. There were also several American Natural History societies, whose members, whether they were teachers, professional naturalists or enthusiastic amateurs, were active and busy.

But the arts and sciences of agriculture in America as a whole lagged behind those of Europe; in fact much of the exploitation of the American soil was not worthy of the name of agriculture. It was all too often a reckless, improvident, and half-barbaric skinning and stripping of the land. The 'natural husbandry' of the early settlers was to be likened to that of the Germans at the time of Christ.[1] And even towards 1870 when vast new areas were being opened up by the rapid extension of the railways, much of the agricultural land was still cheap as dirt, and it was being treated with as little respect or care. Crops of wheat, or cotton, or Indian corn were grown year after year until the land was exhausted, and then new clearings were made further and further west, while the 'used' land was left behind to recover as best it might under a deckage of weeds. At such a stage in the occupancy of a continent the extreme finesse of the botanists' work on microscopic fungi would have seemed to the generality of American farmers, had it been brought to their attention, something very fancy and remote from the rough business of life. The devastations caused by swarms of locusts were something that all could see and understand; the locusts descended upon the fields,

[1] By Sir John Orr.

munched with a million mouths, and left them bare. The invasion of the wheat by the vastly more numerous spores of *Puccinia graminis*, putting out germ-tubes to penetrate and establish choking webs of spawn within the very tissues of the stems and leaves, sapping the nourishment of the grain – this was a phenomenon which only the microscopists could clearly visualize. To the farmers the Red Rust on the wheat seemed innocuous, and the dreaded Black Stem Rust was ruin in the mist.

In the twentieth century, with the United States Department of Agriculture the greatest organization of its kind in the world – using every resource of a vast network of schools, colleges, experiment stations, magnificent laboratories, the press and the radio, for the diffusion of scientific knowledge among the agricultural community – it would require an effort of the imagination to appreciate what the Americans thought of their pioneers in the natural sciences at the time of Bret Harte. The geologist was a figure of fun, the entomologist was a harmless lunatic with a butterfly net, the mycologist – what sort of animal was he? When Louis Tulasne, devout Catholic, writing in Latin, deep-set in the enduring culture and learning of Europe, drew the cover over his beloved microscope for the last time, he left behind him this apology for the way that he had spent his working life: ' "No wise man," says Linnaeus, "will dare any longer to say that those are doing no good and wasting their time, who by collecting mosses and flies contemplate the wonderful works of the Creator and teach us how to turn them to their appointed use." In the meantime you may consider how much care and solicitude are daily employed in collecting the words of persons in authority, of a scholar or a learned man, or in noting and subtly explaining the acts of kings, even the smallest and those of no importance, and then you will decide whether a simple and pure investigator of nature, a candid admirer of the divine work, should be rightly disdained by those who delight to exalt the mere deeds of mortals or the imperfect monuments of literature and art, and to worship none but the lords of the earth.'[1]

But Louis Tulasne could not write more sympathetically of the naturalist than did Bret Harte. There was a difference: the words of the one were fragrant with the clove-oil of the botanical laboratory, those of the other recalled the mountain rocks and the open prairies of a continent yet to be explored:

'There is none to whom recognition comes so tardily, or from whom popular interest is so long withheld as the Naturalist. Whether his practical pantheism takes him out of the plane of human sympathy; whether there is a

[1] Grove's translation.

secret and divine compensation for his human forgetfulness in the fascination of his study, or the acquisition of special knowledge; or whether a certain heroism is always to be found in combination with this taste, we cannot say. The world only knows that out of a life of exile, and often of danger, out of self-imposed wanderings and mysterious labour, he at last lays at its feet a technical catalogue and a sheaf of special pictures, more or less monotonous in subject, which only a very small portion of its people are able to appreciate, and a still smaller part able to purchase and possess.'[1]

Of all naturalists, those who concerned themselves with minute fungi, were, in America as elsewhere, about the last to be recognized as *useful* members of society, and, in truth, the investigation of the diseases of crops was only a part of the work which waited upon the growing up of the young Department of Agriculture. At first its principal concern was the distribution of seeds, and its progress by 1868 might be judged by the fact that it was housed in one largish country residence, with an entire personnel, including the office boys and those who cleaned the stairs, something short of fifty people.

In England, there was no Department or Ministry of Agriculture at all. The old 'Board of Agriculture' which had made a brilliant start in 1792, and was a product of the personal enthusiasm of Sir John Sinclair, Arthur Young and others, had been dissolved in 1822. The Royal Agricultural Society carried on some of the work of the old Board after its incorporation by Royal Charter in 1840. But the members of the Society were hamstrung from the start by a clause in the Charter which 'regulated their purposes by the strictest exclusion from their councils of every question of discussion having a political tendency'. The clause was no doubt inserted with one eye on the conditions in Ireland; and its effect was to make sure that the Society should *not* be a *ministry* for agriculture in any sense of that word. As none of the real issues affecting the prosperity of its agriculture could conceivably be divorced from the politics of the country as a whole, the work of the Society was drastically restricted, and the papers that it was able to publish on such topics as the condition of farm labourers, land tenure, and the relative importance to the national economy of agriculture and the manufacturing industries, made very frowsy reading. The Society had on its council, and as its patrons, members of the land-owning English aristocracy, many noble personages, and its general attitude towards the farmers was that of the landlords towards their deserving tenants. The Society organized annual agricultural shows, and did great work in encouraging the improvement of stocks, the scientific

[1] *The Story of an Ornithologist.*

use of fertilizers, and, generally, in raising the level of agricultural production. The investigation of diseases of the crops, and the recommendation of the best means whereby they might be prevented, was admittedly within the legitimate scope of the Society's activities, but in this direction it did little, and in offering prizes now and then for remedies for such plagues as the Potato Blight, its noble patrons showed little understanding of the problems which were perplexing some of the best scientific minds in Europe. The advancement of plant pathology required a very different form of encouragement from that represented by giving your tenant a rosette and a piece of plate for a prize heifer at a show.

There was, however, one event during the sixties which drove in the first pile of the foundations for a Ministry of Agriculture in Great Britain. Some Russian cattle imported from Esthonia brought with them the Cattle Plague, the Rinderpest. The plague was first discovered in these cattle at Islington market in June 1865; it spread epidemically and with amazing rapidity over the whole country. It reached some twenty-seven thousand separate farms, and three out of every four of the cattle on them perished. Nothing was known of the cause of the disease or of any cure for it; the only way of stamping it out was by the unhesitating slaughter of every infected or suspected animal. An Act giving powers for this purpose was rushed through Parliament in 1866; the death-cries of the murdered cattle went up over the land; but the terrible measure was successful, and by September 1867 the country was declared free of the disease. The Contagious Diseases (Animals) Act of 1869 was then passed, with the object of preventing the recurrence of such plagues, by regulating imports of animals from countries where disease was rife. This was in effect the beginning of the Veterinary Department of the future Ministry, and the powers taken to prevent the introduction of animal diseases were later extended to destructive insect pests, and ultimately to parasitic fungi causing plant diseases – but that was not to be for another forty years or more.

In England, during the sixties, *The Gardeners' Chronicle* and the Royal Horticultural Society were almost alone in paying attention to plant diseases, and fortunately agriculture in England was not then suffering from very much *economic* ill-health; it did not require much legislative assistance, for, in agriculture as in industry, *laissez-faire* and free competition were still working beautifully. About 1870 there were some three-and-a-half-million acres under wheat in the United Kingdom each year, producing three-quarters of the country's requirements; and the price of wheat fluctuated about the comfortable average of 53s. per quarter. Very little meat was imported, and frozen mutton was unknown. The carcasses of sheep were still being boiled down for tallow in Australia, and in 1873 there was an interesting article in the Journal of the Royal Agricultural Society, by Dr. Voelcker, 'On Australian Concentrated Mutton-soup as food for pigs'. The English farmers, little troubled by foreign competition, were getting good prices for both their grain and their live-stock, and apart from the Potato Blight, and the Rinderpest of the cattle, the losses due to diseases were not very significant – they took a tithe of the produce, but, then, they always had done so, and it was not until after the Great Depression that any organized endeavours were made to survey them, let alone to combat them.

The Golden Age was a fool's paradise. The ominous significance to English agriculture of the penetration of the railways into the great wheat belt of North America, the lowering of ocean freights, and the opening of the Suez canal in 1869 – the short cut to the granaries of the East – these developments disturbed but few people; they were fine for the shareholders of the railway and the shipping companies. It was not until the beginning of the eighties, when the influx of cheap imported wheat had dropped the price from round about 53s. to less than 30s. per quarter, and the good arable land of England was going down to grass at the rate of a hundred thousand acres every year that the Government began to wake up and equivocate about the causes of the Depression.

The English high-farmers had a very nicely balanced system of agriculture – one of the finest, indeed, that the world had ever known – which depended in great measure, and in ways that were not perhaps wholly apparent at first sight, upon the cultivation of cereals, especially of wheat. In the typical rotation of crops, it was only once in four years that the wheat-land bore wheat. But the wheat was the cash-crop, for which the other crops, mostly consumed by sheep or cattle on the farm, prepared the land. Wheat represented the perfect stage, the end-product in the cycle. It could fairly be called the 'teleutocrop'. Without the wheat the whole cunningly interrelated system broke down. In the commonest form of the Norfolk rotation, roots were succeeded by barley, barley by red clover, clover by wheat. The roots of the clover enriched the soil with combined nitrogen in preparation for the wheat – though just how they did so was then still a mystery. The top-growth of the clover fed sheep, and their droppings served as a dressing of manure. The 'roots', turnips or swedes, cleaned the land of weeds and they provided a large weight of food for the winter-feeding of stock; they enabled the straw of the cereal crops to be used up for litter and returned to the soil in farmyard manure. There was a vital inter-dependence between the several crops and the livestock, and except for a little milk and some of the barley, not used for feeding but sold to the maltsters, only the substance in the grain of the wheat and in the carcasses of the animals was drawn off from the land. Practically everything else was returned; the clover provided a positive enrichment, the farmyard manure maintained and increased the necessary humus, and, with an occasional dressing of lime to keep it sweet, a small make-up of potash and phosphorus, the English land would go on feeding its fair quota of mankind in perpetuity. But what would happen when it was no longer profitable to grow wheat? What would happen to this conservative system of agriculture – in itself the highest manifestation of western civilization – during that *limited period of time* when virgin soils in excess of the needs of their populations were being plundered, even to the point of their reduction to desert, by the barbaric practice of grabbing cotton after cotton after cotton, and especially wheat after wheat after wheat?

A little wheat represented the concentrated produce of much land; the earth did not provide any finer food for man than that in the exquisite nutty kernels of the wheat plant; it was rich in protein as well as in starch, but the yield of solid food from an acre under wheat was comparatively low. Even in England, where the average yield was twice as good as that in the United States or Canada, wheat produced only about three-quarters of a ton of grain per acre, less than one half of the *solid* foodstuff obtainable from, say, potatoes, after duly allowing for the high water-content of the latter. Indeed those nations were prosperous which could afford for their staple food, not rice or maize or rye or potatoes, but wheaten bread. One reason why the emigrants to North America sighed for the heavy wheat land of England which they had left behind, but grew more and more wheat on the comparatively poor soil of the prairies, was that the grain was a compact and easily transportable form of wealth. It could not be carried in the pocket like a nugget of gold from Colorado, but the produce of several acres would go into a single wagon, and it did not deteriorate during shipment to Europe. The English manufacturers were glad to be paid, and the English investors were glad to receive their tribute of interest, by way of this seed-gold that was plundered from the American soil. But it came to be devalued by its very abundance, and the cash-crop of the English farmers was no longer worth the working. This was the catastrophe towards which events were leading up in the sixties and early seventies: the ruin of high-farming in England – and the despoiling of vast territories in America, for which, a century later, the American people would be paying very dearly in floods and dust-storms and barren wastes.

What had all this to do with the history of plant pathology? Nothing, perhaps, for those imagining that the growth of a science was not conditioned by the needs it served. But for others, the history of any science would seem ghostly, abstracted and unreal, without some reminiscence here and there of its total historical background. In the story of plant pathology

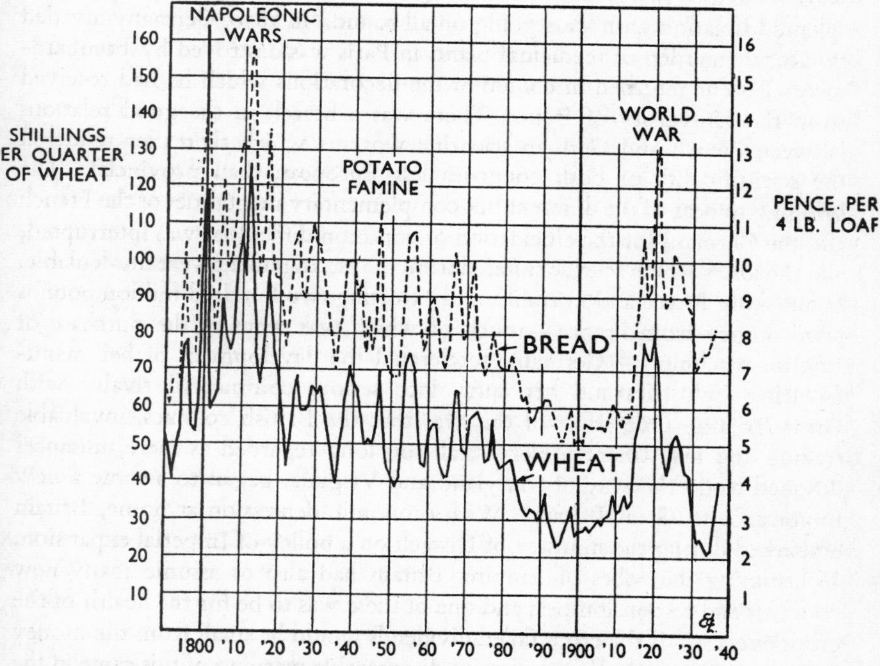

FIG. 25. The price of bread and the price of wheat in England, year by year, since 1790. Concern for the health of the crops was aroused when prices were very low (foreign competition) or very high (famine scarcity).

From data given in John Kirkland's *Three Centuries of Prices of Wheat, Flour and Bread*, 1917, *The London Gazette*, *Ministry of Labour Gazette* and other sources.

it was not so much the history of wars and princes that mattered, or the history of political intrigue and the rise and fall of governments. It was the history of agriculture and the price of food. Would it not be worth while to study the chart for the price of wheat and the price of bread, year by year, over the whole period of the story? (Fig. 25). It would be like a map when one was on a journey, telling the more the longer it was regarded: showing the years of good harvests and of bad, the price that was paid in hunger for wars, the increased share taken by the millers and bakers in the last two decades despite their improved machinery, and withal, the careless times of prosperity, and the times when the crop-doctors would be called in.

Since the affair in the Crimea, England had been at peace – except for a few punitive expeditions, such as that in 1868 against the Negus of Abyssinia who wanted to marry the widowed Queen Victoria – pursuing a policy of splendid isolation with wars going on all round. In 1870, Germany invaded France; the garden of medicinal plants in Paris was destroyed by bombardment; Pasteur returned in contempt the decorations which he had received from the University of Bonn. There was a breach in the good relations between French and German scientific workers which thereafter rendered the scientific life of both countries less European than provincial. The bringing to bear of the different but complementary mentalities of the French and the Germans for the elucidation of common difficulties was interrupted, and the losses which science suffered from the estrangement were incalculable. In annexing Alsace and Lorraine, and extorting two hundred million pounds prize money from France – much of which was spent in the purchase of English machinery – Germany accelerated the development of her manufacturing industries and her entry into serious commercial rivalry with Great Britain. One effect of this was that the British colonies, invaluable trading and investment preserves, all too long regarded as mere nuisances destined to go the way of Maryland and Virginia, began to assume a new importance to Great Britain. With economic depression at home, Britain embarked during the ministry of Disraeli on a policy of Imperial expansion. In assuming the robes of Empire, Britain had also to assume many new concerns and responsibilities; and one of these was to be for the health of the crops overseas. If the crops failed dividends would be small from the money invested in them. A sharp and most disagreeable warning of this came in the early eighties, when a fungus disease of the coffee had ruined the principal industry of Ceylon.

But the next great visitation upon the crops, in historical order, was one that passed England by; it affected only a few nurserymen in the British Isles and was some time reaching Australia and the Cape; it travelled from the east of the United States to France, and then back to California; it laid waste the vineyards, and after it had passed the grand wines of France were never quite the same again; it was the dreadful Phylloxera, drying up the vines.

CHAPTER XI

PHYLLOXERA OF THE VINES

'A NEW enemy of the vine, more disastrous than the Oidium, now menaces the vineyards of several *Départements* in the valley of the Rhone. This evil, which we call *étise*, because it has for external sign the emaciation of the stocks, leads rapidly to the total loss of the vines attacked, and its ravages may already be counted by hundreds of hectares. In the neighbourhood of Orange, of Chateauneuf-du-Pape, of Graveson, of Saint-Remy, and of St. Martin-de-la-Crau, near d'Arles, the evil has spread each year since 1865, the well-authenticated date of its first appearance . . .'

It was Monsieur Planchon speaking, in a communication to the Academy of Sciences in Paris, on August 3rd, 1868. . . .

'In the months of May or June, vines which have so far been vigorous and luxuriant suffer an arrest of growth which is accompanied by a certain yellowing or by an abnormal reddening of the leaves; the primary leaves – those of the principal shoots – wither and fall towards the end of July, or in August and September. The secondary shoots or laterals seem to make an effort to survive, but they are stunted in their turn. The Black grapes remain red, and only partially ripened; the winter interrupts this languishing growth, and the next season, finding only a few enfeebled buds, sees the total or almost total death of the entire stock. This is the spectacle presented at St. Martin-de-la-Crau, by seven or eight hectares of young vines, on the property of M. de Lagoy – a veritable cemetery of dried and withered plants.'

From the beginning to the end of this new trouble on the vines there seemed at first to be no sign of any external cause – no parasitic fungus and no insect pest. The only apparent symptoms were those of starvation. Planchon dug up a number of the sick plants and sought for a possible cause of the trouble at their roots. He found that some of the roots were completely devoid of their fine absorptive rootlets, and where these remained they were often black and carious. The adventitious roots at the base of the stem, instead of having their usual growth of fibres, were swollen up here and there into irregular nodules, which gave to them a coral-like appearance. With their roots in this condition it was no wonder that the vines were dying.

But what was the cause of the trouble? M. Gasparin attributed it to deficiency of nourishment, owing to continuous drought followed by a long and rigorous winter. There was the usual chorus of people who suggested unhelpfully that it was due to some miasmic 'Disease' or blight in the atmosphere. Some blamed the late frosts in May 1868, although the trouble had made its appearance in 1865. The Rev. M. J. Berkeley, commenting in *The Gardeners' Chronicle*, said that whatever its cause the trouble was spreading, and it would mean a serious loss to the nurserymen if it obtained a foothold in England. It would be wise to dig up and incinerate both the plants and their surrounding soil in all suspected areas. In France such advice was already too late.

M. Planchon saw the significance of the contagious nature of the 'disease'; it advanced through the vineyards in lines parallel with the first rows of vines attacked, as though something were creeping forward underground. He was led to look for a living cause. There were some who believed that the mycelium of a destructive fungus was attacking the pith and roots of the afflicted plants, robbing them of their substance. There *was* a fungus disease of the vine roots, called *le pourridié*, which had a somewhat similar effect. But this grey fungus was easy to detect on the roots when they were dug up; the roots of plants suffering from the *étise* had no such fungus spawn in them or upon them. Planchon found instead that there were a number of yellow corpuscles on the roots, and when these were carefully examined under a lens it became apparent that they were caused by insects – by a species of aphis; there were eggs and adult females.

The insects resembled other aphides or 'plant-lice' of which several species were known to infest the roots of artichokes, grasses and pines. But these other aphides were usually accompanied by ants, which milked them of a sugary excretion. There were no ants associated with the yellow *pucerons* on the roots of the vines, and, moreover, they laid eggs where other aphides brought forth living young. They appeared to be aphides of a new generic type, and Planchon, claiming priority for their discovery, described their characteristics in half a page of Latin, naming them *Rhizaphis*, or 'plant-lice of roots'. To this generic name he added the specific epithet '*vastatrix*', because, as he was convinced, these insects were the veritable cause of the starvation, death, and devastation of the vines.

Two forms of the insects were to be found: wingless and winged females. A little further examination of the winged females showed that they were assignable to a genus for which one Fonscolombe had already coined the name '*Phylloxera*' – shunt-Greek for [that which causes] the drying-up of leaves – and, as in matters of priority all good children of science played fair, Planchon re-christened the insects *Phylloxera vastatrix*, adding as an afterthought '*nuper Rhizaphis* (Planchon)'. Even so, the important matter of naming the invaders was not altogether settled, for a Mr. Westwood had found an exactly similar insect causing galls on the *leaves* of some vines at Hammersmith in 1863, and he had described it, in a paper read before the Ashmolean Society at Oxford in the spring of 1868, under the name of *Peritymbia vitisana*. In America the insects went by yet another name. It was never very clear who really did first describe the insect satisfactorily according to the rules, but the name finally adopted for it, by usage and accord, was Phylloxera. And that also went for the havoc it caused.

Strictly speaking, the Phylloxera did not concern the mycologists or those working on plant diseases; it was not a 'disease' of the vines, fungus or otherwise, it was a plague of plant-lice, and its story would belong to the history of applied entomology. But the greatest disaster to a cultivated crop in Europe since the outbreak of the Potato Blight taught many lessons to those working in the sister science of mycology. The ways of the insects and of the fungi threw light upon each other; in their life-histories they exhibited the same phenomena in nature; later on, the plant pathologists would have good reason to be interested in the aphides as conveyors of pathogenic viruses from plant to plant, and the measures, legislative and cultural, found to combat the Phylloxera, were adaptable to the uses of those whose job it would be to defend the crops against subsequent invasions of true plant disease.

The observation of the habits and of the stages in the life-cycle of these devastating vine-lice, these Phylloxerae, proceeded rapidly, and already in 1868, three years after their first appearance in the Gard, Planchon had elucidated the first half of their story. The insects were a tenth of an inch long, plainly visible to the naked eye when one knew what to look for, and they were much easier to follow through their metamorphoses than were the microscopic fungi which caused the Rust of the Wheat, the Oidium of the Vines, or the Potato Blight.

The wingless females dug their proboscides into the roots of the vines and gorged on the sap. This puncturing and sucking caused abnormal local proliferation of the cellular tissue with the production of knotty swellings or galls. When these swellings occurred at the ends of the finer rootlets they did not do much harm, but when they occurred on the main roots they cut off the sap supply from the rootlets beyond them, which atrophied and decayed while the plants as a whole were starved. The actual galls, at first intact, soft and yellowish, soon rotted, thus further contributing to the destruction of the roots. The wingless females on the roots were so many living egg-factories, tapping the sap of the roots at one end for food, and turning out eggs at the other. They laid eggs continuously, sometimes at the rate of thirty a day. There were no male insects; the females were agamic, and the reproduction was entirely parthenogenetic. After a few days the eggs hatched and the new generation of agamic females began to crawl about. For a while they were in a vagabond state, feeling their way over the still-living parts of the root system with their antennae, like blind men with sticks. When they had found a good site they settled down to suck more sap, to produce more galls, and to lay more eggs, which in turn produced another brood of agamic females, which . . . etc. (Fig. 26). This partheno-genetic reproduction of the plant-lice, responsible for the increase and spread of the pests over the roots of the vines through the spring and summer, was very closely paralleled by the asexual reproduction of the Oidium or the Rust fungus, spreading over the foliage of the vines or the wheat by means of vegetative, summer spores.

But after the prolific reproduction of the wingless agamic females of the Phylloxera had been going on for some time, nymphs appeared. These crawled up from the roots, and after divesting themselves of their last moult, became elegant little winged flies. These also were females destined for virgin-motherhood; they laid fertile eggs, but had no mates. They rarely used their wings, but the wind could carry them for considerable distances. The spread of the Phylloxera through the vineyards was therefore proceeding in two ways. The 'apterous-or-wingless-females' — as the entomologists loved to call them — were creeping from root to root under the ground. The winged females were being carried across the roads and over the countryside by the breeze. Thus the spread of the insects along the valley of the Rhone was explained. The mistral of Provence blew from north to south; that of Languedoc blew north-east and rejoined the Rhone in the plain of Arles. The south-east winds dashed down the insects with the rain and so did not assist their spread.

Whether this neat theory of the winds was correct or not, the Phylloxera rapidly spread from le Gard into every vine-growing district in France, and thence to every other European vine-growing country. In 1885, it had also reached Algeria, Australia and the Cape. In France, it no doubt found opportunity, in the preoccupation of the human population with the Franco-Prussian war, of establishing itself quickly in many localities where its march might otherwise have been arrested. By about 1875 it was causing a loss of some fifty million pounds sterling per annum to the French wine industry, about two and a half million acres of vines were ultimately affected, and from the point of view of material damage, it would have been difficult to say which was the worse invasion, that of the Phylloxera or that of the Prussian armies.

In 1875, two whole pages of the index to the *Comptes Rendus* – the Proceedings of the Academy of Sciences in Paris – were taken up with references to the Phylloxera. Mathematics, chemistry, astronomy, physics – nothing mattered so much then as the work on that little *puceron* which was ruining the vines. Commissions for investigation and action were set up in every vine-growing locality; the Ministry of Agriculture, all the Academies of science, *savants*, officials, *propriétaires* and peasants, everybody was seeking desperately for ways and means to lessen the calamity. Vineyards were flooded to drown the insects; carbon disulphide, a volatile and poisonous liquid made in chemical factories by passing the vapour of sulphur over white-hot carbon, was injected into the soil in an attempt to 'gas' the ever-multiplying pests. But the real help, the practical measure that ultimately made the further cultivation of the vine possible in France, came from America. It was the first great contribution from America to the art and science of defending the crops.

Charles Valentine Riley, of graceful presence, looked like a poet or hero of sentimental fiction. He was born in London, went to school in France and Germany, and at the age of seventeen made his way to the States as an emigrant. Struggling against ill-health and adversity, his passion for drawing, and for collecting insects, together with a little journalistic experience, at last stood him in good stead, and he became the first official Entomologist to the State of Missouri. He was one of those who made lonely excursions with butterfly net and specimen bottle, and who lived alert to the movements of insect populations threatening the produce of the cultivated land. He wrote about the curious Mexican 'jumping beans'. He wandered on the grassy slopes of the Rocky mountains listening to the stridulent sex-calls of the locusts, seeking their breeding grounds. He said 'turn out your animals to graze upon these slopes, or cultivate them, and then there will be no more swarms of locusts, for they will have nowhere to breed'. And when the Phylloxera was reported from France, he was among the first to recognize it as a native of America, and to perceive that it was on American vines, introduced into Europe for experiments in hybridization, that the insects had crossed the Atlantic Ocean.

The plant-louse which inhabited the American vines attacked them in so different a way that it was at first thought to belong to a different species. It chiefly infested the leaves, while the 'Phylloxera' in France infested the roots. The American insect was called the Grape-Leaf Gall Louse. Its wingless, agamic females, pricking and sucking at the undersides of the leaves, caused the growth of small leaf-galls, which, as they were hollow, served the insects well as snug nests within which to go on feeding and laying their eggs. The American vines were not the same as the European; in Europe there was only one species of vine, *Vitis vinifera*, modified by centuries of cultivation into some two thousand strains or varieties; in America there were eighteen distinct *species* of vine — *Vitis riparia* (the River Bank), *Vitis Labrusca* (the Northern Fox), *Vitis vulpina* (the Muscadine), to mention only three of the commonest. It was not unreasonable to suppose that among the different American vines the Gall Louse could find a desired succulence in the leaves, while on *Vitis vinifera* it found it in the roots. The Gall Louse and the Phylloxera might be one and the same. Indeed it soon appeared that they *were* the same, for although the Gall Lice *preferred* the leaves of the American vines, search revealed that they also infested the roots.

Riley argued that it was only because comparatively few of the insects made their way to the roots that the American vines were not affected in the same way as those of France. During the long centuries of their association in the New World a degree of natural balance had been established between the needs and numbers of the Gall Lice and the vines. The preying of the former upon the latter was of such a kind that *both* could survive. But Riley saw in the Gall Lice the cause of the deterioration of the American vines themselves. Except in California, where the insects had not yet penetrated, *Vitis vinifera* had failed in every state, and several of the better species of native grapes had declined. His theory would be laughed at; but that was only to be expected. What did it matter what a mere bug-hunter said? The most ignorant were always the most sceptical. Look at Pasteur, even Pasteur, *he* had now not only discovered the cause of the *Pébrine* disease of the silkworms, but a practical remedy for it. He had sacrificed his health in that work. Were the silk-farmers grateful to him? Not at all; the majority of them received his findings only with coldness and suspicion.

By 1872, Riley had been over in France, he had seen the dying vines, talked at length with many French scientists and growers. He had spoken with knowledge of the Gall Louse in America and pointed to the significance of the fact that the American vines in France seemed to be spared though some of them had the galls on their leaves. Already, a few enterprising French growers were importing vines from the United States.

But to replace the immortal French vines with American stocks was emphatically *not* the solution. Such wine as could be made from the

American grapes was raw and horrible. To the palate of a connoisseur it came as an affront, almost an insult. If that was all that could be done the export trade would be lost anyway, and at home, in France, it might even be better to forego wine altogether; to follow the English example and cultivate a grim taste for beer. It would be hard to get used to that dilute, bitter and sottish drink, of which you had to swallow a quart to get as much stimulant as there was in half a bottle of good wine. The English pot-houses with their necessary urinals were unspeakably disgusting, but still – the English put up with beer, some of them had a great liking for it. Perhaps it would not be necessary to go to extremes – it might be possible to make something more like the German lager. Pasteur was at work on brewing. There was much panic and sorrowful foreboding over the fate of the vineyards, for viticulture was more than a great industry in France, it was an integral part of the whole social life of the people. There were only a few, at first, who saw, in the very experiments which had caused the disaster, the germ of a remedy. Riley addressed himself to this clear-headed few.

The possible remedy was drastic and fraught with many difficulties, for it involved nothing less than an attempt to re-make the vine plants; to put together new kinds of vines which would have American roots to resist the Root Lice and French foliage to resist the Leaf Lice and to produce grapes that would make drinkable wine. By grafting, hybridization and careful selection, stocks might be built up in course of time which would not only resist the Phylloxera, but which would produce wines worthy of the great Châteaux. This was to be the salvation of viticulture and the wine industry, not only in Europe but also in the New World. Riley, on the American side, rendered great assistance to the French Government in the selection of the best American root-stocks for importation, in pointing out those species and varieties of vines least susceptible to the Phylloxera in its country of origin.

Meanwhile, Riley had taken back to Missouri with him specimens of both the winged and the wingless insects found on the French vines. They were in small tubes, preserved in acetic acid. He set them beside the Gall insects from American vines, compared them closely in detail and confirmed that they belonged to the same species. He contributed to the work of elucidating the complete life-history of the species of which the wingless and the winged agamic females represented but two of the stages. Many papers were written, many doubtful points had to be argued out by the entomologists, on both sides of the Atlantic, before agreement was reached.

After the root-inhabiting wingless females had been multiplying parthenogenetically through the spring and early summer, nymphs appeared, which crawled up the stems of the vines and grew into winged females (Fig. 26). What happened next? The wings at this stage enabled the insects to migrate to new feeding grounds – a very necessary provision for a species which often killed the host on which it fed. The winged females laid their eggs on the aerial parts of the vines, and at this stage the sexual reproduction began. The eggs were of two kinds, large ones and small ones, which hatched out respectively into female and male, wingless insects. In some mysterious way their virgin-mother brought forth males and females, both unlike herself. It was the function of these males and females to copulate, and for each female to lay one, single, fertilized and precious, egg. It was the egg which had to survive the winter; it was nearly as large as the insect which laid it, and it had a hard shell. Deposited in some crevice in the bark of the vine stock above the ground it endured the frosts and the rain. In the spring it hatched – and there came forth from it? One of the wingless, agamic females, which crawled down again to the roots of the vine and there laid eggs which hatched into brood after brood of unloved females like itself, on into the summer. So the sequence of sexual and asexual generations went on.

But the species had an alternative way of surviving the winter: the agamic females could lie dormant but alive on the roots, and start laying again in the spring. The species could dispense with sexual reproduction, but it was doubtful for how long. It could be assumed that there was some vital reason for that beautiful and elaborate provision of males and females and of the winter egg. Perhaps, by the sexual division and subsequent fusion of its living substance, the Phylloxera underwent some restorative process, which helped it to survive the wear of centuries. But to say even that was to guess at far more than was known. It was possible to watch the insects copulating and laying their eggs; it was possible to dissect them and see how both eggs and sperm were formed; even, later on, to trace some of the changes undergone by the nuclei of the first cells, but there was much that could not be seen, and no man knew the why and the wherefore of it all.

To compare the life-forms and stages of development exhibited by different living organisms was another matter. And when Man, as a species, had to contend with those organisms, in defence of his own food supplies, it was a severely practical, necessary and work-a-day undertaking. Was there not a remarkable similarity between the life-cycle of the Phylloxera on the vines and that of the Rust fungus on the barberry and the wheat? (Fig. 26, p. 155, and Fig. 24, p. 134). The winter eggs of the insects and the winter spores of the fungus could be seen to have almost exactly the same function: they both ensured the survival rather than the multiplication of their kind, and they both constituted a resting stage, at once the beginning and the end of a sequence of developments. The single, hard-shelled winter egg of the Phylloxera might well be called the 'Teleuto-egg'. Then the summer eggs, laid by all those broods of agamic females — did they not serve exactly the same purpose as the summer, or Uredo-, spores of the Rust? Both were short-lived, both represented a stage of prolific asexual reproduction, both ensured

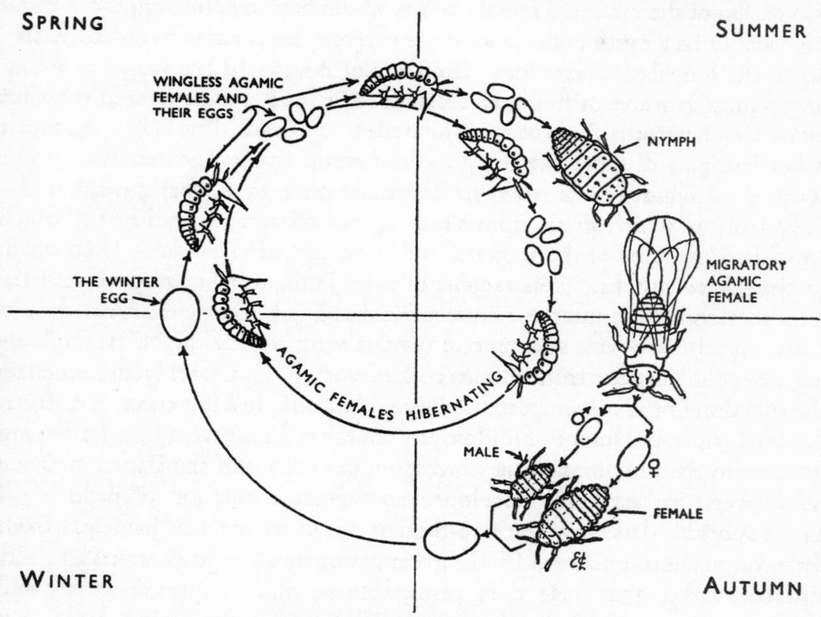

FIG. 26. Life-cycle of the Phylloxera of the Vines.

the increase in numbers of their kind, rather than their survival. By means of its summer spores, the Rust, once established on a few wheat plants, could sweep across the prairies. By means of its summer eggs the Phylloxera multiplied underground and advanced from root to root and from row to row of the European vines.

What of that very definite inner-loop in the life-cycle of the Phylloxera, the alternative way of survival which short-circuited the sexual phase and depended on wingless agamic females resting dormant on the roots over the winter? Had the Rust fungus anything corresponding to *that*? Unfortunately, when serious attempts came to be made to combat the Rust in practice, the plant pathologists were to discover that it most certainly *had*, and that for this reason the destruction of barberry bushes would never entirely suppress the Rust on the wheat. In warm regions and in favoured localities the Rust could survive the winter in its summer stage not only on cultivated cereals but on several of the wild grasses.

Had the Rust fungus a sexual stage? Had it anything corresponding to the eggs which were laid by the winged females of the Phylloxera, and to the copulation of the male and female insects which hatched out from those eggs? This was to be a moot point among the mycologists for two or three generations. At long last, after Oscar Brefeld had developed the art of growing single-spore cultures of fungi, and Blakeslee in 1904 had discovered what he called the 'heterothallism' of the Mucorales, or Bread Moulds – after much water had passed under the bridges – the sexual process of the Black Stem Rust of the wheat was at last revealed. Blakeslee showed that the individual fungal plants which grew from single spores of some species of the Bread Moulds were some of them 'male' and some of them 'female'. Their *thalli*, or vegetative systems, their tangles of mycelium, were of two sexes, they were 'heterothallic', and their perfect fruits or zygospores were formed only when mycelium of one sex came in contact with that of the other. Following up the indications from this and other work, J. H. Craigie reinvestigated the function of the spermogonia of *Puccinia graminis*, in a fine piece of research for the Degree of Doctor of Philosophy at Manitoba University, after having discovered the functions of the corresponding organs of the Rust fungus on Sunflowers, in 1927. He developed an ingenious method of picking off single sporidia (less than one five-thousandth of an inch in diameter) from the promycelium put forth by the germinating teleutospores Fig. 22, p. 130, and Fig. 24, p. 134). He then planted these minute sporidia singly and one at a time on barberry leaves. He found that they germinated, but with the formation of flask-shaped spermogonia the course of development stopped. It was only when two of the sporidia were planted, close together, so that the nectar and spermatia from *two* of the little flask-shaped organs could mingle on the surface of the barberry-leaf, that the growth of cluster cups followed and the line of life went on. It was not any two sporidia that would give rise to this result: it seemed that the sporidia themselves were of two kinds, respectively male and female, or, rather, plus and minus, and that one of each of them had to be picked out. The indication being, in the end, that the line of descent divided between two sexual carriers on the germination of the teleutospores of the Rust fungus, just as it did during egg-formation in the migratory winged females of the Phylloxera.

Although the entomologists and mycologists of the seventies did not go in very much for the kind of 'blue-prints' or 'flow-sheets' of insect and fungal life here sketched in Figs. 7, 24, 26 and 51, it was quite certain that they were tracing out all the sequences and making all the then-possible comparisons in their heads. They had knowledge of the sequences of development of many other organisms to guide them: ferns, tape-worms, yeasts, thousands of species of fungi, algae, legions of insects, green plants, and animals large and small. Certainly, so far as the smaller living things were concerned, that figure of the life-line, with its inner loop representing asexual propagation, and its outer loop dividing at some point into two and representing sexual reproduction, could be regarded as the Mystic Figure and basal pattern of continuing life. Of course it was never really a closed cycle, but a helix winding through time. In the survival of a plant by continuous growth and *also* by seeds; or of an insect by parthenogenetic multiplication and *also* by fertile eggs, there was nothing abnormal. On the contrary, it was the norm. And in 1939 it could be seen that again and again in studying the small fungi causing diseases of plants, the botanists would not have gone far wrong if they had sketched in the typical figure first and then sought in nature for *all* its stages. The details would be different for every species, in some instances a part of the succession would be non-existent or long undiscovered, but it would be possible to represent by dotted lines on the diagram the part of the cycle not found completed in nature and then there would be food for thought in attempting to account for its absence. In this, resort to theories of evolution would be of undoubted assistance.

The strategist, planning the defence of a crop, over a whole country, with a chart of the life-history of the invading pest or parasite open before him, was a public servant unknown in the seventies. But what could be read from the life-history of the Phylloxera as it was gradually being charted then? Was it not apparent that in attempts to reduce the numbers of the insects, it would pay better to destroy one winter egg than several hundreds, or even thousands, of agamic females on the roots? 'Gassing' the insects with carbon disulphide injected into the ground was an expensive, laborious, and withal a clumsy method, because it was attacking the species at the stage where its carriers of life were most numerous. Parasitic fungi on various plants could also be attacked with sulphur when they were putting forth their multitudinous summer spores; but this method was also clumsy, and for the same reason. *Preventive* measures were required, and any good general would seek to attack both the fungi and the insects in narrow defile — where their life passed through a bottle-neck. It was necessary only to think for a moment of the familiar wasps, inviting themselves to a picnic in August or September. One could lay about with swatters and kill hundreds of them, and still more would come. But if a single wasp was seen in June it was worth chasing a mile, for it was almost certain to be a queen, and if it escaped there might well be some eight or nine thousand more wasps to cope with in September. The few overwintering queens could be regarded as the 'bottle-neck' through which the life of the wasps passed in its annual cycle. Among the Phylloxera, the bottle-neck was represented by the overwintering eggs; among the Rust fungi by the winter spores.

Much good could be done by painting the stocks of the vines with a ring of sticky tar, to catch the few females hatching from the winter eggs when they were on their way down to multiply on the roots; just as it was well worth while to destroy the straw or the hay which carried the black spores of *Puccinia graminis* through the winter. But the great defensive measure, which ultimately saved the vineyards of France and was later to be applied with greater or lesser success against almost every fungal parasite of the crops was that of *starving the invader*. And the way of using this weapon of starvation was to build up, by selection, grafting or breeding, new varieties of agricultural plants which yielded the kind of produce desired but which suited the parasites no better than French vines with American roots suited the Phylloxera.

CHAPTER XII

THE WATER FUNGI

1872 . . . More than a quarter of a century had passed since the Potato Blight first spread over Europe, and still there was no remedy for it. Even the life-history of the causal fungus was still half unknown. Whole families of the Rust fungi, the Smut fungi and the Powdery Mildews had been traced from spore to spore; the dread Phylloxera of the vines was losing its mystery, and a remedy for it was already just within sight, but the Potato Blight fungus defied the wits of man. It was but half an organism: just mycelium that grew in the tubers and the leaves, and the external fringe of down, laden with delicate, asexual, summer spores. Where was the rest of it? Where were its sexual organs? Where were its winter or resting spores? How did it survive from year to year?

Between 1872 and 1875 the problem was tackled again, the Royal Agricultural Society of England this time taking the lead. There were several reasons why the Society concerned itself with the Potato Blight just then, after having virtually ignored it since 1847. Earl Cathcart, one of the Vice-Presidents, was something of a natural philosopher, and in 1871, for the first time, the Society retained the services of a Consulting Botanist, 'with a view of applying, through his advice, botanical science to agricultural problems'. The 'Consulting Botanist' was William Carruthers, of the British Museum, and a Fellow of the Royal Society. Though his principal job was to test seeds for the farmers, he began by drawing attention to some of the neglected fungus diseases of the crops. Then 1872 was a very bad 'Blight' year, the potatoes suffered severely throughout the British Isles, and in some districts of Ireland a recurrence of famine was threatened. This last was nothing new, and the danger was less now that death and emigration had reduced the numbers of the Irish by some two and a half million souls. The reduced population was no longer so dependent for sustenance upon a single crop. Again, since the American Civil War, Emancipation had been in the air, and there was a real disposition on the part of Great Britain to extend a certain measure of relief to the Irish. It was Gladstone's policy to mollify them; the disestablishment of the Protestant Church had relieved them of the burden of paying for spiritual ministrations they did not want; and adherence to the Catholic faith was no longer a bar to the holding of public appointments. More significantly, the Land Act of 1870 did to some extent curb the rapacity of the landlords; the tenants had to be compensated when they were turned off their holdings, and the improvements they might have made upon them could no longer simply be stolen. The slow progress towards a wiser and more humane Irish policy was cutting at the root cause of distress in that country, and the action of the Royal Agricultural Society in seeking a remedy for the Potato Blight, which so often acutely accentuated the distress, was in the spirit of the time. But it would be a mistake to exaggerate the weight of straws in the wind: the actual sum, in cash, which the Society at first proposed to spend on its good work, was exactly one hundred pounds.

Undeterred by the total failure of such tactics in 1847, Earl Cathcart offered a prize of that amount for the best essay throwing light upon the undiscovered stage in the life-history of the Potato Blight fungus. The essays were to be in by November 1st, 1873, and it was hoped that the offer of so munificent a reward would promptly lead to the discovery of some way of palliating, if not of altogether preventing the Potato Disease. In which case the prize-money would have been quite well invested.

Ninety-four essays were received, mostly from farmers who had not yet heard that the Blight was caused by a fungus at all. The prize was withheld, and Earl Cathcart was left dangling his hundred pounds.

The Council of the Society, provoked by failure, then decided to apply the money towards the cost of a very different, and much more intelligent, kind of investigation, which was to be in three parts. First, they persuaded and commissioned a really competent mycologist, namely the celebrated Professor Anton de Bary of Strasbourg, to resume his researches on *Peronospora infestans*, and, in his own time to send them a report. Second, they sent a questionnaire to a hundred experienced potato growers, to ascertain whether any of them had struck a way of escaping the Blight, either accidentally, or by any special method of manuring or cultivating their land. Lastly, as many seed-potato merchants were doing a profitable business in so-called 'Disease-resistant' potatoes, they offered a prize and a splendid advertisement for any potato variety that would resist the Blight when grown for three years in succession, at twenty different places in the British Isles, under the supervision of qualified inspectors appointed by the Society. It was quite a plan of campaign.

The answers to the questionnaire came in first, and they yielded a vast amount of detailed information about potato growing, which was sifted by Mr. Jenkins, Secretary to the Society. He discovered one interesting, but highly misleading, coincidence. It appeared that sixty-two of the farmers took' potatoes after a grain crop that had followed clover, while twenty-two of them took potatoes directly after clover, and only two: Mr. Myatt of Evesham and Mr. Knowles in Lancashire, had taken potatoes after a crop which thoroughly cleared the land, to wit, after turnips or cabbages. It was a remarkable coincidence that these last should be the only two farmers claiming to have suffered no loss at all from the Potato Blight. Did this mean that the missing stage of the Potato Blight fungus was to be found on the straw of grain crops, or on clover? Did the fungus require two host plants for its complete development, as did the Rust of the Wheat? Was it 'heteroecious'? And was it to be avoided simply by growing potatoes after turnips or cabbages, instead of after clover or barley or wheat? This was certainly an *idea*, but the evidence was somewhat slight — especially as Mr. Myatt was selling potatoes which he claimed to be disease-resistant, so that his statement about there being no Blight on his crops had to be taken with a prudent shovelful of salt. A more valuable indication from this part of the investigation was that some varieties of potato were rather less susceptible to the Blight than others. Patterson's Victoria, Skerry Blues, Rocks, and Myatt's Early Kidney received favourable mention in this respect; while Lapstones, Leathercoats and Pink-Eyed Radicals were not so good.

Hence the great interest attaching to properly conducted trials for disease-resistance, over three successive years and under the supervision of umpires that it would not be easy to bribe. Six varieties were entered for the prize: Gloucester Kidney, Ash-top Fluke, Red-Skin Flour Ball, General Grant, Gleasson's Late, and Peach Blossom. Each entrant sent a ton of his potatoes, done up in twenty hundredweight bags, and one bag was sent to each of the carefully chosen farms in England, Ireland, Scotland and Wales. The competing potatoes were grown alongside the farmers' ordinary potato crops, receiving the same treatment in every respect. When July came round excitement began to run high in the trade; it was a sporting event, and dealers were chalking up the odds on Red-Skin Flour Balls, Peach Blossoms, and Ash-top Flukes. Would they go down with the Blight or would they not?

At the end of July, William Carruthers started out on tour. He visited the farms in the south and west of England first, then those in Wales, and so to Ireland, to Munster, Leinster, Connaught and Ulster, back to Lancashire, up to Scotland, to Ayr, Elgin, Perth, and then back home again down the east coast. The suspense did not last long; all six of the varieties in all four of the trials in Ireland were attacked by the Blight before the middle of August. They were all out in the first round.

In due course the entire crops grown from each hundredweight bag of 'seed' were dug on all the twenty farms, the potatoes were sorted into 'Blighted' and 'Sound', and then sent to London for exhibition at the Agricultural Hall. The principal conclusion to be drawn from the results was that *the Potato Blight fungus flourished in the wet*. In Ireland and throughout the west, where the rainfall was highest, the Blight was most severe; at some of the farms on the east side the potatoes had escaped the Blight altogether. The trials served a useful purpose in warning farmers against paying fancy prices for so-called 'disease-resistant' seed potatoes, especially as the seed planted by the growers for their ordinary crops had on the whole given better yields than any of the expensive competing varieties. There was no variety immune from the Blight, and the opportunity of determining the *degree* of blight-resistance among the competing and other varieties was lost by the perfunctory abandonment of the trials after a single year. One minor point which the trials had cleared up was that it made *no* difference whether the potatoes were grown after wheat or after turnips: the severity of the Blight attack depended in the main upon the weather. The 'heteroecism' theory of Mr. Jenkins was best forgotten.

It might seem that unless de Bary was going to produce a first-rate scientific discovery to order, the whole programme was fated to lead nowhere – but that would be to reckon without the contributions of Mr. W. G. Smith.

Worthington George Smith was the principal artist on the staff of *The Gardeners' Chronicle*. He was forty in 1875. He had begun life as an architect, dabbling in botany and gardening in his spare time, and studying the larger fungi, toadstools and the like, 'as a mental exercise'. His hobbies had gotten the upper hand, and some time prior to 1865, when he was awarded the Banksian Gold Medal of the Royal Horticultural Society for drawings of flowers, he had switched over from architectural draughtsmanship to botanical – without altogether changing his style. When he had occasion to draw a tomato in a hurry to illustrate some advertisement in the *Chronicle*, it looked exactly like an ornament off a wrought-iron gate, and so realistic you could almost lift it off the page with a pair of tongs. But that was by the way. Worthington G. Smith was in truth a very competent artist, a master of the botanical woodcut, and, withal, he was a man of parts. He made the fine drawings of the fungi to be seen in one of the galleries of the Natural History Museum at South Kensington; he wrote essays on such subjects as 'Man, the Primeval Savage', and he once excavated a palaeolithic floor. He was always fascinated by the forms and shapes of the fungi, and read a good deal about them. He was a Fellow of the Linnean Society and one of the shining lights of the

Woolhope Naturalists' Club in Hereford. This Field Club, as celebrated in its way as the Pickwick Club, or the Society upon the Stanislaus, instituted, in 1868, what it was pleased to call its 'Fungus Forays'. They went on for about a week at a time, the members hunting the fungi all day in the woods and meadows, crying 'Thalli Ho!' or some such thing when an uncommon species was discovered in its proper habitat, and themselves returning to a suitable hostelry in the evening. The day's 'bag' of fungi was laid on the table, and after the haunch of mutton and caper sauce, the (more-or-less) learned gentlemen settled down in a generally congratulatory and convivial atmosphere to listen to each others' papers on fungology. Following a high scientific tradition personalities were excluded from the subsequent discussions, and a thoroughly good time was had by all. The great Mr. M. J. Berkeley went out with the Club sometimes, and Mordecai Cubitt Cooke, M.A., was one of its members. Cooke started a small, scientific, and rather dry periodical called *Grevillea*, in 1872, which was exclusively for fungus-lovers by fungus-lovers. It paid its way, and ran until 1894. Its early numbers were chiefly made up of lists of fungi collected in the British Isles and in North America, with some snippets from de Bary's *Morphologie und Physiologie der Pilze* translated into English for the first time. The members of the Woolhope Club, and later of the Caledonian Cryptogamic Club, and the Essex Field Club, readers of *Grevillea*, were in the main neither amateurs nor distinguished original workers; they were field botanists and collectors, who between them added many hundreds of species to the catalogues of the world's cryptogamic flora.

On July 10th, 1875, Worthington George Smith, of the Woolhope Club as aforesaid, startled the scientific world with the announcement that he had discovered the missing resting spores of *Peronospora infestans* (Mont.) Casp., the Potato Blight fungus.

Accounts of this momentous and long-awaited discovery, from Mr. W. G. Smith's own pen, were published at once in *Nature*, *The Gardeners' Chronicle*, the *Quarterly Journal of Microscopical, Science*, and the *Journal of the Royal Agricultural Society*. On July 12th, the Royal Horticultural Society bestowed upon Mr. W. G. Smith the Knightsian Gold Medal. He became famous overnight. And it was more than personal fame: the Royal Horticultural Society, with sadly reduced gate-money from its pleasure gardens in Kensington, was passing through hard times. The editor of *The Gardeners' Chronicle* said: 'We heartily felicitate the R.H.S. that in this period of deep depression and dire confusion, a member of its Scientific Committee should have cast so much lustre upon it.'

And how was the great discovery made? Mr. Worthington G. Smith held back nothing of the story. The Potato Disease appeared unusually early that year and he had followed its progress with attention because of a private theory of his that the Blight was nothing other than that older disease of the potatoes which was called the Curl. On June 16th he had the first clue, when M. J. Berkeley exhibited some diseased potato leaves at a meeting of the R.H.S. with a sketch of certain nodulous or warty bodies which he had found on them, and which he thought to be spores of a fungus different from that which caused the Blight. It was then that the idea came. Might not these be the missing spores of the Blight fungus after all? He, Worthington G. Smith, had hastened to Chiswick and made a searching examination of the plants from which the leaves had been obtained. The warty bodies looked very like the resting spores of the White Rust fungus on the mustard, which de Bary had figured in his paper of 1863, and which he said the missing spores of the Blight fungus might resemble. They were also very like some curious spores found on a potato plant by Dr. Montagne, way back in 1845, supposed to belong to a fungus bearing the appropriate name of *Artotrogus hydnosporus.* Conviction dawned on Mr. Smith: Berkeley and Montagne were both wrong, the present warty bodies and Montagne's *Artotrogus* were one and the same – the veritable winter spores of *Peronospora infestans.* De Bary had said that the resting spores should be sought within the tissues of the potato leaves. Smith therefore macerated the suspected leaves and happened to leave them under water for a week. He found that the fungus grew profusely under water, and on examining his preparations under the microscope, found egg-cells, or oospores, and some smaller bodies which could be only male parts or antheridia, in contact with them. Here was the sexual stage of the Blight fungus exactly as required. He had discovered it *in copûla.* The submersion in water did the trick: *the Potato Blight fungus was aquatic in one stage of its existence, and in that stage the resting spores were formed.* This was something like a discovery.

The long article about it, in *The Gardeners' Chronicle*, was illustrated with several hopeful drawings by the author. In one of them (here copied without the fine shading and to a slightly reduced scale, Fig. 27) a section through a fragment of blighted potato leaf was represented, magnified 250 diameters. The section was drawn upside down, and the two dangerous-looking horns (H) were minute hairs on the *underside* of the leaf. The mycelial threads of the fungus were shown felted among the leaf-cells and bearing immature resting spores or oogonia, here and there. One of these was evidently being fertilized by a smaller, male body, or antheridium (A) in contact with

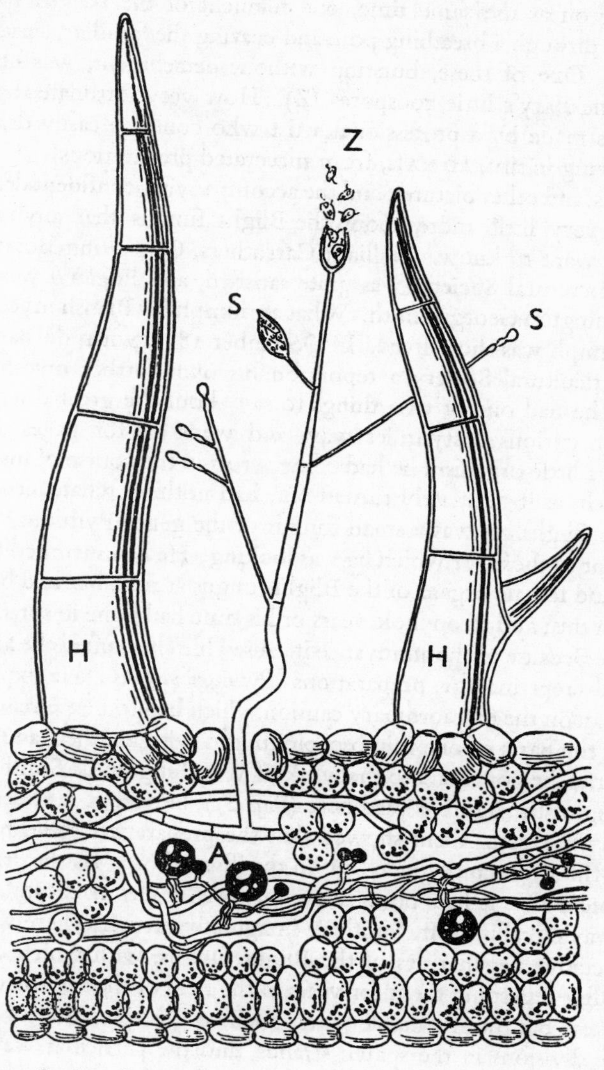

FIG. 27. Section of a fragment of potato leaf showing alleged sexual organs of the Potato Blight fungus. (× 200) After Worthington G. Smith, 1875

it. And to make the picture complete, of sexual and asexual reproduction both going on at the same time, one filament of the fungus was shown pushed out through a breathing pore and bearing the familiar, aerial summer spores (S). One of these, bursting without detachment, was liberating a swarm of de Bary's little zoospores (Z). How very fortunate that the discovery was made by a professional artist who could so easily draw all the parts, growing in situ, AD NAT., from macerated preparations!

With this, and other pictures, and the accompanying confident descriptions, there was very little more about the Blight fungus that anybody could reasonably want to know. William Carruthers, Consulting Botanist to the Royal Agricultural Society, was quite satisfied, and England was proud of Mr. Worthington George Smith. What a triumph for British mycology!

The triumph was short-lived. In December 1875, when de Bary sent the Royal Agricultural Society a report on his own further investigations as promised, he had one or two things to say about the great discovery. He began in a curious nasty-quiet way, and went on for pages and pages, describing a little organism he had come across in the course of his investigations, which, as it ultimately turned out, had nothing whatever to do with the Potato Blight. It was a small fungus of the genus Pythium, which had parts similar to those for which he was looking. He had surmised them to be the male and female organs of the Blight fungus at first, but had been unable to confirm this; and two whole years of his time had gone in sorting the two fungi out. Because of the annoyance it caused him he named the alien fungus which had crept into his preparations '*Pythium vexans*'. He expanded in a general way on the extraordinary caution which had to be exercised to avoid confusing the parts of one microscopic fungus with another, and after these preliminaries, he got round to the work of Worthington G. Smith.

Speaking of the figure copied here (Fig. 27), he said 'it represented things which on the face of them showed that the preparation could not possibly have had the appearance given to it in the illustration'. As the drawing bore the statement that it had been made AD NAT. or 'from nature', this was a smooth way of calling Mr. Smith an imaginative artist. There were a lot of little vegetative peculiarities of the Blight fungus, with which one became familiar after regarding them for years in the field of the microscope – small peculiarities, but unmistakable ones, such as the presence or absence of transverse divisions in the spawn strands, and the particular way in which the summer spores were carried on their 'stalks'. Mr. Smith had produced drawings which might 'look all right' but which were anatomically all wrong. It was the two distinct sets of spawn strands, thick ones and thin ones, shown in the drawings, which really gave the game away. That sort of thing did not happen in any of the families of fungi to which the Blight fungus could conceivably belong.

In macerating his blighted potato leaves, and leaving the preparations about, Mr. Smith had permitted some other fungus to get in. Then, unfortunately, he had been incompetent to distinguish between the two different growths. De Bary examined one of Worthington Smith's actual preparations labelled 'Oospores and antheridia of *Peronospora infestans*' and found it to be merely an amateurish mess, containing a few bladder-shaped objects wholly different from those depicted in the periodical *Nature*, and probably belonging to some common mould. The warty bodies which Berkeley had originally pointed out, might just possibly be mature resting-spores of the Blight fungus, but there was nothing to connect them with what Mr. Smith had found in his macerations.

Professor de Bary's refutation of Worthington Smith's 'discovery' did not make much difference in England, where mycological science was now already sadly behind the times. People of mediocre intellect prided themselves on thinking that one man's word was as good as another's, they could not tell the difference between the genuine and the spurious, the best and the second-rate. It seemed there was then no botanist in England sufficiently experienced in the new methods of research – or with the initiative – to check the work either of de Bary or Worthington Smith. The learned societies and scientific journals which had so hastily published the 'discovery' had to save face, and for twenty years Worthington G. Smith retained the reputation of having solved the riddle of the Potato Blight. On the strength of this reputation he became an authority on plant diseases in general, and sat on several Government Commissions.

So far, the Royal Agricultural Society's drive to force the pace of discovery, by cheese-paring methods, instead of by setting up the necessary continuous and careful research, had led to negative and even unfortunate results. What contribution did they get from de Bary himself? Did their commission and their little *pourboire* cause him to find out anything that he had been unable to find under the impetus of his own sufficient enthusiasm and desire for knowledge? Well, it would be hard to say. No doubt happy to oblige the Society by giving them something of importance to publish, de Bary availed himself of the occasion to separate the Potato Blight fungus from the genus Peronospora and to erect a new genus for it, which he called 'Phytophthora'. There was a marked difference between the two kinds of fungi, in that there was definite branching of the conidiophores or spore-bearing 'stalks' of the former, while in the case of the Potato Blight fungus the spores were first borne at the tips of the stalks, and then pushed to one side as the stalks grew on (Fig. 28).

The Potato Blight fungus had now to be called *Phytophthora infestans* instead of *Peronospora infestans*. The reasons for a change of name were good enough, but 'Phytophthora' on being translated meant only 'plant corrupter', and as that designation could equally well be given to *any* fungus causing a plant disease, the naming of the new genus was not a particularly brilliant piece of applied neology. The name was, however, adopted, and *Phytophthora*

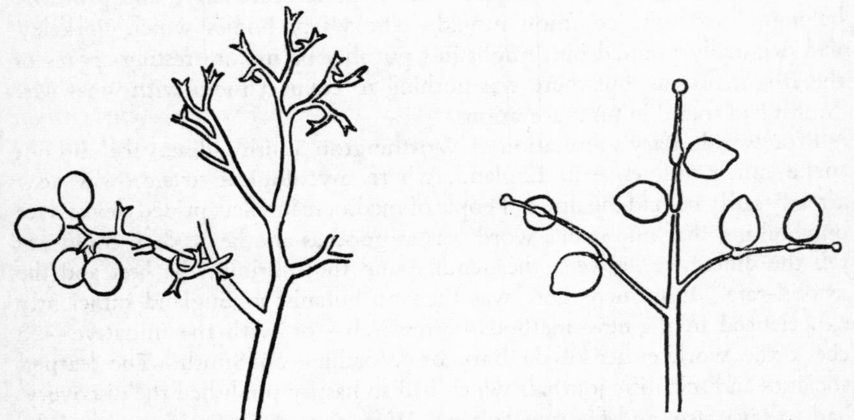

FIG. 28. Distinction between Peronospora (left) and Phytophthora (right) (× 200). After de Bary, 1876

infestans still meant the Potato Blight fungus in 1939. At any rate the important business of naming the fungus was settled for a long time. De Bary did *not* succeed in finding the 'perfect' stage of the fungus. Although he made a further exhaustive examination of a great number of diseased potato plants, he found neither the sexual organs nor the winter spores. He merely confirmed what was already known in 1863, namely that the fungus could survive by means of its living spawn in seed-potatoes over the winter. The mystery about *that* was that blighted sets commonly gave rise to perfectly healthy plants, and though de Bary was able to show how, in a sufficient number of instances, the Blight *could* infect the shoots and thus reach the surface, the fact remained that for all that was known of the Blight fungus it was still only half a living organism.

The interesting drift of thought behind de Bary's work did not lead directly towards the discovery of any way of preventing the Blight, but it did bring to the surface some underlying realizations about the position of the Blight fungus in nature. *Phytophthora infestans* had a partial resemblance to the White Rust fungus on the mustard, but it also had a very marked resemblance to another kind of fungus, called *Saprolegnia, which lived entirely under water.* They were both conspicuously provided with those free-swimming zoospores, and as the Potato Blight fungus had spores that could swim, might it not, at some time in its evolutionary history, also have lived under water? Perhaps it had not always lived parasitically on the potato plant. If theories of evolution were to be trusted at all, the cryptogams came first and the flowering plants much later. The primeval ancestors of the Blight fungus might have been in existence for ages before there was anything resembling the potato on which they could grow. Suppose the fungus once lived, or did still live in some part of the world, under water, along with the algae and such fungi as Pythium and Saprolegnia. Would not that account for its love of humidity, and for the way it flourished on the potatoes in districts of high rainfall? And did not this train of thought lead to the suspicion that the missing fruits of the fungus might be formed only when it lived under water? This idea, at least, de Bary shared with Worthington Smith.

De Bary placed slices of blighted potato tubers under clear spring water, and also in wet soil. The fungus grew vigorously under such conditions, until the slices of potato began to rot, when its further growth was stopped. The fungus was apparently one that could not live on dead or decaying matter. The gradual death of the cells in the submerged pieces of potato, threatening death for the parasite with their own demise, might have hastened the sexual conjugations between the spawn strands and the formation of survival-spores. Death walked always beside life, and at its early beckoning children were born. But when de Bary examined the rotting pieces of potato, the perfect fruits, the survival-spores of the fungus were not there.

It was disappointing, but it might mean only that he had failed to find just the right conditions. The significant resemblance between the known organs of the Blight fungus and those of the Water Moulds remained. De Bary was more inclined to work freely among these last, than to stick too closely to the problem set. Those who commissioned investigations could never understand that the advance of knowledge was like the advance of an army, you could not reach a single objective without first occupying a good deal of the adjacent territory. Very important strategically were the Water

Moulds. Gustave Adolphe Thuret, the great French botanist who discovered so much about the marine Algae, had described and beautifully figured the zoospores of one of the Water Moulds as far back as 1850, and Pringsheim's studies on Saprolegnia in two famous papers of 1858 and 1860, had immediately preceded de Bary's discovery of the zoospores of the Potato Blight fungus. Saprolegnia had been in the background for a long time, and quite soon it was to become notorious in its own right.

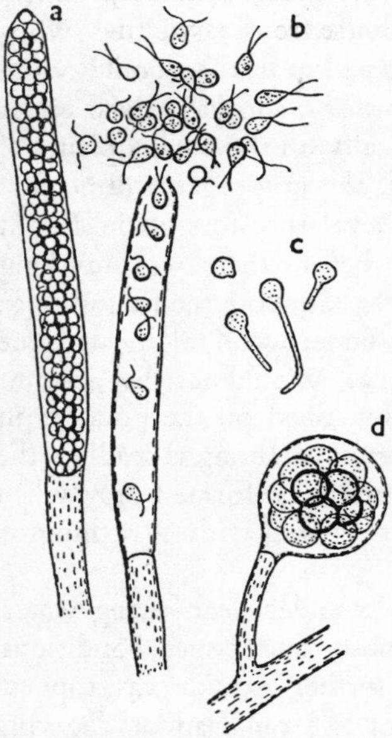

FIG. 29. The Water Mould, *Saprolegnia ferax*, found growing on dead flies and on fish. (*a*) cartridge-shaped zoosporangium, (*b*) discharge of zoospores, (*c*) germinating zoospores, (*d*) eggs or oospores. (× 160)
After Thuret, 1850

There were several species, and they were to be found growing on dead leaves, dead flies and other decaying material in the water of ponds and rivers. Some of the Water Moulds could be regarded, fancifully, as very successful attempts on the part of Nature to produce cartridges of living grape-shot, but, more seriously, as demonstration pieces in which she exhibited very plainly some of her best arrangements for the alternate sexual and asexual reproduction of the fungi.

The plasm inside the tall, cartridge-shaped zoosporangia of the Water Moulds divided into a number of small pellets, each containing a vital nucleus. The pellets grew into small motile zoospores with hairs which enabled them to swim about. The cartridge-cases burst open at the top when they were ripe, and the swarm of zoospores dispersed in the water, to germinate and grow when they came to rest on suitable material. This was the asexual stage of the reproduction, and much the same thing happened when the lemon-shaped spores of the Potato Blight fungus ripened under water. But when winter was approaching the Water Mould produced its second kind of fruit: small globular bodies borne on short lateral 'stalks'. The globular bodies were oogonia, containing at first unfertilized eggs or oospheres, and later fertile eggs or oospores. The arrangements for fertilization of the eggs of the Water Moulds were various; they seemed to include all the possibilities. In some of the very closely related species – if they were to be regarded as distinct species at all, which was dubious – parthenogenesis was the rule, and there were no male organs. In others an antheridium borne on a thin 'stalk' which wrapped itself several times round the oogonium, but which came from a different part of the mycelium, effected the fertilization. But perhaps the most interesting arrangement was that in de Bary's *Saprolegnia monoica*. Here the female organ and the male organ both branched off from the same stalk. The whole structure looked rather like a child's drawing of a thing with its hand over its head; and it fertilized itself as it were by sticking a finger into its own ear. In other words, the antheridium, borne on the self-same stalk as the oogonium, fertilized the egg-cell therein by means of a fine tube which it pushed into the interior. The idea that conjugation took place between two outgrowths from two separate mycelial strands, which might belong to two different plants in a fungal colony – thus effecting a cross – had here to be left behind. Why it should be so important for the organism to divide its own substance into two parts, and then put them together again immediately afterwards by an act of self-fertilization, nobody knew. Ultimately, it might even be a purely mechanical dodge on the part of Nature, but at any rate, after self-fertilization the oogonium developed into a perfect fruit, with a protective covering and containing the stuff of survival-spores. This perfect fruit became detached from its stalk when it was ripe, to lie in the mud or wash about the bottom of the river, awaiting the following spring.

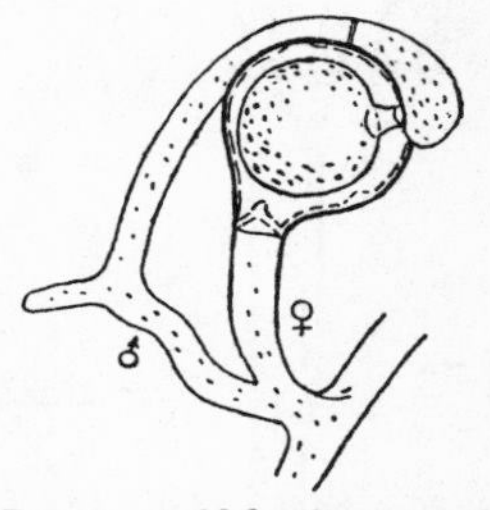

FIG. 30. Self-fertilization of the Water Mould, *Saprolegnia monoica*. (× 300) After de Bary, 1881

So far as the investigation of the Potato Blight fungus was concerned, the upshot of all this was that the fungus might have sexual organs and resting spores more closely resembling those of the Water Moulds than those of the Peronosporaceae or the White Rust of the cabbage and mustard. In which case the spores were not necessarily to be sought for *within* the tissues of the blighted tubers or leaves. Only one thing was certain: the longer the resting spores of the Blight fungus eluded discovery, the more likely it seemed that they were to be found somewhere. When so many of the algal fungi had an apparently indispensable sexual method of reproduction, it was almost inconceivable that it should be entirely lacking in the Blight fungus alone. Even if it had become vestigial – where were the vestiges of it?

At this, the work on the great Potato Blight Problem rested in 1876, and there was no further advance, either in knowledge of the causal fungus, or in methods of lessening its ravages, for another ten or fifteen years, when help came from an unexpected quarter. De Bary's 'perennial mycelium' theory pointed to the inadvisability of planting seed potatoes that were in the least degree touched with the Blight; and the belief, in England, that Worthington G. Smith had discovered the resting spores in blighted potato foliage pointed to the desirability of removing and destroying the diseased haulms – never ploughing them into the soil. But these measures, in so far as they were practicable, had long since been advocated on general grounds. The attempts to produce disease-resistant varieties by hybridization were continued by the potato breeders, with the sufficient incentive of profit. 'Potato fancying' was well under way, and seed potatoes of new varieties for which virtues including disease-resistance were claimed, would sometimes command fabulous prices – as much as a guinea a pound on occasion.

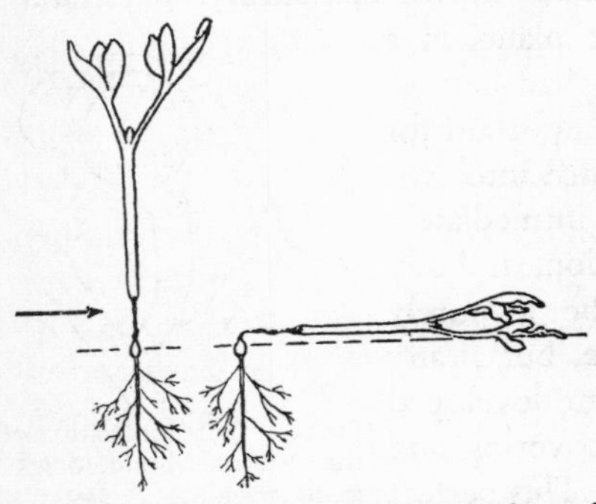

FIG. 31. A seedling attacked by *Pythium de Baryanum* (Damping-off Disease).

De Bary had wasted much of his time in studying that vexatious little fungus which he called *Pythium vexans.* But to say that he had 'wasted' his time was hardly to use the right word. He had been interested in the fungi of the genus Pythium ever since Pringsheim distinguished them from the true Water Moulds, and gave them their name in 1858. De Bary had done most of the earliest work on the genus and discovered several species. Some of them grew parasitically on water weeds, some on decaying material; in a way they were intermediate between the Potato Blight fungus and Saprolegnia. They had spherical zoosporangia instead of the cartridge-shaped bodies of the latter. Their mycelium ramified within the tissues of their hosts as did that of the Blight fungus, but they formed resting spores in abundance and their sexual processes were easily to be observed. They appeared of much botanical but little economic importance until 1874, when another German worker, Hesse, found an omnivorous species attacking many cultivated plants at the seedling stage. This fungus, which he called *Pythium de Baryanum*, in recognition of de Bary's work on the genus, was soon found to be the principal cause of innumerable 'damping-off' diseases, collectively almost as serious for the nurserymen and market gardeners as the Potato Blight was for the farmers. The resting spores of *P. de Baryanum* lurked in the soil of seed-beds and frames and attacked the stems of young seedlings near the ground, withering them, and so causing collapse (Fig. 31). Seedlings of lettuce, cabbage, conifers, and ornamental plants were attacked with great impartiality, and the fungus was even rather fond of the evil-smelling Geranium. But because of its semi-aquatic habit, it required plenty of moisture. Any gardener who had his seedlings overcrowded and growing in too damp an atmosphere could observe the infant mortality of plants caused by *Pythium de Baryanum*, and later on, when a science mistress wanted a typical parasitic algal-fungus, or Phycomycete, for her class to examine she would not choose the Potato Blight fungus, which was 'imperfect' and only readily obtainable in the summer months, but *Pythium de Baryanum*, which she would be almost certain to obtain, at any time of the year, simply by planting the 'cress' of 'mustard and cress' in unsterilized wet soil, and keeping it unventilated.

Phytophthora, Pythium, Saprolegnia – they were three of a kind – three genera of the algal-fungi which loved the wet and were all of them provided with free-swimming zoospores for dispersal under water. Phytophthora blighted the potatoes in the dew and the rain; Pythium damped-off the nurseryman's seedlings; and Saprolegnia, the Water Mould – what mischief did *that* do?

It was the fungus that grew on fishes' sides. In 1877 there was a serious outbreak of disease among the salmon in the rivers Conway and Tweed; within two years it had spread into most of the salmon rivers of the British Isles, causing widespread consternation among gentlemen, fish-wardens and gillies. There were but few members of the literate public at that time who did not hear of *Saprolegnia ferax*. The salmon were dying in the rivers by the thousand, and when they were taken from the water they were found to be marked by great white patches of the fungus – sometimes shrouded by it from head to tail.

It seemed that the Saprolegnia was spreading under water among the fish as in 1845 the Blight fungus had spread over the potato fields. And this particular epidemic of fungus disease threatened to deprive the wealthy of a favourite pastime – it touched England to the quick. The unimaginable catastrophe of some fungus disease rotting all the grass on the playing-fields of Eton could not have been much worse. A commission of inquiry was set up by the Rt. Hon. Richard Aubertin Cross, the Home Secretary, in 1879. No pains were spared in collecting evidence from fishery inspectors, river wardens, and fish-and-gamekeepers. Distinguished English scientists of every sort – irrespective of whether they knew anything about the fungi or not – were invited to say their say about the causes of the disease. It was a national emergency.

The result was an appalling revelation of the ignorance about pathogenic organisms which prevailed among the English scientists of the time. There was not one who got at the truth about the Salmon Disease. Even the great Thomas Henry Huxley went astray.

About what happened to the salmon there was little doubt. A patch of the fungus, about the size of a sixpenny piece, usually appeared first on some part of the fish's body not covered by scales – on the top and sides of the head or on the soft skin at the bases of the fins. The patch of fungus then increased in area, keeping its circular shape, and when it was an inch or more in diameter the central part could be lifted or rubbed off like wet paper, taking the outer skin of the fish with it, and leaving a bare, sore area exposed. Particles of sand or grit adhered to this sore place, causing great irritation and pain. The fishes rubbed themselves persistently against the stones, and dashed about so distractedly in the water that some people said a sort of rabies had broken out among them. Often tails and fins were rotted, and exposed bone and gristle were to be seen where the fishes had managed to tear the 'white night-caps' of the fungus away from their heads. In the last stages of this terrible affliction, the weakened and sluggish fish sought the shallows near the banks of the rivers, and there died.

The fungus was easily identified as *Saprolegnia ferax*; the cartridge-shaped zoosporangia were unmistakable under the microscope; and indeed it was well-known that this fungus grew upon fish. Franz Unger had found it on carp in the botanical gardens at Gratz, and described it with figures in the *Annales des Sciences naturelles* for 1844. It had often been observed on salmon in the rivers of Canada and Siberia; while in California, the Indians crossed their arms, regarded the distant horizon with dignity, and said their ancestors had known about it since time began – they added that the fungus came only on spent or injured fish. In England, everyone who kept goldfish had, in fact, seen patches of this same fungus on *them* at one time or another. It was very common in streams and rivers, especially on the bodies of dead insects. Why had it suddenly begun to cause so much injury to the salmon? Why had it changed from its common scavenging, saprophytic habit, and taken such a liking to living parasitically upon fish that it had caused an epidemic?

Some said the rivers had become too small for the fish, owing to the low level of the waters in 1877–78; some said the pollution of the rivers by factory effluents was the cause, and they pointed to the Tweed near Galashiels, where the water was often blue with indigo, and turbid with soap and arsenic and tar from the wool-scourings. Many, like the Indians, said the fungus attacked the fish only when they had been bruised or injured in some way – as by unsuccessful attempts to jump the weirs, or in the fighting which went on between the males at spawning time. Yet others said that wild ducks were carrying the spores of the fungus from river to river in their crops or on their feet. And practically everybody blamed the Game Preservation Laws, which made the removal of dead or diseased fish from the rivers an offence.

Mordecai Cubitt Cooke, of *Grevillea* and Woolhope Club fame, had swallowed the Grand Darwinian Theory whole, and *he* thought the disease of the salmon was due to the extermination of the otters. The otter was the natural enemy of the salmon, and the otters had been hunted until few remained. The protection of the salmon had caused a diseased race, since before man's intervention the otters had naturally eaten any salmon that were too languid to get away, and thus had kept the rivers free of disease. The same thing, he said, was happening to the grouse on the moors; they too had a disease which was becoming 'more serious' year by year. The remedy was to restock the moors with peregrine falcons to pick out the sickly grouse, and to restock the rivers with otters to devour the ailing salmon. The great law of the survival of the fittest would then operate to 'keep nature's numerous family in a healthy and prosperous condition'.

And that was that. But the early literature on the Salmon Disease would be for ever distinguished by the contribution that was made to it by Thomas Henry Huxley. That grand old rationalist, the Hamlet of his time, who had meditated for so long, not on the skull of Yorick, his friend, but on the colder remains of prehistoric man – he should never have rubbed dead blue-bottles on mouldy salmon from the Tweed. It was not in character, it was *infra dignitatem*, and it was scarcely in his line.

Huxley was dissatisfied with the findings of the Commission of Inquiry, which left the cause of the disease uncertain and indicated no remedy. As it was manifest that England had no Pasteur or Robert Koch to undertake the investigation, he decided to try his hand. His account of the epidemic, for its precision and practised simplicity of style, was a contribution to literature as much as to science, and as a skilled anatomist he was able to state exactly which organs and tissues of the fish were affected. But when it came to finding the part of the fungus in the causation of the disease, he was out of his depth. He saw that no one had really proven that the species of Saprolegnia on the fish was *identical* with that which grew on decaying matter. Hence his experiment with the dead blue-bottles. He wanted to know whether the fungus on the living fish would grow on dead flies, and *vice versa*. He therefore rubbed the corpses of the blue-bottles against the fungus on the sides of the fish, and then put them into glasses of water to watch developments. The spores of the fungus germinated and it grew copiously on the dead flies, enveloping them in white mould. From this he drew the unguarded conclusion that the fungus, normally saprophytic, was living as a true parasite on the fish and causing the disease. How times had changed since 1845! For now a fungus found associated with a disease was so readily taken to be the cause of it, when in those days the orthodox view would have been that the growth of fungus was a mere consequence of some pre-existing morbid condition. What was true of the Potato Blight was not necessarily true of the Salmon Disease. And there Huxley slipped up.

He went on to propound a wonderful 'dead-fly theory' of the disease. A single dead fly in a river could easily have on it one thousand of the cartridge-shaped spore cases of the fungus; assuming that each of these liberated twenty zoospores, and that the fungus ran through its full course of development from zoospore to zoospore in twelve hours, then there would be forty thousand zoospores released into the water, per dead fly, per diem. Enough to infect a whole pool in a shallow stream where salmon were spawning. And if a single dead fly could do that, a single dead salmon, covered with the fungus, could infect a very large volume of water indeed – in fact forty such salmon would be enough to infect every pint of water in the Thames. The *theoretical* remedy, said Huxley, was to extirpate every diseased fish as soon as possible, but he hastened to add that it would be cheaper to put up with the malady, and to let Nature take her course.

There was, incidentally, one *chemical* way by which the fungus was kept down in nature. Those salmon which did not die after spawning, but made their way back to the sea, were promptly cleaned of the fungus. Against *Saprolegnia ferax*, sea water was a most efficient fungicide.

The true relation of *Saprolegnia* to the Salmon Disease was not discovered for another twenty years. In 1903, Hume Patterson, Bacteriologist to the Corporation of Glasgow, found a bacillus which obtained entry into small wounds in the fish and so affected their skin that the fungus could grow upon it. The spores of the fungus were almost universally present in the rivers; it was a true saprophyte responsible only for a secondary stage of decay. Patterson isolated pure cultures both of the bacillus and of the fungus. He put healthy salmon into tanks of water free from the bacillus and fed them on pieces of liver. On introducing the pure culture of the fungus it grew so profusely on the pieces of dead liver that after a while he could scarcely see through the water, but the fish were totally unaffected. He then rubbed the fish here and there with sandpaper, causing slight abrasions of their skin, and put them back in the tank. They were still unaffected. But when he then introduced the pure culture of the bacillus, the ubiquitous Water Mould grew rapidly on the abraded places, and very soon all the fish were covered with it.

The methods used by Paterson in obtaining his pure cultures were hardly known in 1882 (their derivation is here referred to in a later chapter) and as bacterial diseases in general were then only just beginning to be explored, it was not surprising that the bacillus of the Salmon Disease went undetected; but Huxley's error was of a different order – it was as old as neolithic man. Because *some* parasitic fungi caused plant diseases he was tacitly assuming that the fungus growing on the salmon was parasitic and that it caused the Salmon Disease. Discovery as ever, waited upon the testing of the tacit assumption.

CHAPTER XIII

CLUB ROOT AND ANTHRAX

MICHAEL STEPANOVITCH WORONIN was a wealthy Russian. He was born in St. Petersburg in 1838. He had a German tutor as a boy, was sent to the University as a matter of course, graduated comfortably at the age of twenty, and, as he was of a solitary disposition and had never to contemplate the tiresome necessity of earning his own living, he prepared himself serenely for the enjoyment of an intellectual life. He had a taste for the natural sciences, botany was the most alluring at that time, and when it came to choosing where he should go to complete his education abroad, he selected Heidelberg, for botany under Holle, and later Freiburg i. B. under Anton de Bary. He was a brilliant pupil of the latter, and on his return to St. Petersburg he settled down to mycological research 'in the steps of the master'. He had a laboratory in his bedroom and for over thirty years he lived apart from the noise and clamour of the world. But he became Secretary of the Natural Science Society in St. Petersburg, and about once a year he went to Finland, to search among the heather and the pines for certain elegant Cup-fungi (Sclerotiniae) of which he made a hobby.

He worked on many fungi causing plant diseases in Russia, notably on the Sunflower Rust, which was driving peasants out of a traditional sunflower-growing industry, and also on the fungus disease of Rye which was responsible for the 'intoxicating bread' of the S. Ussurian region. But his greatest original contributions concerned nodules and abnormal swellings on the roots of plants. He found the bacteria associated with the nodules on the roots of lupins and other legumes and thus paved the way to the discovery of the living processes by which these plants enriched the soil with atmospheric nitrogen. And, a little later, he found the remarkable causal organism of the Club Root of cabbages and other Brassicas.

This disease, also known as 'Anbury' or 'Finger-and-Toe', was common in England, France, Germany, Russia, Spain. It caused much loss among the cabbage, cauliflower, mustard, swede, and turnip crops, especially on sour or wet land. The Germans called it '*Kelch*' or '*Kropf des Kohles*'; the Russians '*Kapoustnaya kila*'. In Spain, because of the fantastic and often obscene-looking swellings on the roots, which characterized the disease, it was once thought to be nothing other than syphilis which had spread to the cabbages

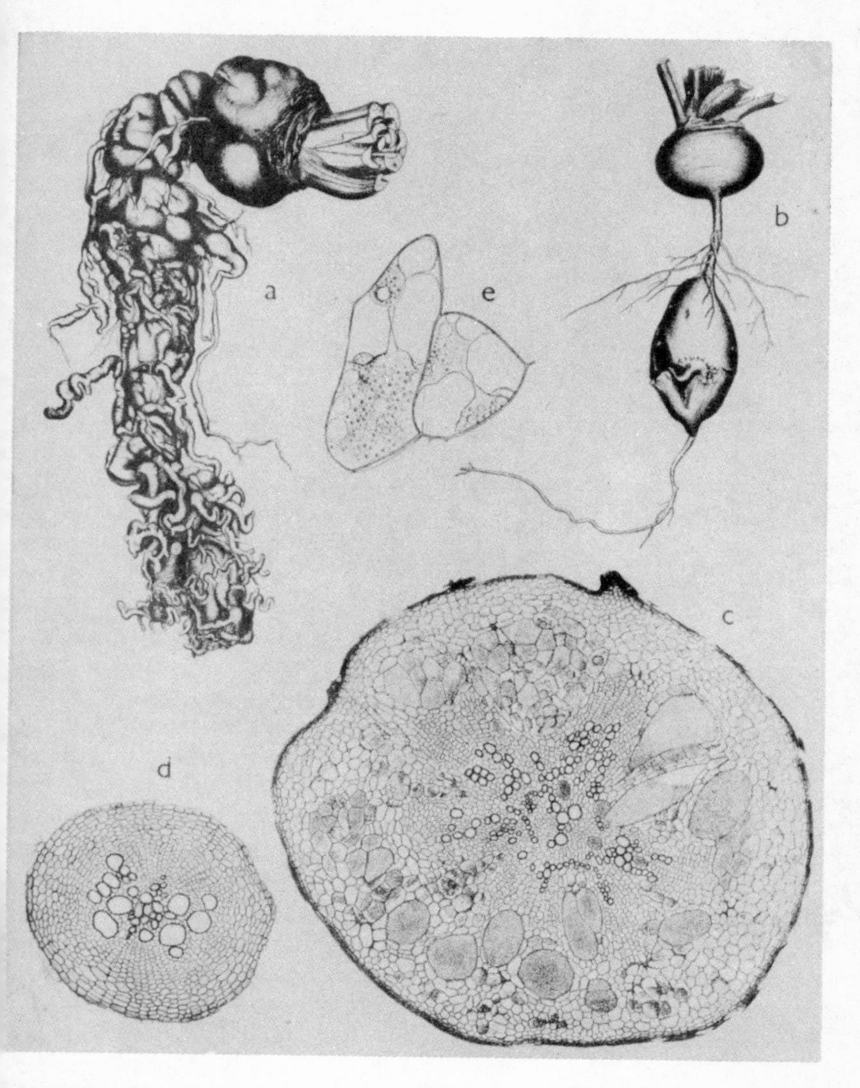

PLATE II. The Club-Root Disease of Cabbages, Turnips and other Brassicas. (*a*) and (*b*) turnips affected; (*c*) cross-section of a diseased root as seen under the microscope; (*d*) cross-section of a healthy root for comparison; (*e*) two cells of a diseased root, further enlarged, showing plasmodium of the Slime-fungus, *Plasmodiophora Brassicae*, within them.

Woronin, 1878

by way of certain dirty waters flung into the garden by mankind. Ruiz Diaz de Isla, one of the earliest writers on syphilis, said that at Baija in his country, the outgrowths on the cabbage roots so much resembled the chancres of the '*mal francais*' that the amiable children cut them off with scissors and stuck them on their faces in imitation of the disease. In the twentieth century it was found that certain compounds of mercury – which was introduced into medicine by Paracelsus, principally for the treatment of syphilis – were very effective in killing the causal organism of Club Root, but, in truth, the

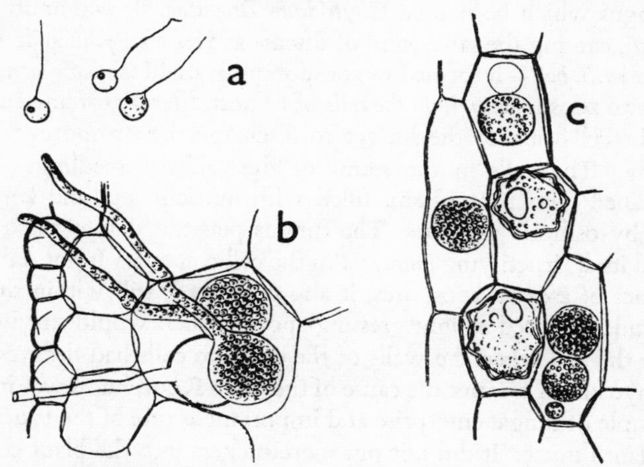

FIG. 32. *Chytridium brassicae*, growing within the cells of a cabbage seedling. (*a*) free zoospores (further enlarged), (*b*) Zoosporangia, (*c*) resting spores.
Woronin, 1878

disease had nothing whatever to do with syphilis, and in the seventies, before Woronin's investigations, it was generally regarded as a kind of hernia of the roots, brought about by physiological disorders and not by any living, or infective, principle.

Cabbages suffering from this hernia could not possibly thrive. The plants were sickly, stunted, and quite incapable of forming those gargantuan buds which the gardener called 'hearts'. The swollen and distorted roots eventually rotted into a foetid and semi-liquid mass. The disease was widespread in Russia, where cabbages were very extensively grown, and in 1872, the market-gardeners about St. Petersburg were losing half their cabbage crop every year. The Royal Russian Gardening Society offered a prize for the scientific investigation of the trouble. Woronin did not compete, but he stacked his laboratory-bedroom with diseased cabbage roots, and set to work.

His discoveries had the quality of the unexpected, for the cabbages showed none of the familiar signs of fungal attack.

In the spring the young cabbage seedlings often died in the hot-bed; the stems withered and the seedlings toppled over on to the ground, presently going rotten. This trouble might easily have been confused with the Club Root – taken perhaps for an early stage of it. But Woronin, who attacked the investigation with very great skill, began by clearing this possibility out of the way. The seedlings suffered from a 'damping-off' disease, caused by a little fungus which he named *Chytridium Brassicae*. It was another of the water-fungi, causing the same kind of disease as Hesse's *Pythium de Baryanum* (Fig. 31, p. 172), *but* – it formed its zoosporangia, small sacs of plasm destined to divide into zoospores, *within the cells* of its host, merely forcing small tubes through the cell-walls to the surface to discharge the zoospores when they were ready. The cells in the stems of the cabbage seedlings were like bladders, lined with protoplasm, filled with nutrient sap, and kept rigidly distended by osmotic pressure. The fungus penetrated into these bladders and helped itself, fructifying *immersed* in the cell contents. It not only formed there its sacs of asexual zoospores, it also copulated, still within the cells of its host, and produced tougher resting-spores which would survive and be set free in the soil when the walls of the cabbage cells had decayed.

This Chytridium was not the cause of the Club Root, but it was interesting as an example of fungal enterprise and important as one of the types of fungi causing plant disease. It did not put mere suckers into the plant cells to rob their juices and so deflate them; it lived wholly immersed. And if one could imagine just such another organism, but without membranes enclosing its parts, a cell-inhabiting slime-mould . . .

Woronin left the 'damping-off' disease, and went on with his search for the cause of the Club Root. He cut thin sections of healthy young roots, and also of some which were a little older and already swollen with the '*Kapoustnaya kila*'. These sections when examined under the microscope appeared as shown in Plate II, *d* and *c*. The holes where Dame Nature seemed to have been dropping stitches in the delicate cellular lacework, were the cavities of tubes which conducted the sap through the roots to the stem. But what were those enormously enlarged and bloated cells full of granular material in the diseased root? No wonder the root was swollen at the place where that section was cut! It would be worth while to take a look at the contents of those cells under a higher magnification.

Woronin found that the bloated cells were filled with a living slime alien to the cabbage plant. In some of the cells this plasm or slime was colourless and fine-grained. In others it contained innumerable, equally colourless, spherical bodies. To the fine-grained plasm he gave the name 'Plasmodium', and the small spherical bodies which took shape in it, he recognized as its spores. To the whole organism he gave the name *Plasmodiophora brassicae.*

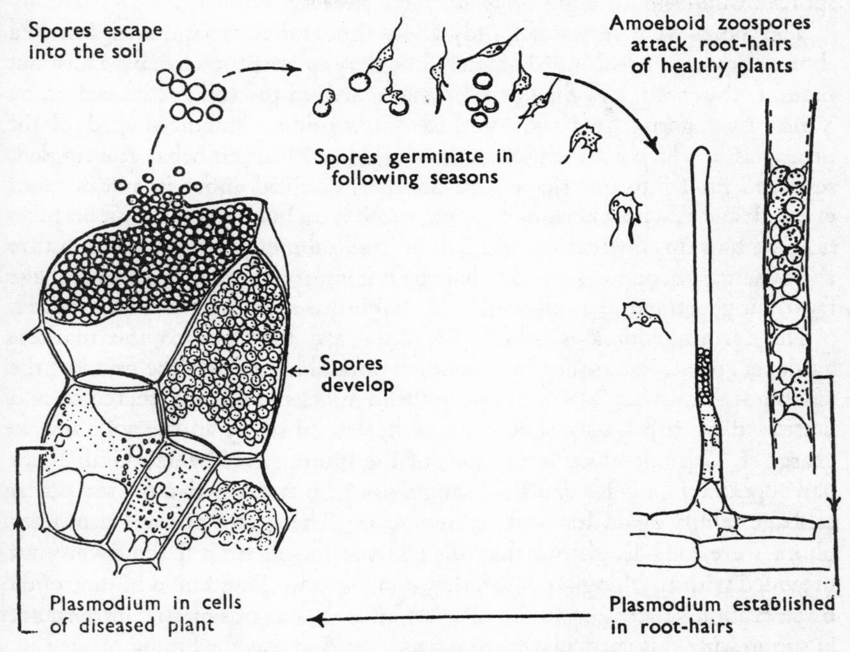

FIG. 33. Life-history of the Slime-fungus, *Plasmodiophora Brassicae*, causing Club Root of cabbages, turnips, etc. Not to scale, parts of diagram enlarged as necessary to indicate detail. Based on Woronin's figures, 1878

This Plasmodium was in constant, slowly-streaming motion; it made its way from one cell of a cabbage plant to another, living on their contents. There was no membrane around this amorphous living slime; it never developed any spawn strands or mycelium; it was just a formless mass of naked plasm, full of little nuclei, which became the centres of the spores into which it broke up when it was ripe or mature.

The growth of this organism not only caused many of the storage cells in the cabbage roots to increase in size, it also caused them to divide and proliferate abnormally, and it twisted the veins in the roots in such a way that their provender went for its own nourishment and not for that of the cabbage plant. Hence the visible swellings on the roots and the symptoms of hernia. Cabbage and Slime-fungus contended for the available nourishment for some while, but in this unequal struggle the cabbage usually lost. The root-cells began to die, the cell-walls rotted away, and millions of the spores of the Slime-fungus were liberated into the soil.

The spores were very small, only about three microns, or one-eighth of a thousandth of an inch, in diameter, but they were protected by a distinct membranous wall, and they could remain alive in the soil for several years. When they germinated they pushed out a minute spindle-shaped bit of protoplasm, which behaved for all the world like a little amoeba. It wriggled, squeezed itself into one shape after another, doubled about its middle, and even advanced with a curious stepping motion by holding on to soil particles now with its tip and next with its tail. It lived submerged in the soil moisture and when it encountered a root-hair belonging to any plant of the cabbage family it penetrated the cell-walls and established a new plasmodium within.

The recommendations which Woronin had to make to the market-gardeners of St. Petersburg were evident enough, now that the cause of the trouble was known. The 'clubbed' cabbage roots should be gathered up and destroyed by fire – they should never be left to decay in the soil, and so charge it with uncountable millions of the spores. And where Club Root had appeared in a field, that field should not be planted with any crop of the cabbage family again for four or five years. The spores of the Plasmodiophora were long-lived, but they died in the soil in time if they were not provided with anything on which they could grow. They could be destroyed by starvation. Attention to the rotation of crops was of supreme importance in suppressing this particular plant disease. And so was the liming of the soil.

The chemists were mistaken in their belief that all plant diseases were attributable to excesses or deficiencies of particular chemical compounds in the soil; this dogma retarded progress in plant pathology, especially in England, for a very long time. But there was one instance in which the chemists were *not* mistaken, and that was in their contention that this Club Root of cabbages and turnips was related to a deficiency of lime in the soil. In 1859, Dr. Augustus Voelcker, consulting chemist to the Royal Agricultural Society of England, had analysed the soil and found a very trifling supply of lime where the Club Root was present; while in fields where the plants were healthy he found much limestone gravel. Later he found that the application of lime, or chalk or marl, to the soil would prevent the reappearance of the disease. Much later, this fact became widely recognized, and in 1898, for example, Halstead in New Jersey, published the results of a careful series of experiments by which he showed that even in localities in which the disease was prevalent cabbages could be grown year after year on the same soil if it was kept thoroughly well limed. The spores of the slime-fungus preferred a slightly acid medium, and germinated best when the soil was sour.

In England, until about the end of the seventies, most of the farmers kept their land well limed as a matter of routine; supplies of chalk and limestone were abundant in England, and anyone who looked at the enhanced vigour of the grass about the chalk line on an old cricket pitch could see the difference it made. But with the Great Depression the liming of the English land was neglected more and more. For a while this appeared to make little difference, but as the calcium reserves in the soil were slowly exhausted, bracken and sour docks invaded the grass land, spurrey and corn marigold spread on the arable, and the cabbages and turnips were affected increasingly with the Club Root. It was one of the surest indicators of lime deficiency.

The parasitic Slime-fungus which Woronin found to be the causal organism of the Club Root disease was very low in the scale of living things. It could be regarded as one of the earliest forms of life – primitive naked plasm just sufficiently organized to divide itself up into unicellular spores for the purpose of dispersal and reproduction. It was necessary to conjure with definitions to decide whether the organism was really animal or vegetable; it had resemblances to the simpler living things in both those rough and ready categories. Anton de Bary conceived of it as belonging to an order of Mycetozoa, or fungal animals; others – whose opinion prevailed – called it a Myxomycete, or Slime-fungus. There was to be the same doubt about the bacteria; regarded by the botanists as Schizomycetes or fission-fungi, many of them lived on animal rather than vegetable substance and were themselves more flesh than fungi. The workers on the lower fungi and now the pioneer workers on the bacteria were reaching different parts of the same border-line.

In 1876 Woronin's final communication on *Plasmodiophora Brassicae* was made to the Natural Science Society in St. Petersburg, and in that same year at the Institute of Ferdinand Cohn in Germany, a be-spectacled young district surgeon from Wollstein demonstrated the complete life-history of the Anthrax bacillus. Another great original worker had entered the lists – his name was Robert Koch. In obscurity, with little more than a microscope and some home-made apparatus, with many other calls on his time, and within only four short years of his return from service in the Prussian army, Koch had made a series of beautiful experiments which turned many searchlights upon Anthrax and the bacillus associated with it. It was with Anthrax that the investigation of the bacterial diseases of animals, as such, began; just as it was with the Potato Blight that the investigation of the fungus diseases of plants had begun in earnest, thirty years before. As it happened, the bacilli of Anthrax were among the largest of pathogenic bacteria, and they were the first of these to be seen. Davaine and Rayer observed them in 1859, and called them 'bacteridia'. Koch cultivated them in suitable media on microscope slides and demonstrated their growth into long filaments, and the formation within those filaments of oval, translucent bodies – resting spores. He showed also how these resting spores grew again into the typical rod-shaped cells of the bacillus. Following Koch's discovery, Pasteur also began to study Anthrax with a very particular interest, and in a few years both Koch and Pasteur had established that the bacillus was indeed the living cause of the disease.

Between 1872 and 1875, the botanist Ferdinand Cohn published his celebrated researches on the bacteria, grouping them into genera, and species according to their life-forms; and, as with the fungi in the time of Tulasne, it was found that polymorphism or pleomorphism existed among them. What was taken to be a distinct species would confound expectations by developing into the characteristic form of another. Koch found that the Anthrax bacillus went through a series of metamorphoses in its life-cycle just as did the Hop Mould or the White-Rust fungus on the cabbage and mustard. The bacillus also had its phase of vegetative reproduction – the multiplication of the anthrax rods by fission – and it also had its resting spores. These last were very hard to kill; they would remain viable after immersion for hours in boiling water, and their longevity accounted for the persistence of Anthrax in infected pastures.

The hunt was out for the bacteria now; de Bary, Cohn, and several other leading botanists turned from their work on the algae and the fungi to search into this little-known part of the world's microflora – or was it microfauna?

The formidable difficulty with the bacteria, however, was that of sorting them out. A single drop of liquid could contain a million mixed bacteria; they were visible only under a very high magnification. How was it possible to isolate a single species? How could mixed lots of bacteria conceivably be analysed? It would seem impossible, and yet, unless it could be done, the specific effects of different species in the causation of disease, or in bringing about fermentative and other chemical changes in nature, their individual properties and life-histories could never be determined with certainty. The result of working with impure cultures could be nothing but confusion – not only of one kind of bacterium with another, but even with the common moulds, whose spores all too easily drifted into the preparations.

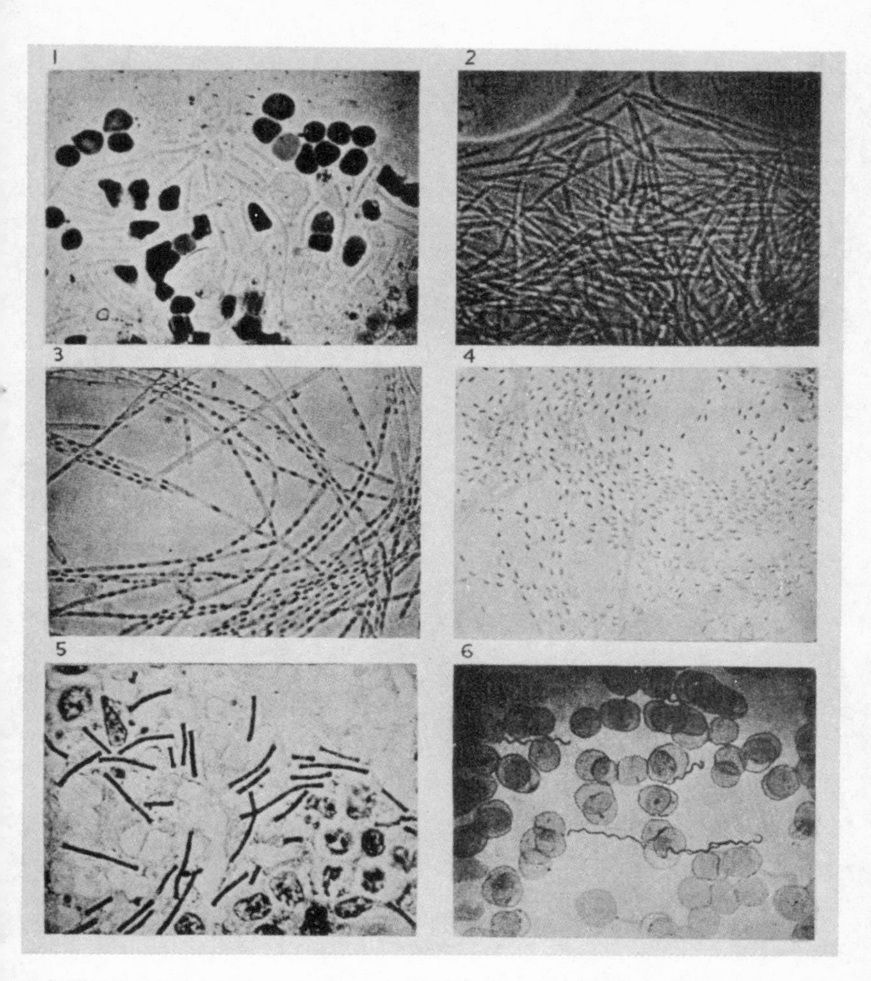

PLATE III. The historic photomicrographs which first told the life-story of the Anthrax bacillus. 1. Living Anthrax bacilli in the spleen of a mouse that had recently died of the disease. The dark bodies are red blood corpuscles. 2. The same after incubation for 24 hours at 18°-20°C. The rod-shaped bacilli have grown into a dense tangle of long filaments. 3. Filaments cultivated in aqueous humour, showing formation of resting-spores. 4. A further stage: the filaments decompose, leaving the resting-spores, which remain viable for 5 years after drying. 5. Illustrating effect of differential staining. Same material as used for (1) but treated with Aniline Brown and glycerine. The red blood corpuscles are decolorized, while the bacilli stand out dark. 6. Spirochaetes, another type of bacteria, photographed in the course of the experiments. The causal organisms of Relapsing Fever and Syphilis were later found to be of this kind (all × 700 in original, here × 600).

Robert Koch, 1876

So long as experiments continued to be made with cultures which were mixed or 'impure', 'evidence' could be adduced for almost any kind of theory about the nature of fungi and bacteria that it was desired to propound. Ernst Hallier, for example, whose work on plant diseases, his *Phytopathologie* of 1868, had not been too successful, courted fame by providing the Darwinian extremists with a first-class 'missing-link'. According to him, bacteria would evolve into fungi while you waited. It happened, he said, in his cultures, and, of course, if it was possible to watch one kind of organism actually developing into another, there was no limit to the extent to which such developments might be supposed to have occurred in nature in the course of unlimited time. Such extrapolation was still very much in fashion. Hallier's beautiful edifice of error was destroyed by the criticism of his arch-enemy, Anton de Bary; it did not mislead anybody for very long, but it was quite sufficient to reveal the fantastic mistakes that could be made simply by confusing one microscopic organism with another. Even Pasteur's cultures were almost certainly impure; he had the Gods on his side, but what a wealth of work would be left for plodders to do in clearing up after his inspirations! The progress of bacteriology demanded routine methods of segregating different sorts of bacteria that any worker of average skill could employ.

Over that period of their greatest perplexity, from 1876 to 1881, Koch and the other bacteriologists were assisted greatly by the chemists, who had by then prepared a number of new synthetic dyes. Methyl violet, methylene blue, fuchsine and Bismarck brown, were all available. Paul Ehrlich, Weigert, Koch and others found methods of staining dead bacteria and also parts of the higher fungi with these dyes, so that they could be very much more readily seen under the microscope, and various parts of their substance could be differentiated by the colours they took up. And now all those working on the physiology of the higher plants were also falling over one another to reap the rich harvest of discovery which followed the use of these new methods of differential staining. So far, the cellular architecture of plants had received the greatest attention; now, with dyes which picked out the different contents of the cells, by tinting them so beautifully in different colours, it was what happened *inside* the cells that mattered. Particularly what happened to that mysterious bit of denser plasm which was called the nucleus. With the new dyes, sets of colourable bodies, or 'chromosomes', within the nucleus, stood out clear and distinct, and the division of these chromosomes preceding the division of the cell as a whole, came to be regarded as perhaps the most significant phenomenon of life. By tracing out the division and sharing of chromosomes much came to be learned of the intimate mechanism of growth and sexual and asexual reproduction in plants, including the fungi – and, incidentally, the use of the new stains led to the confirmation of most of the conclusions about the sexuality of the fungi, which de Bary drew from the behaviour of the cells.

Differential staining led to great advances in every department of biology, but the delicate art of tinting dead bacteria did not remove the difficulty in obtaining pure cultures of live ones. How in the world could it be done? How was it possible to pick out a single organism, a coccus say, one twenty-fifth of a thousandth of an inch in diameter, and grow it *alone*? This was the apparent impossibility with which Koch, Pasteur, Lister, Brefeld, Cohn and many others were confronted in the late seventies. A method *was* to be found, and in the end it would be so simple that a child could understand it. The special materials and apparatus necessary would scarcely cost five shillings, and yet it was to lead directly to the discovery of the causal organisms of tuberculosis, cholera, typhoid, the Plague, and at long last it was to solve the mystery of the Salmon Disease and reveal the missing resting spores of the Potato Blight fungus.

In the meantime, had Koch's work on the bacillus of Anthrax in sheep any direct relation to diseases of plants? Well, in 1877, before it was so much as proven that the interesting bacillus was the true causal agent of the disease in sheep, Professor Burrill of Urbana in Illinois, was writing about 'Anthrax of Fruit Trees' and attributing this plant disease to certain bacteria which he found in association with it. Then, and indeed for nearly twenty years after the bacterial diseases of animals were recognized, it was commonly held that bacteria could or should not cause disease in plants. But Burrill found one plant disease at least in which the causal organism was not a parasitic fungus with a mycelium, or even with a plasmodium like that of the Club Root of the cabbages, but, apparently, a species of bacteria resembling the Anthrax bacillus or, as he said, the *vibrions butyriques* of Pasteur. And this plant disease was by no means a pathological curiosity without economic importance. It was the Fire Blight of the Apples and Pears: one of the most serious troubles with which the American orchardists had to reckon. It was prevalent from the Great Plains to the Atlantic seaboard. The Fire Blight was worse on the pears, and the afflicted trees looked as though they had indeed been swept by fire. The leaves were blackened, the fruit trusses were blasted and burnt, and the twigs died. The bark of the older limbs was also affected, and on the diseased parts there were drops or tears of sticky exudate. Burrill found, on examining this exudate under the microscope, that it was teeming with small rod-shaped bacteria in ceaseless oscillating motion. He found these bacteria in all the affected parts of the trees. In 1880 he made inoculation experiments in an orchard comprising ninety-four healthy young pear-trees, twenty apple trees and one quince. His method was to dip the point of a penknife into the sticky exudate from a diseased tree, and then by means of a small cut, to introduce the organism into the bark of the healthy trees on which he was experimenting. Sixty-three per cent of the inoculated trees took the infection; the typical symptoms of the Fire Blight appeared on them nine days after inoculation, and within a fortnight their leaves began to blacken. Unless the exudate also contained some virus or other contagious principle, there was very little doubt that the bacteria caused the Fire Blight. Burrill did not inoculate his trees with Koch's Anthrax bacillus, which was in fact a different species; the Fire Blight of the fruit trees would not cause Anthrax in sheep or *vice versa*; but while there were so many rod-shaped bacteria, which looked pretty much the same, and had not yet been sorted out, it was reasonable enough to speak of 'Anthrax of Fruit Trees'. Both Anthrax and the Fire Blight were bacterial diseases and that was Burrill's point. Later he gave his bacillus the name of *B. amylovorus*, and in 1883, as soon as practical methods of obtaining pure cultures had been found, another American worker, Arthur, isolated the bacillus and confirmed Burrill's results by inoculating the trees with it alone.

CHAPTER XIV

CANKER OF THE LARCH

THE larches in all the woodlands and forests of northern Europe came originally from the high Alps and the Carpathian mountains, where they grew wild. It was not until the seventeenth century that a few of them were planted elsewhere, as ornamental trees, and it was not then thought that they would be of much value for timber. The Dukes of Atholl, in Scotland, were among the first to recognize their worth, and from about 1730 onwards, they planted larches extensively on their great timber estates of Atholl and Dunkeld. The tree flourished, it grew straight and quickly, and for many purposes, including that of shipbuilding, its timber proved superior to that of the Scots Pine. A fine naval frigate, the *Atholl*, was built of it in 1820, for comparison in service with another, the *Nieman*, built of Baltic fir. Fifty-five years later an Admiralty inspector reported that the *Atholl* was sound long after the timbers of its competitor had succumbed to the action of the seas.

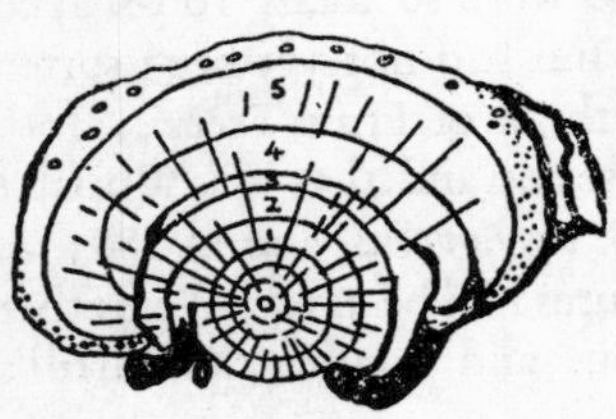

FIG. 34. Cross-section of the trunk of a young larch, showing a canker of five years' standing.
After Hartig, 1880

The larch steadily increased in favour among foresters from the latter part of the eighteenth century until about 1860, when it was at the height of its popularity. It was planted widely in Britain, and in Germany there were larch woods of all ages from the Alps to the coasts of the Baltic and the North Sea.

Then things began to go wrong. By the time the trees had grown large enough to be cut for railway sleepers their foliage was often seen to have become unhealthy, and when they were felled it would be found that their trunks had been penetrated by the spawn of a fungus, so that nothing remained of sound wood except the growth of the last ten years or less. This was the 'Heart-rot', described by the Rev. M. J. Berkeley in 1859. The Heart-rot was one thing; the Canker was another. The purpose of Berkeley's article in *The Gardeners' Chronicle* at that time was to describe the Canker, which had then recently been brought to his attention by one Sir W. C. Trevelyan.

In its advanced stage, the Canker took the form of large depressed scars on the trunks and branches of the affected trees, flanked by swollen growths, and accompanied by sorrowful weepings of resin. When there were several of these cankers on the trunk it was deformed to such an extent that the

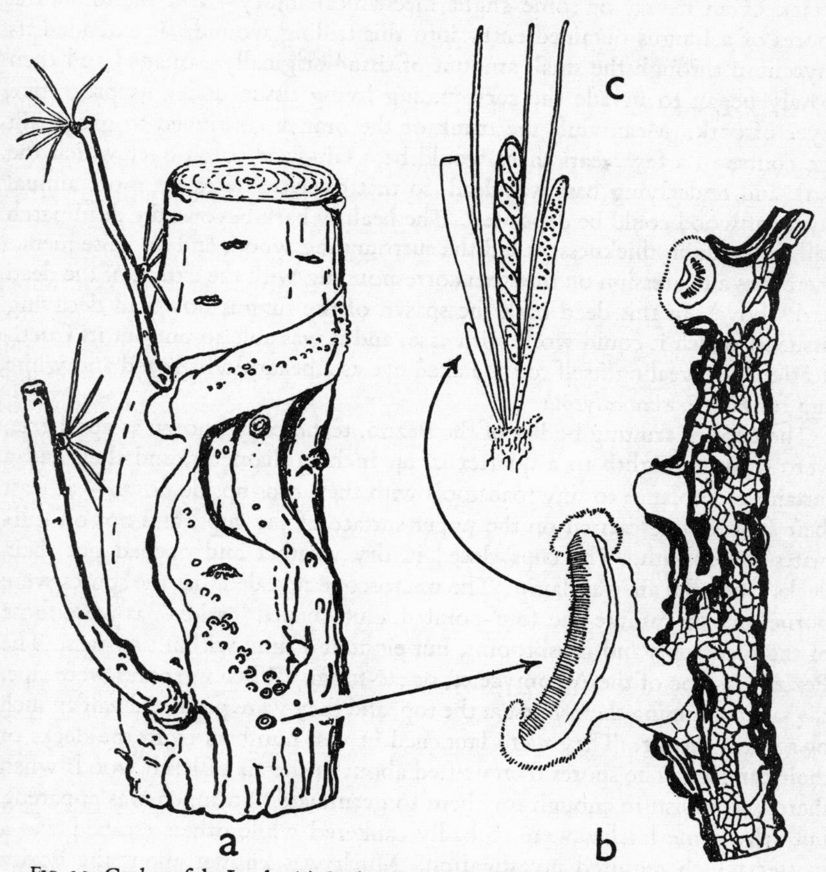

FIG. 35. Canker of the Larch. (*a*) Cankered young trunk, natural size. (*b*) a portion of the diseased bark, enlarged 20 diameters, showing the Cup Fungus, *Peziza calycina*. (*c*) the spore-sacs or asci which cover the upper surface of the Cups, enlarged about 300 diameters. *b*, after Willkomm, 1867; *a* and *c*, after Hartig, 1880

timber was of little value. As with the Club Root of the cabbages, it was then by no means apparent that any parasitic fungus was responsible for the malformations. Something rather like these scars and swellings might have been caused by animals eating away the bark in places when the tree was young. But the specimens which Berkeley examined revealed the disease in its early stages.

A small portion of the bark first suffered from some unknown cause – the attack of an insect, or some slight mechanical injury – and the air-borne spores of a fungus obtained entry into this trifling wound. It extended its mycelium through the small amount of tissue originally damaged and then slowly began to invade the surrounding living tissue under its protective layer of cork. Meanwhile the trunk or the branch continued to grow. In the course of a few years there would be a fair-sized patch over which the bark and underlying bast was dead, so that over that area no more annual layers of wood could be deposited. The healthy bark beyond the dead patch still increased in thickness, as did the surrounding wood, and in consequence there was a depression on the stem corresponding with the extent of the dead bark above. In this dead bark the spawn of the fungus now had decaying tissue in which it could work with ease, and it was able to put out its fructifications – revealing itself to the naked eye as a beautiful little red and white cup fungus, *Peziza calycina.*

The cups or fruiting bodies of the Peziza, technically known as apothecia, were from an eighth to a quarter of an inch in diameter, and they had a certain resemblance to tiny toadstools with their caps upside down – at least their spores were carried on the upper surface of the cups, and not on gill-plates underneath. The cups closed in dry weather and opened out their decks when the air was damp. The microscope revealed that the spores were borne, not on minute and four-pointed, club-shaped 'basidia', as were those of the toadstools and mushrooms, but eight at a time within tiny sacs. The Peziza was one of the Ascomycetes, or sac-fungi. When its spores were ripe, the sacs containing them burst at the top, and they were projected half an inch or so into the air. They were launched in vast numbers from the decks of their carriers. The spores then drifted about in the air of larch woods when there was moisture enough for them to germinate. So much was apparent, but why some larches were so badly cankered while others escaped was a matter which required investigation. Much was known about the Peziza fungi themselves, from the works of the brothers Tulasne and others, but they usually lived as saprophytes on decaying material only, and it was by intuition rather than from any certain knowledge that Berkeley put his finger upon *Peziza calycina* as the cause and not the consequence of the Larch Disease. Intuition was not enough, and he remarked that it was highly important that such affections of economic trees, in consequence of the spread of destructive fungi in the forests, should be studied by competent persons.

Robert Hartig, who took up the investigation of the Larch Disease in earnest during the seventies, was a 'competent person' in Berkeley's sense. His father and his grandfather before him were foresters, the understanding of trees was in his blood; he served his apprenticeship in the forests before taking his Doctor's degree in botany at Marburg, and afterwards held responsible appointments in the forestry service. He became professor of botany at Eberswalde, and in 1879 he was elected to a newly-created chair of Forest Botany at Munich, which he occupied until his death in 1901. Like Julius Kühn, he combined botanical knowledge with great practical experience, and brought both to bear throughout his working life, upon the problems of plant disease. He did not merely study parasitic fungi for their own sake; he studied them in relation to environmental factors and to the damage they caused. He was one of the rare bridge-men who worked for the establishment of plant pathology, as such, inspired perhaps by a hope that in time to come the *applied* science of defending cultivated plants of every kind against disease, would have foundations as sure as navigation or engineering. Hartig's book on the principal diseases of forest trees, his *Wichtige Krankheiten der Waldbäume*, published at Berlin in 1874, was, with a few emendations in later editions, to be a standard work still in 1939. It was not only one of the best books ever written on the diseases of trees, it was a model of the clear and practical way in which other books on plant diseases, from the destroyers of food-crops to the spoilers of garden flowers, could with advantage be written. And Hartig, in studying the pathogenic species among all the diverse fungi of the woods, added much to the existing knowledge of fungal enterprise and resourcefulness in the struggle for life. There was, for example, the pretty Honey Fungus, whose clumps of yellow toadstools grew on old tree-stumps. The fungi, in general, had no roots, from the least to the greatest of them they arose from a tangle of mycelium or spawn, but Hartig discovered that *this* fungus, to suit its ends, could compact masses of its spawn filaments into root-like straps, in appearance resembling black boot-laces and push them out a few inches under the ground for yards, to reach for the roots of living trees, or start another clump of yellow toadstools some distance away. The fungus did not only grow on old stumps; it was not only a saprophyte on dead wood, it attacked living trees by their roots and destroyed them as surely as the root-lice of the Phylloxera destroyed the vines. The Honey Fungus dismayed the forester wherever it was seen, for though the old stump could be destroyed and its toadstools burnt, it still spread like cancer in the soil under the trees. But now that the 'rhizomorphs' and their ways were known, the progress of the fungus could be stopped by digging a shallow trench at a few yards radius round the stump, which the outgrowths could not pass. The false roots of the Honey Fungus had their counterparts in the glistening strips of compacted spawn with which the fungus causing Dry-rot in the woodwork of buildings crept along brick walls and through crevices to reach the floors beyond. Various indeed were the ways of the sylvan fungi, that, out of the false tissue of com-

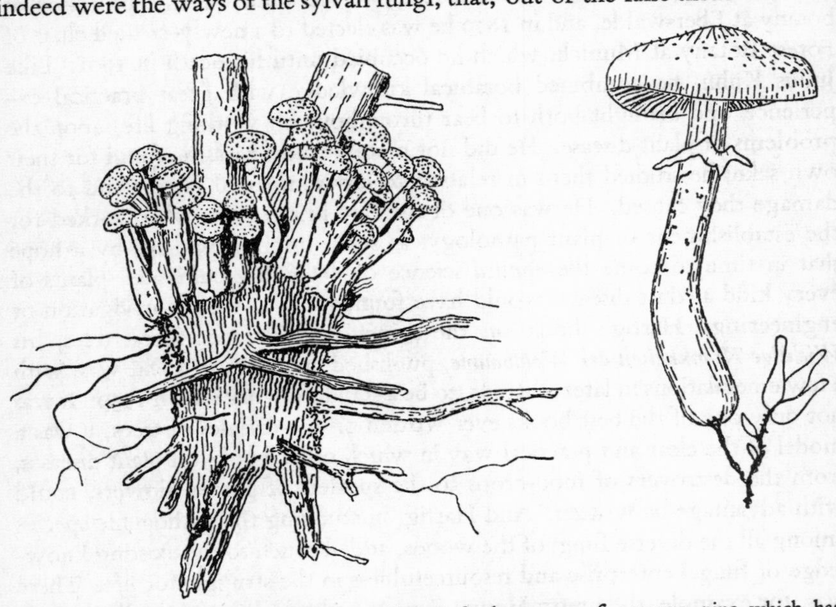

FIG. 36. The Honey Fungus, *Armillaria mellea.* Left, the stump of a young pine which has been killed by the fungus, showing the black rhizomorphs extending into the ground. Right, one of the sporophores or toadstools of the fungus which has developed on a rhizomorph.
After Hartig, 1874

pacted spawn strands, could build gay toadstools, giant puff-balls, brackets rigid as wood, and root-straps to creep under the ground. Some parasitic species attacked the heart-wood of oaks, leaving trunks and branches hollow shells, others rotted the pines so that they rattled leafless in the wind and their brittle spars could be pushed over with one hand. Cankers on stems and branches were only one of the forms of damage caused by the fungi in the woods.

In studying the epidemic canker of the larch, Hartig used the inoculation methods of Anton de Bary. An earlier German worker, Willkomm, who described and figured the fungus in his *Mikoskopischen Feinde des Waldes* of

1867, had already made inoculation experiments, but his method had been crude – rather like that of planting pieces of mixed fungal spawn in a mushroom bed. He cut holes in the bark of healthy larch trees and then plugged them with pieces of bark containing living spawn cut from trees suffering from the Canker. These experiments proved that the disease was transmissible in this way – which could hardly occur in nature – but they did not show what the causal principle or organism might be. There might have been spawn of other fungi besides the Peziza in the diseased bark, and there might have been some other, non-fungus, pathogen in it as well. Hartig grew young larch trees in pots, made small cuts in the bark, and carefully 'planted' *spores* of the Peziza fungus only, in the cuts. That was in September 1879. By January of the following year the early symptoms of Canker appeared on the young trees, and by the middle of February the Peziza was visibly growing on the bark – there were the small apothecia, the little toadstools with inverted caps, bearing the next generation of spores. The causal relation of the Peziza fungus, later to be known as *Dasyscypha calycina*, to the Larch Disease was formally proven.

But why was it that the larches, which had promised so well for a time, were now suffering so badly from the attacks of the fungus, that very few of them were any longer being planted? The Peziza had always been present among the larches on their native Alps, and except in damp localities and by the shores of lakes, it there did very little harm. Why should it spread down from the Alps and ravage the larches on the lower hills and plains? There was nothing inherently sinful in taking seed from the larches on the Alps, and attempting to establish such beautiful and useful trees elsewhere. The timber was especially valuable for its water-resistant properties, and the larch plantations were extensions, not strippings of the woodlands. There was no apparent reason why God or Mother Nature should frown upon so sensible an enterprise on the part of necessitous Man. It was not even that the foresters had been greedy in planting larches so extensively. They were wind-planted extensively enough upon the Alps. The notion, never far below the surface of the European mind, that all disease was some sort of punishment for sin, did not provide any inspirational explanation of the failure of the larch. To get at the true causes it was necessary to *think*, and in the explanations advanced by Hartig there was nothing facile.

Because of the extremely cold winter on the Alps, the larches there remained quiescent until May, when their buds opened very rapidly, and within a fortnight the young needles were no longer tender and delicate, but hardened-off and ready for the short, brilliant summer. The spring was short. On the plains, however, the larch buds would open as early as March, and in the tardy spring the foliage would be two months in passing through its incomparably beautiful – but unfortunately very vulnerable – stage. Insects, both beetles and flies, attacked the young foliage when it was tender, and it also suffered from late frosts. The spores of the Peziza could infect the damaged shoots, and on the plains it had two months instead of two short weeks for the work of invasion. Its growth was also favoured by the damp and mild atmospheric conditions. Thus it was that the parasite, relatively harmless to the larches on the Alps, had advanced slowly year by year through the larch plantations elsewhere, until the Larch Disease assumed epidemic importance. The only trees to escape it were those planted in mixed stands – here and there among hornbeam and beech – those in exposed situations, where the fungus had not the advantage of damp stagnant air, and those which by good fortune had attained the age of twenty years before the fungus reached their locality, for the greatest damage was to the young trees. Where the larches were wind-planted on the mountain-sides there were trees of all ages, and this was another reason why the Canker was less prevalent among them.

Hartig's theories accounted for the spread of the disease through the plantations, and for the formation of the cankers on the branches, but it did not so convincingly account for the cankers on the *trunks* of the trees, which were, after all, those which mattered most to the timber merchant. Hartig said that the force of the wind, or the weight of snow on the branches in the winter, caused small cracks at the junction of the branches with the trunks, and that the spores of the fungus drifting into such cracks in the spring, started the formation of the trunk-cankers. As the fungus could obtain entry to the soft tissues under the bark by any wound, the lower branches should never be cut away before they were dead.

Hiley, of the School of Forestry at Oxford, re-investigating the Larch Disease some thirty or forty years later, perceived another, and entirely different way by which the fungus might attack the trunks of the trees. The Peziza grew readily on dead wood, and it was commonly to be found on the dead under-branches of the young trees. Why should not the spawn of the fungus make its way along these dead branches until it reached the living trunk? The cankers would then be in the position in which they were almost invariably found when the trees had grown up. The only difficulty was that the tree insulated the soft tissues of the trunk from those of the dead branches by means of a ring of cork, which the spawn of the fungus would have to get under or over or round. But there were ways in which it *could* do this;

and that it did so was more probable than that the spores of the fungus entered by cracks made by the loading of the branches with snow. In many districts where the larch was grown there was not much snow; its load would not be considerable on the branches of young trees, and any cracks that might be caused in this way were promptly sealed up with resin.

Far from leaving the dead branches on the trees, some positive good could be done by cutting them away. Affected bark could also be cut out and the wounds painted with tar. But no real cure was to be found for the Larch Disease, except to plant the trees very sparingly in mixed stands, or in dry exposed situations. A little Cup Fungus crossed the will of man, and the great larch plantations passed away.

CHAPTER XV

COFFEE RUST IN CEYLON

WHILE the Phylloxera was starving out the European Vines, and the 'Water-fungi' with their relatives were respectively corrupting the roots of the cabbages, blighting the potatoes, and shrouding the salmon in the rivers, the Rust fungi had not been idle. The Rusts of cereals advanced with their hosts in North America and Australia, flourishing unchecked in new fields of opportunity. A species of Rust fungus, not previously seen in England, the *Puccinia Malvacearum* of Dr. Montagne, attacked the hollyhocks in the gardens about 1874, and for a while threatened the almost total loss of those well-beloved Chinese flowers. The fungus, a native of Chile, had reached Europe by way of Australia. But the Rust which caused the greatest alarm towards the close of the seventies, and was most significant in the history of plant pathology, was that which attacked the coffee-trees in Ceylon.

As far back as November 1869, the Rev. M. J. Berkeley had described in *The Gardeners' Chronicle* an interesting and rather pretty microscopic fungus, received from Dr. Thwaites of the Royal Botanical Gardens at Peradenija. Berkeley's collection then already included some eleven hundred different species of fungi from Ceylon, but this resembled none of them. Indeed it had no very marked resemblance to any other fungus which had by then been found anywhere. In form and habit of growth it seemed to be intermediate between the True Moulds, such as Mucor, and the Rusts. Berkeley proposed a new genus for it, which he called 'Hemileia' – referring, no doubt, to a peculiarity of some of its spores, which were 'half-smooth'.

This Hemileia had been found on coffee-trees in the Madulsima district where it appeared to be associated with a premature fall of the leaves, which was causing some anxiety. Fears were entertained for the crop over the two or three acres affected. Berkeley, who had seen the spread of the Potato Blight, and of the Oidium of the Vine, considered these fears well-grounded, and with the gloomy promptitude of a Jeremiah, he had tacked '*vastatrix*' on to the name of the fungus. It was to be known as *Hemileia vastatrix*. Berkeley's faithful 'Dr. Watson', Mr. Broome of Bristol, had made a sketch from the specimen, and this was published with Berkeley's first description, which was not in Latin but in a kind of English – for once.

'HEMILEIA VASTATRIX (Berk. & Broome), *forming little white orbicular patches on the underside of the leaves, consisting of minute tufts of flexuous threads surmounted by a single subreniform spore attached obliquely at the base, rough externally with wart-like papillae, quite smooth on the side near the flocci. The upper portion of the leaf above the patches looks as if it were burnt. Our figure represents a group of threads with young immature spores highly magnified together with one of the tufts as seen from above, and spores in different positions.'*

As this fungus was growing on the undersides of the leaves, with its spawn system within the leaf-tissue, Berkeley pointed out that it would be difficult to combat once it had been allowed to spread. He suggested the immediate application of sulphur 'by means of one of the instruments now in use in the Hop yards in Kent, or spraying with one of the sulphurous solutions, recommended for the extirpation of Hop Mildew'.

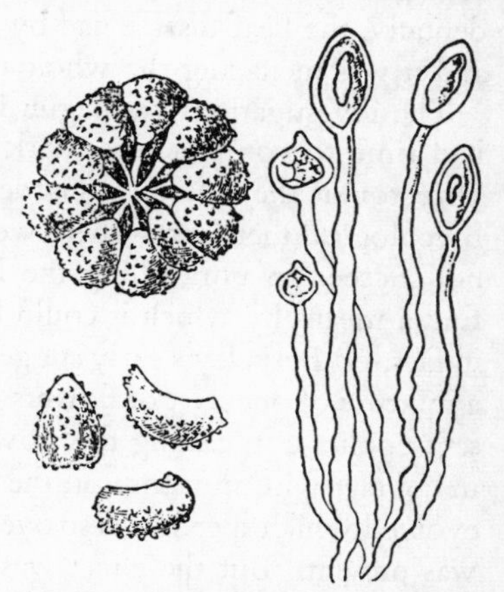

FIG. 37. The Rust fungus found on Coffee trees in Ceylon (about × 250). Berkeley & Broome, 1869

That was in 1869. It was a pity that neither the planters nor the Ceylon Government took any particular notice of Berkeley's warning at the time, for within five years the Coffee-leaf Disease, as it was called, had spread over the whole island and no plantation was free from it. The fungus had so sly a way of attacking its host that the planters were constantly encouraged to hope that it would disappear as mysteriously as it had come. The fungus never *killed* the trees. Sometimes it would strip them bare, but in the following season there would be a fine new flush of leaves, the blossom would be perfect, and as often as not there would be a fairly good crop. Although the coffee tree was an evergreen, it was quite normal for there to be a heavy cast of yellowed leaves in the 'autumn', and the premature leaf-fall did not at first affect the crop of 'coffee-cherries' as much as might have been expected. It was true some people said the fungus caused the fall of the leaves, but the planters regarded that as an open question, and even Dr. Thwaites was very doubtful about it. Parasitic fungi were supposed to love the damp; it was in the hot, dry weather that the rusty spots appeared and the leaves fell. And what became of the fungus afterwards?

It was not until the too-frequent casting of leaves had caused exhaustion, and the crop-bearing capacity of the trees began seriously to decline, that the planters took alarm. Until 1871 the average annual yield of coffee on the island had been about 4.5 cwt. per acre planted; in the five succeeding years the average dropped to 2.9 cwt., until in 1878 it was 2 cwt. only, and the monetary loss was to be reckoned at over £2,000,000 per annum.

The Ceylon Government set up a Commission of inquiry in 1879 and appealed to Kew for trained workers on the fungi to investigate the disease. This action was taken ten years too late, and the workers arrived just in time to attend the post-mortem of the principal industry on the island. Incidentally, the Leaf-disease had by then spread over southern India and Malay, and it was menacing the whole of the coffee in the East.

The investigation was begun in Ceylon by Daniel Morris, but before he had time to complete his work he was transferred to Jamaica, to become Director of the Botanical Gardens there. He was not a master of the new mycological methods – there were exceedingly few who were – and he did not succeed in unravelling the life-history of the Hemileia; though he did find a means by which it could be held to some extent in check. He acted, in fact, on Berkeley's early suggestion that sulphur should be tried. He made a mixture of one part of flowers of sulphur with two parts of quicklime, and sent coolies out, casting this powder by hand over the trees. When it came in contact with moisture on the leaves, gaseous compounds of sulphur were evolved which speedily destroyed most of the superficial fungal growth that was present. But the effect was transitory, re-infection soon occurred, and the trees were as bad again. Repeated application of the mixture might have prevented the disease from becoming epidemic, when it was first noticed over a small area at Madulsima; but now that the Monsoon winds were blowing the multitudinous spores of the fungus backwards and forwards through all the plantations, to apply a little lime-sulphur mixture here and there was like brushing your hat in a sandstorm.

The preliminary account which Daniel Morris gave of the habits of the Hemileia was worthy of a place in the history of vampires. He found that the coffee-trees before a Rust attack were completely enmeshed in a web of fungal strands; not only the leaves but the trunks, the ground, everything was covered with this web. The fungus entangled and netted its prey before it began to feed. The web grew superficially over the trees in wet or 'steamy' weather; when the hot, dry days came, innumerable root-threads crept out from the web and penetrated everywhere into the tissues of the leaves, seeking therein not only food but protection and moisture. Within a week or two the mycelium within the leaves produced its fructifications – the orange-coloured rusty spots – and a new crop of mesh-engendering spores began to blow about. The leaves, weakened by loss of substance and moisture, succumbed to the heat and the drying winds, and fell in showers from the trees. The effect of the sulphur, said Daniel Morris, was to destroy the *external* web of the fungal vampire before it began to feed.

This web-theory, which accounted for the sudden appearance of the Rust in dry weather, was plausible enough, and no doubt it would have remained current for some time had it not been for the very careful work of Mr. Morris's successor.

Harry Marshall Ward was a young man who found in science a career open to the talents. On leaving school he had attended classes in the Science and Art Department at South Kensington; he wanted to be a science teacher. His abilities soon attracted the attention of the Professor of Botany – W. T. Thiselton Dyer – who encouraged him to make a particular study of de Bary's work on the fungi, and gave him a job as a Demonstrator to assist with the classes. In 1876, this working lad won an open scholarship to Christ's College, Cambridge, and three years later walked off with a First in Botany at the Natural Science Tripos. His services were recommended to the Ceylon Government, by the authorities at Kew, and he went out to investigate the Coffee-leaf Disease early in 1880. He was then twenty-five, a young plant-doctor entrusted with a case on which he had a chance to make his reputation.

The first thing that impressed him about Ceylon was that it was *not* populated exclusively by planters, coffee-trees and the fungus *Hemileia vastatrix*. The number of other living species co-operating or contending with each other for existence on the island was quite remarkable. One had also to reckon with jungles, Cingalese, mountains and monsoons. His problem, defined on paper with the help of a few dried specimens in England, appeared very different when he was out among the coffee-trees and talking to the planters. There were the coffee-rats, for example, which were supposed to come out of the jungle every seven years when the Nillor tree died: that was 'a fable invented by the people', but other things besides rats came out of the jungle – it teemed with insect and fungus life. There was the Black Bug on the coffee; it fed on the leaves and left behind what was politely called 'honey-dew'. This sweet and sticky excretion was food for a small black fungus, which grew over it, thereby sometimes covering the leaves with 'Black-wash'. The bugs fed not only on coffee but on guavas, Hibiscus, Justicias, oranges . . . carrying fungus spores about on their feet. The bugs themselves were attacked by many parasites, swarms of minute and vividly coloured wasps and flies. The small fungi on the coffee-trees were even more numerous than the insects, and it was by no means easy to sequester one species from the embarrassing variety.

How much of the general fungal growth belonged to the destructive Hemileia? That was Ward's first problem – to disentangle the 'fungal web'. He analysed the local microflora, *à la* de Bary and Pasteur. Instead of catching the spores for examination by Pasteur's method of drawing the air through a filter plug, or into vacuum flasks, he hung small gummed glass slips – microscope slides – on the branches of the trees in the position of leaves. These strips became moistened with dew, and their 'catch' gave a fair indication of the number and variety of spores which were drifting about.

On taking his 'glass leaves' down from the trees in the early morning and examining them under the microscope he found that the *number* of individual spores caught reached astronomical figures; and on one of his slides he was able to distinguish fifty-one different *kinds* of spores, the characteristic kidney-shaped spores of Hemileia and fifty others. By incubating various of the spores in glass vessels, either allowing them to germinate simply in water, or nourishing them with sugar or Pasteur's solution, he was able to reproduce good specimens of the 'fungal web' which Daniel Morris had truly observed over the trees. But – this web was not produced by the spores of the Hemileia; it belonged to other fungi altogether.

Hemileia had its peculiarities, but it was plainly one of the Rust fungi, and no more or less sinister in its ways than those which attacked wheat, sunflowers, roses, hollyhocks and other plants. The spores germinated on the leaves in humid weather and when the dry periods came the fungus was in the leaves and ready to put out its fructifications – the visible Rust. It then drew on its host plant for all the moisture it required, and the drier the weather the more damage it caused. Its successive crops of spores, liberated from the Rust patches on the undersides of the leaves, carried off the leaf-substance in the form of this spore-dust. Then the drying winds, and the demands of the developing coffee-cherries came to complete the work of desiccation and the leaf-showers began.

One peculiarity of the Rust fungus on the coffee was the vigour, and the curiously 'coral-like' growth of its spawn filaments within the leaves. Normally, when the spores germinated, they put out quite short germ-tubes – they formed no sort of preliminary and external web – but sometimes, when there was plenty of moisture and the advancing end of the tube could find no stoma to get through, the external germ-tube was abnormally long and already coral-like. On the end of it there was a little vesicle, into which all the plasm from the spore was gathered, leaving an empty tube and an empty spore-case behind. The vesicle fitted exactly over the breathing-pore in the leaf, in preparation for the act of penetration. The plasm was then forced through and the coral-like growth continued within. It put out definite suckers into the leaf-cells as it crept past them. There was no doubt about the parasitism of *Hemileia vastatrix*.

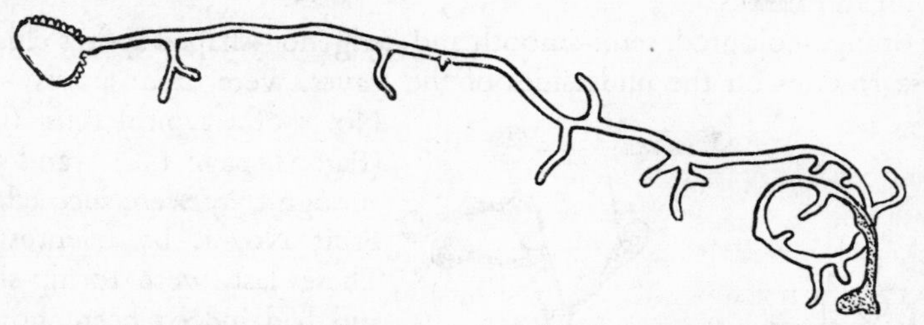

FIG. 38. Coral-like germ-tube put out by a Uredospore of *Hemileia vastatrix* after 40 hours immersion in a film of water (× 250). Marshall Ward, 1882

Ward inoculated the leaves of healthy young coffee plants, under glass, with the Rust spores and found that the characteristic Rust spots appeared where, and only where, the spores had been sown. He cut sections of the leaves and traced out the progress of penetration and inter-cellular growth of the fungus up to the production of new rosettes of spores (Fig. 39). All this

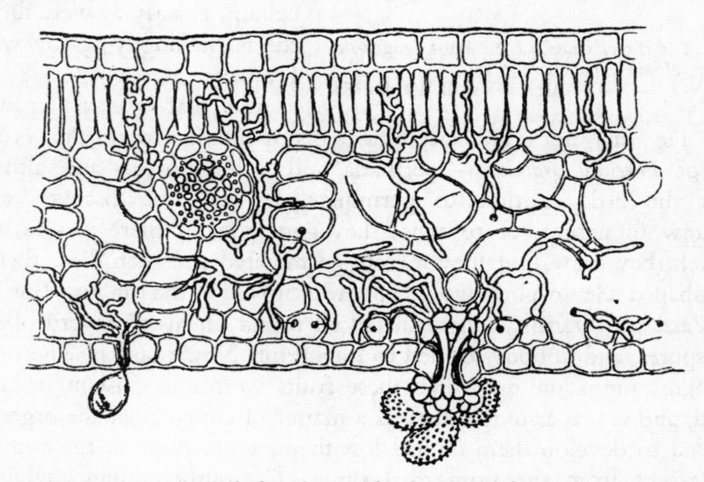

FIG. 39. Section of a leaf of Arabian coffee showing (left) the germinal tube from a Rust spore penetrating the lower epidermis; (centre) the coral-like mycelium growing in the intercellular spaces; and (right) spore-bearing threads put out through a stoma (× 250). Marshall Ward, 1882

after de Bary. The exercise in the application of the master's methods was beautifully done. Such facts as it had taken a century to establish about the Rust on the wheat, could be determined by Ward in a few months, for the Rust on the coffee, now that the way was known. On his return to Europe, Ward took his results over to de Bary, who approved them, and, as it were, gave him full marks.

The orange-coloured, semi-smooth and hedgehog-shaped spores clustered in those rosettes on the undersides of the leaves, were uredospores – Fruit No. 5 of a typical Rust fungus (Fig. 24, page 134) – and surely enough they were succeeded by Fruit No. 1, by teleutospores. These last were turnip-shaped and had indeed been shown in Berkeley & Broome's figure of 1869 (Fig. 37). Ward 'discovered' them in March 1880, and by watching their germination in water observed for the first time the little sporidia, carried on four spicules put out by the promycelium, exactly as were those of the Rust fungus of the wheat: Fruit No. 2.

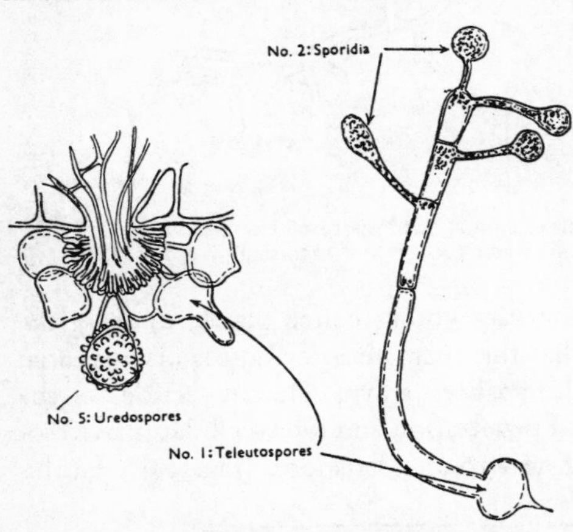

FIG. 40. The three 'fruits' of the Rust fungus on the coffee, *Hemileia vastatrix* (× 250)
After Marshall Ward, 1882

And that was as far as he went. He did not find anything corresponding to Fruits Nos. 3 and 4 of *Puccinia graminis* – spermatia and æcidiospores – and although he got the little sporidia to germinate, he did not discover where they grew in nature, or to what they gave rise. If there was no plant on which they grew, but they merely germinated and then died, then the turnip-shaped teleutospores would appear of no use to the fungus. But Marshall Ward was warmly congratulated all round on his discovery of these teleutospores, and nobody seemed to miss Fruits Nos. 3 and 4. There were many Rust fungi among which these fruits were non-existent or undiscovered, and it was assumed then, as a matter of course, that the organisms had failed to develop them or had lost them, somewhere in the course of their descent from the primordial slime. Curiously enough, while the cryptogamic botanists were so much concerned about the sexual processes of *Puccinia graminis* and the Potato Blight fungus, nobody bothered about the sex-life of *Hemileia vastatrix*. It was just marked absent.

Perhaps it did not matter so much, because the asexual summer spores or uredospores of the coffee Rust were adapted to serve also as survival spores. They were well-protected in a hard rind; they were not easily destroyed by heat or dried out by the wind; and they remained viable for six months or more. Attention could well be concentrated upon these seed-like uredospores which waited for the rains and blew about the plantations numberless as grains of sand in the Sahara.

Ward noticed that the coffee-trees growing in sheltered places were often free from the Rust, while those which were swept alternatively by the S.W. and N.E. monsoons suffered most. The fallen leaves were covered with the clusters of Rust spores, which broke loose as the leaves were blown about, and were taken up into the air in invisible clouds. The first measure to reduce the number of these spores was to collect and burn the fallen leaves – but to do this over the whole island was an impossible undertaking. If only the planters had left belts of trees to break and filter the winds! When they carved out their estates they had stripped the mountain-sides completely of the virgin forests, and, all unwittingly, they had left a clear way over their miles of coffee for the aerial drift of fungus spores!

There was an idea among the planters that the object of Ward's investigation was to discover some superior chemical which would cure the disease locally wherever it was applied. They had called in a plant-doctor and they expected him to prescribe a bottle of medicine. There was more in it than that. Ward saw that the opportunity of experimenting with various chemical treatments was too good to be missed, but he knew that none of them could now save the coffee. It was sad, and it was not the sort of thing that it would be tactful to say in his reports, but the real usefulness of his investigations was that they might be the means of saving other cultivations – and not only of coffee – in other parts of the world. As a botanist, Ward had already done well; he had discovered those teleutospores, found out a great deal about a new Rust fungus – enough to start his scientific reputation. But what did *that* matter? It was for him to read the lessons of catastrophe, to find out how the epidemic had begun and why it had spread beyond control. He had been called upon to act as a plant pathologist, he was consciously exercising a new profession, and he had his own ideas of what that implied. He was not out on a mere 'Fungus Foray'. It was the seriousness and sense of responsibility in young Harry Marshall Ward which made people use the word 'character' so often in speaking of him. He made no pretence of offering the planters a remedy where he could see none, but his observations on the cause and course of the Coffee Rust, as a typical epidemic of plant disease, won for his reports to the Ceylon Government (Colombo Sessional Paper No. XVII, 1880 et seq.) a place among the great historic and fundamental contributions to his science.

The fungus, so recently named *Hemileia vastatrix*, had almost certainly been present on wild coffee in the jungles of Ceylon for centuries. The outbreak of the Leaf-disease in 1869 was *not* to be attributed to the introduction of a parasitic organism from some other part of the world. How was it that this fungus, which had not done much harm to the wild coffee, caused such havoc when it got into the plantations? An important question to which the probable answer was simple. In the jungle, coffee trees were to be found here and there, separated by much other vegetation. The spores of the fungus were prevented from travelling far, and, as they failed to grow on nearly everything except coffee, the propagation of the fungus was held severely in check. Both the Rust fungus and the coffee tree had to contend for existence with countless other living species. None was favoured but many survived in the grim democracy of Nature.

As soon as the land was cleared of its mixed wild flora, and attempts were made to reserve it for plants of a single desired species, the multiplication of all the pests and parasites of that species was enormously favoured. They were provided with unlimited food, and many of their natural enemies were destroyed. There was nothing to stop their spread until they reached the limit of the clearing, or came to another crop on which they could not grow. In short, specialized cultivations *invited* epidemics of plant disease.

In mixed cultivations, where different crops were grown in rotation and fields of wheat, for example, were bordered by fields of turnips, or of barley, or of potatoes, the 'run' of the various pests and parasites was constantly being broken. In specialized cultivations, where fruit-trees, or coffee trees, or vines, or cereals, were grown for mile after mile and year after year, there was nothing except uncontrollable variations in the weather to prevent the advance of the insects and the fungi across a whole countryside. This was the explanation of the spread of the Hemileia in Ceylon, and it was a grim warning of one of the dangers which threatened specialized cultivations everywhere. It was no use nagging the planters, like a Dutch grandmother, about their too hasty stripping of the hillsides. Where land was found specially suited for the cultivation of a particular crop, it was but natural that it should be used as far as possible for that purpose. Planters, and those financing them, were not natural philosophers; they had not the knowledge to lay out estates with much regard to questions of ecology. Plant disease was only one of the factors involved – there would be great losses from soil erosion on the hillsides of Ceylon a little later. The wise exploitation of the different agricultural terrains of an empire required an informed and far-sighted administration. Governments were too much preoccupied with division of immediate gain and with the rule of turbulent populations. In pointing to the exclusive cultivation of single crops over unbroken areas as one of the chief causes for the advance of the fungi, Ward did not put forward any panacea; he stated a fundamental truth.

It was not the only matter, of general significance, which he underlined in his reports on the Coffee-leaf Disease. He also clearly stated, for the first time, a very important principle which was to underlie the successful control of many fungus diseases by spraying. The planters were trying the lime and sulphur dust recommended by Daniel Morris, and they were also making attempts to 'disinfect' the trees with Condy's fluid, and Lister's carbolic acid. Ward watched the application of these substances, and asked himself what exactly they were supposed to do. Some of the planters were mixing carbolic powder with mud and plastering the mixture round the trunks of the trees, with the idea that the acid would penetrate into the sap, and so get at the spawn of the fungus within the leaves. He had the greatest difficulty in persuading them that this was a mistake; and that all the mixture did was to cause the bark to peel off where it was applied. The application of Condy's fluid and carbolic acid to the foliage certainly killed any 'fungal web' there might be about, but unless the solutions were very weak they also caused severe injury to the trees. And as the Hemileia did not form an external web, their effect was at best a momentary clearing of all the fungal growth except that which really mattered. The lime and sulphur treatment was more rational, as the mixture did remain on the trees for a while, even after rain, and it was comparatively harmless to the foliage. The main things to be determined about the sulphur treatment were *when* they should be applied, and with what precise object.

Ward went back indoors and pondered over what he knew of the life-cycle of *Hemileia vastatrix*. The fungus was not very vulnerable; its spores were encased in hard rinds; its spawn was buried in the coffee leaves. But there was just one chink in its armour; one short period during which a vital part was exposed – and that was *after* the spore, germinating on the leaf-surface, had put out its delicate germ-tube but *before* this germ-tube had time to penetrate through a breathing-pore into the leaf-interior. 'The life of the parasite', he said, 'is so arranged that as short a time as possible shall intervene between the well-protected spore condition and the safely ensconced mycelium.' In devising any direct way of attacking the fungus, the toxic material would have to be applied so that it was '*already on the leaves when the spores were germinating*, at which period the delicate tubes were easily destroyed and offered scarcely any resistance to weak caustic or poisonous solutions'.

This was a vital realization, for these words of Marshall Ward's marked the emergence of the idea of *preventive* treatment of *foliage* with chemical substances to combat those kinds of parasitic fungi whose spawn grew *within* the leaf. Of such fungi, the Hemileia was only one; another was that which caused the Potato Blight. One of the key realizations which were to lead at last to the finding of a remedy for the Potato Blight in Ireland, was made by Harry Marshall Ward when working on the Leaf-disease of the coffee in Ceylon. No doubt the same idea occurred independently to other workers; Millardet, in Bordeaux, claimed it for his own a few years later – but there, in Marshall Ward's reports of 1880-81, the principal function and purpose of a protective fungicide for application to foliage was defined. It remained for others to find the ideal material; perhaps it was a pity that Ward did not read Bénédict Prévost's paper of 1807, just then.

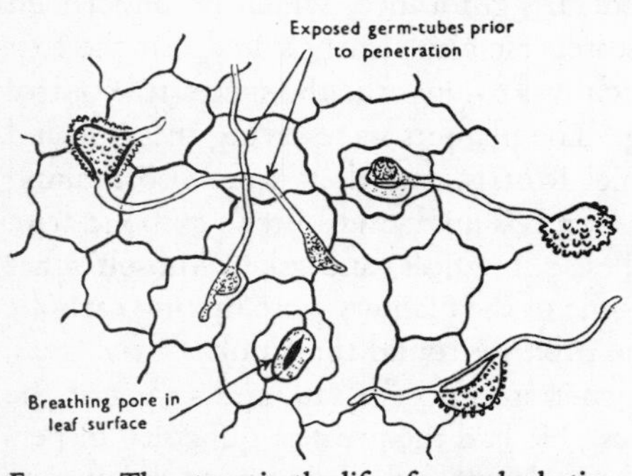

FIG. 41. The stage in the life of an endophytic fungus at which it is vulnerable to chemical attack. (× 200) Marshall Ward, 1882

But the sulphur and lime, *applied at the right time*, did about as much as any chemical mixture could have done to save the coffee. On the Harrow Estate at Pundolu-oya in 1880, timely sulphuring raised the yield of coffee-cherries from 36 to 48 bushels per acre. But in the main it was a losing fight with the spore-laden winds. What was the end of the story? The productivity of the trees went down and down until their cultivation was no longer profitable on the island. The planters were ruined and the Oriental Bank went smash in the general confusion. The Leaf-disease spread throughout the East, destroying the finest, the Arabian, coffee first, and then the Liberian and less valued kinds. In Africa, the disease restricted the cultivation of coffee to particular altitudes and districts, everywhere rendering it more expensive and difficult. The centre of gravity of the world's potential coffee production shifted from the British empire to Brazil. In after years the hillsides of Ceylon came to be more extensively planted with tea than ever they had been with coffee – one reason why Indian tea was to remain the principal caffeine stimulant of the English people. In the barmy thirties of the twentieth century, when instances of waste were required to point this or that argument about the state of world-finance, it became habitual to refer to the deliberate burning of coffee berries in Brazil, but there were few who ever gave a thought, while they stirred their tea, to that little fungus which ruined the entire coffee-producing industry of the Indian Empire.

CHAPTER XVI

AFTER FORTY YEARS

THE decade between 1880 and 1890 was the period of the Seventh Plague, when much had been learnt from a long series of disasters, many searches came to fruition, and the necessity for organized resistance to the 'advance of the fungi' could no longer be ignored. The issue was one of survival: unless more and more cultivations were to be abandoned, and more and more herds were to be lost, measures had to be taken to combat, not the fungi alone, but the insects, the bacteria – all those small but multitudinous pests and parasites which were contending with man for the produce of the land. Passing over the ancient Rust and Smut and Ergot of the cereals, and beginning with the Potato Blight in 1845, there had been full seven plagues, more widespread and more destructive than any Pharaoh knew. They came in the wake of the industrial revolution, with the specialized cultivations, and with the growth of maritime trade. Some were ancient, some were new, they were no mere visitations; where they were introduced they came to stay. The Muscardine and the Pébrine of the Silkworms, the Potato Blight, the Oidium of the Hops and the Vines, the Phylloxera, the Locusts, the Canker of the Larch, the Rinderpest of the Cattle and the Anthrax of the Sheep, the Salmon Disease, the Hemileia on the Coffee – and now the Colorado Beetle and the Peronospora or Downy Mildew of the Vine. Yes, assuredly, by 1885, there had been forty years of plague.

In 1845, when the Blight laid waste the potatoes, the scientists of Europe watched its progress aghast, unable to propose any remedy, uncertain of its cause. They could work no magic, and they did not pretend to do so; instead they turned to the closer investigation of the fungi associated with plant diseases, and of the fungi as a whole. They built upon a heritage of knowledge from the past. For forty years their search continued; the detailed contributions from a thousand greater or lesser investigators were laid down in the archives; the pure science of cryptogamic botany had first to be firmly established, and beside it the search went on for the causal organisms of disease. The company of seekers had begun to divide into mycologists and bacteriologists, some empirical remedies were known or found by the way, but, as though by a common understanding or consent the search was always first and primarily for the *causes* of disease, whether in plants or in animals –

when the cause was known a remedy would reveal itself or could be sought for with more hope of success, and the empirical would be explained.

After 1880 came long-awaited revelations, and there was a great change in the direction of the total activities of those working for the conquest of disease. The search went on, it branched in many directions, the field opening up before it was vast, pathogenic agencies with particles smaller even than the bacteria were yet to be found; but, with the discovery, one after another, of effective new methods of *preventing* disease, there was other and different work to be done. It demanded the diffusion of knowledge by education and the participation of whole populations through their Governments in the cost of organized research and executive action. During the eighties a network of Agricultural Experiment Stations was set up over the whole of the United States, and a new Board of Agriculture began its work in Great Britain. In Bordeaux a method was discovered of protecting the vines from the Mildew and the Potatoes from the Blight. In Paris the Institut Pasteur was founded, marking the conquest of Anthrax and hydrophobia.

The decade opened with the greatest single advance ever made in the technique of search for the causal organisms of disease. Robert Koch at last found a way of analysing mixed lots of fungi and bacteria, and preparing pure cultures of individual species from among them, which was about as simple as planting a packet of mixed seeds to make a 'Japanese Flower Garden' and then, when the flowers were up, separating the poppies from the anemones, the stocks from the marigolds. There was now good reason to suspect that the causal organisms, not only of Anthrax, chicken cholera, and the *Pébrine* of silkworms, but also of many infectious diseases of man, were to be found among the bacteria. The study of these organisms, no less than of the fungi causing plant disease, in truth involved a kind of gardening. To find out how they grew, how they differed from one another, how they could be killed, to what diseases they gave rise, and what changes they brought about in the media in which they grew, it was necessary to 'plant' them and to cultivate them. They could be grown in the living plants or animals which they normally parasitized, and most of them could also be grown in artificial media – in broths and other nutrient solutions contained in glass vessels. One way of obtaining more or less homogeneous cultures of deadly bacteria was to inject mixed lots of them into the bodies of mice, rats, guinea-pigs, sparrows, dogs and other small animals. Some of the bacteria would live and multiply in the blood of a particular animal, while others would not, so that by passing the bacteria through animal after animal, a partial sorting of the bacteria could be effected. But in general it was preferable to do the mere sorting in glass dishes and to plant the bacteria in animals only when it was necessary to study their pathological effect, which could not be determined in any other way. The medical workers were ready enough to 'use' a hundred animals for anything their living organs would do, but to inflict suffering wantonly, where other means were to be found of achieving the desired results, was to debase the ethics of science to those of the grouse-moor or the battlefield. The botanists' methods of cultivating micro-organisms in glass flasks and dishes when they wanted them, and of attempting to obtain pure cultures as gardeners selected desired kinds of seeds, was not only more civilized, but in many respects it was more instructive. In glass the organisms were easier to observe, and by providing them with richer or poorer nourishment than they normally obtained they could sometimes be made to reveal stages of growth rarely encountered in nature.

Pasteur's method of cultivating the Anthrax bacillus was to take a drop of blood from a diseased sheep and put it in a flask containing sterile beer-wort or urine. The urine was simply 'manure' for the Anthrax fission-fungus in the blood. The microscopic plant grew rapidly within the flask when so nourished, and there was soon a dense tangle of its threads. Pasteur then took a very small portion of this growth and transferred it to another flask of sterile urine, where it continued to grow. So on, through as many as forty flasks, until, as Pasteur made out, he had a pure culture of the organism, anything else in the original drop of blood having been long since left behind. The Anthrax bacillus, so long cultivated in this way outside the animal body, infallibly caused Anthrax when inoculated into a healthy sheep. About this Koch and Pasteur were agreed, but there was a flaw in Pasteur's argument; even after passing through forty flasks his culture of the bacillus was still not necessarily pure. In the smallest portion he could transfer from one flask to another, there could be myriads of living cells and it did not follow that they were all of the same kind.

Oscar Brefeld was perhaps the most successful fungus-gardener of the seventies. Beginning in 1872, and at intervals of a year or so from then until 1912, there were published eighteen profusely and beautifully illustrated volumes, recording the results of his labours. He studied not so much the bacteria as the common moulds, and the kinds of fungi which caused plant disease. For an example of his methods there was his work on the destructive Honey Fungus of the woods. Hartig discovered the 'rhizomorphs' of this fungus in 1874, but as these root-like extensions of interwoven spawn-filaments crept forward under the ground, it was not at all easy to observe them in process of growth. Brefeld took a single spore from one of the yellow toadstools and planted it in clear, sterile, nutrient solution in a glass flask. It was easy to look through the walls of the flask and watch what happened: a circular patch of branching mycelium grew out round the spore, and from this arose the same black rhizomorphs which Hartig had found in the ground. They increased in length by about an inch a day, and when roots of a tree were put into the flask, the way in which the fungus attacked them was apparent. It was necessary only to take out the roots after a while, cut the usual thin sections from them for examination under the microscope, and there the spawn threads of the fungus were to be seen, invading the root-tissues from the point of contact of the black rhizomorph.

From his long experience of cultivating fungi in glass vessels, Brefeld was able to point out some of the working principles upon which success in obtaining pure cultures depended. To cultivate one particular microfungus and not a mixture of several it was necessary to *start with a single spore*, to plant it in a *suitable* nutrient solution, taking care that this was (*a*) *sterile*, and (*b*) *transparent*, and then, and all the time, to *keep the spores of other organisms out*. The rules were sound, and the method worked admirably when the spores of the fungus were just sufficiently large for it to be physically possible to pick out a single one of them to begin with. When it came to the bacteria, however, whose individual cells were so small that a million would not make up the volume of a pin's head, there was an obvious, and for years apparently insurmountable difficulty. Dr. Lister, in England, sought to overcome it by taking a drop of broth containing some million living bacteria, and then diluting it with a million measurable parts of water. In some of the millionth parts of the dilution which could be drawn off drop by drop, there would, by the mathematical laws of probability, be one living bacterium and one only. If a sufficient number of cultivations were made, starting with these drops, *some* of them would be pure. It then remained only to determine which were pure and which were not . . .

Robert Koch improved upon the methods of Brefeld. He began by taking advantage of an ingenious dodge first used by Davaine, as far back as 1859. If a little gelatine was incorporated when making up the warmed nutrient solutions they would set solid when cold, so that any organisms in them had to grow where they happened to be – they could no longer swim about freely in liquid. While experimenting with gelatine in this way, Koch conceived the idea of melting a sterile nutrient jelly and pouring it thinly over glass plates, where it set solid, forming an ideal 'seed-bed' on which to grow bacteria. He was still unable to plant them one at a time, but by dipping a clean platinum wire into a solution thinly populated with a mixture of them, and then dragging the wire across the surface of the jelly, individual bacteria were wiped off and planted at random along its track. Or, a few bacteria in a drop of medium could be added to the jelly while it was still liquid, so that they dispersed in it, and remained so dispersed after the jelly had set. Each bacterium grew where it chanced to be sown and gave rise to a colony of its own kind in that immediate neighbourhood. Supposing that some of the bacteria were red in mass and others white, then there would be distinct red and white colonies on different parts of the jelly. It was then a simple matter to take some of the bacteria from a red colony and streak them out on another plate; and in this way pure cultures of the red and the white bacteria could be obtained with remarkably little trouble from mixtures of the two. There were many criteria, besides that of mere colour, by which different species of bacteria could be distinguished, once they were sorted out, and this method of analysis by cultivation – equally applicable to the kinds of fungi causing plant disease, and to the benign bacteria of the soil – marked the beginning of practical bacteriology, and the culmination of the mycologists' long-continued endeavours to find the best way of cultivating *their* particular garden.

Koch's 'plate-method' was described and demonstrated before Lister, Pasteur, the English veterinary-surgeon Burdon Sanderson and others at the historic International Medical Conference at London in August 1881, and thereafter the art and science of determining the causal organisms of disease developed with astonishing rapidity. The plate method was improved in one or two simple ways, which might well delight everybody of a practical turn of mind. If it was desired to cultivate bacteria which normally lived at the temperature of the animal body, it was evidently necessary to keep the jelly at that temperature. But, just as table-jellies made with gelatine melted in the mouth, so those gelatine bacteria-beds of Robert Koch's melted likewise as soon as they were warmed. The method would have come to grief, but for the bright idea, on the part of one of Koch's assistants, of replacing the gelatine with a vegetable jelly obtained from certain kinds of seaweed and called Agar-Agar, which was not liquified so readily. Then another of Koch's assistants, Dr. Petri, replaced the flat glass plates with shallow flat glass dishes, provided with glass covers – 'Petri dishes'. The cultures could thus be moved about, conveniently visible, but protected from drying-out and accidental contamination. Yet another practical and inexpensive way of making bacteria-beds, by the thousand if need be, was to pour small portions of the melted jelly into sterilized test-tubes and leave them to cool on the slant.

The bacteria could be cultivated on the sloping flat surfaces of jelly, the colonies to which they gave rise were readily seen through the walls of the tubes, while plugs of scorched cotton wool kept out extraneous organisms but admitted the necessary air for those which were being grown. Bacteria-farming demanded extreme cleanliness and care in manipulation: all the glass tubes, dishes, and small implements had to be sterilized, notably by baking them in ovens or passing them through flame; the right conditions of 'soil', moisture, temperature and air supply for the different species had to be found; but the intrinsic difficulty in obtaining pure cultures had been overcome. In 1882, Koch isolated the bacillus of tuberculosis, and by 1890 the causal organisms of Asiatic cholera, typhoid, diphtheria, the Plague, and many other infectious diseases of man and beast, had been isolated and identified.

But at that International Medical Conference in 1881, the cheers had been not so much for Robert Koch as for Louis Pasteur, who in June of that year had such a triumph over his opponents in the dramatic test of his preventive inoculation of sheep against Anthrax, staged at the farm of Pouilly le Fort. He had made a discovery of the first magnitude, which now concerned not the mere causation of infectious diseases, but their *prevention*. Some two or three years previously he had been sent the head of a cock that had died of chicken-cholera, a disease then very prevalent among the fowls. He found the head teeming with a bacterial organism, which he cultivated in a broth of chicken-gristle. The smallest drop of this culture, when freshly made, was sufficient to kill a chicken, so virulent was it. But, by a lucky accident, Pasteur had inoculated some fowls with a culture of the bacillus which had been allowed to stand about for some time, an old preparation, and this did *not* kill the fowls – it caused only a mild indisposition from which they soon recovered, and thereafter inoculations with the most virulent, freshly-made cultures still did not kill them. They had acquired immunity from the disease. Inoculation with the old culture, which though still containing *living* bacilli had become so mild that it would not even kill a sparrow, had much the same effect on the fowls as Jenner's 'vaccination' with cow-pox had in conferring immunity from small-pox in man. By yet another divine or merely lucky accident, Pasteur had also inoculated some sheep with a culture of the Anthrax bacillus which had been overheated, by a few degrees Centigrade, during its preparation. The sheep recovered, and when subsequently inoculated with a virulent culture they too survived.

Thus Pasteur had struck the daring, and at first seemingly fantastic method of saving animals from death by bacterial disease, by injecting into their blood-streams attenuated but still-living cultures of the very disease germs themselves. No wonder there were some who distrusted these 'vaccines' of Pasteur's, and who sought to expose him as a charlatan! But he knew what he was doing; the *premier vaccin* injected into those sheep at Pouilly le Fort, was so innocuous that it did not kill baby guinea-pigs; the *deuxième vaccin*, which followed, was less attenuated, until, on the great day when he was to be exposed, the 'vaccinated' sheep were unaffected by the virulent test-inoculations of Anthrax, while the unvaccinated died before the eyes of the crowd. The Gods smiled upon that crucial experiment, for as Koch insistently pointed out, the 'purity' of Pasteur's cultures was dubious. But Pasteur's luck *did* hold, and over the next ten years, in France alone, some three million sheep and half a million cattle were treated by his method. The mortality from Anthrax dropped from 20 per cent in sheep to less than 1 per cent, and from 5 per cent in cattle to less than ½ per cent. One of the most formidable and ancient endemic diseases of the flocks and herds was vanquished. But this was not all, vaccine-therapy was to be used successfully against many other diseases; it was in 1885 that Pasteur first inoculated a child, who had been bitten by a mad dog, with attenuated viruses of hydrophobia. The child recovered.

The problems confronting the medical profession and those concerned with the diseases of the crops now had much in common. A man, suffering from one of the identified bacterial diseases, was a large and elaborate living organism contending for life with millions of minute unicellular parasites, *of known kind*, in his blood stream. The pathologist had to think coolly of his fellow-creature in distress; emotionally undisturbed by all the atmospherics of pain, mental suffering and apprehension of death, he had to use his wits to find means of killing the parasites without killing the man. This would be to effect a *cure*; and what was perhaps of even greater importance, he had to find hygienic measures which would prevent those parasites from invading other people – beginning with himself. The personal factor did not enter into the plant pathologists' work – he stood in no danger of contracting Potato Blight – but his problem was otherwise the same; he had to find means of killing the spores of the Blight fungus without killing the potato plants, and of preventing one blighted plant from infecting others.

It seemed that Pasteur was making parasitic bacteria cause the poisoning of their own kind within the bodies of their animal hosts. Many crop-destroying fungi also poisoned themselves – or, rather, changed plant tissues so that they could no longer live on them. That did not immediately suggest any method of control, but it was worth bearing in mind. What was the rationale of the vaccine-therapy? *How* did Pasteur make pathogenic fission-fungi work their own destruction? Every living thing had to take in food, use a part of it to elaborate its own substance, and reject the rest. The Anthrax bacillus notably affected the spleen, but without going into too much physiological detail it could be said that the bacillus lived on and in the 'blood of sheep'. Then, as the substance of the bacillus differed from that of the blood of sheep, it followed, algebraically, that what it rejected into the bloodstream differed from blood. This new substance had its effects (*a*) on the sheep, and (*b*) on the bacillus. The bacillus could not only be poisoned by its own effluvium – as the further growth of yeast cells was inhibited when the alcohol they had produced reached a certain concentration – it could also be poisoned by the products of interaction between its own effluvium and the sheep's blood. Sheep which had recovered from mild attacks of Anthrax were immune from further attack because their blood was so charged with such products or modified by them that the bacilli could no longer live or multiply in it. Thus, if it was desired to protect healthy sheep against Anthrax, one way of doing it was to make their blood antagonistic to the bacilli by treating it with the effluvium or waste products or ground dead bodies of the bacilli to start with. Pasteur's method was to generate these waste products *in situ* by injecting 'vaccines' containing the enfeebled but still-living organism itself. Another method, used with notable success a little later against diphtheria – after Kitasota's revealing discoveries, *circa* 1890 – was to inject the serum or fluid part of blood in which the organism had been, but was no longer, living.

In both cases the substances which killed the bacteria – 'antitoxins' and whatnot – were produced in consequence of the growth of the bacteria themselves, as parasites, within their animal hosts. Apart from such messiness as that of mixing up horse-serum with that of man, preventive inoculation introduced nothing that was really extraneous or new, it merely assisted the process by which animals recovered from bacterial disease, when they did so, and made that process more certain. Thus the very success of preventive inoculation led to a much closer inquiry into the unassisted natural processes of recovery. It was one thing to shift vaccines and anti-toxins about from one animal to another; the central problem was how those substances came to be produced within the animals at all. Some animals and some people had much greater powers of resistance to particular bacterial diseases than had others. Why? And then again, it had long been known by experience that hereditary, nutritional and environmental factors all affected the power of the animal body to resist and overcome diseases. How did they do so? The answer was to be sought in the effect of all these factors on the stuff within the tissues of the animal body which actually nourished or poisoned the specific invading bacteria. The problems of disease had to be referred down to the microscopic scene where the bacteria and the cells of the host organism were contending for life. If the relations between macroscopic and microscopic could only be determined, then by breeding from particular stocks, and exercising an informed choice of environment and nutrition, the physiological defences of animals against specific pathogens could be reinforced as surely as by any injections of serums and vaccines.

In the world at large there were many who had no patience with all this talk of specific pathogens; there were many who went off into cackles of amusement at the very idea that there could be as many distinct kinds of disease-producing bacteria as there were contagious diseases; there were many who still preferred to generalize about Disease with a capital D, as an absolute principle, which could be exorcised in all its manifestations by calling upon the powers of another principle of Healthy and Natural absolute Good. Such people were never at a loss for short-cuts and panaceas. According to the notions of what was absolutely Healthy and Natural, in fashion at one time or another, Disease (in man) could be prevented by keeping windows tight-shut to exclude raw air – or by flinging them wide open in the depths of winter; by living on a diet of port-wine and beefsteak – or on nuts and lettuce-leaves; by indulging all the carnal appetites with exuberance – or by resort to chastity and prayer.

The same divergence between scientific thought and preconceived opinion was still apparent in the eighties over the diseases of the crops. In England, Earl Cathcart of the Royal Agricultural Society, and John Lawes of Rothamsted, were surrendering ground that had been very hard won, when they encouraged farmers to believe that parasitic fungi were of secondary importance only, and that the causes of plant Disease were wholly to be sought in soil deficiencies, errors of cultivation, senile degeneration of stocks, adverse weather conditions and so on. It was abundantly true that all these factors affected the prevalence of fungus diseases and the resistance of predisposition of cultivated plants to them – but to belittle the importance of the parasitic fungi, and the study of them, was to reject the only means by which the exact part of the various environmental factors could be determined. The issue was put in a very different way by Marshall Ward and his friend and mentor Thiselton-Dyer of Kew. *They* said that the Rusts and the Blights and the Smuts and the Mildews were truly and indeed caused by specific kinds of parasitic fungi. But whether these fungi spread or not, whether they gave rise to great epidemics or harmlessly attacked a few plants here and there, depended solely upon whether or not they found conditions favourable for their increase. If the environmental conditions were favourable any pest or parasite might give rise to a plague. The time was past for argument in the dark about factors which might or might not predispose plants to noumenal 'Disease'; it was now necessary to distinguish the particular species of fungi associated with specific plant diseases, to determine the conditions which favoured their increase, and then, if possible, to alter those conditions to the disadvantage of the fungi and the advantage of the crops. And this was equally true for the pathogenic bacteria which had their habitat, not in green leaves, but in the veins and capillaries of animals.

After 1881 new species of bacteria were being distinguished and named almost every day; but, even so, the number of known species of bacteria were very few compared with the multitudes of known fungi. Some years before 1880, the great Italian cryptogamic botanist and scholar, Saccardo, decided to bring together into one vast work of reference the descriptions of all the fungi so far recognized. Often the same fungus had been described under a score of different names, and these descriptions were to be found in all the European, and several of the oriental, languages. To ascertain what was really known of any particular fungus, whether it was a pretty toadstool or a parasite causing a plant disease, meant years of tedious research, which few were qualified to undertake even if they had the time. Saccardo essayed the stupendous task of gathering all the descriptions together, comparing them, setting them side by side, and translating them uniformly into Latin. And he lived to do it; though he could scarcely keep pace with the new species found after he began. The first volume of his *Sylloge fungorum omnium hucusque cognitorum*, concerning one of the groups of fungi, called the Pyrenomycetes, was published in 1882. As the other groups were dealt with, one by one, in further volumes, 'Saccardo' gradually became the first and richest source of information for those attempting the diagnosis of fungus diseases of plants. The work was continued up to Saccardo's death in 1920, and thereafter as an institution.[1]

The beginning of Saccardo's great *Sylloge fungorum* during the eighties marked the phase of gathering-in, the harvesting of scattered knowledge about all the species of the fungi; in that decade also there was another development to be noted. In consequence of the better understanding of the nature of contagious diseases of man, great improvements began to be made in sanitation and public hygiene. The better part of preventive medicine

[1] Volumes XIX and XX are perhaps the most helpful for the novice as they list most of the published Figures of the fungi from antiquity to 1910, and 'all the best papers have Figs'.

was the removal of sources of infection. Open drains were closed, filth and garbage on which disease germs could grow were more diligently sought out and removed by municipal enterprise, rats and lice and blow-flies which carried germs about with them were more clearly recognized as unclean, Ibsen wrote *An Enemy of the People* (1882), hospitals were no longer pest-houses, 'Condy's fluid' and 'carbolic' became household words, and the literate public in every country began to exhibit a lively consciousness of the 'germs' about them. Quarantine measures were everywhere tightened up, tropical diseases began to be investigated, and new precautions were taken to prevent the spread of disease from one part of the world to another. Epidemiology was no less important than pathology; and this was true also of the diseases of the crops. To peer down the microscope was not enough — it was necessary to look out of the laboratory windows over the land. The mass-movements of parasitic fungi and insect pests about the world were now beginning to receive the most anxious attention.

It was but natural that after the Potato Blight and the Phylloxera, one of the questions the European workers were asking was: what other pests and parasites have you, on your crops in *America*, which have not yet reached us over here? The question found workers competent and ready to answer it on the other side; among them were Charles Valentine Riley, Entomologist for the State of Missouri and later of the U.S. Department of Agriculture; and William Gilson Farlow, who founded the department of cryptogamic botany at Harvard.

Riley watched and reported on the spread of the Colorado Beetle, *Doryphora decemlineata*, of the natural order Coleoptera. A yellowish-brown beetle, about half an inch in length, marked with five black lines on each of its wing-cases, and having delicate, rosy-coloured wings which it exposed only in flight. The adult beetles and their grubs devoured potato foliage, sometimes stripping the plants to the ground, and in the States they had become an even worse plague than the Potato Blight. The beetle had been discovered as far back as 1824, feeding harmlessly on wild plants of the Potato family on the eastern slopes of the Rockies, in Colorado. The American farmers, pushing farther and farther to the west, at last reached those slopes with their fields of cultivated potatoes. The beetles descended from the mountains as though by invitation, and finding an abundance of food that they had never known before and which they liked much better than their old diet, they increased in numbers prodigiously. Their surplus population began to travel east. By 1861 they had reached Iowa, by 1865 Illinois. They invaded the streets, the bars, and the sitting-rooms of the houses. In 1861

FIG. 42. The Colorado Beetle. The insects on the leaf are shown somewhat enlarged, those below are natural size. *a* and *b*, larvae or grubs; *c*, pupa; *d*, *e*, and *f*, adult beetles; *g*, eggs.
C. V. Riley, 1877

they crossed into Canada, and were to be seen making their way over the Detroit River and Lake Erie, on ships, chips of wood, and all floating objects. In 1873 they had reached Quebec, Vermont and New York. In the American newspapers the accounts of the Beetle were highly coloured and sensational, but it was only too true that in some districts potatoes were so scarce that they had become a luxury. In St. Louis market they fetched two dollars a bushel. Farmers thought twice about planting potatoes, merely to feed these 'coleopterous immigrants from Colorado'.

The Governments of France, Germany, Belgium, Russia, Holland and Spain all took alarm, and passed laws prohibiting or restricting the import of potatoes from North America, on which it was supposed that the eggs, larvae or adult beetles might be brought over. Riley was in communication with the European naturalists, and his work on the life-history of the beetle, helped on the one hand to allay unnecessary scare measures, and on the other to indicate how the embargoes might be made effective. The beetle was unlikely to survive the crossing in the form of grubs or eggs – it was the adult beetle for which Europe had to watch out. In England the risk of the beetle obtaining a footing was not at first regarded as very serious. In the States the beetle had confined its operations to a belt of territory between parallels of Latitude 35° and 44°. The northern limit, though passing near Toronto, was comfortably clear of the British Isles, crossing France down by Bordeaux. And what was the use of prohibiting the import of some fifty tons of special seed-potatoes a year from America, when the adult beetles were swarming in the shipping quarters of New York, and could as well make the crossing on any other kind of merchandise? Their food was the foliage of the potatoes, not the tubers. To be on the safe side, however, the Royal Agricultural Society issued coloured pictures of the beetle to the English farmers in 1875, requesting them to report any they might find. By 1877, following the news that a few of the beetles had already reached Germany, the English Government was sharing the general alarm and an Act was hurriedly passed in that year, prohibiting the sale of the live beetles in the British Isles (for some of them were actually being sent to collectors), providing for the examination of agricultural produce at ports of entry; giving powers to restrict or prohibit imports, and so on. Such measures taken in face of the particular danger of admitting the Colorado beetle into the potato fields of Europe, were later greatly extended and they marked the beginning of one of the most important checks to the advance, not only of the insect pests but of the parasitic fungi – *legislative* control of the movements of produce capable of carrying them across the natural barriers of the seas.

What happened to the potatoes in the United States, after they had been overrun by the beetles? At first the beetles had it all their own way; then their enemies began to multiply also. The rose-breasted grosbeaks ate them, and so did the toads. Domestic fowls acquired a taste for them, and when turned loose in the fields, devoured them in great numbers. Had the potatoes, the beetles, the insectivorous birds and the toads been left to fight it out among themselves, a natural balance would have been established – but the yield of potatoes under such conditions would have been very inadequate to satisfy the needs of the human population. Where some animals had fangs and others claws Man had only his wits. And Man's method of intervening in that particular conflict was to make himself a box on the end of a long pole, fill it full of copper aceto-arsenite or Paris Green, and then walk up and down between the rows of potatoes, scattering this highly poisonous green powder over them. A few grains of Paris Green on a potato leaf were sufficient to provide several beetles with a fatal meal. The treatment was laborious and expensive, and it was not altogether without danger to those who had to do the work, but it reduced the number of beetles very considerably, and enabled the cultivation of potatoes to be continued. Some thought that this copper aceto-arsenite, applied to destroy the beetles was also to some extent protecting the potatoes from the Blight. Was it the arsenic in the compound, or was it the copper? The Paris Green was acid, and sometimes 'scorched' the potato foliage rather badly; this drawback was overcome by mixing it with lime. In a few years the Americans would have discovered the 'copper' remedy for the Potato Blight, but the credit for that was to belong once again to France. The invention and use of '*Bouillie bordelaise*' was her response to the invasion of her already-stricken vineyards by the American, or so-called (Downy) Mildew of the Vine, the Peronospora.

In 1872, William Gilson Farlow, in preparation for teaching cryptogamic botany at the new agricultural college, the Bussey Institution, attached to Harvard, sailed to Europe to prime himself in the subject. He visited many of the foremost workers on the Continent and worked with de Bary at Strasburg. He obtained a very good idea of the latest developments in the pure science and of its applications in plant pathology, and his students had the great advantage of hearing what was known in 1874 without too much of the English controversial backwash. His own scientific papers, examining some of the fungus diseases of America in the light of the new knowledge were much-needed contributions to the world literature.

It was in March 1876 that he wrote on the American Grape Vine Mildew, which was then believed to be confined solely to the United States. Surely enough, it had first been described by the Rev. M. J. Berkeley – it was *Peronospora viticola* Berk. & Curt. It attacked all the species of vine in the States, east of the Rockies, and usually made its appearance at the beginning of August, on the undersides of the leaves. Its spawn grew *within* the leaf-tissues, and except that its resting-spores were readily to be found, it bore a very close resemblance to the Potato Blight fungus. Farlow used it to demonstrate the production of zoospores for the benefit of his students. The summer spores, borne in clusters near the ends of the aerial filaments (Fig. 28, p. 168, left), divided their plasm, as did those of the Blight fungus, into a number of free-swimming zoospores when immersed in water. They did this with unfailing regularity, always within two hours, which was convenient when getting things ready for a class. Farlow often sat with his watch beside him, timing the emergence of the little zoospores: they issued one by one, started off in the water by movement of their two propulsive hairs, kept going for fifteen or twenty minutes, and then slowed down, putting out their small germ-tubes in the hope of penetrating a vine leaf. De Bary's classical experiments, which had been a nine days' wonder during the sixties, were being repeated year after year now by Farlow's students, as a regular part of their course. Science was moving west.

Although very prevalent, the Grape Vine Mildew in America did little harm to the crop, and indeed its effects were sometimes regarded as beneficial. Farlow said: 'Our native vines have a luxurious growth of leaves, and the danger is that in our short summers the grapes will not be sufficiently exposed to the sun to ripen. The Peronospora appears at the happiest moment to shrivel up the leaves so that the direct rays of the sun may reach the grapes.' But he added that if the fungus were introduced into Europe the case might be very different. In the moister climate, and attacking the vines earlier, the Peronospora might well prove as disastrous as the Phylloxera.

The fungus was first observed in France by Millardet and Planchon in 1878. No one could say exactly when, where or how it had been introduced; it was possible that it had passed unobserved for several years; but with the importation of American stocks to counter the ravages of the Phylloxera, its appearance sooner or later had been almost inevitable. It spread rapidly after 1878, and it became even more destructive than Farlow had feared. By 1882 it was in every vine-growing district of France, with the exception of the Midi, and progressing fast over the vines of Italy and Germany.

The ominous brown patches appeared on the upper surfaces of the leaves, early in the growing season in Europe; on the undersides of the leaves were the corresponding frosty patches of the Mildew. The exceptionally wet seasons of the late seventies favoured the spread of the Peronospora, just as those in the late forties had favoured the Oidium and the Potato Blight. The leaves of the vines shrivelled and fell, the young grapes deprived of nourishment ripened poorly or not at all. The grapes themselves were attacked: when green and very small they were often covered with the grey Mildew, and when the Mildew developed later, when the grapes were larger, a proportion of them would hang withered, deflated and brown in the bunches: the Brown Rot. The miserable crop that might at last be gathered at *la vendange* would be tainted with the Mildew, and the wine made from it had an unpleasant taste.

With the coming of the Peronospora any people less dogged than the French might well have given up the cultivation of the vine in despair. There was all the sulphuring against the Oidium, more and more vines were succumbing each year to the Phylloxera at the roots. It was not known yet whether all the expensive pumping of carbon disulphide into the soil, the floodings of the vineyards, and the replacements with American root-stocks would be successful against the Phylloxera in the end. And now, superimposed disaster upon disaster, came this Mildew and Rot to ravage what was left of the vines, as the Potato Blight had ravaged the potatoes in Ireland in 1845. If the system of land-tenure in France had been anything like that in Ireland the vineyards of France would have passed away. But in France most of the land was owned by those who worked and lived upon it; and men would fight for what was their own. Neither the plant-lice nor the fungi were going to dispossess the French people of their viticulture and their wine.

On June 1st, 1882, Pierre Marie Alexis Millardet, Professor of Botany at Bordeaux, and yet another of those who had studied under Anton de Bary, presented to the Society of Physical and Natural Sciences at Bordeaux four young vine seedlings in a flower pot. The seedlings were only eight to fifteen days old, but the Mildew was already established on the lower sides of their pairs of seed-leaves. The seeds had been planted under a layer of dead vine leaves containing the resting spores of the Peronospora, which had infected the first leaves as they pushed through to the surface. Here was one of the ways in which the Mildew could start anew each year; grape pips cast on the ground by man or birds among mildewed leaves, could give rise to mildewed seedlings from which the summer spores would drift on to the vines in bearing. But this was only one of the ways in which the Mildew spread; there was little mystery about the life-cycle of the causal fungus. Millardet had found its winter-spores by December 1880; for the rest it was but the Potato Blight all over again. History had begun to repeat itself, but now this other 'Blight' fungus, advancing over the vines, found men prepared by a generation of grim experience to investigate it at once, wise to the ways in which such fungi performed their work of destruction. It was the time of the Seventh Plague; Man's wits were sharpened, and his heart hardened unto effective resistance. There was no Exodus. The French vinegrowers armed themselves with a new and deadly weapon against the fungi and went to war.

CHAPTER XVII

BORDEAUX MIXTURE

TOWARDS the end of October, in the year 1882, Professor Millardet was strolling through one of the vineyards of Saint-Julien in Médoc. There had been much Mildew in the locality that year, and he was surprised to notice that the vines beside the path were still in leaf, while elsewhere they were bare. He paused to examine these leaves which had escaped the common fate, and he found traces on them of a bluish-white deposit, as though they had received some chemical treatment. This was interesting, and he made inquiries about it of Mr. Ernest David, who was the manager of the vineyards at the Château Beaucaillon. He learned that it was a custom of the vinegrowers of Médoc to bespatter the vines beside the paths with a conspicuous and poisonous-looking substance, to discourage the passers-by from pilfering the grapes. For this they used either verdigris or a mixture of copper sulphate and lime. Mr. David had never given the matter a thought, but now that the Professor mentioned it, those vines beside the paths, for all that they were so disfigured, did appear greener and more healthy than the rest. Certainly, he would make a few experiments next year. If they only could find something that would stop the Mildew . . . He would try anything the Professor cared to suggest.

Millardet was excited. In studying the life-history of the Peronospora he had come to the same realization as Harry Marshall Ward, working on the Coffee-leaf Disease in Ceylon. He perceived the stage in the life of the leaf-inhabiting fungus during which it was vulnerable to chemical attack. The delicate summer-spores of the Vine Mildew readily lost their germinative power; their zoospores and their germ tubes, before they had succeeded in penetrating the vine leaves, were naked and exposed. Millardet was looking for some substance which could be applied as a protective coating on the leaves, so that the fungus spores drifting on to them would be killed before they could accomplish their work of infection. Now it seemed that chance had put the very stuff into his hands. The verdigris, the bluestone – they were salts of copper. He would try these and other copper salts as *preventives* of the Mildew. During the winter he made his plans; he would also try salts of calcium and of iron; he would try the bluestone by itself and also mixed with lime.

But when the summer of 1883 at last came round there was little Mildew about; it followed after rain and that summer was dry. The protective effect of the treatments could not be fully revealed, but for all that there was so little Mildew, it was apparent that they did *some* good. Especially the bluestone and lime. The bluestone, or copper sulphate, when it was used alone burnt the young shoots of the vines. It was the same with Mr. David's trials in a vineyard at Dauzec, and with his own in his garden.

To continue, he had to wait for yet another year, hoping that in 1884 the Mildew in the locality would be severe. It was not. But there was enough, and all the preparations on which he had been working were tried on the vines: carbonate, acetate, sulphate, phosphate and sulphide of copper, with and without lime, lime alone, and the green vitriol or sulphate of iron. He was now convinced that the mixture of bluestone and lime was the best; trials on a more extensive scale and in a really bad season were necessary, but already rumours of his success were beginning to circulate in the district and to make their way over to his scientific rivals in Burgundy. There was no little fame at stake: if he had indeed found a prophylactic against the Mildew he would save the vines of France. And . . . oh, yes, he could see it now . . . he would also have found a remedy for the Potato Blight. The Blight fungus was so very similar to that of the new Mildew of the Vine. And many other fungus diseases also – of tomatoes, of fruit trees, even of roses – would also be prevented by the protective treatment of the foliage with his copper mixture. The discovery that had eluded every worker for forty years might now be his. In May 1885, Millardet communicated his precious formula to the Society of Agriculture for la Gironde.

8 kilos of copper sulphate crystals were to be dissolved in 100 litres of water. In a separate vessel 15 kilos of good fat quicklime were to be slaked and stirred up with 30 litres of water. The 'milk' of lime was then to be poured into the solution of copper sulphate, while stirring, to produce a bluish paste. This was the first Bordeaux mixture, or *Bouillie bordelaise*.

In 1885, following the publication of the remedy, many of the principal vine-growers in Médoc submitted it to test. Mr. Johnson, for whom the enterprising Mr. David was manager, treated a hundred and fifty thousand vines at Dauzec and Beaucaillon alone. That season was wet and the Mildew very severe. The treatment came through its first large-scale trials with flying colours. On October 3rd, the leaves of the treated vines at Dauzec were healthy and of a beautiful green, the grapes black and perfectly ripened. The rows of untreated vines left between them for comparison were in a wretched state; the majority of their leaves had fallen, the few remaining were dry and shrivelled, and the grapes were still red, unfit for anything but sour wine. The contrast could not have been more striking, and the same spectacular results were obtained not only in the other vineyards of Médoc, but as far away as Italy, where M. le Marquis G. Pinelli of the Château Tagliolo, had treated eighty hectares.

This dramatic success was to be compared in significance only with Pasteur's triumph over the Anthrax of sheep, at the farm of Pouilly le Fort, four years before. There were some who said that it was not Millardet who discovered the *Bouillie bordelaise*, but that God, working in his mysterious way, had revealed it by the miracle of an accident to his children of Bordeaux – as a reward for their sweet and charitable disposition, perhaps, in only *pretending* to poison the grapes that might tempt the passing stranger; others claimed that they, individually, had anticipated Millardet by a month or a year. In Burgundy, copper sulphate had been used as a wood-preservative for the poles on which the vines were trained; there was a belief that this had some effect in warding off the Mildew from the vines themselves, Ricaud and Paulin had published a note about it in the *Journal de Beaune* in September 1884; it was in Burgundy that copper sulphate had first been used against the Mildew of the Vine! Monsieur Estéve of Montpellier, who was selling a proprietary mixture containing copper sulphate among other of its ingredients, and called 'Sulfatine', claimed that this had been found effective as early as 1882, and that therefore it was to him that the credit was due. Paul Olivier had certainly tried copper sulphate on the foliage of fruit trees in 1881. And in December 1884, six months before Millardet, M. le Baron Chatry de la Fosse had also drawn the attention of the Agricultural Society of the Gironde to the good effects of a mixture of copper sulphate and lime. '*On a l'habitude en Médoc, de salir, avec ce mélange, les pampres et les raisons, le long des chemins, pour éloigner les grappileurs.*' How many times that story was repeated! It was the legend of the *Bouillie bordelaise*. A tale that in after years would be told to children in school. Millardet was jealous for the credit of his discovery, and in writing the history of it, in the *Journal d'Agriculture pratique*, in that excited autumn of 1885, he eulogized his own achievements in the style of a French obituary notice. If it had not been for the many sound and careful papers that already stood to the credit of his name, Millardet's self-appraisement would have been unseemly; but, as it was, nobody could take it for anything but the outburst of a very sober man, momentarily affected by the excitement of a great success, and yearning to be carried on the shoulders of his countrymen and acclaimed with a noise of trumpets and drums:

'I claim the honour', he said, 'of having been the first to conceive the idea of the treatment with copper; the first to experiment with it, and the first also to recommend its use in practice. And may I be permitted to add – for these things are for us *savants* our titles and our most precious trophies – that in 1878, simultaneously with Monsieur Planchon, it was I who first observed the presence of the Mildew in France, and that since then I have been constantly on the alert. To this my works bear witness.'

The trouble was that Millardet had not been quite quick enough in communicating his formula to the Agricultural Society. It had leaked out before it was published over his name, and to prove that he really was the first to think of using copper salts on the vines he had to refer to a remark he made in the *Zeitschrift für Wein- Obst- und Gartenbau*, of Alsace and Lorraine, in March 1883. It was not altogether tactful to do this, for in France at that time, if one wanted to insult a dog one called it *allemand*.

But in all the squabbling over priority, which really did not matter two sous, nobody looked very closely for the real genesis of the idea. Millardet expanded at length on the wonderful conceptional processes by which he had come to realize the fungicidal effects of copper salts, after having taken the first hint from those bespattered vines along the paths. He obtained confirmatory evidence, he said, from his observation that the fungus spores would not germinate in the water from a well in his garden which was lifted by an old copper pump. In *this* his countryman, Bénédict Prévost, had in fact anticipated him by over three-quarters of a century. And then those salts of copper, lime and iron – had not Millardet heard of their use as fungicides before? They were the substances used in *le chaulage*, in the steeping of seed wheat as a preventive of *la Carie*, or the Bunt. Their well-known function, also defined by Prévost in the case of the salts of copper, was to prevent the germination of the spores of the Bunt fungus on the seed grain. All that Millardet really did, in principle, was to apply a treatment that had long been in common use to prevent fungus infection of seed wheat for exactly the same purpose on green foliage. It had taken mankind just three-quarters of a century to discover that what would kill fungus spores on seed wheat, without causing too much injury to the seed itself, would also kill fungus spores on green foliage without causing too much harm to the leaves. And even then the discovery was made only by accident. So much for the sapience of Man.

There was, however, a considerable difference between the practical operation of dipping seed into copper sulphate solution and then mixing it with lime, and that of mixing the copper sulphate with lime first and then applying the mixture to foliage. The seed for many acres of wheat could be treated in an hour or so, and all that was required for it, besides the materials, was a few tubs and baskets and a little space on a stone floor. The Bordeaux mixture, however, had to be deposited over the growing vines, row after row, and mile after mile, out in the open vineyards.

In 1886 and 1887, while the chemists of Burgundy and Bordeaux were rivalling each other in attempts to improve upon Millardet's formula, the agricultural implement makers, village blacksmiths and brassworkers were busy inventing contrivances for projecting the mixtures on to the vines. The original method described and at first advocated by Millardet was for the labourer to make his way along the rows with a can of the mixture in one hand and a small switch of heather in the other, flicking the stuff to right and left over the foliage, avoiding the grapes as much as possible. It was considered neither necessary nor desirable for the leaves to be *covered* with the mixture; a few drops of it on each were quite sufficient, for the idea was that the deposits of almost-but-not-quite-insoluble cupric mixture, which adhered fast to the leaves where the drops had dried, would contaminate any film of moisture on the leaf-surface with the very slight taint of copper necessary to prevent the development of the fungus spores. Even so, it took a very long time to treat all the foliage in a large vineyard by the can-and-brush method. To go round with a syringe and a pail was almost equally impracticable. What was required was some inexpensive, portable, one-man-power machine, that would blow or otherwise project the mixture on to the vines in the form of a fine spray. Competitions for such machines were held by Agricultural Societies in many parts of France.

One of the first contrivances, invented by M. Armand Cazenave of la Réole, had a revolving brush, operated through a train of gear-wheels and fed with mixture from a portable copper tank to which it was attached. On turning the handle, a stirrer went round in the tank, the brush went round in its trough, and a scraper pressed against the bristles caused them to project the mixture in fine style (Fig. 43). Millardet spoke of the *absolute* merit of this device, but was reticent about its *relative* merit, as compared with some of the other inventions. Then there was the '*Mélangeur-pulvérisateur automatique*' of M. Meyer. This comprised an air-tight copper tank – containing the mixture – which the operator carried on his back, and which was connected by two lengths of rubber tubing to a brass nozzle which he held by a hook on the end of a stick and directed at the vines – or the fruit trees – as the case might be. The mixture was projected from the nozzle by pneumatic pressure, generated by two small bellows attached to the operator's feet. The upper sides of the bellows were strapped to his shoes and the lower were made like sabots. The bellows were connected to the tank by more india-rubber tubing which ran up his trouser-legs, and as he walked along or marked time, the bellows worked, the tank was pumped up, and the mixture came out of the nozzle in a spray (Fig. 44). When demonstrating this outfit to prospective purchasers the operator smoked a pipe, and took it out of his mouth now and then to show that he had one hand free (Plate IV, *c*).

Most of the inventions, however, incorporated some form of pump or

FIG. 43. Cazenave's apparatus for applying Bordeaux Mixture. 1886

bellows which had to be worked continuously by hand, and the unfatigued expression of the gentleman with the bellows on his feet was not reflected on the countenance of the peasant using *Le Projecteur Audebert* (Plate IV, *d*). He had to hold out a heavy pair of domestic bellows in front of him, and puff away with them all the time, atomizing a thin trickle of the mixture which ran down into the nozzle through a pipe connected to a tank on his back.

The simplest and most practical types of knapsack sprayer were very soon sorted from the rest, improved, and put on the market. They all had a brass or copper tank to contain two or three gallons of the mixture, which was carried on the back, some form of hydraulic or pneumatic pump built into the tank and worked by a lever with the left hand, while the spray-lance was

PLATE IV. The French people defend their vines against the Mildew – some of the first knapsack spraying machines. (*a*) Noguès sprayer; (*b*) Noel sprayer; (*c*) Meyer pedomatic apparatus in action; (*d*) Audebert pneumatic sprayer. (From the *Journal d'agriculture pratique*, Paris 1886–7.)

held in the right. These simple sprayers – when fitted with a good nozzle – were convenient and efficient in use, and they could be purchased for 35 francs or thereabouts. One of the best of them, soon to be known in every part of the world, was the 'Eclair', made by the brassworker Vermorel of Villefranche. The secret of its success, apart from the Vermorel nozzle, was that it had a diaphragm pump, small, but working on the same principle as those used in chemical works for shifting just such slurries as Bordeaux mixture. There was no piston in contact with the liquid and very little to get out of order. With the efficacy of the copper *bouillies* apparent, and suitable machines available for their application, spraying against the Mildew became one of the recognized and indispensable operations of viticulture. In France it was called '*le Sulfatage*', and by about 1888 the French peasants with knapsack sprayers on their backs were engaged in this new kind of chemical warfare against the fungi, over five million acres of vines.

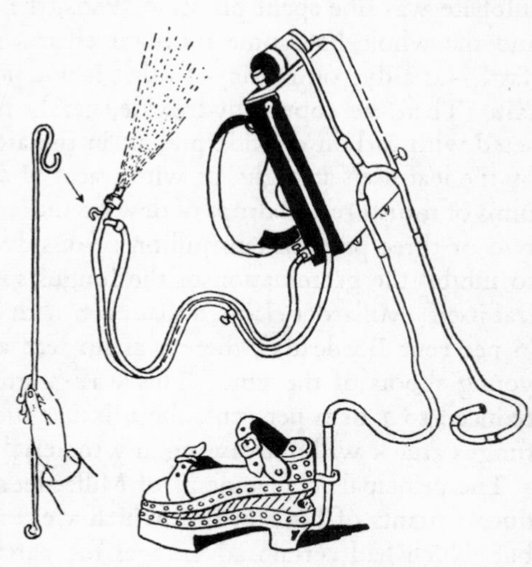

FIG. 44. The Pedomatic apparatus of M .Meyer. 1886

In working out and explaining the action of his Bordeaux mixture, Millardet was assisted by his colleague, M. Gayon, a very able chemist, and the mixture, for all that it was apparently so simple, was in fact a complex and strangely complete invention. Like Stephenson's 'Rocket' – which incorporated all the principal features of the modern steam locomotive – it was not destined to be improved upon in any *essential* respect for generations. At first it was thought by a number of workers that the application of copper sulphate to the leaves was what really mattered, and that the lime was, so to speak, thrown in. In Burgundy there was a tendency to sniff at the lime mixture of Bordeaux; the use of copper sulphate *per se* was a Burgundian idea – had they not used it on the props before ever Bordeaux mixture was heard of? They would spray their vines simply with a weak solution of copper sulphate. This certainly killed any fungus spores on the leaves at the time of application, but unfortunately, unless it was used at a very feeble dosage it also severely injured the leaves. And, as it was wholly soluble in water, it was washed off the leaves by the first rain and had no lasting effect.

Millardet and Gayon pointed out that in their *Bouillie bordelaise* there was no copper sulphate at all. The lime interacted with that substance, and in Gayon's view the mixture actually deposited on the leaves was composed of copper hydroxide, calcium sulphate and some unaltered lime. The calcium sulphate was like spent plaster of Paris, the lime 'set' like mortar in a wall, and the whole had some mordant effect on the leaf-cuticle which held it 'fast' – as a dye on fabric – so that it was *not* washed off at all easily by the rain. Then the copper hydroxide, nearly insoluble in water, slowly interacted with carbon dioxide present in the atmosphere or with that given off by the leaf itself at night, or with traces of atmospheric ammonia, to charge films of moisture and drops of dew on the leaf, over a long period, with those two or three parts in ten million of dissolved copper which were sufficient to inhibit the germination of the fungus spores, but powerless to harm the leaf itself. Millardet claimed that even with his very strong original mixture, '6 per cent Bordeaux', there was no fear of harm to the tenderest of the young shoots of the vine. This was sanguine, but when the strength was reduced to 1 or 2 per cent, the mixture did give lasting protection against fungus attack without causing any material injury.

The principal achievements of Millardet's rivals were in the main to produce variants of his mixture, which were neither safer nor more effective, but which had certain advantages for particular practical applications. M. Audoynaud produced '*Eau celeste*', a royal-blue fluid made by mixing copper sulphate solution with ammonia instead of with milk of lime. A pale 'celestial' blue precipitate was first formed and then as more ammonia was added this dissolved, producing the royal-blue *liquid*. This clear liquid passed more easily through the nozzle of the sprayer than did the Bordeaux mixture, in which the active material was merely suspended in water and fairly rapidly settled out. Ammonia, however, was more expensive than lime, and, as it remained to be discovered later, the *Eau celeste* tended to injure some kinds of foliage more than did the *Bouillie bordelaise*. Then in 1887, Professor Emile Masson of the School of Viticulture at Beaune, and Dr. G. Patrigeon, published their formulae for what was later to be known as 'Burgundy mixture', in which ordinary washing-soda was the alkali employed. Soda, thanks to Ludwig Mond's exploitation of the Solvay process, was getting cheaper, and sometimes it was easier to obtain in small quantities than *good* lime. The mixture when freshly prepared was more gelatinous and less gritty than that made with lime, and it was a little less liable to wear and block up the nozzle of the sprayer. It was supposed to be more adherent to the foliage than Bordeaux mixture, and it contained hydrated carbonate of copper which liberated dissolved copper rather faster, when deposited on the leaves, than did the hydroxide. It was a stronger mixture, useful on foliage that would stand it. The so-called 'Modified Eau celeste', which was cheaper than Audoynaud's solution, was made, in effect, by adding a little ammonia to Burgundy mixture to dissolve the precipitate in it and so obtain a clear fluid.

One of the most interesting variants of Bordeaux mixture was that proposed by Michel Perret in 1889. It was tried about that time and then generally abandoned as no improvement, but it was a forerunner of certain developments in copper fungicides which were regarded as new half a century later. Perret added *molasses* to the mixture. Firstly, to make the liquid part of it more viscous, so that the active material would not settle out so quickly in the sprayer; secondly, to make a mixture which could be kept for some time before use; thirdly, to improve the adhesion of the mixture to foliage because of the 'sticky' addition; and fourthly, to make the mixture more active by reason of the fact that some of the copper would be combined with sugars in the form of soluble sucrates. A curious thing happened to this mixture when it was allowed to stand for a few months.[1] From being of a dirty olive colour – a pale blue precipitate in a brown solution – it turned first yellow and then distinctly red. The reducing sugars in the molasses ultimately reduced the blue cupric compound to red cuprous oxide, a substance differing materially in its chemical nature from all the basic copper salts in the other *bouillies*.

One fairly successful way was found of using copper sulphate alone without the addition of alkali. This was to soak inert talc in strong copper sulphate solution, and then to dry and grind it to produce a powder which could be dusted over the vines. It was quicker to treat the vines with a fine dry dust than to spray them with a liquid mixture. The dust could be applied by means of the bellows which the vine-growers were already accustomed to use for putting on sulphur against the Oidium; an impalpable dust drifted into the recesses of the foliage better than a liquid spray, and if it was blown over the vines when the leaves were moist with dew, it gave a very good protection against the Mildew for a short while. When the Mildew was spreading rapidly, and the peasants had to work against time, the quick application of the copper-talc powder, or 'cupric-sulphosteatite' as it was called, had obvious advantages. But the application of talc which was

[1] Assuming that 'molasses' in 1889 was not essentially different from 'molasses' in 1939.

merely soaked in copper sulphate had most of the disadvantages of the treatment with copper sulphate alone; the active material was fairly rapidly washed out of the talc and off the leaves by the rain, and it injured the young leaves. It was the principle of applying the copper in the form of dust, as an alternative to spraying, that was of importance. The copper-talc was about the first of these dusts; in the twentieth century it was replaced by others which gave deposits on the foliage of much the same nature as those which resulted from spraying with Bordeaux mixture.

There was of course a loud outcry in 1885 and 1886 that the copper splashed on to the grapes, through this new practice of spraying the vines against Mildew, would poison the wine. It was an interference with the dispensations of Nature, and so on. But in fact, as M. Gayon showed, the wine made from grapes which had been sprayed contained only about one-third of a milligramme of copper per litre. The water raised by the copper pump in Millardet's garden contained fifteen times as much copper, and, though he and his family had been drinking it for years, it had never done any of them the least harm. Minute quantities of copper compounds, as of many other substances poisonous when taken by the teaspoonful, were harmless and indeed necessary for the proper alimentation of both plants and animals. Many foods, notably meat and chocolate, contained relatively large amounts of copper.

It appeared that copper had a unique toxity to fungus spores. Millardet found that where only two or three parts of copper sulphate in ten million parts of water were needed to prevent the complete development of the spores of the Peronospora, one hundred parts of sulphate of iron or one thousand parts of lime would have to be employed to achieve the same result. Copper was no rare metal, its common salts cost only a few pence a pound, but because of its effect on the spores of fungi causing diseases of the crops it was indeed a precious element. The discovery of its prophylactic properties, and of ways of turning them to account, was no less significant in the war against disease than the later discovery of radium. Which was to be of the greater value – radium with its limited usefulness in the treatment of cancer; or copper which was to save annually throughout the world some millions of tons of the foodstuffs necessary to sustain human life? A question for the philosophers! But in the tally of the magnificent contributions towards the conquest of disease, made by the children of France, there would surely be an honoured place for those who discovered the fungicidal properties of that precious metal which could protect the wheat from the Stinking Smut, the vines from the Mildew, and the potatoes from the Blight. In whatever way the credit of discovery might be apportioned between Bénédict Prévost, Millardet, and Millardet's contemporary workers on the vines, it belonged indisputably and entirely to France.

But to see who first perceived the full significance of the discovery, and set about with the greatest energy to adapt and employ copper-containing sprays for the defence of every kind of crop, it would be necessary to turn to America. In the United States the losses of agricultural produce, caused by plant diseases, were becoming both increasingly serious and more widely recognized, and on July 1st, 1886, a section of Vegetable Pathology was established at Washington as a part of the Division of Botany in the United States Department of Agriculture. The Rev. M. J. Berkeley, writer on 'Vegetable Pathology' thirty years before, just lived to see that consummation of his hopes. He died in retirement in 1889. The Section was in charge of F. Lamson-Scribner, with, as his principal assistant, Beverley Thomas Galloway. Both these men were live wires. They were in communication by every mail with the principal workers on the European mainland, and they wasted no time at all in bringing the new copper treatments under trial in France, to the notice of the American farmers. Already, in 1886, they had circulars out, giving the formulae of some eight or nine of the rival mixtures, and requesting the co-operation of the farmers in testing them, not only on vines, but on potatoes, tomatoes and fruit trees. Scribner and Galloway did not take Millardet's or anybody else's word as to which of the mixtures were the best; they imported the lot – together with a sufficient number of Vermorel spraying machines for their trial application – and set about finding out for themselves. The rivalry between Burgundy and Bordeaux was not their affair. They distributed the sprayers among the best of the farmers who volunteered to help, and in a very short time they had devised a first-class sprayer for themselves, with a cyclone jet invented by C. V. Riley, and called the 'Eureka'. They collected, correlated, checked and counter-checked the results of the various experiments; they figured out how much the spraying cost in cents per application per vine-plant or per tree; and they were not long in perceiving that the strength of the mixtures could sometimes be greatly reduced without loss of efficiency, thus saving material and money. They studied the 'scorching' of foliage caused by some of the sprays, and decided which of them could safely be recommended for general use on this, that, or the other crop, and which could not. They cut out plain copper sulphate solution straight away. They ascertained the times in the growing season at which the spraying could be done to the best advantage, according to the life-cycle of the particular fungus concerned, and drew up programmes accordingly. '*Eau celeste*' they translated as 'Blue Water', and '*Bouillie bordelaise*' as the 'Copper Mixture of Gironde'.

The first outstanding success with the copper sprays in America was once again on the vines. Not against the Mildew as in France, but against the Black Rot, which was caused by another fungus altogether. In the States the Black Rot was the devil. It seemed to go directly for the *grapes*, attacking them during June when they were still hard and green. In the autumn the bunches would consist of a few sound and ripe grapes among which hung many that were blackened, shrunken, and hard as stone. Spraying would not have prevented this particular Rot, if investigation of the causal fungus had not shown when it had to be done. It would have been of little use to spray the grapes. In reality the fungus first attacked the young leaves; when these were examined with care there were to be found on them small brown or grey patches curiously dotted with tiny black spots. The same black dotting was also found on the grapes – it was the characteristic symptom of the disease. There was no downy growth of mildew. The Black Rot fungus produced its spores in little conceptacles, buried in the tissue of the leaves, with their mouths open at the surface. These conceptacles or pycnidia were the black dots visible to the naked eye. The spores issued from them, drifted in the air, and given the necessary moisture, started the Rot on the grapes. The proof of this was that the grapes could be saved by enclosing the clusters in paper bags in the early summer; the grapes ripened perfectly inside the bags, and remained wholly free from the Rot. The infection of the grapes from the leaves was a 'secondary infection' brought about by the summer spores of the fungus. The copper treatment had to be applied to prevent the *primary* infection of the young leaves. Hence the great importance of knowing the whole life-history of the fungus. The blackened grapes and the diseased leaves fell to the ground in the autumn, and in them there were small hard lumps of living fungus tissue, which survived the winter and developed in the spring into the perfect fruits of the fungus, perithecia, containing numbers of little sacs each with a charge of eight spores. These sac- or asco-spores, liberated into the air in the spring, caused the primary infection of the young vine leaves; and the secret of successful spraying was to repeat the applications at short intervals to keep pace with the growth of the vines, until the time when the grapes changed colour, after which they were no longer subject to infection.

The Black Rot was the second distinct type of fungus disease to yield to the copper treatment, and this success in America was second in technical and economic importance only to the victory over the Mildew in France.

The Black Rot of the Vines was yet another of the plant diseases of the New World whose introduction had long been dreaded in France, and surely enough it came. It was first observed on some vines at Montpellier by Professor Viala in 1885. It might have caused yet another crisis, another panic, but this time a remedy was known beforehand and promptly applied. Spraying against the Mildew could be done in such a way that it would prevent the Black Rot also. In 1887 Professor Viala went to America, on behalf of the French Government, to compare notes with Lamson-Scribner. For nearly six months these two men worked and travelled about together; through such embassies and the exchange of scientific papers, France and America had become the closest of allies in the war on plant disease. The breach between the French and German workers still gaped wide, but French-American scientific relations were animated by mutual respect and friendship. And theirs was a powerful combination; they were attacking common enemies simultaneously now, on both sides of the Atlantic ocean.

Great Britain was no partner in this working alliance; the exchanges between the United States and the Continent passed England by. That the *Bouillie bordelaise* was likely to prove as effective on the potatoes as on the vines was foreseen by Millardet and announced by him in the *Journal d'Agriculture pratique* in 1885. It might be supposed that the agricultural authorities in Great Britain would at once have seized upon so promising a remedy for the Potato Blight. But it was not so. Six years passed before any of the copper mixtures were even submitted to preliminary trial on the potatoes in Ireland, and indeed it was not until 1890 that the Journal of the Royal Agricultural Society of England contained any mention of the new use that had been found for copper in France and America. The *Journal d'Agriculture pratique*, one of the oldest and best-known of the agricultural journals of Europe, contained the fullest particulars of all the mixtures and the machines, and the publications of the U.S. Department of Agriculture were neither inaccessible nor obscure. Indeed, *The Gardeners' Chronicle* did not fail to publish several notices of reports by Prillieux on potato-spraying experiments in France between 1885 and 1889, but so far as the English Government was concerned it might all have been happening on the moon. The credit of finding the best way of employing Bordeaux mixture for the prevention of Potato Blight, even of recommending the exact strength of the mixture ultimately to be adopted, went once again to France. The experimental work was practically finished in France, and Belgium, before the British farmers were informed that it had begun.

From 1885 onwards, a number of the French growers tried spraying their potatoes with the copper mixtures, at various strengths, some at the right time and some when it was too late to do much good. There were few who bothered to weigh their potatoes and to obtain comparative figures from sprayed and unsprayed plots. The composition of the mixtures used was erratic, and when the copper sulphate was only partially neutralized, with insufficient lime, the plants were injured and sometimes the crop was reduced. But the drift of the early results was shown by a trial made by Prillieux – Inspector-General of Agricultural Education in France and Professor at the Institut Agronomique – in 1888. He treated the foliage of nine potato plants with very strong Bordeaux mixture (6 per cent) during the month of August. He obtained from these plants 115 sound and healthy potatoes. From 10 neighbouring plants left untreated he obtained 53 potatoes only, of which 17 were diseased.

The first systematic trials were made by Aimé Girard in 1888 and 1889. Girard had been working for many years to increase the French potato crop. He had worked out a special system of cultivation which involved deep-ploughing and a generous manurial treatment. Many growers, both on a large and a small scale, co-operated with him, and while the average yield of potatoes per acre, over the whole of France, worked out at only a little over three tons, many of those who adopted his system obtained twelve tons per acre or more. Some rational means of preventing losses from the Blight was all that his system lacked, and he was not slow to incorporate spraying with Bordeaux mixture. Some thirty-three farmers collaborated with him in his first trials, and he worked in conjunction with the Institut Agronomique. In 1888, among other of his field experiments, were trials on four different varieties of potato on a farm at Clichy-sous-Bois. Plots of equal area (125 square metres) were marked out, and for each variety there was one plot sprayed and one left unsprayed for comparison. In the autumn the potatoes from each plot were weighed and the blighted separated from the good. The effect of the spraying differed considerably on the different varieties, on none of them did it prevent the Blight attack altogether, but on each of them it resulted in a substantial increase in the yield of sound potatoes. The gains due to spraying on the four varieties were respectively 14.3, 22.9, 13.5 and 17.2 per cent. And this was in a season when the Blight was not particularly severe. The actual mixture employed by Girard in 1889 was made up, in English units, of 20 pounds of copper sulphate and 10 pounds of quicklime per 100 gallons of water. The Bordeaux mixture officially recommended as the best for spraying potatoes in Ireland in 1939 was to be made up of 20 pounds of copper sulphate and 10 pounds of quicklime per 100 gallons of water.

Girard said that the spraying should be done preventively, before the Blight appeared, and recommended two applications of his mixture at the rate of 130 gallons per acre. The 1939 recommendation was to spray with the same mixture, preventively, before the Blight appeared, and to give at least two applications at 120 gallons per acre. So much for the accepted improvements on the original treatment which were to result from fifty years of research; and so much also for the extent to which the art of potato spraying had developed in France before any news of it had reached the British Isles.

CHAPTER XVIII

DANISH 'HOT WATER'

JENS LUDWIG JENSEN, a Danish schoolmaster, was a man of initiative and imagination. He ran an agricultural magazine from 1868 to 1880, and in 1872 started a company for selling scientifically tested seeds. He never held any official Government position, but in 1881 organized his own agricultural researches at a private institute which he called the 'Bureau Ceres', in Copenhagen. He was not a brilliant controversialist; it was sometimes said that his writings were long-winded and prosy; he never raised any great noise about his discoveries, but his imagination of what constituted plant husbandry was deep and wide and fair as the unfenced fields of Denmark. He could see as one whole phenomenon the rise and growth of crop from seed to harvest, and in his view the health of a crop was never to be guarded by performing any *one* particular operation but only by tending the plants with long-sighted skill over their whole period of growth. Every plant pathologist, indeed every practical farmer, would hasten to protest that in this there was nothing new: that it was only common sense. But how many acted upon it? And the sense of living things, of plants or of men, extended in time from conception to maturity, was by no means common; it was, on the contrary, very rare. The historic contributions made by Denmark, through Jensen and Rostrup, to the art and science of raising healthy crops, were quite unique and almost different in kind from those of any other nation.

Just before the discovery of Bordeaux mixture in France, Jensen wrote a pamphlet in English on '*How to Overcome the Potato Disease*'. He had been studying the various ways in which the Blight fungus affected the potatoes through the course of the year, and he advocated three measures as parts of one whole protective system of cultivation. There was then no way of preventing the Blight from spreading over the potato *foliage* once it had started in a field; with the partial or total destruction of the foliage the further growth of the tubers underground was retarded or stopped, but the tubers were only *blighted* where the fungus spores from the foliage were washed down to them through the soil. This could be prevented by 'protective earthing-up'. This measure had been proposed before, but its efficacy depended on the depth of soil piled over the potatoes to filter out the spores carried down by the rain. Jensen made some experiments: he poured a measured quantity of water containing 100,000 spores through a tube containing a one-inch bed of soil; 6289 spores passed through. With two inches of soil, only 598 were washed through, and with five inches not a single spore passed. To obtain such a protective cover over the potatoes in practice, he spaced the rows thirty inches apart, and, immediately the Blight appeared, he drove a special moulding-plough between them, piling up the ridges four inches higher than was usual. When it could be managed he employed women in the fields to push over the potato haulms to an angle of 45° facing the sun and to shape the ridges in such a way that the spores from the leaves would be washed into the furrows and not on to the tubers. Next, for 'protective lifting'. If the potatoes were dug before the blighted haulms were dead, and while the spores of the fungus scattered over the surface of the soil were still alive, then it was evident that the potatoes would become infected. The spores would be distributed all over them. This was one of the reasons why potatoes, quite sound when lifted, became blighted in storage. Lifting should therefore be delayed until two or three weeks after the haulms had been cut down and removed, or after they had withered naturally at the end of the season when the short-lived summer spores of the fungus would be dead. Finally, there was 'protective storing'. The seed-potatoes should be kept apart from each other, in layers of dry sand.

So far, the only thing that was new about these measures was the deliberate and rational use that Jensen made of them. But he next turned his attention to reducing the number of points from which the Blight could start in the fields – to removing the sources of primary infection. It was only in England that much credence was given to Worthington G. Smith's 'discovery' of the resting spores of the Blight fungus; on the Continent, Anton de Bary's demonstration that the fungus could survive the winter by way of its living spawn in blighted seed-potatoes was regarded as much more significant. *Some* of the blighted tubers sent up blighted shoots which started the new season's spread of the fungus over the foliage. Was there any way in which the spawn of the fungus, deep-buried in the tissues of seed-potatoes, could be killed without injury to the potatoes themselves?

Jensen was now attempting something of far greater intrinsic difficulty than merely killing spores on the surface of leaves, as they were doing with their copper sprays down in Bordeaux. Here no *superficial* treatment could be of the least avail. What was there, under Heaven, that could be put into a potato to kill a tangle of fungal threads interwoven among the cells, without causing harm to the potato itself?

The answer to this conundrum was 'Heat'. All living things could be killed by heat, and thermal sterilization could be used for nearly everything from surgical instruments to jam. The lethal temperature varied according to the organism that was to be killed. Jensen discovered that the temperature which would kill the fungus within the seed-potato was some degrees lower than that which killed the potato itself. Thus, in differential thermal sterilization, he found a way of ensuring that his seed-potatoes were free of the Blight.

By 1883, he had devised a practical apparatus for use on the farm and communicated particulars of his method to the *Société Nationale d'Agriculture* of France. The *Société* awarded him a Gold Medal and published a full account of his work in their *Mémoires* for 1887. He found that the fungus spawn within the potatoes was killed when they were immersed in water at 40° C. (104° Fahrenheit) for four hours. But after this steeping in warm water the potatoes would not keep, their skins were soaked and softened, and they were very liable to rot. It was necessary to use *dry* heat, and this was easily contrived by suspending covered, water-tight, cylindrical tins filled with the potatoes in a tank containing water at 42° to 56° C., and leaving them there until a thermometer with its bulb down among the tubers registered 40° C. for four consecutive hours. With such simple apparatus, occupying very little room, Jensen was able to treat two lots of four hundredweights of seed-potatoes per day; and the work could go on steadily all through the winter until within about six weeks of planting time, when all the potatoes should be laid out to sprout. As a result of the treatment, and of allowing the potatoes to sprout before planting – another of Jensen's recommendations – he obtained an average increase of yield over fifteen trials in different parts of Denmark of about one ton per acre. The benefit was most pronounced when the Blight came early.

One interesting point about this heat-disinfection of potato tubers was that it might occur in nature. Perhaps, thought Jensen, it was responsible for the centuries of delay before the Blight fungus followed the potatoes from South America to Europe. When the ships were weeks passing through the tropics any potatoes on board would be very thoroughly heat-treated; but when, as in the early forties, the tropics were crossed in nine days, the spawn within the potatoes had a better chance of reaching Europe alive.[1]

Jensen's heat-treatment worked very well; but what was the good of a farmer going to all the trouble of 'de-blighting' his seed-potatoes when his

[1] This theory was challenged later by Reddick (*Phytopathology*, XVIII, 496, 1928), who pointed out that the temperature in the holds of the small ships of the forties would approximate to that of the surface waters through which they were passing. Information obtained from the U.S. Weather Bureau and other sources showed that this temperature could rarely have exceeded 30° C. during any part of the voyage, or at any time of the year.

neighbour planted untreated seed and so started the Blight in the next field? Full advantage of the method could be taken only by co-operative action over a large area. Rostrup, of the Royal Danish School of Agriculture, proposed that the heat-treatment of seed-potatoes should be made obligatory by law, throughout Denmark, in a bold attempt to eradicate the Blight fungus altogether, solely by attacking it in its over-wintering stage. It was a little difficult to see how outbreaks of Blight at the end of July were related to the Blight on a very few shoots from diseased tubers, which came up in May. To bring the possible connection home to the imagination, he advanced an interesting 'let's suppose' theory.

Let's suppose, he said, that the whole of Denmark's two thousand million seed-potatoes are planted on May 1st. Unnoticed among these there are, at a guess, one million which contain living spawn of the Blight fungus. By May 25th the green shoots of the potatoes are above ground everywhere, and, let's continue to suppose, only one in twenty-five of the Blighted tubers have given rise to blighted shoots. That gives forty thousand plants with blighted shoots, among the two thousand million potato plants in the Kingdom of Denmark. Not very many. From the diseased shoots the first generation of Blight spores begin to blow about. They reach other potato plants, and, assuming that there is sufficient moisture and the average temperature is about 59° F., they germinate and give rise to inconspicuous disease-spots which produce a second generation of spores within five days. Let's suppose then that a disease-spot gives rise to only three more disease-spots on neighbouring plants within five days – a very modest estimate indeed. At this rate the number of disease-spots on the potatoes over the whole of Denmark will multiply by ten every ten days. A mathematician might make it thirteen, but never mind, we'll assume that three of the spots go out of action meanwhile. The disease-spots multiply by ten every ten days. So by June 4th there are forty thousand, by June 14th four million, and by July 14th four thousand million – which makes two to every potato plant in the Kingdom. By this time the disease-spots have begun to be apparent and it is said that Blight has broken out. By July 27th there are twenty spots or 'units' of disease on each plant and its growth is being checked. By August 3rd, with two hundred units of disease each, the plants are half-spoiled, and by August 8th with six hundred units they are substantially destroyed.

Thus the Blight could start on a very small number of blighted shoots from untreated seed-potatoes in the spring, pass unnoticed through a long period of increase, and appear to 'break out' towards the end of July. Nothing would be left of Rostrup's *joie d'esprit* when those of elephantine wit had finished trampling all over it; he was quite well aware that the Blight did not present so spotty a picture as he had drawn, of course it did not increase in regular geometric progression over the whole period, it probably dawdled at first, and it was throughout influenced by the weather. But it was there all the time and with that potentiality of increase. The idea of eliminating the Blight from Denmark altogether was probably a dream, but by delaying its small beginnings if only for a few weeks early in the season, the damage later on would be greatly reduced. The heat-treatment of the seed-potatoes, assisted by 'protective earthing-up' and 'protective lifting', would reduce the losses from the Blight to a very small proportion of the potato crop.

The Danish way with potatoes was not destined to be adopted to any great extent outside Denmark; it was soon thrown into the shade by the new method of spraying the potato foliage with copper mixtures, which did not demand that kind of co-operative enterprise for which the Danish farmers were famous. The heat treatment *for potatoes* was likely to be reconsidered in subsequent generations, only in countries which for one reason or another *ran short of copper*. But the treatment first worked out for the potatoes was soon to have a world-wide application for the prevention of seed-borne diseases of the wheat, oats and barley.

In the work of the brothers Tulasne and others on the Smut diseases of cereals during the fifties (Chapter V, herein) there was a gap, a major problem left unsolved. It concerned the fungi which caused the *Charbon* or (Loose) Smut diseases of cereals, especially of the barley and the oats. Unlike the Bunt, or Stinking Smut of the Wheat, such diseases could not be prevented by treating the seed with fungicidal solutions, and the reasons for this had escaped detection for over thirty years. The spores of the Loose Smuts were not enclosed within the skins of the corrupted grains, only to be liberated at threshing time; they blew about freely from the smutted heads, when their host plants were in flower. This was well-known, but the curiously sinister purpose behind the liberation of the spores at flowering-time had passed unrecognized. Jensen followed up an idea that it might be a habit of those spores *to cuckold the pollen of the corn*.

When the oats (and likewise the barley and the wheat) were in flower the female organs, the ovaries, put out moist, feathery stigmas to catch the drifting pollen from the stamens hung out by the same or other flowers in the head. When a pollen grain was caught it germinated and sent a fine germ-tube down into the ovary to effect fertilization. Such were the nuptials of the corn in the pleasant days of spring. The stigmas were exposed in naked expectancy fearing no wrong. But the black spores of the Loose Smut fungi, borne like the pollen on the gentle air, came to violate and corrupt. They too germinated on the moist stigmas and sent, not the good other half of life, but the hyphae of an alien fungus down the styles into the ovaries of the flowers, there to remain while the nuclei of pollen and ovary had their conjugation and the ovaries developed into apparently sound and healthy grain. And there to remain still, dormant as the seed itself, until it was sown in the soil. As the seedling grew and the stalks of the plant pushed up, the mycelial strands of the awakened fungus crept among the tissues, to fructify within the ovaries of the following season, 'smutting' them and reducing them to dust – adulterous dust that drifted once again on to the stigmas of uncorrupted neighbouring flowers.

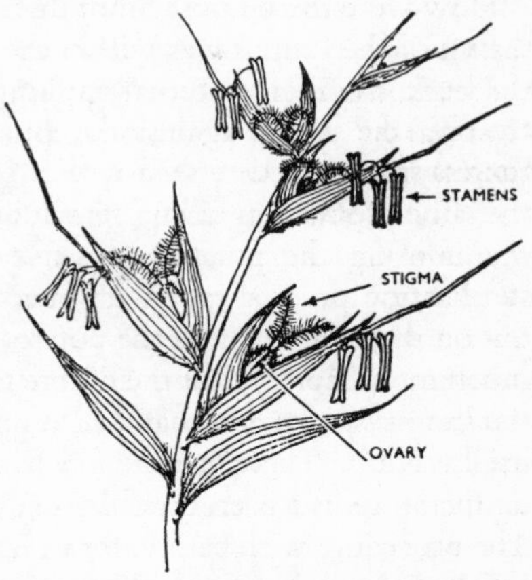

Fig. 45. Oats in flower. A spikelet opened out to show the parts.
Line drawing by Dr. E. S. Gyngell

Was this idea too far-fetched? Too bad to be true? At first Jensen thought so. The flowers might be infected by the Smut spores in quite another way. When the feathery stigmas were put out to receive their pollen the husks or glumes which enclosed the young grains – of barley and of oats – opened by a crack, and through this crack the Smut spores might get in. Having done so they might remain there unaltered, while the grain matured and ripened, and until it was eventually planted as seed. To test this possibility, Jensen stripped the husks from seed-barley and seed-oats, and then dusted the naked kernels with Smut spores. The plants that grew up from these seeds were infected with the diseases which Jensen later clearly distinguished as the 'Loose Smuts' in exactly the same way that wheat was infected with the 'Covered Smut' or Bunt. It was the husks, the natural protective sheaves round the kernels of barley and oats that saved them from external infection by the spores, and the fungus penetrated this armour at its only opportunity – when it was opened at flowering time. This could explain the infection of the oats and the barley but not of the wheat – for the wheat kernel was not enclosed in a husk. On the wheat, the Loose Smut fungus was indeed an adulterer, and its living spawn was within the substance of the kernel itself.

It was Jensen who discovered that there *were* two Smuts of barley, 'Loose' Smut and 'Covered' Smut, and he was able to confirm that the Loose Smut of the oats did not affect the barley or the wheat, and indeed that the Loose Smut fungi on the three cereals were specific and distinct. There was not one fungus, *Ustilago segetum*, attacking wheat, barley and oats indifferently; there were *Ustilago Tritici*, *Ustilago nuda* (on barley), and *Ustilago Avenae*. This was in itself an important fact established, for it meant that the Loose Smut on the oats did not endanger nearby fields of wheat or barley, and so on, *mutatis mutandis*. The three fungi kept to their specific hosts.

How were these Loose Smut diseases to be prevented? Whether the living spawn of the fungus was within the seed, or its spores were protected under the husk, the mere external application of fungicides to the seed-coat, as in treating the wheat against the Bunt, was equally unavailing. But to kill fungus spawn inside a seed without injuring the seed itself presented exactly the same problem as killing spawn of the Blight fungus within a potato without injuring the potato. Jensen tried his method of differential thermal sterilization on seed grain. In one respect the treatment was easier to carry out on the grain than on the potatoes, for the heat penetrated the small seeds much more rapidly, but the difference between the temperature which killed the fungus spawn and that which injured the germinative power of the seed itself was less. There was, however, just sufficient margin, and when the right temperature had been carefully determined the treatment worked perfectly. The procedure with barley, for example, was to soak the seed in water which just had the chill off, which was to say at 68° F. to 86° F., for half a day, in order to rouse the fungus within the seed and render it vulnerable, and then to plunge this soaked seed for five minutes into water at a temperature between the precise limits of 127° F. to 137° F. The seed was then cooled by pouring cold water over it, and dried in readiness for sowing by spreading it out on a floor. The seed was but little injured by this treatment, and in the resulting crop the number of smutted ears was *nil*.

Not only did the Hot Water Treatment kill the spawn of Smut fungi within the seed, it killed spores between the kernel and the husk, and spores on the surface of the outer seed-coat as well. It would not only prevent the Loose Smuts, for which no remedy had ever before been found, but it was as effective as the copper-sulphate steeps against the Bunt of the wheat. All the Smut diseases of cereals, Loose *and* Covered, without exception, could be prevented by soaking the seed for some hours and then plunging it for a few minutes into warm water, at a carefully predetermined temperature.

The method was developed rapidly in Denmark, and, as it happened, news of it penetrated into the British Isles without the usual delay. Jensen could write in English, and he was in correspondence with C. B. Plowright who brought his work to the notice of the readers of *The Gardeners' Chronicle* and the *Journal of the Royal Agricultural Society*. Jensen's historic paper on 'The propagation and prevention of Smut in Oats and Barley' was published in the latter journal in 1888. It was in the United States, however, that the method was most promptly investigated and put to use; as one might see by turning up the U.S. *Farmers' Bulletin*, No. 5, of 1892, by W. T. Swingle.

CHAPTER XIX

THE LEAD OF THE U.S.A.

DURING the eighties, agriculture, and everything connected with agriculture, in Great Britain, was miserably low and depressed. In the particular field of plant pathology, Berkeley had retired, Cooke and Plowright were more interested in the fungi for their own sake, and Worthington G. Smith seemed to have the subject almost to himself with his little book on *Diseases of Field and Garden Crops* of 1884. This book contained many clear figures, for W. G. Smith was certainly a fine draughtsman, but for the rest it was chiefly remarkable for the account it contained of his famous squabble with de Bary over the resting-spores of the Potato Blight fungus. He was still smarting from de Bary's criticisms, and he also managed to quarrel with Jensen. What little he knew of the work that was being done on the Continent he refused to acknowledge; he stuck his head into the insular sand, and for this reason his book was already years out-of-date when it came from the press. With the possible exception of Charles Plowright, who wrote a valuable botanical monograph of the British Rust and Smut fungi (1889) and whose judgment when he touched on plant diseases was generally considered pretty sound, the only English worker who could fairly be included in the first rank was Harry Marshall Ward. But on his return from Ceylon, Ward became a professor of general botany at Cambridge, and did only occasional research in plant pathology. His own reflective and philosophical books on the subject, and his memorable contributions on host-and-parasite relationships, were not written until the next decade. It was true that after twenty years, on the occasion of its second and much-amplified German edition, Anton de Bary's fundamental work was at last translated into English and published by the Clarendon Press: *Comparative Morphology and Biology of the Fungi, Mycetozoa and Bacteria*, 1887. But English publications on the recent developments in the *applied* science, which the Germans called '*Phytopathologie*' or '*Pflanzenschutz*', were to be sought for in vain.

The fungus diseases of the crops, however, had only an accessory part in the causation of the great agricultural Depression of the eighties. There had been a succession of bad, wet seasons when all the diseases, both of the crops and of the livestock, were at their very worst – acutely accentuating the farmers' difficulties. Just as the misery in Ireland after 1845 was at bottom attributable less to disease and bad seasons than to economic and political

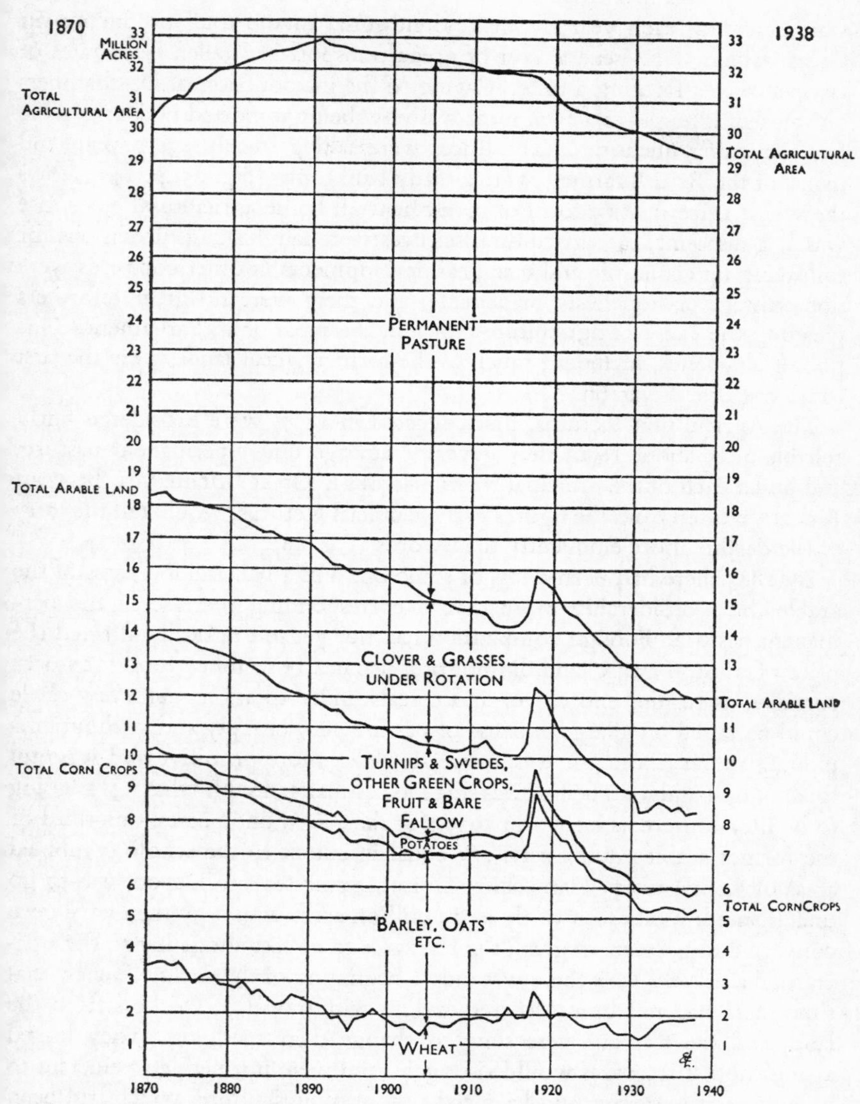

FIG. 46. The Decline of Agriculture in Great Britain. Each division of the vertical scale represents one million acres, an area only slightly less than that of the whole of Somerset (1,031,365 acres).

causes, so it was in England now. In the United States wheat production was increasing each year by an amount equal to the total production in Great Britain. The general cost of ocean transport had fallen from rates of twopence to a farthing a mile. Owing to the introduction of ice-chambers on ships and freight-cars even meat was now being imported in considerable and increasing quantities. The prices were falling steeply every year, and many of the British farmers were already bankrupt. (Fig. 25, p. 145, shows the wheat prices.) As a form of investment all home agricultural enterprise was at a discount, the agricultural sciences were languishing, provisions for following up economic and technical developments in other countries were non-existent or hopelessly inadequate, and there were no great reformers pleading the cause of agriculture either in the press or in Parliament. The poorer clay lands, including much of the former wheat lands, were the first to go out of cultivation.

The Agricultural Returns, first collected in 1867, were considered fairly reliable after about 1870; they gave the acreage under permanent pasture, and under each of the principal rotation-crops in Great Britain, year by year. A chart, plotted from the figures in these official Returns, would tell the story of the decline more eloquently than words (Fig. 46).

By 1885 there had been a loss of some one and a half million acres of the arable, but considerably more than a corresponding increase in the permanent pasture. Foreign competition had not yet so drastically affected the price of meat. Pasture land did not produce nearly so much food for stock, per acre, as turnips and clover and cereals under rotation; but a few cattle could be raised on a large expanse of pasture very cheaply and without employing much labour. It was a reversion to a more primitive and wasteful form of husbandry. The loss was small in comparison with what it was going to be fifty-four years later – in 1939; for then *six* million acres, one-third of the former arable land, a territory equal in extent to the whole combined areas of Kent, Sussex, Hampshire, Dorset, Somerset and Devon, was to go uncultivated. Only four of these six million acres would by then have been converted to permanent grass; the rest were to be lost altogether to the agricultural area. By 1885 there was only a beginning of the decline, but by that time there had not been a corresponding withdrawal of workers from the land, and the farmers were slow to change their methods. They hoped against hope that prices would rise again, and were instinctively reluctant to give up a conservative and balanced system of agriculture, which had been the pride of their fathers, and which indeed produced an enviable yield of honest bread and meat from the land without impairing its fertility. In 1885 the farmers' distress was severe; there was Depression, but not yet prostration and despair. That kind of spiritual decline which caused a great nation to regard with complacency the neglect of six million acres of its arable land, while two million of its people were unemployed and ten million in want, was something then unknown in the world.

But only one-sixth of the total capital invested in agriculture was in the hands of the farmers, and available for the actual working of the land. The other five-sixths was the landowners' share, represented by the more or less static ownership of the land itself and the permanent buildings thereon. The first charge on all that the farmers could earn was the interest on the landowners' capital, and unless the tenants were going to relinquish their farms altogether this interest had to be paid alike in prosperity and in times of depression. The rents had been racked up to a very high level during the Franco-Prussian war, and the slump in prices and the run of bad seasons which followed hit the farmers first. It was not until the payment of rents had become an impossibility, and farms were standing vacant on every hand, that the landowners began to squeal. No one ever squealed for help so loudly as a landlord deprived of his rents; when that happened the Depression was really serious, and there was a more insistent pressure on the Government to 'do something about agriculture'. Some of the landowning aristocracy who acknowledged ties of sentiment to their estates, did assist their tenants by making rent-concessions with a good grace when there was no help for it, and by making 'permanent improvements' on their land. But in the main the landowners, unable to draw their full revenue, were 'impoverished' and not only unwilling but impotent to finance the changeover from high-farming to dairy-farming and specialized cultivations that would be necessary if home-agriculture was to hold its own in the face of the ever-increasing foreign competition.

The development of agriculture by private enterprise had been a jealously guarded privilege of the land-owning aristocracy in the past; but now there was agitation for the setting up of a Board or Ministry of Agriculture in Great Britain. The Royal Agricultural Society, with its annual Shows, and 'half-yearly epistles from Hanover Square to the Agricultural world', was not enough. The plight of agriculture demanded the attention of Her Majesty's Ministers of State. There was an opportunity then for a little government in the best sense of the word, for wise direction of the country's affairs and a judicial balancing of conflicting interests in such a way that the very real advantages of cheap food, which were a consequence of Free Trade, could be retained without ruining the farmers. The population of Great

Britain was increasing at the rate of a thousand a day. Every year a third of a million more mouths had to be fed. The importation of increasing quantities of food was imperatively necessary; the increasing consumption of food per head of the population was an excellent thing – it meant that the misery of partial starvation was diminishing in the land. With all this increasing demand for foodstuff, surely the home farmers should have been enabled to contribute all they could, leaving still a very substantial excess to be imported from overseas? To contrive this by pulling at the right strands in the tangled skeins of finance was the job for a wise government and a great statesman. The need found neither the government nor the man. The simple requirements were lost sight of, or deliberately obscured, in the prolixities of parliamentary business and the discreditable vociferations of purely sectional interests. No one got his head out of the skeins.

In 1878, a proposal that there should be a department of Agriculture and Commerce, with a Minister in the Cabinet, was mooted in Parliament. This promised well, for if the Department could hold the scales fairly between the interests of Agriculture on the one hand and Commerce on the other, and influence the national economy accordingly, it would do exactly what was required. But, of course, if it ever did come to function effectively, it would be running the country; for there was precious little in the work of government that was not in one way or another subservient to the needs of Agriculture and especially Commerce. Perhaps for this reason the proposal was strenuously resisted by the Conservative Party, but a Bill was passed. It did not become operative however, and nothing further happened until 1883, when Mr. Gladstone approved a resolution to draw the work of a number of scattered Government offices together, and to establish a Committee of the Privy Council for the consideration of all matters relating to agriculture. The Committee was formed, and the main practical outcome was that the existent Veterinary Department of the Privy Council took over the job of issuing the annual agricultural statistics from the Board of Trade, and called itself the Agricultural Department. Issuing statistics was only documenting the losses, but the building-up of an organization round the old Veterinary Department and the expansion of its functions was well-conceived. The Department was active and it had already rendered some positive assistance to the farmers. Called into being after the outbreak of the Cattle Plague in 1865, it had been armed with extensive powers to suppress contagious diseases of livestock, and the farmers co-operated surprisingly well with its officers, because in a world of Free Trade it was giving them a certain measure of Protection on the sly. Free Trade had thrown open the ports to live cattle and sheep from the Continent, and these had brought with them the sheep-pox, which the farmers promptly called 'Peel's Pox', and the Rinderpest. The officers of the Veterinary Department, and their predecessors, closed the ports to stock from a number of continental countries, and these measures taken to exclude disease, suited the farmers' pockets very well. From operating with a firm hand against the diseases of sheep and cattle, it was an easy step to extend such operations to check insect pests and diseases of the crops. The Veterinary Department was not run only by clerks and politicians; the veterinary surgeons had a say in what was to be done – and they were doctors, men of scientific training and outlook; they constituted a good nucleus for the technical and scientific organization of a Ministry of Agriculture.

The Government failed to tackle the central problem; the unregulated importation of foodstuffs, for sale at prices with which the home farmers could not compete, represented many things: interest on British investments overseas, all kinds of brokerages and commissions, insurance premiums, and freights, as well as payment for exports of manufactured goods. Nothing could be permitted to stand in the way of Great Britain's imperial money-lending, shipping, and manufacturing businesses; they, too, were 'depressed' as other countries were beginning to exploit the industrial machinery that had been sold to them. But to quieten the everlasting complaint that something should be done about agriculture, the Government looked round for a formula that would sound like a policy, and for some ostensible action that would not disturb the *status quo* or involve any appreciable expenditure. The formula was the alternative to Protection: there had to be 'an endeavour to bring back agricultural Prosperity, not by any action of Parliament, not by the fostering care of a Department, but by bringing home to the farmers that knowledge and power by which they themselves might work out their own deliverance'. And the action, that was to look like doing something but not to cost anything, was to set up a Board of Agriculture. This Board would be constrained to mind its own business, which was to bring home to the farmers the aforesaid knowledge and power.

In 1889, the Land Commission Department, which dealt with tithes, enfranchisements of copyholds, and enclosures, was lumped in with the Agricultural Department and transferred to the new Board. The Board was planned on the same lines as the Board of Trade, and was to consist of the Lord President of the Council, the First Lord of the Treasury, the Chancellor of the Exchequer, and a number of other high functionaries which it would be superfluous to enumerate, because in fact the Board, as such, never met.

It began its work under a President at £2,000 a year, and the first estimate of its annual expenditure was £55,000, just £7,000 more than the combined estimates for the old Departments of which it was composed. All the money it had to spend for rescuing the agricultural industries was a grant of some £5,000 for agricultural and dairy schools. Fortunately the Board included a few individuals, constitutionally incapable of doing nothing, who determined to take it seriously. A Board, or Ministry, or Department, of Agriculture – call it what you pleased – had at last been shuffled ingloriously into existence; its powers were pathetically limited, but so far as rendering technical assistance to the farmers was concerned, they were going to be exercised and extended.

Curiously enough, the very first really useful thing the Board found itself able to do, was to take a hand in resisting 'the advance of the fungi'. By a piece of secret service work inspiring wondering admiration, an 'intelligence officer' of the Board got to hear of the copper mixtures which were then being used on the vines all over France, and of Aimé Girard's experiments on the control of the Potato Blight. In 1890 the Board drew the attention of the authorities in Ireland to these experiments, and with the assistance of the Royal Agricultural Society it succeeded in getting Bordeaux mixture submitted to test on the potatoes at a considerable number of places in Great Britain during the years 1891 and 1892. The result was to introduce the practice of potato spraying; and this was in truth giving the farmers power to help themselves – at least to the extent of saving about a third of their potato crop in wet seasons. And *Phytophthora infestans* was not the only fungus that interested the Board; it promptly held an inquiry into the Rust or Mildew of the Wheat, and within a few years all the fungus diseases as well as the insect pests of the crops were to come under review. They were depriving the farmers of a tithe of their produce – perhaps ten per cent would be about the extent of the loss, taken by and large – but on some crops, in some localities, and in bad seasons it was very much more. If the Board could recommend ways by which that wastage could be reduced, it would be giving the farmers real assistance to meet foreign competition. They would have better produce to sell and more of it, for a given expenditure on cultivation. This form of assistance was, moreover, politically and economically unexceptionable. It was playing the Free Trade game. Nobody was lending any money or selling manufactured goods to the insects and the fungi. The Board took courage when it found there was something practical it could do; and its campaign to save that ten per cent of the country's agricultural produce was, alone, a more than adequate justification for its existence.

Another important thing the Board could do was to provide technical assistance for those farmers who were lucky and flexibly-minded enough to be able to give up the traditional production of bread-plus-meat and go in for producing commodities for which the market was not yet spoilt – dairy produce, for example, green vegetables, salad stuffs, apples, pears and soft fruits. There was a growing demand for a more varied dietary, especially in the large centres of population; the development of market-gardening and fruit-growing would not make any appreciable difference to the rate at which the arable land was going down to grass; these cultivations were, and would always be, a very small part indeed of the country's agriculture as a whole; the acreage devoted to them would hardly show on the chart, but they provided opportunities for an enterprising few, and were by all means to be encouraged. The difficulty was that high-farmers able to make the change-over, had to learn their job anew. Fruit-growing and market-gardening were specialized arts, demanding a relatively enormous amount of technical assistance. The farmer needed as much special knowledge to raise a couple of acres of raspberries successfully as he did for five hundred acres of wheat. The Board, at first, had not so much as a Journal of its own, the sums it had to spend for agricultural education were trifling, but, with the Royal Agricultural and the Royal Horticultural Societies, it did manage to help here. Incidentally, when the beam of attention was squarely turned on fruit-growing, parasitic fungi and insect pests were revealed as far worse troubles than foreign competition and Free Trade.

In setting out to encourage specialized cultivations, and to reduce the losses from pests and diseases, the Board of Agriculture was entering upon a long, slow, and elaborate fight. The greatest success that could possibly attend these endeavours would hardly offset the rising cost of agricultural labour, which was another factor, besides the high rents and low prices, against the farmers. Science was going to be called upon as never before to help the agricultural industries. Some of the benefits of scientific discovery could be reaped in practice without any significant capital outlay – it cost no more to plant and grow a high-yielding variety of wheat, for example, than a poor one. It was on such improvements that the Board was forced to concentrate. There were other and even more important methods of cheapening production which would certainly help the farmers to meet competition. The central drift of the Royal Agricultural Society's work for fifty years had been to show how generously the land responded to the sinking of even a little additional capital in it. But now, in time of Depression, capital was unavailable or withheld, and in fact the farmers were forced to draw recklessly on their last reserve – the unexhausted fertility in the soil. It was one of the consequences of relinquishing the functions of government, and leaving the country's vital affairs to be shaped according to the blind operation of a half-understood 'financial system', that capital was never available for an industry at the times when it was most required in the interests of the people. Adherence to the principle of Free Trade, as though it were some inviolable

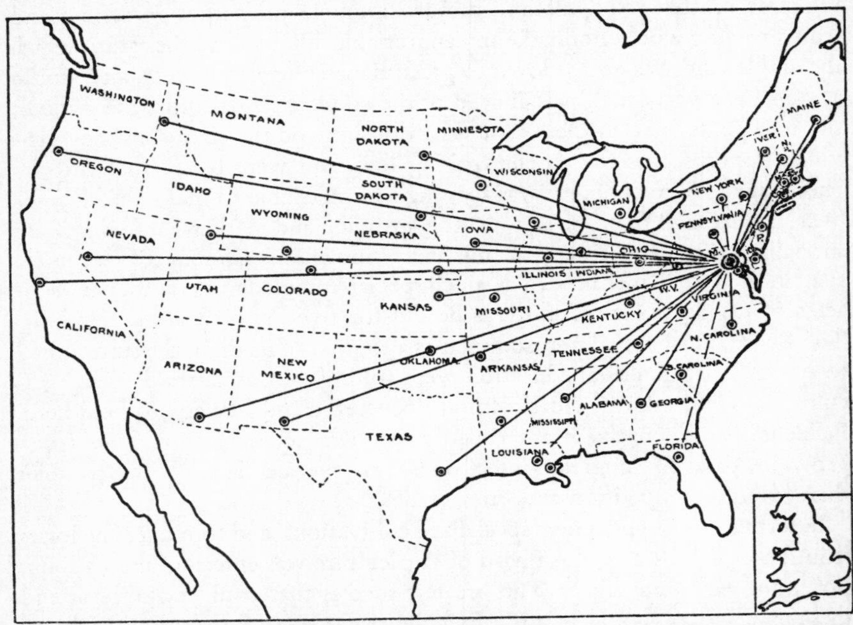

Fig. 47. Agricultural Experiment Stations in the United States, set up by the Hatch Act of 1887. The linkages indicated are with the U.S. Department of Agriculture through the Central Office of Experiment Stations in Washington. Each station is also linked directly with all the rest through the medium of the U.S. Mails.

law of nature rather than a mere conspiracy of non-intervention between conflicting greeds, did not lead to the survival of the fittest, but merely to the survival of the survivors. Science could do much to help agriculture, but, the capital withheld, this help could be only marginal. It could not compensate for political neglect and gross economic folly. The future for the Board, and later for the Ministry of Agriculture in England was most unenviable: it was wedded to our Dame Agriculture, not in her years of vigour but at her turn of life.

In 1888, when these depressing and poverty-stricken nuptials were being arranged in England, the Hatch Act was passed in the United States of America. It provided for the setting-up of Agricultural Experiment Stations in conjunction with the Land Grant Colleges in every one of the forty-eight States, ordered their necessary financial assistance from federal funds, and linked their work together through a central liaison office which was to be a part of the U.S. Department of Agriculture at Washington. With one great and far-sighted legislative Act, centres of research and channels for the diffusion of scientific information in the service of agriculture, were established over half a continent. The proud Department of Agriculture in Washington had something like a bride.

In 1862, during the presidency of Abraham Lincoln, and while the country was torn with civil war, Congress not only created the U.S. Department of Agriculture, but, by what was known as the Morrell Act, it appropriated out of the public lands of the U.S.A. some eleven million acres for the endowment and maintenance of colleges 'to promote the liberal and practical education of the industrial classes in the several pursuits of life'. Each State received land or land-script to the extent of 30,000 acres for each of its representatives in Congress under the census of 1860. It was a charter of technical education of unprecedented scope; a mighty act in the makings of a nation. The land was cheap then, its average value only a dollar and fifteen cents an acre, but the grants were made at the right time; the land was due to appreciate in value very rapidly. The effect of the Act was to provide each State with one or more 'Land Grant Colleges' at which agriculture was usually the principal subject of instruction. Some of these colleges, further assisted by grants from the individual States, and by private endowment, had grown within twenty-five years into flourishing universities. Some of them, colleges or universities as the case might be, had provided themselves with small agricultural experiment stations before the passing of the Hatch Act, but thereafter *every* State was to have its Agricultural College with Experiment Station attached. Education and research were to go hand in hand. The Federal contribution was $15,000 a year for each Station, and in 1890 additional financial assistance was provided for the Colleges. By the end of 1888 there were 46 Experiment Stations in the United States, and by 1900 the number had increased to 60, including Stations in Hawai, Puerto Rico and Alaska.

The purposes, objects and nature of the experiments to be made at the Experiment Stations were not specifically defined in the Hatch Act. It said, in effect, 'There you are, boys, you've got your Experiment Stations; the rest is up to you'. They were to conduct 'such experiments or researches, bearing on the agricultural industry, as might be advantageous having regard to the varying conditions and needs of the respective States or Territories in which they were located'. The Stations had no flash buildings of their own, set off by mown lawns, smelling of floor-polish, and stuffed with expensive equipment. They were humble parts of the Agricultural Colleges; most of the indoor experimental work had to be done in the ordinary laboratories used by the college students, and the field experiments either on the college farm or on lands belonging to neighbouring, friendly farmers. The work of the Stations was in no sense controlled or directed from Washington; the small teams of experimenters, typically an organizer, a botanist, a chemist, a clerk, and sometimes by good fortune an entomologist and a mycologist, were usually also teachers in the College, and they were under the administration of the College authorities. The area of the States they served was often greater than that of the whole of England and Wales; many of the Stations were out on the unbounded prairies or on the slopes of tremendous mountains, thousands of miles from the capital and from each other. But they were linked together by the U.S. Mails, which carried all their publications free of charge. The Act stipulated that each Station was to publish at least four Bulletins, or progress reports, each year, and copies of these were to be sent not only to the Central Office of Experiment Stations at Washington – which formed the link with the Federal Department of Agriculture – but also to all the other Stations from California to Carolina and from Texas to Maine. Each Station was also to send copies of its publications to the newspapers in its own State, and, of course, to supply them to farmers wherever they could be of practical assistance.

Four Bulletins a year from each little team, mostly of inexperienced experimentalists, who were teaching as well as running the Experiment Stations, was an excessive demand. At first there was a great traffic in mere paper, for the teams could not possibly do enough first-class experimental work for the results of it to fill a presentable Bulletin every three months. The newspapers, inclined to criticize what they regarded as a lavish expenditure of public money on a fancy scheme, wanted to be shown results – immediate results. There was a natural temptation to yield to this demand; so that much of the early work was showy, full of premature conclusions and of little real value. But at least the teams were teaching themselves how to write Bulletins; the Central Office at Washington was tactfully pumping into the system a great deal of sound information about the more scientific work that was being done by the Department and by well-established research stations in Europe; while those of the experimenters who had a natural aptitude for organizing good field trials, or for carrying out original research, were setting a constant example to the rest. The system encouraged enthusiasm and initiative. Mathieu Tillet, expressing his humble opinion, in 1755, that making practical experiments might be a way of solving agricultural problems, must have rejoiced, in the world of departed shades, when news came down of all those Experiment Stations getting under way in America – although for years there were but few of them that had anything by half so fine to show as his single-handed work on the Corruption of the Kernels of Wheat in the Ear. The promoters of the scheme were not so sanguine as to believe that great original discoveries were going to be caught, except by chance, in any net of organization. The making of experiments was to serve many ends besides that of advancing original discovery: it was to teach both professors and students the realities of agricultural science; to provide visual demonstrations for the farmers; to afford means of comparing one variety of wheat with another, one fertilizer with another, one method of combating disease with another, and so forth, for all the different crops and soils of the States.

In September 1889 the first number of the *Experiment Station Record* was published in Washington. It was already a brochure of fifty-six closely-printed pages, but it contained short abstracts only of all the Bulletins that had been published by the Experiment Stations during the previous three months. There was No. 3 from Alabama on Analyses of Fertilizers; No. 26 from Indiana on the Rust of the Wheat; No. 6 from Kansas on Silos and Silage; No. 2 from Tennessee on Diseases of the Irish Potato; No. 10 from Dakota on the Germination of Frosted Grain; No. 6 from Colorado on Insects and Insecticides; No. 52 from New Jersey on the worst weeds in that State; No. 4 from Iowa on Wild Plums. As the years went on, and the fat bound volumes of the *Record* began to reach along the shelves, so the Bulletins whose contents they reported, came to deal with every conceivable activity in the agricultural life of the nation. At first there were hundreds, then thousands, of Bulletins. No man could read them all. In 1890 began the vast work of correlating all this information and turning it to practical account. The Central Office began to publish its series of *Farmer's Bulletins*, written in semi-popular style, explaining to the farmers the ways in which their practice might be improved, in the light of the work done at the Experiment Stations.

Although the trained mycologists and entomologists working with the teams at these Stations were as yet so few, it was significant that from the very first there were more Bulletins on the Insect Pests and Fungus Diseases of the crops, than on any two other subjects of investigation whatsoever, with the possible exception of Fertilizers and the Diseases of Cattle. It was the same with the Bulletins issued by the (Federal) Department of Agriculture. Nos. 2, 5, 7, 8, 9, 10 and 11 from the Division of Botany were contributed by the Section of Vegetable Pathology. In 1890 this 'Section', under the direction of Beverley Thomas Galloway, became the Division of Vegetable Pathology, to work side by side and on an equal standing with the Division of Entomology under C. V. Riley. In Riley the Department had the world's leading Economic Entomologist; in Galloway, not only the leading but perhaps the first public servant who could fairly be called an Economic Mycologist. Galloway's team of co-workers included, or came to include among others A. T. Woods, E. F. Smith, N. B. Pierce, M. A. Carleton, C. O. Townsend, W. A. Orton, W. T. Swingle, and R. H. True, all of them noteworthy pioneers in their respective fields.

CHAPTER XX

POTATO SPRAYING

In the course of introducing Potato Spraying into the British Isles, the new Board of Agriculture had occasion to seek out the existent facilities for agricultural experimentation which had grown up in the country as a result of private enterprise, and both the solid merits and the gaping deficiencies of these insular provisions were shown up. By 1890 there was every reason to believe that spraying with Bordeaux mixture would prevent, or at least greatly reduce, the losses caused by the Potato Blight. Thienpont, for the Ministry of Agriculture in Belgium in that year, supervised some ninety-five field trials, and as a result of timely spraying he obtained increases of crop ranging from three to as much as six tons per acre. This meant that in a year when the Blight was bad many hundreds of thousands of tons of potatoes could be saved in Belgium alone – a significant item in that country's total food supplies. What could be done in Belgium could be done in Britain; but between knowing a remedy for a disease and getting it adopted in practice there was all the difference in the world. When the Board of Agriculture had Aimé Girard's results from France, complete with full directions about the composition of the mixture, the amount to be applied, and the times when the spraying should be done, it first passed this information on to the Irish Commissioners of National Education. Three small trials were arranged in Ireland that year, at the Albert Model Farm at Glasnevin near Dublin, and at the small agricultural and dairy schools in Munster and Connaught. Although the spraying was done too late, and in a very haphazard way, it did appear to keep the plants green longer than those which were unsprayed. Nothing could really be said about the effect on the crop.

The Board of Agriculture then asked the Royal Agricultural Society of England whether they happened to know of any trials made with the copper mixtures in Great Britain, and, if not, whether they would be kind enough to arrange a few, on behalf of the Board, during 1891. The Board also appealed to the Royal Highland Society of Scotland, to the Authorities in Ireland again, and seedsmen and independent growers were invited to send in particulars of any trials they might make privately.

The Royal Agricultural Society rose to the occasion and organized model field trials in six places, including Devonshire, Cheshire, Lincolnshire, Kent and Bedford. Each trial plot was to be a whole acre in area and to form part of the ordinary potato crop of an experienced farmer in each locality. The Society would supply the materials and knapsack spraying machines imported from France, and employ a trustworthy man to go round the farms making up and applying the mixture in exact accordance with Aimé Girard's directions. There were to be three one-acre plots at each place, the first of which was to receive two 'preventive' sprayings, respectively at the beginning and the middle of July, the second, a single 'curative' spraying in mid-August when the Blight had already made considerable progress, and the third was to be left unsprayed as a check or 'control'. When the time came to lift the potatoes, the whole crop from each plot was to be sorted into 'sound' and 'blighted', and both lots were to be weighed. The trustworthy man could be provided with forms on which to record the results, and in order that the Consulting Botanist to the Society might be able to follow the progress of the Blight, specimen leaves were to be sent to him from time to time.

There was a considerable amount of Blight about in 1891, and except that on some of the plots three 'preventive' sprayings were given instead of two, the whole project was carried out very much as planned. The cost of the treatment, both for materials and labour, was carefully estimated in each instance, so that it could be deducted from the increase in value of the crop, if any, to obtain the net gain or loss in £ s. d. The materials, bluestone and lime, cost 3s. 6d. per acre for each spraying, and the labour 5s. 0d., reckoning an agricultural labourer's wages at the then current rate of 3s. 0d. a day, so that the total cost of treatment per acre was 17s. 0d. or £1 5s. 6d., according as the spraying was done twice or three times.

When all the data had been collected, and the table of results made out, it was found that there was a wide variation in the figures from the six trials. In Kent, three preventive sprayings increased the crop from 8.7 to 12.6 tons per acre, decreased the proportion of blighted tubers from 6.5 to 1.6 per cent, and resulted in a net gain to the farmer of £12 17s. 6d. per acre. In three other counties, the net gains were respectively, 6s. 0d., £2 6s. 10d., and £3 14s. 7d. per acre. But in Cheshire the sprayings appeared to have *reduced* the crop by 1.45 tons, and to have resulted in a net *loss* of £5 5s. per acre.

These were the first organized trials ever made in Great Britain of a practical remedy for the Potato Blight. If the coming of the Potato Blight in 1845 had been an historic event, so also was the coming of the remedy in 1891. The lay-out of the trials was admirable, the six locations were chosen to cover conditions in different parts of the country, the devotion of a whole acre to each trial plot was generous, and the careful weighing and sorting of the crop from each plot was designed to show up the practical and cash results of the spraying. But there was a flaw, which made the trials of much less value than they might have been. It was one of the consequences of the all-pervading caste system in English social life that even in so important an experiment as this a 'trustworthy man' was left to do all the practical work while the scientific gentlemen in top hats and frock coats stayed in London and did the interpretation. In America, where Jack was as good as his master – unless he happened to be coloured – such an arrangement would appear funny enough; but no English gentleman could for the life of him see what was wrong with it. What was in fact wrong, in this particular instance, was that the interpreters had no means of relating the variations in the results to their natural causes. Something had gone very wrong in Cheshire, for example. The potato plants there had been severely injured by the spraying, and no one would ever know whether this was due to some defect in the copper mixture, to acid fumes in the atmosphere, to preceding insect attack, or to some abnormality of the plants themselves. Such experiments needed experienced and thoughtful scientific workers, out among the potatoes, following the spread of the disease, seeing for themselves its relations to the weather conditions and the state of the plants, looking on the spot for possible reasons of success or failure of the spraying tactics employed. As it was, the interpreters could not speak from any direct personal experience of what had happened, and they strayed into the legal and parliamentary but very unscientific method of seeking a consensus of opinion.

Much of the evidence available by the end of 1891 was thoroughly entangled in 'human nature'. One firm of seedsmen, who were selling what they claimed to be disease-resistant potatoes, reported that they had tested Bordeaux mixture very carefully and found it no use at all. Another firm, who no doubt intended to sell the materials for making the mixture as a profitable side-line, said it was an absolutely perfect preventive. The Royal Highland Society of Scotland, who somehow or other managed to get their Bordeaux mixture quite black, and by the description unlike any Bordeaux mixture ever seen elsewhere, reported that 'it had entirely failed to have any restraining effect whatever on the Potato-Disease'. Some of the most careful experiments were made in Ireland by Professor Carroll at the Albert Model Farm. He obtained an increase, by spraying, of 3.5 tons per acre with one variety of potato that was very sensitive to the Blight, and only about 12 cwts. per acre increase from other varieties which were less susceptible. He *was* out among the potatoes, and he did not seem content to spray so soon by rote and formula, exactly according to the French directions; he thought it desirable that a closer study should be made of the propagation of the Blight itself. The Agricultural Department of the Irish Land Commission thought they ought to promote some trials, but could not bear to spend the money necessary to do it properly. They purchased twelve and a half cwt. of some stuff called 'Anti-Blight Powder' which, as it contained copper sulphate and lime, ought to do, and handed this out among some twenty-five potato growers, together with cheap indiarubber distributors to puff the stuff on with. The Anti-Blight powder made no appreciable difference to the Blight, but it served to strengthen the prejudices of the farmers against all such new-fangled ideas.

The consensus of opinion, according to the Board of Agriculture, was that spraying the potatoes with the French mixture did not prevent the Blight, but that when it was done thoroughly, and at the right time, it checked the progress of the disease and decidedly increased the yield of potatoes. The advantage was not wholly or chiefly derived from the prevention of disease in the tubers, but from the prolongation of the life of the plants, which not unnaturally went on growing longer and accumulating more food reserves in their tubers, when the destruction of their foliage by the Blight was delayed for several weeks. Further experiments were desirable.

But there was another consensus of opinion, among practical potato growers and breeders, to the effect that much so-called Potato Disease was not due to the Blight fungus at all, but to the Degeneration of potato varieties in cultivation. A good new variety of potato, produced by cross-fertilization and reared up from true seed – in the small tomato-like fruits of the plant – would do well for ten or twenty years, and then its productivity would begin to decline; it would become prone to disease as though worn-out and tired of life. Perhaps it was debilitated by continuous vegetative propagation, and the potato plant like other living things could only maintain its vitality by the occasional passage through a sexual phase. A 'seed-potato' was only a swollen part of an underground stem, its eyes were buds; so that potatoes grown from tubers were like plants raised from cuttings; after twenty years of such propagation the resulting plants were, in fact, twenty years old. There were some who thought that the potato simply wore out with age, but what the nature of this wear might be, nobody could say. It was more probable that the potato picked up various diseases, of kinds not yet understood, in the course of its long life, and that these diseases were left behind when the potato was raised anew from its true seed. The only occasions on which this natural cleansing and renewal was allowed to take place were when the potato-breeders crossed one potato variety with another to obtain new hybrids.

Perhaps it was the same with potatoes as with politicians: one way of improving the parliamentary stock was to plant some younger ones in Parliament occasionally, to replace those whose minds had become excessively full of corruption with the passage of years. The improvement was not necessarily due to the introduction of any new sap: even the replacement of old politicians by their own offspring, though highly undesirable, was theoretically capable of doing a certain amount of good. The inheritance of acquired characteristics, upon which Darwin had pinned his faith, was now regarded as improbable, and even the child of a politician by the daughter of a politician, as it was raised anew from Weismann's immaculate and immortal 'germ-plasm', could be an honest and decent human being, *at birth*.

The debilitative diseases and corruptions which the potato picked up in the course of its long life were more mysterious in their nature than those affecting the minds of politicians, but the degeneration was plain enough. A potato variety that had been in cultivation for many years would frequently yield several tons per acre less than when it was first introduced. It was a matter of experience that this was so, and the fact, as yet unexplained, could not be gainsaid. The loss of crop due to 'degeneration' could be as great as that due to the Blight. And, indeed, the new and vigorous variety 'Champion', raised by Nichols in 1876, had withstood the disastrous Blight in Ireland during 1879, to a very remarkable degree. Earl Cathcart, who wrote a prophetic essay 'On the Cultivated Potato' in 1884, considered that much more attention should be given to that older disease of the potatoes, the 'Curl', which had caused ruinous losses of the crop long before the Blight came to Europe, and which had never by any means disappeared. 'Stephens, in his *Book of the Farm*', he said, 'characterizes the Curl as weakness; the leaves curl and crumple; when virulent they shrivel; the tubers are small and rot; the herbaceous stems are puny; and a small insect feeds on them; some call this the cause. A few plants curl one year; planted the next, half the crop will prove diseased; the disease is hereditary. Degeneration is not only a disease, but the predisposer to acute disease, the struma of the potato . . . '

A part of Earl Cathcart's essay was retrogressive, in that he threw doubt on the causal relationship of the Blight fungus to the Potato Blight, which had long since been established beyond question. He also confused the Blight, the Curl, Degeneration, and other ailments of the potato, together, and resurrected that old phantom of Disease with a capital 'D'. But out of this very confusion a new and most significant idea could be seen to be taking something more than nebulous shape. It was that senile degeneration, in respect of the potato at least, was not the result of mere age or wear, but of the accumulation of miscellaneous diseases. It was just beginning to be perceived that the potatoes were subject to two different and distinct kinds of disease. One kind was caused by parasitic fungi, and the worst of this kind was the Blight, which after 1891, it seemed, could be checked by spraying. The other kind could not be associated with any causal organism; in practice it seemed to result from growing the same variety of potato too long in the same locality. What the causal principles of degeneration might be remained a complete mystery, but there was plenty of evidence that it could be lessened or avoided by obtaining seed potatoes from another locality – as when English growers obtained seed from Scotland – and by the change of old varieties for new.

At the last Government inquiry, in 1880, into the state of the potato crops – following the very bad 'Blight' year of 1879, when the loss was estimated at £6,000,000 in Ireland alone – there had been a proposal to set up an experiment station in the British Isles for the study of potato varieties, and the investigation of possible means of reducing the disease in the potato crops, by methods of breeding and selection. Now that this new method of checking the Blight by spraying had come along, the authorities congratulated themselves on having done nothing about that earlier proposal. But the grounds for such satisfaction were very dubious. Apart from the possibility of obtaining partially Blight-resistant potatoes, the investigation of the vexed question of Degeneration would alone justify the relatively small cost of such a station. Earl Cathcart, in 1884, had dared to suggest yet further expenditure. He pointed out how exceedingly little was known about the habits of the wild potato in its natural habitat, and thought that 'inquiry should be pushed in the direction of the South American home of the plant: if you desired to study a Frenchman you would visit his own grand country. You certainly would not hunt up a specimen at the Sablonière in Leicester Square!' It seemed passing strange to him that Great Britain, mistress of the seas, with her trade spread over the entire world, could not afford to send an expedition out to South America, to study the potato there, and perhaps to find kinds of potato growing in the varied climates of that mountainous continent, which would be less subject to disease in the British Isles than the ordinary domesticated sort. Darwin had observed wild potatoes growing on the Chonos peninsula; there were a few words about them in his *Voyage of the Beagle*. It did not reflect much credit upon a nation of explorers that it should be content with *that*, quoting that one meagre reference again and again and again, and never sending a party off to explore the interior.

As soon as the new Board of Agriculture tried to do something about the Potato Blight, in 1891, it found that the introduction of potato spraying was only a part of the work on that crop that demanded attention. All the proposals made in previous years came up again, and the question, 'What ails the potato?' still dead-central in the now-widening vistas of plant pathology as a whole, did not refer only to the Blight.

Perplexed by all this, the Board appealed to the Foreign Office to obtain information, not only about potato spraying, but about the very cultivation of the potato, in other countries. Her Majesty's diplomatic and consular representatives, ever ready to oblige, made a discreet note of the correct way to spell *Phytophthora*, and then set about collecting a mass of most valuable information from Denmark, Holland, Germany, Belgium, France, Italy, the United States and Austria-Hungary. The reports, while revealing the substantial progress that had been made in checking the Blight by spraying, in France and Belgium, and by the heat-treatment of tubers and 'protective cultivation' in Denmark, indicated that rather more was known in *England* about potato *varieties* than in any other country. If the Board of Agriculture wanted to investigate the degeneration of potato varieties, and to seek methods of improving the stocks, there was nothing for it but to finance some original research and to set up the potato-breeding station mooted in 1880. As this project would involve the expenditure of several thousand pounds a year it required prolonged consideration – and in fact no such research station was started in England for another quarter of a century. As for sending explorers out to collect potatoes in South America – the wealth of the Indies did not provide any money to be spent on that sort of thing. The progress of *potato spraying* in other countries encouraged the Board to press ahead with that relatively inexpensive part of the programme.

In 1892, the spraying trials or demonstrations were continued in the British Isles, and a number of individual farmers, educational authorities, County Councils, commercial firms and agricultural societies lent their assistance to the Board. The Royal Agricultural Society again organized trials in six counties, this time on Early and Middle Early as well as Main Crop potatoes, and they also made field trials on a smaller scale at Woburn, where the generosity of the Duke of Bedford had provided them with an experimental farm. They tried Bordeaux mixture with the addition of molasses, as advocated by Michel Perret, and a mixture made with equal quantities of copper sulphate and lime as advocated by various other French workers, but decided that the modifications increased the cost of the mixtures without making much difference to their effectiveness. Aimé Girard's mixture, containing 20 pounds of copper sulphate, 10 pounds of lime and 100 gallons of water, remained the best. Dr. Voelcker, Chemist to the Society, considered the chemistry of the mixture and advanced a theory that the actual copper compound in it was an oxysulphate of copper and not the hydroxide, as Millardet and Gayon believed. He also pointed out the necessity of using reasonably pure copper sulphate crystals in making up the mixture, which was important, as much of the commercial salt then on the market contained considerable amounts of deleterious iron as an impurity. Masson's mixture, made up with soda instead of with lime, the 'Burgundy mixture' which was later to be used extensively on the potatoes, was not included in the Society's trials at that time. The formula had been published in 1886, but no French worker had yet sufficiently stressed the point that it was as good on the potatoes as on the vines.

In Ireland the Land Commissioners now provided proper knapsack sprayers and materials for trials on nine or ten farms, and, during the month of June, issued a circular on Potato Spraying. Directions were given for spraying 'Champions', which were now being grown in Ireland to the practical exclusion of almost every other variety. At the Albert Model Farm, Professor Carroll not only continued the spraying trials to formula, but performed an experiment that was pleasingly original. To test whether spores from partially blighted foliage really did wash down with the rain to infect the healthy tubers underground, he covered the soil round a number of potato plants with a layer of cotton-wool to serve as a spore-filter. He marked off an equal number of plants which he left uncovered by way of comparison. When the tubers were dug in the autumn, those which had grown beneath the soil covered with cotton-wool numbered seventy-five sound and none diseased; while those which had not been so covered numbered forty sound and thirty-three diseased. This experiment went some way to explain why some of the tubers were still blighted, even when spraying had kept the greater part of the foliage green until autumn. Quite small patches of Blight on the leaves missed by the spray would provide plenty of spores to wash down into the soil with the rain and infect tubers here and there. It would pay to combine the French method of spraying with some of the protective methods of cultivation advocated by Jensen in Denmark.

The summer of 1892 was fairly dry, and, except in Ireland, the Blight was not very prevalent. But it was a remarkable fact that in nearly all of the many trials made in the British Isles that year, the increase of crop which resulted from spraying was more than sufficient to repay the cost of treatment. It had been anticipated that in localities where little or no Blight happened to appear, spraying would do no good, and the cost of it would be a net loss to the farmer. The spraying had to be preventive, *before* the Blight appeared, if it was to be effective, and in some districts no one could say whether the Blight was likely to be prevalent or not – it depended on the weather. As the cost of spraying was recouped in increased crop, even when the Blight attack appeared to be slight, there were grounds for thinking that the copper had a stimulating effect on the potato plants apart altogether from its effect on the Blight fungus. However this might be, it was fortunate from the point of view of getting spraying adopted, that the farmers could confidently be recommended to spray their potatoes as a matter of routine, *every* year. It was the very best kind of speculative investment, for if there was little Blight the stake was returned, and if the Blight *was* severe, the gain was about ten to one.

The spraying cost about £1 an acre, and nearly all the trials in Ireland in 1892 showed a net gain of £10 per acre. In England, in localities where there was little Blight, the spraying made a difference of only some 7 to 15 cwt. of potatoes per acre; but where the Blight attack was of normal severity the gain was from two to three tons. There were one or two cases in which the spraying resulted in a loss, but the overwhelming majority of the experimenters, both in the British Isles and on the Continent, were agreed that it paid, and paid well, to spray the potatoes whether severe Blight was to be anticipated or not.

Thus, and for this reason, the potato growers of the British Isles, like the vine growers of France, and the orchardists and vine growers of America, began to take up arms against the fungi – to engage in chemical warfare with *Phytophthora infestans* over two and a half million acres of potato fields. The spectacle presented to the imagination was that of a very few men, at first, out with three-gallon knapsack machines on their backs, spraying an infinitesimal part of that large area, to combat the multiplication of aerial millions of spores of the fungus in its most prolific summer stage. Within a year or two, horse-drawn spraying machines were introduced, which would treat some six or eight rows at a time, but even so, with the help of such cavalry, the proportion of the total acreage sprayed was for many years very small indeed.

How were the advantages of spraying to be brought home to the farmers? How was their traditional reluctance to adopt innovations in farm practice to be overcome? How were they to be instructed in the principles and methods of spraying? The technology of it was simple enough – so far a the farmers were concerned – but success depended upon using properly made mixture and applying it at the right time. One way of diffusing th necessary information was by means of printed leaflets, another way b agricultural colleges, schools, and extension lectures. But when the Boar began its work in 1889 there was hardly any such thing as agricultura education in England. A great many of the farmers in England and in Ire land – though not in Scotland – were still illiterate. There were sma agricultural schools established by private enterprise at Cirencester, Downto and Aspatria; the lectures and examinations in Agriculture by the Scienc and Art Department at South Kensington, being intended for teachers, wer theoretical and did not involve any practical training. At first the Board ha only £5,000 a year to spend on agricultural education, and for a time i distributed only a fraction of that small sum by way of grants – but it helpe the University College of North Wales at Bangor, for example, when a agricultural department was started there.

The chance of helping the farmers, in the matter of potato spraying c anything else, by way of elementary agricultural education, seemed some what remote. But England was a country in which everything got done i time; usually in the most bizarre ways and as a consequence of trying to d something quite different. It was the 'whisky money' that put Englis elementary agricultural education on its feet. In 1890, the Governme imposed additional duties on beer and spirits, in the hope of using the pro ceeds to extinguish liquor licences with compensation – to reduce th amount of gin-drinking and the number of pot-houses. There was such a outcry from the brewers and the distillers that the proposals had to be with drawn, and the Government was left with a windfall of £750,000 a year o its hands. This was by way of being real money, and it was divided up amon the County Councils, the sop to virtue being that they were authorized t use it for the betterment of technical and agricultural education. Some o them did so. Meanwhile, the Board of Agriculture encouraged 'highe agricultural education, so far as it could, by grants to colleges of Universit rank, which took the initiative of opening agricultural departments. Betwee 1890 and 1896 such departments were started by University Colleges a Leeds, Newcastle, Aberystwyth, Cambridge, Nottingham and Readin The Agricultural College at Wye, serving the very important hop and fru growing district of Kent, and associated with the University of London, w founded in 1896. In time all these places were to become centres of agr cultural research as well as of education, but progress was slow, the number o students was small, and their influences for change on the agricultural practice of the country as a whole was not marked until well into the first decade of the twentieth century. One of the things that the Board of Agriculture by no means neglected to do was to send somebody to take a look round the Agricultural Colleges and Experiment Stations of the United States: it published an envious report about them in 1895. In 1894, the Board issued the first number of its own *Journal*, which was destined to continue later as the *Journal of the Ministry of Agriculture*. Slowly, and with opportunism, the Board made its own arrangements for following up technical developments in other countries, and for the diffusion of useful information at home. The policy enjoined upon it was to encourage and foster a 'natural' growth of agricultural research and education in the British Isles, rather than to attempt its promotion by any bold legislative action. There were some advantages in this, and the time-lag behind other countries might not have mattered a great deal if the agricultural land had not been going out of cultivation so very rapidly all the time.

CHAPTER XXI

FUNGI IN THE ORCHARDS

THE next parts of England's all too green and mossy land to receive the attention of the Board of Agriculture were the orchards and fruit plantations. The increasing demand for fruit in the big towns seemed to offer an opportunity for some increase in the acreage devoted to fruit-growing; it would never make much difference to the rate at which the arable land was tumbling down to grass, for all the orchards in the country did not occupy a quarter of a million acres, but any increase would be to the good, and home-grown fruit could have a freshness and flavour unrivalled by any imported produce. Of all the kinds of fruit—apples, pears, cherries, plums, gooseberries, currants—apples were the most extensively grown in England; apple trees were as much a part of the English countryside, as the cherries were of Switzerland and Southern Germany, or the vines and the peaches were of sunnier France. The English soil was capable of producing the finest apples in the world. But it was a lamentable fact that most of the English apples could not compete on the market with those which were being imported from America. Despite the cost of shipment, three thousand miles across the Atlantic Ocean, and all the deterioration to which the fruit was subject in storage and transit, the American apples were actually cheaper, sounder, more attractive in appearance, and better in everything except flavour, when they reached Covent Garden, than the great bulk of those from the Kentish orchards forty miles away. The English fruit-growers grumbled about this foreign competition, but the unwelcome truth was that despite obvious handicaps, the American growers were beating them, on their own doorstep, solely by superior skill in cultivation, and care in marketing what they had to sell.

In 1898 there were 224,000 acres of orchards in Great Britain, of which 218,000 were in England. Most of these orchards consisted of grass-land planted with fruit-trees, chiefly apples and pears. As a writer in the *Journal of the Board of Agriculture* pointed out, it was evident from the very appearance of these grass-orchards, even to those who knew little of fruit-culture, that a large proportion of them were not producing by one-half so much as they should, and that much of the fruit was of common kind and inferior quality. Even in Kent and Worcester, where there were some progressive growers, there were in fact all too many trees as miserably neglected as those which still remained to be seen, in 1939, in old gardens, and in the cider-apple districts of Devonshire and Normandy.

The trees were pruned carelessly or not at all; they were encumbered with a crowded growth of wood, much of which was dead; the limbs and trunks were green with mosses and lichen; the twigs were cankered, rough with swollen wounds, and infested with the Woolly Aphis; the apples, though they might be numerous, prettily-coloured and of good taste when picked from the trees, were small, often misshapen, maggoty, and blemished with the black spots of *la Tavelure*, or Apple Scab. 'Mummied apples' from the previous season were to be found hanging on the trees, and there were many soft-rotten ones with concentric rings of fungus pustules on their brown skins. Many of the leaves had the same dark Scab marks on them that there were on the apples; caterpillars of various kinds ate into the fruit-buds, rolled up and perforated the leaves, stretched themselves on webs in which they enshrouded half-eaten shoots, or let themselves down on silken lines. On the younger trees, which were not already cankered and rugged, a white or greyish superficial mildew – the Apple Mildew, similar to the Powdery Mildews so common on rose bushes and young oak trees – was very destructive. It covered the spur-shoots in the spring as with flour-paste left to dry, curling up the leaves and crippling the fruit trusses. Such neglected orchards were veritable jungles of parasitic fungi and insect pests.

The trees also suffered much from partial starvation, for there was a curious notion among the English farmers that fruit trees were not as other plants. They were supposed to have very deep roots which could draw all the nourishment they required, indefinitely, from the interior of the earth. They were rarely given any fertilizers or manure other than that which they got back from lean pigs turned loose to fatten off the grass beneath them.

The only thing to do with some of these old orchards was to grub them up and start again, planting good marketable sorts of apples, and seeing that the trees received proper nourishment. That would greatly increase the yield of saleable fruit – when the trees came into bearing – but it would not of itself keep down the insects and the fungi; the new trees would be as infested as ever, and where intensive methods of cultivation were adopted – bush or half-standard trees, all of the same kind planted close together in their hundreds – some of the pests and parasites could well be expected to *increase*.

The Americans owed much of their success to the cultivation of the soil beneath their trees, and to the very careful grading and packing of their fruit for market; but they were aided more than by anything else, by the methods which the practically-minded scientific workers of the U.S. Department of Agriculture had developed for combating the insects and the fungi. If the English commercial fruit-growers were to remain in business they would have to follow this lead, and the job of the Board of Agriculture was to help them to do so, by arranging for the investigation of all that seemed best in the American practice, and its adaptation, by way of such trials as were now beginning at Wye College, to English conditions. The work on individual orchard pests and parasites was already voluminous, but before getting down to that it was necessary to make a thorough and general clean-up of the orchards, a systematic depopulation of the jungle.

First of all, by pruning and cutting out dead and diseased wood, not only was more light and air admitted to the fruit and the sap-supply directed to the best advantage for its alimentation, but many sources of fungus infection and resorts of insects were removed at the same time. The pruning of fruit-trees was a highly developed art by the time of Queen Elizabeth, let alone by the eighteen-nineties, but its part in the suppression of such diseases as the Canker and the Scab was not appreciated until the life-histories of the fungi causing those diseases were uncovered. The Canker was one of the oldest diseases of the apple trees, and it was to be seen at its worst, by no means on the wild crabs, but in orchards which had been cultivated up to a point and then left to the care of Nature. It somewhat resembled the Canker of the Larch (here already discussed in Chapter XIV), especially in its mode of attack on the young wood. It was caused by a fungus whose spores could infect the living bark wherever the protective layer of cork was cut or broken, or where it was punctured by insects. At first the growth of the fungus spawn in the underlying tissues caused concentric weals on the surface, about the point of infection, then a patch of dead bark fell away in the centre, exposing the bare wood. The surrounding bark then became swollen and rugged, and the fruit on the cankered branches was starved owing to the restriction of the sap supply. Where the canker completely 'ringed' the branch, the wood beyond it died. The causal fungus, a species of Nectria, closely related to the Coral Spot Fungus so common on dead wood, was studied by the brothers Tulasne and also by Anton de Bary, who established the important point that it could live both as a saprophyte and as a parasite — on both dead and living tissue. It was studied also by Robert Hartig, and described in his classical work on the diseases of trees. When the Canker became very troublesome in France, on apple trees planted in some districts to replace vines destroyed by the Phylloxera, Millardet gave it his attention and contributed a long paper on it to the *Mémoires* of the Society of Sciences at Bordeaux for 1875. Although the farmers called any kind of ruggedness or swelling on the apple branches a 'Canker', and the botanists gave the name of *Nectria ditissima* to what would be distinguished in 1939 as *Nectria galligena*, there was not much mystery in 1890 about the life-history of the Apple Canker fungus. Both its summer and winter fructifications were easily to be found on the affected bark; the former had sickle-shaped spores, the latter small red perithecia visible to the naked eye, and housing a number of microscopic sacs containing ascospores. The two kinds of spores were respectively washed down the twigs by rain and liberated into the air from the cankered branches, thus spreading the infection through the orchards. When Woolly Aphides probed the bark of the apple shoots with their needle-like proboscides to feed on the sap, they caused the formation of galls, which when massed together and cracked, had in themselves a canker-like appearance. The spores of the Canker fungus in fact very frequently obtained entry by way of these cracks, so that the Woolly Aphides with their flecks of cotton-wool-like secretion, cracked woody galls and true cankers, went together. It was evident that the Canker could be checked to some extent by destroying the Woolly Aphides, and this was one of the reasons why the control of fungus disease in the orchards was indisseverable from the total process of cleaning-up the trees; but the principal weapon against the Canker was simply the pruning knife. A very desirable refinement being to make the cuts cleanly and in such a way that water would not lodge on them; or, better, to paint the wounds with a protective coat of tar – aseptic tree-surgery. The part of pruning in combating that other fungus disease, the Apple Scab, which spotted the fruit, was seen, somewhat tardily, when it was realized that *one* of the ways in which the Scab fungus survived the winter was by means of inconspicuous cushion-like growths of toughened spawn on the young wood. Some, but not all, of that wood could be removed by very careful pruning without sacrificing too many of the all-important fruit-buds.

Along with the pruning, went the still fairly obvious measure of removing any 'mummied' or otherwise diseased apples remaining on the trees, and of clearing away and burning any dead wood on the ground. Also by sweeping up and burning the dead leaves in the autumn, or turning them into the soil when lightly ploughing up the hungry weeds and grass, further sources of fungus infection could be put out of action. It was well enough known by this time that many of the parasitic fungi survived the winter in fallen leaves. That was the first place to look for their perithecia, oospores, teleutospores, sclerotia, hibernating mycelium, and so forth. By mere pruning and cultivation most of the English orchards could be made a great deal healthier and

cleaner and more productive than they had ever been in the past, but th
trunks and branches were still encumbered with growths of mosses and liche
and often rough with loose bark, harbouring the eggs and grubs of man
destructive insects.

The next step was to scrape away any loose bark, and to wash or coat th
trees when they were dormant in the winter with something that would ki
the lichen and moss. The English growers sometimes lime-washed the tree
thereby giving them a sepulchral appearance by day and a positively ghastl
look on a winter's night. The lime-wash did a certain amount of good, bu
by about 1895 a very much more effective treatment had been found in th
U.S.A. It was to wash the trees during the winter with a solution of causti
soda, or caustic soda and potash. The effect was very striking: the moss an
lichen disappeared as though by magic, and when the 'winter-washing' ha
been continued for a year or two the branches had a smooth grey glint. Th
washed and well-pruned trees, waiting for the spring to put forth thei
foliage again, looked as clean and functional as gear on the deck of a battle
ship.

At blossom-time such apple orchards were, to the passer-by, spectacles o
indescribable loveliness; but as the petals fell and the young fruit began to fil
out, it was apparent that the control of the insect pests and the fungi was ver
far indeed from complete. Nothing had yet been done that affected th
tightly-closed perithecia and other over-wintering growths of the fungi
there were still eggs of insects unharmed in the bark, adult insects and pupa
hibernating in the soil, fungus spores from external sources still drifted int
the orchards in the spring. Some of the insects which hibernated in th
ground, notably Winter and Codling Moths, could be trapped on their wa
up the trees by bands of sticky material tied or painted round the trunks
and something more could be done in the autumn and winter by spraying th
trees with kerosene emulsified in water.

All the numerous kinds of insects with which fruit-growers – and farmer
and gardeners – had to contend could be sorted for practical purposes int
two main categories. There were those, like the Green-flies, the Capsid-bugs
the Woolly Aphides, the Phylloxera and the Scale insects, which puncture
plant-organs and fed by sucking up sap through mouth-parts resemblin
small hypodermic needles. And there were those, like the caterpillars
beetles, locusts and earwigs, which ate the leaves and had mouth-part
adapted for tearing and biting. Some of the 'biting insects', namely th
beetles, had gizzards like the hollow cones of coffee-mills, furnished wit
horny blades, which ground up their food very fine and made it go a lon

way; other of the 'biting insects', namely the caterpillars, had no such gizzards, they bolted their food, much of which passed through undigested, and that was one of the reasons why they were such voracious feeders. But whether the biting insects had gizzards or not, they could all be killed by depositing poisonous substances on the leaves which they were going to eat. The 'sucking insects' could *not* be killed in this way, for with their needle-like proboscides they probed delicately through any surface layer of poison and fed on untainted juices from the interior of the leaf. The sucking insects could not only cause disastrous direct damage to crops – witness the Phylloxera on the vines, and their near cousins, the Woolly Aphides in the orchards – but, as it was later to be discovered, they were most diabolical agents for carrying about the causative agents of certain plant diseases.

It was not surprising, considering the number of oil-wells in the United States,that the Americans were the first to use oil-sprays for the destruction of sucking-insect pests. By the nineties they had two kinds of kerosene (or paraffin oil) emulsion in use, both in the citrus and the apple orchards. The emulsion most generally favoured was made up with soap and water; the other, of great historic interest, was made with sour milk. These were the simple and homely prototypes of all the elaborate oil sprays which would be used in fruit-growing in the twentieth century. The idea of using sour milk was a good one, as the milk contained casein, which was in some respects a better emulsifying agent than soap, for it did not form curds in hard water. The emulsion was made by putting two gallons of paraffin oil and one gallon of water in which half a pound of soap had been dissolved (or one gallon of sour milk), into a tub and then pumping the mixture backwards and forwards by means of a force pump or a syringe with the nozzle submerged. The effect was to break up the oil into very small globules, producing a thick milk or cream of paraffin oil, which could be diluted with more water for use.

These oil emulsions, sprayed upon the fruit trees in the winter, served to burn, dissolve, suffocate or bedraggle any sucking insects there might then be upon them. The minute oil-globules in the spray ran together on the insects' bodies, covering them with a continuous film of oil. This not only put them into something of the plight of sea-birds after resting on oily waters; but it suffocated them directly by covering up the spiracles, or air pores, along the sides of their bodies, through which they breathed. The oil also dissolved some of the greasy or waxy protection of the insects, and some of the insects' eggs in the crevices of the bark; and it was nearly as effective as the caustic soda washes in destroying mosses and lichen. Unfortunately the paraffin oil sprays could not be used with safety in the summer, as they often caused severe injury to the foliage, but they could be used at any time after the fruit had been picked in the autumn and before the buds broke in the spring. They were particularly valuable for the suppression of the Scale insects, and the gall-producing and Canker-spreading Woolly Aphides.

With the thorough cleaning of the trees in the winter, new environmental conditions were set up for all the remaining pests and parasites. The lichen and mosses vanished, the Canker and Woolly Aphis retreated, and the Apple Scab, Codling Moth and, later, the Red Spider came to the fore. All the small wild flora and fauna which escaped the winter campaign multiplied in the spring and summer, and ways had to be found of combating them when the foliage was on the trees. Nobody could take exception to the American practice of spraying the bare trees with caustic soda or with paraffin and milk or soft soap. It was otherwise with the next part of the programme, which was to attack the 'biting-insects', i.e. the leaf-eating caterpillars, and the maggots before they could get into the apples, by spraying the trees with arsenical compounds in the spring.

This practice had arisen out of the successful use of Paris Green against the Colorado Beetle on the potatoes; it was first tried against the larvae of the Codling Moth on apple trees about 1879. By 1891 or '92 spraying with Paris Green, or with white arsenic, or with London Purple – an arsenical waste product of the synthetic dye industry, tinted with residues of the dye – had become almost universal in the American orchards. It was highly effective, and as it was done before the apples were as large as peas, the risk of any dangerous amount of arsenic remaining on the fruit when it was fully grown need not have alarmed anybody. A few of the English growers were just beginning to use arsenic in the same way, about 1895, and in another fifteen years or so there would be scarcely an apple grown in any English commercial orchard that was *not* treated with arsenic in the spring. But there was a great outcry in the English press about arsenic on the *American* apples. As Riley, of the Department of Agriculture in Washington, did not fail to point out, it was easier to raise this scare, and even to entertain hopes that the importation of American apples might be prohibited, than to compete fairly with them in price and quality. He estimated that it would be necessary to eat thirty-eight barrels of the apples, cores and all, to absorb any dangerous amount of arsenic from them.

Because of the copper in the Paris Green, spraying with this substance to kill the grubs and caterpillars had also some effect on the parasitic fungi. As Professor Goff, of the Experiment Station at Madison, found in the course of trials between 1888 and 1891, Paris Green while almost completely preventing damage by the Codling Moth, also checked the Apple Scab. But the real part which the introduction of spraying with insecticides played in the war against the fungi was that it provided all the necessary machines for spraying the trees in the spring with fungicides as such. In 1887 there were only some half a hundred growers in America using spraying machines, by 1892 there were fifty thousand fruit-growers alone, from the Atlantic to the Pacific and from the Great Lakes to the Gulf, spraying in accordance with the recommendations of the Department of Agriculture. The apparatus devised and recommended by Riley and his co-workers for the application of insecticides was ready to hand in the orchards for the application of copper fungicides just as soon as Galloway and his team had shown them to be effective. The machinery was not very complicated but it had to be *there*. Usually it comprised a barrel, mounted on a low horse-drawn cart, and fitted with a force-pump which was operated by one man, while another, armed with a spray-lance, connected to the pump by a length of rubber hose, worked over the trees. The vital part of the equipment was the nozzle from which the spray was projected. The perfect nozzle, as Lodeman pointed out in 1896, was simply the end of a hose and a man's thumb. By varying the pressure of the thumb, the spray could be made fine or coarse, fan-shaped or squirt-like, voluminous or restricted, at will. But unfortunately the human thumb soon tired, and a metal nozzle had to be invented to take its place. Many devices were tried: the liquid was forced between two flat plates of metal pressed together, jets were pulverized by causing them to impinge on deflectors. But about the most practical and satisfactory nozzle of all was Riley's cyclone, in which the liquid was made to whirl round at high-velocity in a small chamber behind the orifice before it emerged. With this nozzle, and a good pressure from the pump, the spray could be made so fine that it would hang in the air like a mist and cover the foliage both evenly and economically. It was only a little bit of brass, but the invention of an efficient nozzle was in fact as important in the history of spraying as that of the bicycle valve in the history of the pneumatic tyre.

With spraying machinery available and the fungicidal effect of copper mixtures known, the American orchardists were ready for the attack on the one remaining parasitic fungus on the apple trees which eclipsed all others in causing disfigurement and loss of the fruit, then known as *Fusicladium dendriticum*, the Apple Scab fungus. In the old days, when the apples were tumbled into baskets as they came from the trees and sold unsorted on local markets, it had not mattered very much about the familiar black spots and patches on the apples. They did not spoil the taste and they were removed when the apples were peeled. But when the fruit had to arrive sound on distant markets, nicely graded into sizes, all spit-and-polish, and of an almost artificial perfection of shape and colour to please the silly eyes of townsfolk, then those apples which were at all noticeably scabbed, though they were perfectly wholesome, became an almost total loss to the fruit-growers. And it was not only that the consumers liked fruit in the shops which resembled as far as possible the wax fruit under glass domes in Victorian sitting-rooms. The Scab fungus did not only affect the mere *appearance* of the fruit; it was a contributory cause of rot during transit and storage, it sometimes half-defoliated the trees, it scarred the apples when they were small, distorting them, and preventing many of them from growing to full size. The yield of fruit was reduced in quantity no less than in quality. It was during the nineties that the real extent of the damage caused by the Apple Scab fungus began to be recognized, not only in the States, but in Canada, Australia, Tasmania, Germany, England – wherever apples were grown. With the progressive industrialization and expansion of the commercial apple orchards, the Apple Scab became as serious a source of loss to the fruit-growers as the Blight was to the potato-growers, or the Rust to the wheat-farmers. It was one of the principal fungus diseases of the crops.

The discovery that a weak solution of copper sulphate would check the development of the Scab fungus on pear trees was made by Paul Olivier, in France in 1881 – two or three years before the discovery of Bordeaux mixture. In 1886, Ricaud, also in France, sprayed a few apple trees with Bordeaux mixture itself, and found that it had some positive effect in controlling the Apple Scab, the causal fungus of which was very similar to but not identical with that on the pears. Thereafter, it was in the United States, and in Canada, that all the early experimental work was done. When Lamson-Scribner and Galloway were 'importing' the new fungicidal sprays from France and getting them tried against all sorts of fungus diseases of plants, it was Goff, of the State Experimental Station at Madison, who turned his hand to the work on the Apple and Pear Scab. He first tried a 1 per cent solution of ordinary photographic hypo, or sodium thiosulphate; and he also tried the old liver of sulphur, or potassium sulphide. Rather too hastily, perhaps, he dropped these experiments with sulphur in favour of the new copper mixtures, and by 1891 he had done enough to show that the latter would unquestionably prevent the Scab, if applied at the right time. Bordeaux mixture was the best, though he had obtained good results also with Burgundy mixture and Eau Celeste. There was, however, a snag: the copper sprays had in some instances caused serious injury to the sensitive foliage of the apple trees and it was evident that much careful work remained to be done in determining the best and safest mixture for general recommendation. Several other workers now joined in, but progress was not so extremely rapid as in the adoption of spraying with copper mixtures for the prevention of many other plant diseases in the States. A great responsibility rested upon Galloway, as Chief of the Division of Plant Pathology; he was as cautious as he was enterprising, and it was a few years before the majority of the American apple-growers had extended their spraying programmes to include the use of Bordeaux mixture, at a reduced strength, against the Apple Scab.

Meanwhile, there was a mystery about the life-history of the Scab fungus itself, and the way in which it caused the superficial spots and blotches on the fruit, though well-known to the mycologists, was by no means self-evident to the growers. According to Charles Whitehead, writing in the *Journal of the Royal Agricultural Society of England* in 1891, the majority of the English fruit-growers, at any rate, had not the slightest idea of the origin of the Scab on the apple trees, and they would probably have smiled at the very suggestion that any spraying with copper mixtures could stop it. The fungus was one which grew at first just under the cuticle of the young leaves and fruit, forming a pad of toughened spawn between it and the underlying part of the outer wall of the epidermis or skin. The cuticle over this pad then broke, the torn edges of it remaining as a fringe – whence the name 'Scab'. A crop of stumpy, dark-coloured spores, each on a very short branch, arose on the exposed spawn-pad, the mass appearing to the naked eye black and velvety. The spawn continued to grow for a time, enlarging the spots by biting under the surrounding cuticle, the edge of which was cut into an indented pattern – whence the specific epithet *dendriticum* in the name then given to the fungus. As soon as the skin of the leaf or of the young apple began to toughen with the advance of the summer, the growth of the fungus was checked. The loose spores drifted away from the Scab spots, leaving a bald area of old spawn-pad. This remained as a permanent scar, stretching a little as the apple grew, but usually restricting growth in its vicinity so that the fruit bulged on the opposite side, if the skin there was unaffected. It was evident that once these bald pads of old 'mushroom-tissue' were on the apples there was nothing that could be done about them. The young foliage and fruit had to be protected against invasion by the fungus in the early spring, when its fructifications were easily recognizable as dark olive green or velvety growths. No one who carefully examined the black spots at this early stage could have any doubt about the Apple Scab being a fungus disease. It began on the new leaves before the flower-buds opened and on the infant fruit as soon as the petals had fallen.

But where did the first spores come from? What was the source of primary infection in the spring? *Fusicladium dendriticum* was one of the *Fungi Imperfecti*; only its summer stage was known — how did it survive the winter? There was the same vexed problem as with the Potato Blight — where were the perfect fruits of the fungus, its 'winter spores'? Or was it a perennial, surviving by dormant spawn? While these questions remained unanswered there was an uneasy feeling that all attempts to combat the disease by spraying were being made in the dark. The function of spraying was to protect the young growth from infection by air-borne spores. Yes. But from infection by spores from *what source*? Failing this knowledge the only thing to do was to protect the foliage by spraying at the time when such protection seemed to be required, and to see whether this treatment proved effective in practice.

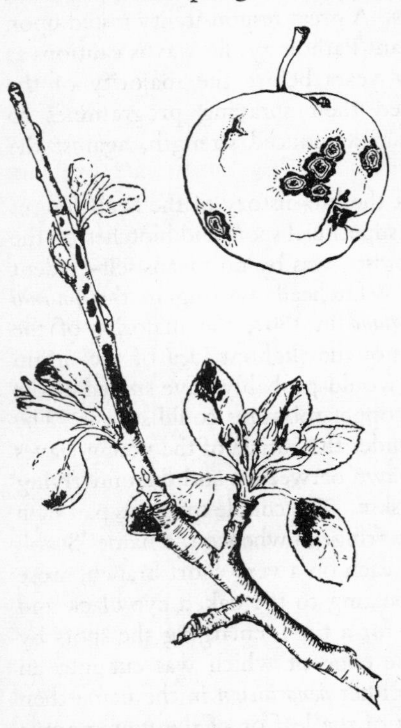

FIG. 48. Apple Scab.
W. A. R. Dillon Weston, 1939

Fortunately it did. By about 1895 it had been firmly established, both in the United States and in Canada, that spraying the trees four times with Bordeaux mixture, (*a*) just as the buds were opening, (*b*) just before blossoming, (*c*) just after the flower petals had fallen, and (*d*) when the apples were about half an inch in diameter, would effectively protect the fruit from damage by the Apple Scab fungus, *wherever its spores came from in the spring*. Some varieties of apple, particularly sensitive to copper, were 'scorched' or 'russeted' to some extent by this treatment — a drawback that remained to be overcome — but the loss on this score was small compared with the enormous gain in having all the apples clean and substantially free from the Scab. The American growers now went ahead, the Canadians and Australians promptly following suit. In terms of cash, the spraying cost thirty to fifty cents per tree, all told, and the net profit was from three to seven dollars per tree. When the number of apple trees in the United States alone was fast approaching two hundred million – the figure in the Census of 1900 – the economic significance of this victory over yet another plant disease was apparent. And it was apparent also how closely every smallest detail of the treatment had yet to be investigated by experiment, for recommendations from the Department which might mean only an average gain of a single cent per apple tree, would make a difference of a million dollars to the national economy. The Experiment Stations in the States, and the new Divisions of the Department of Agriculture, were beginning to pay for themselves many times over.

Sure, the American orchardists saw it in terms of cash; and certainly they wasted no time before adopting a treatment which substantially lowered the cost of production, and gave them yet a further advantage over their less wide-awake competitors. But dollars or pounds sterling were never the proper units in which to express the value of a victory over a disease, whether it was of apples or of man. Everything that the fruit-growers could gain by years of spraying could be lost in an hour by a slump of the market, a change of fiscal policy or a financial manœuvre on Wall Street. The gain, as the plant-doctors and all scientific men saw it, was an increase in the power of man to suppress the jungle and to defy the elements. Ultimately it was no less than that, for in the past the amount of Scab on the apples had depended upon the weather. When the air was humid or wet in the spring, the fungus had spread and there had been much Scab; when it was dry there had been less. Now, good weather or bad, there need be very little Scab. One of the elements of chance in the cultivation of apples had been eliminated.

It was so also with the cultivation of many other fruits: Bulletin No. 6 of Galloway's Division in 1894 reviewed all the plant diseases which had been successfully treated with Bordeaux mixture (or with potassium sulphide) in the United States – Apple Scab, Pear Scab, Black Rot and Anthracnose of the Grape, Pear Leaf Blight, Gooseberry Mildew, the Leaf Blights of Cherries and Plums . . . Behind it all there was a great swirl of technical activity, many workers participating; the accounts of it were all there, in the publications of the Department and the Experiment Stations – Bulletins, Circulars and still more Bulletins. A wealth of scientific and practical detail into which only the specialist, in later years, would desire to delve. The story of the introduction of the French mixtures into America, their formulae, and all that was done with them in the States, up to about 1895, was finely told by E. G.

Lodeman, Instructor in Horticulture at Cornell University, in his book *The Spraying of Plants*, published by Macmillan in 1896. This brought the information in the columns of the *Journal d'agriculture pratique* and other French periodicals and *Mémoires*, into the English language, provided a very complete key to all the French and American literature, and made the study of one chapter, at least, in the history of plant pathology a matter of easy reference for English readers.

The innovation of spraying fruit with copper compounds, no less than with arsenic, at first was met with criticism in Great Britain, designed to prejudice consumers against the American fruit, and the Department had several interesting things to say about traces of copper in foodstuffs. The preserved beans and peas which were a speciality of France, were steeped into a solution of copper sulphate for ten minutes during the course of their preparation, to give them a permanent green colour which made them look very fresh and appetizing. They contained from 11 to 125 milligrams of copper per kilo. Great Britain imported fourteen million pounds of these re-greened vegetables from France in 1890, and they contained twenty times as much copper as there was in all the fruit in the United States combined. Many foodstuffs contained far more copper than did sprayed fruit. Even wheat, which certainly was not sprayed with anything at all, contained over 7 milligrams of copper per kilo; there were in fact no less than ten tons of copper in the 3,263,266,020 pounds of wheat exported in 1890. Those who imagined that traces of copper were poisonous, rather than indispensable for health, had better give up eating bread. And as for chocolate, *that* contained no less than 125 milligrams of copper per kilo. The average, for all foodstuffs, according to Tschirch of Stuttgart, who devoted a whole book to the subject in 1893, was 0.93 milligrams per kilo.

After a practical remedy for the Apple Scab had been found in spraying with copper mixtures, determined search was made into the life-history of the Apple Scab fungus itself. The usual order was reversed. Since it was first reported by the Swedish botanist, Elias Fries, in 1819, the summer stage of the fungus had been described again and again in botanical works; it had been re-named several times as it was shifted out of one generic category into another; it was common in every country where apples were grown, but it seemed that no one had ever seen its perfect stage. The taxonomists, as was their habit in such cases, assigned the organism to that convenient rubbish heap which they called the *Fungi Imperfecti*. That sounded very well, and it more than half conveyed the impression that human ignorance about the fungus was one of its natural attributes. It was in Germany, home of the great morphologists and physiologists, that the search was made. The German workers, deep and slow and thorough, delving down into the darkest mysteries of living things, could never rest content with half an Organismus. It left an ache, a ragged void; it cried aloud to Himmel for its other half.

Herr Dr. Rudolf Aderhold, of the Royal Pomological Institute at Proskau, spent ten years investigating the Apple Scab fungus, beginning in 1891 or thereabouts, but it did not take him ten years to find the missing winter stage. He described it in 1894. It was not so hard to find that the fungus could hide its double life for very long when subjected to any thorough-going cross-examination. In fact Aderhold was neither the first to describe the missing stage nor to recognize it for what it was, and, as he discovered, when searching the literature, it had been *found* long since – by none other than Mordecai Cubitt Cooke, of *Grevillea* and the Woolhope Naturalists' Club.

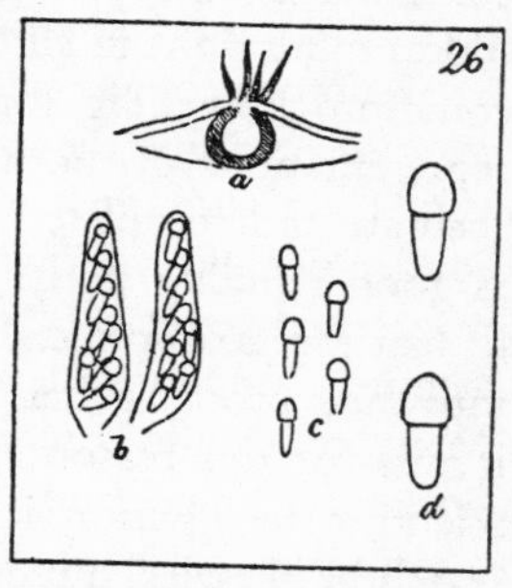

FIG. 49. Winter fruits of a fungus, first called *Sphaerella inaequalis*, found on fallen apple leaves.
M. C. Cooke, 1866

In 1865, Cooke had proposed to his friend, Dr. Capron, of Shere, in Surrey, that they should examine all the minute fungi of the kinds known as *Sphaeriae* and *Venturia*, that they could find on dead leaves in their respective localities during the winter. They poked about under hedges, and in ditches, and between them collected a great many, including some that had never been reported before – a very good 'bag'. Cooke published a list of the finds in Seeman's *Journal of Botany* for 1866, and he included a drawing of each one – very nearly small enough to go on a postage stamp. No. 26 was one of those which were 'new' and had therefore to be described in Latin. Because the two halves of its double ascospores were of different sizes, Cooke called it *Sphaerella inaequalis*. In his figure (here reproduced, Fig. 49) (*a*) represented a section through one of the black conceptacles or perithecia, in actual size rather smaller than a pin's head, found just under the skin of decayed leaves; (*b*) further enlarged, represented two of the minute sacs of spores contained within the ripe perithecia; while (*c*) and (*d*) still further enlarged, represented the spores themselves and showed the characteristic 'inequality' of their two parts. Dr. Capron found this fungus on the dead leaves of *Pyrus Aria*, and Cooke found it on those of Ash, Hawthorn, Pear and Apple. He remarked that 'it was apparently very common', but it certainly did not occur to him that it had anything to do with the Scab fungus found on the apple trees in the summer.

Twenty-one years later, in 1887, a German naturalist and writer on scientific horticulture, R. Goethe, contributed an admirable paper to *Gartenflora*, in which he not only described such perithecia as Cooke had found, on fallen leaves of both apple and pear trees, but unhesitatingly asserted that they were the overwintering or 'perfect' fruits of the Apple and Pear Scab fungi respectively. Goethe's paper was accompanied by a fine double-plate on which he showed the ripe perithecia of both fungi in considerable detail, with stages in their development, together with the corresponding summer or conidial stages, the Scab pustules on the young wood of the trees, and the growth of the mycelium between the cuticle and the outer cell-walls of the epidermis on the young leaves. He did not get the shape of the summer spores quite right in all his figures of them; he was in error in showing one conidium branching forth from the side of another; but for the rest his representations of both fungi, if a little diagrammatic, were remarkably accurate and complete. *Gartenflora* was an old-established journal, of about as good standing as the English *Gardeners' Chronicle*, but Goethe neglected to bait the taxonomists, in that he made no attempt to shift the two fungi into their proper generic category when he figured their perfect stages, and it was for this reason, perhaps, that his contribution failed to receive the scientific recognition it deserved, until Aderhold 'discovered' it. Further search in libraries, museums and herbaria later on, also brought to light von Thümen's *Mycothecia Universalis* No. 1544 of 1880, in which the botanist, Winter, had placed specimens of the perithecia and of *Fusicladium dendriticum* side by side, as parts of one whole, which he labelled, correctly as it turned out, but without a word of explanation, as a species of Venturia.

Aderhold took his cue from Goethe's work, found some of the perithecia which Goethe had described, on apple leaves, and cultivated the Apple Scab fungus from its (asco-)spores sown in nutrient media. He also performed inoculation experiments with these spores on young apple trees. The spores gave rise to growths of the fungus that was called *Fusicladium dendriticum* on the leaves, and thus the truth of Goethe's claim was established. But the fungus was no longer properly to be called *Fusicladium dendriticum*, for that was only the vegetative and asexual stage of the fungus whose 'perfect' fruits were those found on the dead leaves. Aderhold renamed the whole fungus *Venturia inaequalis* in 1897. Although opinions were to differ about the attributions that should be tacked on at the tail — some saying that they should be '(Cooke) Aderhold', others that '(Wallroth) Winter' would be more closely in accordance with the rules of botanical law — and although the English workers went on calling the fungus *Fusicladium dendriticum* for

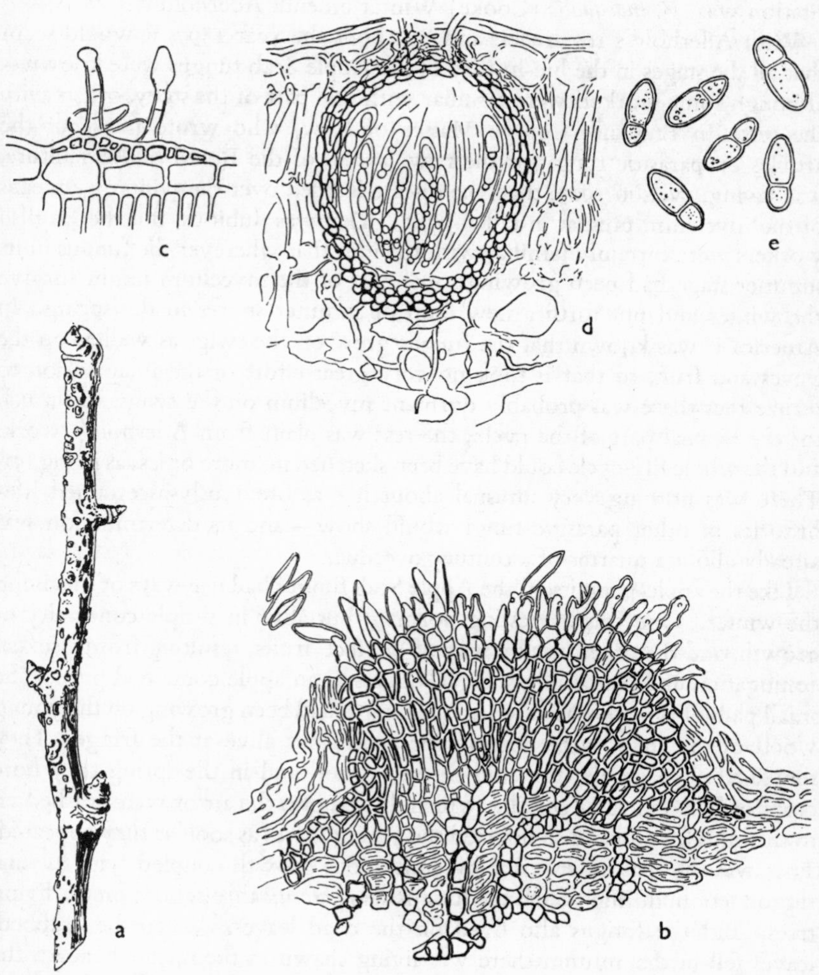

FIG. 50. The Pear Scab fungus. (*a*) Scab pustules on a pear twig. (*b*) cross-section through one of the Scab pustules, greatly magnified, showing the conidia or summer spores and the thickened mycelium reaching into the tissues of its host. (*c*) Mycelium growing beneath the cuticle of a young leaf and putting forth summer spores (Apple Scab fungus). (*d*) Fully ripe perithecium in a fallen pear leaf. (*e*) Ascospores. After Goethe, 1887

another quarter of a century or so, *Venturia inaequalis* was the name by which it would be known everywhere in 1939, when the accepted full-dress author citation was '*V. inaequalis* (Cooke) Winter emend. Aderhold'.

With Aderhold's researches, and by about the year 1897, it would seem that all the stages in the life-history of the Apple Scab fungus were known – although some workers were familiar with one part of the story, others with the rest. In England, George Massee of Kew, who wrote many of the articles on parasitic fungi for the new *Journal* of the Board of Agriculture, was saying, even in 1903, that 'the disease is tided over the winter by means of the mycelium present in fallen fruit'. *That* was dubious, but the English workers were certainly familiar with the idea that wherever the fungus in its summer stage had been growing some part of the mycelium might survive the winter and put forth a new crop of summer spores in the spring. In America it was known that the fungus grew on the twigs as well as on the leaves and fruit, so that it took no very great effort of the imagination to realize that there was probably dormant mycelium on the twigs. So much for the asexual part of the cycle; the rest was plain from Aderhold's work, and the whole life-cycle could have been sketched in, more or less as in Fig. 51. There was nothing very unusual about it – as previously-ascertained life-histories of other parasitic fungi would show – and its determination was already about a quarter of a century overdue.

Like the apple-plant itself, the Apple Scab fungus had *two* ways of surviving the winter. One was by resting dormant but alive in simple continuity of growth, and the other was by way of 'perfect' fruits, resulting from a sexual conjugation and containing survival-spores as an apple contained pips. The small pads of fungus spawn where the fungus had been growing on the young wood of the trees, were dead in the centre but alive at the fringe. They remained alive despite the cold of the winter, and in the spring they bore crops of bud-spores or conidia, which drifted into the air or were washed on to the buds by rain and so infected the young leaves as soon as they appeared. That was the way of survival by continuous growth coupled with asexual reproduction, during which the fungus was *parasitic* throughout on the living trees. But the fungus also lived on the dead leaves. When the 'scabbed' leaves fell in the autumn there was living spawn in them, just beneath the cuticle. As the leaf decayed the underlying cellular tissue softened and the spawn of the fungus extended into it. Thus, on the dead leaves, the fungus lived, as a scavenger or *saprophyte*, and, simultaneously nourished but threatened by the decay that its own spawn would ultimately have to share, it fused certain pairs of its nuclei together – male to female – and began to form well-protected survival fruits. The pairs of nuclei divided into two after fusion, and then into two, and two again, so that there were eight spores – or rather pairs of 'unequal' spores – in each of the spore sacs. Many of these sacs grew up side by side in the developing fruits, and by a process as wonderful as any building of silken cocoons by insects, the sacs were enclosed in a beautiful tight capsule, entirely composed of interwoven and compacted

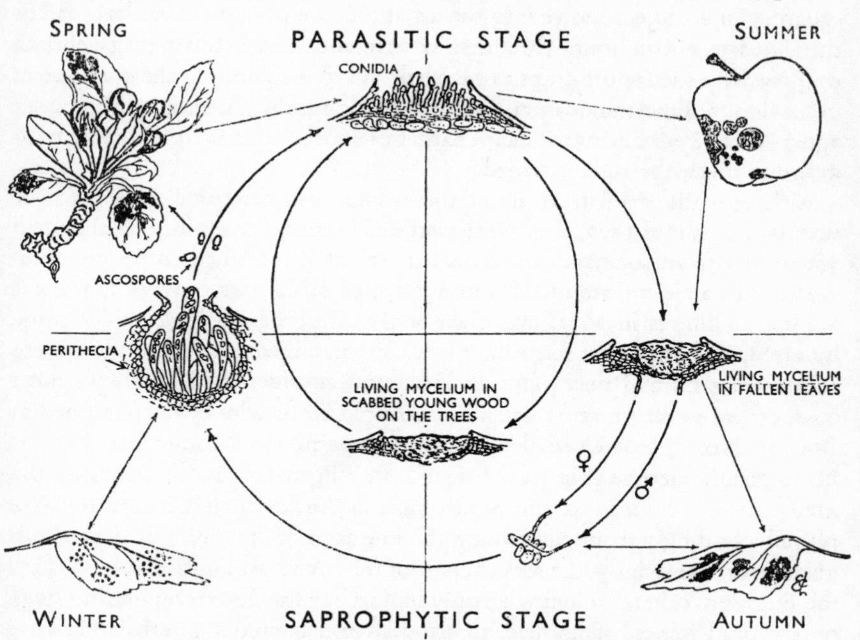

FIG. 51. The Life-cycle of the Apple Scab fungus, *Venturia inaequalis.*

spawn-strands. All through the winter these fruits were developing on the dead leaves, and by the spring they were ripe. Then they opened, and thanks to one of nature's highly ingenious seed-and-spore-disseminating mechanisms they were projected half an inch or so into the air. They were then lofted by the slightest movement of the breeze and some of them reached the opening buds on the trees above, or, when liberated a little later, the young fruit and leaves. They there germinated and gave rise to the growth of the Scab fungus in its familiar summer phase. When these facts were known, the protective spraying of the apple foliage with Bordeaux mixture was no longer a step in the dark. It had to protect the foliage from infection by spores from two sources – the Scab pustules on the twigs and bud-scales, and the multitudinous perithecia on the dead leaves under the trees. Evidently the spraying could be assisted by cutting out as much as possible of the 'scabby' wood and burning or burying the dead leaves. But however carefully the dead leaves might be dealt with, there would always remain a few on the surface, and the perithecia on an area of dead leaf only half an inch square, could project spores into the air at the rate of about five thousand in three-quarters of an hour. Countless experiments were made in the twentieth century with such spore-traps as Marshall Ward used among the coffee-trees in Ceylon, to determine when, and for how long, the perithecia on the dead apple leaves were liberating their charges of spores, so that the spraying programme might be rightly timed.

Although the main facts about the Apple Scab fungus were known or surmised by about 1897, they were scattered, very scattered indeed; they had yet to be drawn together, and a wealth of detail remained to be explored. Aderhold's basic contributions were confirmed by Clinton of the Experiment Station at Illinois in 1901, and even at that time he was able to list some hundred and forty other scientific papers on the subject. By 1913, there were as many again, and they were all listed and considered in Wallace's most comprehensive key monograph on the Apple Scab, which was published as Bulletin No. 335 of Cornell University Experiment Station, in that year. In England, George Massee of Kew, and Professor E. S. Salmon, the Economic Mycologist at the South-Eastern Agricultural College at Wye, played a leading part in confirming the infection of the leaves from the Scab pustules on the twigs – the asexual part of the cycle. But until as late as 1925, the English workers looked with only half an eye for the overwintering stage on the dead leaves. They had a curiously insular conviction that this stage could well occur in the United States and in Germany, but not in Great Britain. When Dr. Ware, of Wye College, disregarded the opinions of authorities, and, in 1925, really looked for the perithecia on the dead leaves, he found them. Not by a rare accident and under a single tree, but under many trees in several different localities in Kent, all in the same year; and he also found the corresponding perithecia of the Scab fungus on the pears. The difference in emphasis upon the two sources of primary infection, in the United States and in England, arose, no doubt, from the fact that several varieties of apples grown in England were more susceptible to Scab on the young wood than the generality of those in the States. But *both* sources of infection were nevertheless operative, in greater or lesser degree, in both countries.

Aderhold had found, by 1896, that none of the four hundred and fifty different varieties of apple grown in Germany was *immune* from the Apple Scab; but in Germany, as elsewhere, some of the varieties were much less susceptible than others. Was there any indication that the troublesome spraying with scabicidal mixtures could be avoided, and that fruit reasonably free from Scab could be obtained, by the method of breeding and selecting Scab-resistant varieties of apple for commercial cultivation? Unfortunately there were great difficulties blocking progress in this direction. An apple tree raised up from seed was several years old before it came into bearing; experiments in crossing Scab-resistant apples with those having desired economic qualities would necessarily take a long time. And then again, such an apple as the Cox's Orange Pippin was already something of a miracle; in ten thousand experimental hybrids an equal excellence in the quality of the fruit might not reappear, and the hope of combining such excellence with the qualities of Scab-resistance was about as remote as that of obtaining sweet vinegar or non-intoxicating gin. Experience was to show that the consumers in the towns would accept tough-skinned and insipid apples provided they had a good colour and appearance – this was to give the breeders and the commercial fruit-growers an important measure of latitude. But there was another, and an intrinsic difficulty in the method of combating plant diseases by the choice of resistant varieties; it was stated, prophetically, by Professor Bailey in the United States as early as 1892. He thought that it might be possible to produce apple-varieties which would be 'Scab-proof' *for a time*. 'But', he went on, 'this is a common history of injurious insects and fungi; they take on new habits to accommodate themselves to new conditions. It is possible a good market apple may spring up that is Scab-proof; but when we have learned to produce such kinds with tolerable certainty, the fungi will have grown cunning too – I fear.'

CHAPTER XXII

WHEAT–SPECIES IN THE MAKING

THE greatest single undertaking in the history of applied Plant Pathology was to be the attack on the Rust diseases of cereals. Not on paper, or by laboratory research alone, but in practice, and over vast expanses of steppes, patunas and prairies. The Apple Scab in the orchards, the Mildew in the vineyards, even the Blight in the potato-fields – these were minor and localized murrains beside the Rusts of the grain crops. In all the great grain-producing countries the Rust epidemics were more disastrous than Fire or Flood; the produce lost was the principal staple foodstuff, the biologic fuel of Western civilization. In Australia, in 1889, following an unusually wet spring and humid weather when the wheat was in flower, there had been a Rust epidemic which in terms of money alone cost the Commonwealth between two and three million pounds. In Prussia, in 1892, the total loss from Rust, on all cereals, was estimated at over twenty million pounds. In the United States, in 1894, Mark Alfred Carleton, when beginning his cereal investigations for the Department, toured the wheat-growing States of the Great Plains and the Mississippi valley, and found Rust so prevalent in some States that the cultivation of wheat was being abandoned. The total loss throughout the States was entirely beyond estimation from any data then available, but it exceeded that due to any other enemy, insect or fungus, and often equalled the losses from all others combined. The Rusts of the Argentine, Russia and South Africa were as yet almost totally unexplored.

The mighty Rust investigations, soon to be world-wide, began in Australia with a series of Rust-in-Wheat conferences, following the epidemic of 1889. There were Cobb and McAlpine out there, and Farrer, a private wheat-breeder who produced some of the earliest improved hybrid varieties. Then, in the United States there was Mark Alfred Carleton; in Canada, William Saunders and his sons; in Sweden, Professor Jacob Eriksson. These were among the men whose names would be remembered.

The classical researches of Anton de Bary and the brothers Tulasne had long since established the parasitism of the Rust fungi, revealed their successive 'fruits', and demonstrated that the Black Stem Rust of the wheat had one of its stages on the barberry. The existence of this stage had been questioned, furiously disputed, and even derided by some workers – by W. G.

Smith in England, for example – and although the great majority accepted it as established fact, all discussion about the Rust on the wheat for twenty-five years, had, as it were, ended up in a barberry bush. The business of 'heteroecism' was so fascinating that that other part of the life-cycle of the Rust fungus, the 'inner loop' of asexual reproduction on the wheat and wild grasses alone, received all too little attention. Supposing it were possible to destroy all the barberry bushes, then, if the fungus had a stage on the barberry, such destruction would seem to be desirable. If the fungus had no such stage, then destroying the barberry bushes would do no good – and so the argument went on. Looking back over the history of the disputes about the Rust fungi, the Apple Scab fungus and the rest, it would almost seem that Man suffered from some psychological inability to see *both* loops in the typical life-cycle of a parasitic fungus (Fig. 52), *at the same time*. The mind went round and round the outer circle, considering survival by sexual reproduction, *or* it went round and round the inner loop, arguing that the organism survived by asexual reproduction alone. It rarely made the *whole* journey at any one time. Now, in the Rust investigations, it was the turn of the inner loop; the outer circle which included the stage on the barberry passing for a while out of mind. That the Rust on the wheat was often very bad in the neighbourhood of such bushes was a well-authenticated fact, but against that, the Rust swept over thousands of miles of wheat in Australia, where barberry bushes were exceedingly rare and the fungus would not grow on them even when they were imported; while in India, if Dr. Barclay's observations were to be relied upon, the Rust was certainly very destructive in the Himalayan regions where there were plenty of barberries, but equally destructive in the South where there were few or none. Except in Denmark, where Rostrup was campaigning for the destruction of the bushes over the whole Kingdom, the barberry was now given the go-by.

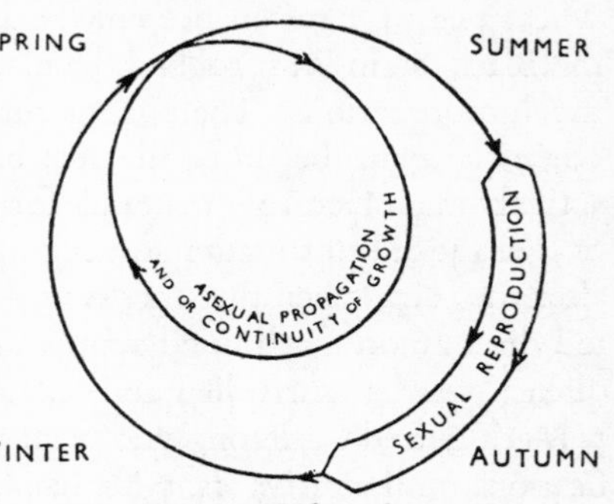

FIG. 52. Life-cycle.

When the great investigations began in the nineties there were two kinds of Rust known on the wheat, and then distinguished by the botanists, but hopelessly confused with each other by the farmers. When it was reported that in this or that territory there was a great deal of Rust, no one could say for certain which Rust was meant. There was the Orange Leaf-Rust caused by *Puccinia rubigo-vera*, and there was the Black Stem Rust caused by *Puccinia graminis*. Both these Rusts had a 'red' and a 'black' stage, corresponding to the production of their uredo- and their teleuto-spores (Fig. 24, p. 134). The one was called the Orange Leaf-Rust because its 'red' or rather 'orange' stage on the leaf-blades was more prevalent and more conspicuous than its black stage which came later; while the Black Stem Rust, which could easily be mistaken for the other in its 'red' or uredo-stage, had an unmistakable and extremely destructive black stage on the stems. The Orange Leaf-Rust did not grow on the barberry at all, though it was said to have a Cluster-cup stage on borage. The distinction between these two different Rusts was exceedingly important, for the Orange Leaf-Rust robbed the wheat plant for sustenance chiefly during the early stages of growth, while the Black Stem Rust robbed the plants later, when the drain upon them was much more serious. There was a turning point in the life of the wheat-plant when the grain began to fill out: before that the leaf and root system was actively manufacturing materials for growth, and if parasitic fungi stole some of them it did not matter so very much as the plant could make more; but after the turn, when the straw was beginning to ripen, the Black Stem Rust fed directly on the limited supplies destined for the grain, which in consequence was left shrivelled and lean.

Mark Alfred Carleton, who went for the main facts first and left the qualifications until afterwards, said that however serious the Orange Leaf-Rust might be in other countries, it did comparatively little damage to the wheat in the United States – it never caused much shrivelling of the grain. The Black Stem Rust was responsible where the wheat was a total loss in Kentucky, Indiana, Texas, Michigan and Ohio: it was *Puccinia graminis* on which one had to concentrate, *that* narrowed the problem down a little, but it brought one back to the everlasting talk about Barberry bushes. Carleton was more than a little impatient with all this talk that led nowhere, and there was another thing that struck him as very queer about *Puccinia graminis* – the number of graminiferous host plants on which it was supposed to grow. Whether it was in America, or Sweden, or Australia, on wheat or oats or barley, or on any one of some thirty-five to a hundred species of wild grasses, the *Puccinia graminis* was supposed to be always the same – a fixed and invariant species. That a single parasitic fungus should be adapted by nature to live on so many different host plants was a very remarkable phenomenon. So remarkable that it merited a little investigation.

As far as it was possible to see by examining specimens with the naked eye or under the microscope, the fungi causing the Black Stem Rust on the wheat, oats, rye, barley and various wild grasses did appear to be pretty much the same. But were they, in fact, the same? That was the question. Between 1892 and 1896 Carleton grew the various cereals in pots in a greenhouse and tried to infect the wheat plants with uredospores from the Rust on the oats. The attempt failed – the spores from the Rust on the oats would not infect wheat, barley, or rye. And with the exception of the Rust on the wheat, which *did* infect the barley, he found that the Rust on one cereal would not infect the others. There was not one *Puccinia graminis* but several, to be distinguished from one another only by the kinds of wild or cultivated grasses on which they would grow.

Meanwhile, Professor Eriksson had pushed such experiments rather further in studying the cereal Rusts of Sweden, and he had already sorted the single *Puccinia graminis* of his botanical forefathers into six specialized forms: *P. graminis sp.f. Avenae*, to be found on oats and some half-dozen wild grasses; *P. graminis sp.f. Tritici*, to be found on wheat and barley and a few other of the grasses; *P. graminis sp.f. Secalis*, on rye, and so forth. These special forms of the fungus which differed so widely in their ability to parasitize the different cereals could perhaps be regarded as species in the making. Forms in which adaptation and natural selection had gone far enough to make profound physiological differences, but not far enough to alter the external appearance of the parts of the organisms, in so far as those alterations could be seen by man with the aids to vision available.

Here was an even sweeter subject for disputative botanists than de Bary's 'heteroecism'. What were these special forms of *P. graminis* on the different cereals properly to be called? It depended upon the views held by the disputant about the ways in which new species did or did not arise in nature. The Origin of Species was a subject about which all naturalists, for some reason or other, felt very strongly, and now that some species had apparently been detected in the act of originating under the group name of *Puccinia graminis*, many jealous passions were aroused. Even Hugo de Vries' mutating Evening Primrose could scarcely cause a greater stir. Were these special forms of *P. graminis* really species in an early stage of differentiation? Sub-species? Adapted species? Physiological forms? Biological races? The trouble was that for all the hypotheses and speculations no one really knew *why* the Rust on the oats would not grow on the wheat, and any name given to that particular form of the Rust was very liable to prejudice the issue and to sanction one botanist's view of what was happening to the exclusion of another's.

Mark Alfred Carleton said, in effect, oh, call the special forms *varieties* and be done with it! Why should there not be varieties of a parasitic fungus just as there are varieties of the cereals themselves? Let's call the fungus which causes the particular Black Stem Rust on the Wheat simply *Puccinia graminis tritici* for convenience of reference, and get on with the job. The wheat cannot be affected by the Rust on the oats or the rye; that's all that matters for the moment – the problem was thus a little further narrowed down.

Some varieties of wheat resisted attack by *P. graminis tritici* better than others. Again, no one knew why, but failing all certain knowledge of how the Rust started in the spring – where there were no barberry bushes – the best hope of combating it was plainly in the selection and breeding of resistant varieties, and their gradual substitution for the more susceptible varieties, district by district and State by State. At best this would be the work of more than one lifetime, and before embarking upon it the U.S. Department of Agriculture had made a number of preliminary experiments by way of clearing the ground.

It was not thought that *spraying* the wheat with liquid fungicides or dusting it with sulphur would ever be a practical proposition; the acreage under wheat was too vast, and it would really need flying machines with spraying tackle on board to cope with such a job. Flying machines that would *fly* had not then been invented. But it was of importance to know whether spraying, even of small experimental plots where it could be done, would check the Rust. Trials were made at several of the Experiment Stations in 1891 and '92. At Garrett Park in Maryland eleven different fungicides, including Bordeaux mixture, potassium sulphide, flowers of sulphur and some unusual ones such as copper ferrocyanide and copper borate, were tested on a hundred and seventy-five plots of winter wheat. The spraying – or dusting in the case of the flowers of sulphur – began in November and went on until May, the young plants receiving no less than seventeen treatments at intervals of ten days over this period. The first signs of the Rust appeared on May 1st and by May 20th all the plots were about equally affected. The spraying was a complete failure, not because the sprays were innocuous to the Rust spores, but for the interesting and unexpected reason that the drops of spray ran straight off the leaf-blades. The foliage of cereals being very glossy, and made up of narrow, upstanding or steeply curving leaves, would not 'take' the spray. Even when a five-cent bar of soap was dissolved in each lot of spray mixture to enhance its wetting properties, the plants were still four-fifths unprotected by any persistent spray deposit. In Kansas they were, however, a little more successful than in Maryland; spraying with Bordeaux mixture did have some effect in delaying the development of the Rust, though in the end it made no difference to the yield of grain.

Many attempts were also made, both in the United States and in Australia, to control the Rust by seed-treatments as used against the Smut diseases. Chemical steeps and the Jensen Hot-Water treatment were tried. The experiments were as unsuccessful as they were misconceived, for there was no real evidence that the Rust spores could infect the plants via the seeds, but much evidence that the infection was started on the foliage by air-borne spores when the plants were above ground. Dr. Cobb, in New South Wales, said: 'As for curing the Rust by treating the seed, the idea is fantastic. It would be just as reasonable to expect to prevent measles amongst mankind by soaking babies in some sort of pickle'.

It was often airily asserted by those concerning themselves with what came to be known in the twentieth century as the 'Rape of the Earth' that the Rust was simply attributable to worn-out or exhausted soil. Unfortunately for these people who wanted to improve upon an already strong case by pointing at the undoubted havoc caused by plant diseases, the Rust, in fact, spread as fast or faster over wheat grown on the richest virgin soil as over that where the soil was exhausted or poor. There was always the consideration that the more luxurious the growth of wheat the better food supply it provided for its parasites. Whether the agricultural practice was virtuous or rapacious, from the point of view of the good-earth-and-all-that, the Rust went its own way. McAlpine, in his work on the Rusts of Australia, pointed out that the best crops were often the worst affected by Rust, and had to be cut for hay. Deep-ploughing yielded heavier crops and thus indirectly *favoured* the development of the Rust. The rotation of crops might tend to reduce the Rust, but chiefly for the reason that it kept down volunteer plants on which the Rust fungus could carry over. Burning or ploughing-in the stubble made no difference. And no manurial treatment was found anywhere in New Zealand or Australia that would prevent the Rust. It was found, both in North America and Australia, that an excess of available nitrogen in the soil, whether from artificial fertilizers, or from farmyard manure, or from the original humus, tended to *increase* the loss caused by the Rust, by delaying ripening of the plants and promoting a lush and rather soft growth on which the fungus could proliferate. Phosphates and potash by toughening the foliage and hastening maturity, tended to have the opposite effect. But the Rust was always present, and the severity of the attack in any year depended almost entirely upon the weather. The only practical way of mitigating the losses, short of planting resistant varieties, if they could be produced, was to sow early and to choose kinds of wheat which matured early in the hope that they would ripen before the destructive Black Stem Rust had time to do its worst.

It was to be expected that where there were no barberry bushes this Rust on the wheat would survive the winter, somewhere, by way of its red uredospores, or by way of living spawn that would give rise to the first generation of these spores in the spring. Searches were made for these overwintering uredospores, but they were not at all easy to find. In the United States it was thought that the fungus might survive by way of these delicate spores in the South, where the winters were mild, and that the spores might be blown northwards by relays in the spring. During the winter of 1892, Carleton went exploring through Texas from the Indian territory to the Mexican line, but no trace of overwintering uredospores could he find, either on wheat or on wild grasses. A little later, in 1894, he did find the summer spores of that other Rust, the Orange Leaf-Rust, overwintering in Texas; it passed a perpetual existence in its uredo stage below latitude 40° without the intervention of any other stage. But that was a different matter. In Australia, according to Dr. Cobb in 1892, it was generally accepted that both the Orange Leaf-Rust and the Black Stem Rust existed in their red, uredo, stage all the year round. They probably survived likewise somewhere in the States, but so far as search had gone, those of the Black Stem Rust were, in the winter, nowhere to be found.

Nor were they to be found in Sweden, and the source of primary infection in the spring, when rusted barberry bushes were absent, remained so obscure, and the disease broke out with such apparent spontaneity in 'Rust weather', that Professor Eriksson was moved to revive in a new form the ancient theory that the disease could be latent within the wheat plant itself. That it could be inherited via the seed, so that it could start from *within*, as well as by the germination on the leaves of the spores from an external source.

This theory, first put forward in the *Comptes Rendues* of the French Academy of Sciences for 1897, survived for twenty years or so, and in the words of Harry Marshall Ward, it caused more flutterings in the mycological dovecots than anything since Koch's discovery of the life-history of the Anthrax bacillus in 1876. It was called the 'Mycoplasm Theory', and it was exceedingly difficult either to prove or to disprove. It was based on the supposition that besides its spawn-threads ramifying among the cells of the rusted wheat plant, the fungus might also have detached bits of its naked plasm *within* the host cells – in the form of 'Plasmodium', such as that of the fungus which caused the Club Root disease of cabbages. Eriksson's idea was that these hypothetical bits of naked fungus plasm might fuse with the protoplasm in the cells of the wheat plant itself, forming a sort of mixed living jelly, to be called 'mycoplasm', which would be half fungus and half wheat.

It was to be supposed that the fusion of the alien plasm with that of the wheat was symbiotic and perfectly amicable, so that the cells of the wheat plant were not in any way irritated or deranged by it, except when the Rust 'broke out'. It did not upset the genetical 'works' of the wheat plant; on the contrary, when the nuclei of the cells divided preceding cell-division, the entangled fungal jelly divided also and was thus smoothly transferred from cell to cell as the plant grew, even to the germ cells of the seed. Alternatively it could be supposed that the fungal jelly was capable of 'streaming' through the cell-walls from one cell to another and becoming generalized throughout the green parts of the plant in that way. In fact any supposition could be made, so long as it did not lend itself to refutation by direct observation, and provided that it helped the theory to work. When the seed from such an internally mixed plant was sown and it put forth its shoots, the plasm of the fungus continued to grow mixed with that of the wheat in the cells of the new plant, and in the spring, when the external conditions of humidity and temperature were right, the fungus plasm came out of partnership with that of the wheat, formed independent bits of its own jelly in the cells, which on maturing put forth walled hyphae which penetrated the host cell-walls from within outwards, and gave rise in the intercellular spaces to a tangle of spawn from which the familiar uredospores were first produced.

As there was, seemingly, no way of distinguishing between wheat plasm and fungus plasm in the contents of the cells, this mycoplasm theory, though quite medieval and full of dubiety, was fairly invulnerable. The sheer imaginative audacity of it prevented even those who liked it least from calling it plain moonshine. One had only to hypothecate the existence of mycoplasm, or to take it on faith, and the apparently spontaneous appearance, not only of Rust on the wheat, but, of course, of any other fungus or bacterial disease, was immediately explained. There was no reason why the train of supposition, once started, should ever be cut short. And why confine it to diseases of plants? Why should not some plasm of the bacillus of tuberculosis be mingled symbiotically with the protoplasm of Man? Then it could be necessary for a man to go only cold and overworked and hungry for long enough — if those were the right conditions — and tuberculosis would 'break out'. The hitherto benign latent plasm would disentangle itself and breed myriads of the virulent bacilli of its kind.

It was even possible to explain some of the phenomena of disease-resistance and predisposition by the mycoplasm theory if one was minded to do so. Suppose the existence of Rust-fungus-plasm mixed with that of the wheat was a necessary antecedent condition for the growth of the spawn of the Rust fungus within the wheat plant from the spores germinating on the surface of the foliage. Suppose the fungus-plasm inside said to the germ-tube of the fungus spore without: 'Come in, brother, I've been in this wheat plant and its ancestors for generations. Professor Eriksson says that except when external conditions tempt me to turn into mycelium and put forth things like you, I don't do the wheat any harm. That's all *he* knows. Of course, I've been subtly altering the juices of the plant all the time, getting them ready for you. Come in, little germ-tube; grow into a well-nourished tangle of spawn, put out successive crops of spores, and then be a mycoplasm with me.' It could well be supposed that the external spore would accept such an invitation, while, if it lighted on another plant, which had none of the plasm of the fungus within, penetration, if it occurred at all, would result only in a restricted growth of the fungus, and the plant would be called 'Rust-resistant'.

The mycoplasm theory grew and grew unchecked in the lovely world of the imagination until about 1902, when Eriksson spoilt it by claiming to have seen the '*corpuscules spéciaux*' which one of the Rust fungi formed within the cells of the wheat plant as its plasm was disentangled prior to the origination of mycelial threads *within* the cells. Marshall Ward, at Cambridge, examined these alleged 'special corpuscules', and said that so far as he could see they were simply suckers pushed *into* the cells by the mycelial threads creeping about in the usual way in the intercellular spaces. He could see no sign of 'an erumpent and aggressive stage of the fungus suddenly manifesting itself', and in the august Philosophical Transactions of the Royal Society he made grand fun of the whole theory. It was not so easily killed, but it withered a little. Because of the great respect that was felt for Eriksson, the theory was discussed in nearly every paper on the Rust for many years, until finally it would have died of doubt, if some of those working on plant virus diseases had not then quietly borrowed it and added many embellishments.

What with the Mycoplasm theory tempting respectable mycologists away from the straight and narrow path of Science into the brothels and gin-palaces of unbridled hypothecation, and the total failure to find any ordinary overwintering stage of the Black Rust fungus, except on barberry bushes, it was small wonder that the more practically-minded workers resigned themselves to the lack of knowledge about the way the Rust really started in the spring, gave up hope of combating the disease by removing sources of infection for the time being, and faced up to the mighty job of trying to produce Rust-resistant varieties. Incidentally, the hope of controlling the Rust by removing sources of infection appeared even more hopeless when the overwintering uredospores *were* found. In 1905, Bolley, of the Experiment Station in North Dakota, was able to announce definitely that the uredospores could remain unimpaired by the action of the drying winds of autumn and the intense cold of the North Dakota winter.[1] He found them surviving on dead leaves, dead straw, and the partly dead or green leaves of living grain or grasses. With these viable spores dusted over an entire countryside following a Rust attack there was no way of destroying them. It might be necessary for the fungus to pass through some sexual stage on the barberry occasionally to maintain its vigour, but this could no longer be regarded as an annual necessity for the survival of the species. A grim example of the way in which a Rust fungus could survive solely by way of overwintering uredospores was provided by the story of the Rust on the coffee in Ceylon.

The difficulty in obtaining Rust-resistant varieties lay in the fact that Rust-resistance was only one of the qualities desired in a good wheat for cultivation. Such a wheat had also to be highly productive, to yield grain of preferred kind for milling and baking; often it had to be drought-resistant or frost-resistant, always it had to be suited to the particular soil and climate of the territory in which it was to be grown. There *were* Rust-resistant varieties of wheat, Einkorn, for example. But that was little more than a tufted wild grass, of scant utility as a grain-producer. The attempts to obtain economically valuable Rust-resistant varieties would necessarily involve much juggling and compromise, and they were inseparable from a greater undertaking – the general improvement of the wheat stocks.

How were improved wheats for, say, Manitoba, or Texas, or East Anglia, or any other given region, to be obtained? One way was evidently to seek for them in other parts of the world, to collect parcels of seed of foreign wheats and to grow them experimentally in the region, in the hope of finding some among them which did better than those already introduced. This was what Mark Alfred Carleton did for the semi-arid districts of the Great Plains when he introduced the hard, drought-resisting Durum wheats from Russia. It was the object of his journeyings in European Russia and the Caucasus in 1898. Some of the Durum wheats not only resisted drought but they also resisted the Rust remarkably well; the significance of this was revealed strikingly enough during the very severe Rust epidemic of 1904. 'Iumillo' Durum, Variety No. 1736 on the Department's list of introductions, under trial in the Dakotas, almost entirely resisted the Rust and gave a yield of about 17 bushels per acre, while a Pedigree Blue Stem variety, as commonly grown in the region, was so badly rusted that it gave only about

[1] Subsequent work showed that they *could* but seldom did (*vide* page 367 et seq.)

6 bushels per acre of miserably shrivelled grain. Two other varieties, only partially resistant to the Rust, one a Durum, the other not, gave about 13 and about 6 bushels per acre, respectively. The desirability of replacing the Pedigree Blue Stem with the Iumillo Durum – from the point of view of combating the Rust – was apparent; in such a season as that of 1904, it would about treble the crop, and the grain would be plump and well-filled instead of being shrunken, light and almost worthless. But the flour from the Durum wheats was more suitable for macaroni than for bread. It had not the quality of 'strength' which was required for bread. The gluten was not white, and it did not hold the bubbles of gas in the dough as they expanded during baking. The loaves were small and heavy. The method of selecting wheats from other parts of the world to suit a particular region, though immensely important, was, after all, only picking out varieties ready-made, and where Rust-resistance was found other desired qualities were generally lacking.

Another method of obtaining improved varieties, which had in fact been exploited by most of those who introduced the great wheats of cultivation, was to take advantage of naturally-occurring mutations. Here and there, and once in a while, among untold millions of ordinary wheat plants, or growing by chance on some bit of waste ground by the wayside, there would be found a single exceptional plant – with unusually large and well-filled ears, or with an unusual freedom from the Rust, or with some other unique and valuable quality. Such plants were 'sports', or mutations, the rare and sudden exceptions to the rule that like begat like, upon which, with the rise of Hugo de Vries 'Mutation Theory' at the close of the nineteenth century, so much of the speculation about the origin of species was now coming to depend. Once the 'sport' was found – by anybody who knew enough about wheat to recognize its good points – the rest was easy. The seed from the single plant, even from a single ear, was carefully collected and kept, for it might be worth ten thousand times its weight in gold. It was sown the next season in a tiny plot, the few plants were watched and tended, and if the 'sport' bred true, the seed from them was again kept for sowing a larger area. After some years of such tended increase there would be enough grain to spare for milling and baking trials, and ultimately to provide seed for commercial cultivation. It was very rarely, however, that a great change in a variety or species would occur at a single mutation. The art of the selector was, in the main, to take advantage of a number of slight mutations, in the desired direction, occurring over many years. The famous rye of Schlanstedt, produced by Rimpau, which was tall, vigorous, with very long heads and kernels nearly double the size of ordinary rye, was produced by this method of continuous selection. Rimpau started in 1866 by picking out the finest heads he could find among his rye and growing the seed from them in a special experimental garden in the middle of his farm. By taking his seed only from the finest heads, year after year, he obtained a rye which differed almost beyond recognition from the original stock, so great was the cumulative improvement. Other farmers in the locality became envious of this rye, and some twenty years after his selecting began Rimpau put the seed on the market. The new 'variety' soon became very popular, for cultivation on moderately good soil, throughout France and Germany.

As it was with Rimpau's improved rye, so it would be with Rust-resistant varieties of wheat. 'Rust-resistance', being in all probability a complex quality, could not be expected to appear in a single mutation. Nature would not shuffle her dice and deposit a Rust-resistant, high-yielding, first-class Bread-wheat ready made, on anybody's campus. It would be necessary to take advantage of many slight and even imperceptible mutations, some affecting the vigour of the plants, others the toughness of the foliage, yet others the quality of the grain, and so forth. This was by no means so difficult in practice as it might appear; the wheat-farmers could do it themselves, in a very simple way, to which Carleton drew attention after the Rust epidemic of 1904. Instead of reserving a part of the general crop for the next year's seed, they could set apart a portion of their land solely for producing seed, and take their seed only from this 'seed-plot'. They could sow their seed-plot each year, not with the common run of grain from the main crop, but with grain from those plants which looked best and freest from Rust at the time of harvest. There was always some of the wheat which was better than the rest, and the seed of any outstanding individual plants, picked out here and there, and thrown into the seed-stock would perpetuate the precious mutations. The effect of these rough and ready selections year after year would be cumulative, and the rust-resistance and vigour of the wheat stocks would go up and not down. It amounted to 'breeding from the best', or assisting the survival of the fittest – from man's point of view.

The third, and perhaps the most important method of trying for Rust-resistant varieties, which yet awaited exploitation, was that of wheat-breeding in the true sense of the word: the deliberate crossing of varieties which had *Rust-resistance* but inferior grain, with other varieties which had little Rust-resistance but *superior grain*, in the hope that hybrids having *Rust-resistance plus superior grain* might appear among the progeny. This was the general idea, but in practice, of course, many other characteristics would have to be bred in or eliminated. Fortunately for the wheat-breeders, crossings between different varieties of wheat were very rare in nature, the female parts of the flowers being so contrived that they almost always received pollen from male parts of flowers in the same ear. Once a new hybrid was 'fixed' it would continue to breed true. To effect a cross it was necessary to perform a delicate operation on ears of wheat in flower: the male parts, or stamens, were amputated while yet immature, and the stigmas of the remaining female parts were dusted with pollen from mature stamens cut from flowers of the other variety. The operation was delicate but usually successful: the 'doctored' ear was enclosed in a waxed paper bag to exclude insects and adventitious pollen, and a few fertile seeds were obtained. When these were sown in the following season they gave rise to cross-bred plants which were often of extraordinary vigour, sometimes they would grow six or seven feet high and tiller so much that they seemed to have received some food of the Gods. All the cross-bred plants from a given pair of parents were alike. But when the self-fertilized seed from them was sown again, the resulting plants, that is to say those of the first generation after the cross, were found to have returned to normal stature but to be of many different hybrid kinds, exhibiting among them all sorts of combinations of characters inherited from their grandparents. The different hybrids were distinguished as far as possible, and the seed from them was kept in separate packets. The next year, some of the seeds would seem to have reproduced the particular hybrids from which they were obtained, but most of them would not do so – the hybrids 'broke'. By growing the more distinct hybrids year after year, for many years, some of them at last became 'fixed', and these were the new 'varieties', whose seed had yet to be multiplied by continued cultivation, before the extent to which they resisted the Rust, and their value as grain-producers could be determined by large-scale trials. This was what wheat-breeding amounted to, before the first decade of the twentieth century – a very haphazard and tedious business indeed.

The famous Marquis wheat of Manitoba, which was not Rust-resistant, but which combined early-maturity – to escape some of the late Rust as well as damage by the frost – with perhaps the finest grain for bread-making ever known, was, however, produced in this way. In 1888, Dr. William Saunders, who was the first Director of the newly founded Experimental Farms in Canada, started cross-breeding experiments for the improvement of the wheat stocks throughout that Dominion. Many hundreds of crosses were made. The Red Fife was then the variety chiefly grown in the west; it was very productive, with excellent milling and baking qualities, but unfortunately it matured late, suffered badly from Rust, and was often frozen in the fields. The Red Fife was crossed, experimentally, with a number of other varieties, one of which was an early-ripening Indian wheat called Hard Red Calcutta. The packets of seeds from the different crosses were kept, and some of the resulting strains were more or less fixed by repeated sowings and selections over a period of ten or fifteen years. The number of them was too great for Dr. William Saunders to follow out, but when his son, Dr. Charles Saunders became Cerealist for the Dominion, all the fixed and partially fixed strains were available at Ottawa as material to work upon. From one of them, eventually traced back to the crossing of the Red Fife and the Hard Red Calcutta, Dr. Charles Saunders obtained the first ear of the wheat which was later to be called Marquis, in 1903. Its seed gave only twelve plants in 1904, with less than a pound of grain. By 1906 there was two-thirds of a bushel, and by 1909, there was sufficient to send out four hundred parcels of the seed for trial by the farmers. By 1913, the Marquis was replacing most of the other varieties throughout Manitoba, Saskatchewan and Alberta, and 200,000 bushels of it crossed the frontier as seed for North Dakota, where, by 1918, it constituted seventy-five per cent of the crop. It took one whole generation of Man to fix, multiply and introduce into cultivation that improved wheat after the first cross had been made, and even then, wheat-breeding to obtain Rust-resistant varieties as such, had not yet begun.

But just as a 'sport', a sudden mutation, sometimes occurred among the wheat, so among the world's annual crops of papers by slow-plodding, conscientious scientists, there sometimes occurred one that was the product of an unpredictable flash of genius – of the sudden unification of two previously unrelated sequences of thought in the same human mind. When such mutative scientific papers were found, and their significance was appreciated, science leapt forward to new positions. Just such a leap occurred in 1900 when Hugo de Vries, and two other workers, Correns and Tschermak, independently, turned up a paper on hybridization experiments with kitchen peas, which the Augustinian priest, Gregor Johann Mendel, had communicated to the Natural History Society of Brünn, in Moravia, during the year 1865. This paper, which linked heredity with arithmetic, or, rather, with the mathematical laws of probability, and provided a scientific basis for the art of plant breeding, had lain neglected for thirty-five years. Not because the transactions of the Natural History Society of Brünn were particularly obscure, but because preoccupation with the origin of species had crowded the problem of what constituted a species, out of court.

It was significant that a full English translation of Mendel's paper was published – in the *Journal of the Royal Horticultural Society* – immediately following the 'discovery' of the German original on the Continent. There was none of the usual delay. The English workers, Bateson and others, indeed took the lead in erecting the great theoretical structure of 'Mendelism' from the clues in Mendel's single paper. And the very first to take advantage of these clues, in breeding Rust-resistant varieties of wheat, were Biffen and his colleagues at the new School of Agriculture at Cambridge. In research on plant diseases and the adoption of control measures, England still lagged behind the times; apart from the historic contributions of the Rev. M. J. Berkeley, very few of the original discoveries and practical innovations in this field had been made by English workers. Perhaps it was not their *métier*. But now, when one of the principal lines of advance in plant pathology involved plant breeding, it was another matter. The English had always excelled in the breeding of animals and plants, from their hereditary aristocrats to racehorses and sheep, and from potatoes to roses. The English had Darwin in their hearts and hereditaments in their understanding.

The wheat-breeding began at Cambridge in 1900, and it was a happy circumstance that the wheat plant was found to be an almost perfect subject for Mendelian experiments. It was self-fertilized in nature; a large number of plants could be grown on a small plot; only one year was required for each generation; and, above all, there were varieties of wheat which differed from one another by pairs of characteristics even more sharply defined than those among Mendel's peas. There were bearded wheats and beardless wheats, wheats with lax ears and wheats with dense ears, wheats with red seed-coats and others with white, wheats with rough chaff and wheats with chaff that was smooth.

In the first, exploratory, experiments a red-grained wheat (i.e. one with a red seed-coat) was crossed with a white-grained one. All the plants of the first generation raised from this cross-fertilized seed bore red grains. The 'red' character was dominant, the 'white' recessive, in Mendel's sense. All the plants from this red seed were self-fertilized in the usual way; and when their seed in turn was sown the next year it gave rise to a mixed crop in which there were, on the average, 3 plants with red grains to every 1 with pure white. The white grains, when again sown, bred true – the white strain was fixed by the first generation after the cross. So far, this might appear to have given back merely one of the parent wheats – the white-grained. But, of course, the parent wheats differed by more than one pair of characteristics. The next step was to cross a white-grained, rough-chaffed wheat with a red-grained, smooth-chaffed one. The result, once again in exact accordance with the Mendelian rule, was that in every 16 plants of the generation after the cross there were, on the average, 9 red-grained and rough-chaffed, 3 red-grained and smooth-chaffed, 3 red-grained and rough-chaffed, and 1 white-grained and smooth-chaffed. The last, the white wheat with the smooth chaff, bred true, and it was a *new* variety of wheat, in which the whiteness of its grandmother was permanently coupled with the roughness of its grandfather. For however long it might be grown, provided only that it continued to be self-fertilized and that no remarkable mutations occurred, there would never be any red seed-coats or smooth chaff among its descendants.

The question now was whether or not 'Rust-resistance' was a unitary inheritable character of wheat, like whiteness of the seed-coat or smoothness of the chaff. One would expect it to be complex, but if by extraordinary good luck it *did* turn out to be a simple Mendelian characteristic, then it could be bred into, or left out of, new varieties of wheat as easily as the redness of the seed-coat or the smoothness of the chaff in the experiments already made.

The Black Stem Rust, due to *Puccinia graminis*, was not common in England, but the Orange Leaf-Rust, or Yellow Rust, due to *Puccinia glumarum* — one of the two species into which the old *Puccinia rubigo-vera* had been divided by Eriksson and Hennings — was quite sufficiently prevalent. It attacked the wheat in the neighbourhood of Cambridge each year with almost unfailing regularity. Biffen therefore experimented on the inheritance of resistance to *Puccinia glumarum*. He began by collecting a number of well-known varieties of wheat and growing them in trial plots to observe how badly the Rust attacked them. They ranged from Einkorn and American Club, which were highly resistant, to Michigan Bronze, which was one of the most susceptible varieties in existence. In 1906, at Cambridge, the Michigan Bronze was so severely Rusted that forty plants did not set a single grain. With markedly Rust-resistant and Rust-susceptible varieties available as parent stocks, Biffen proceeded to cross them one with another, and to trace out the inheritance of these qualities. The accounts of this work, all the ins and outs of it, appeared in the first two volumes of the *Journal of Agricultural Science*, which began in 1905 as a channel for publication of research papers from the twenty-five Agricultural Colleges then at last getting under way in England. Biffen's papers gave the new *Journal* a fine send-off. Briefly, he found that resistance — at any rate to the Yellow Rust — *was* a simple Mendelian character, which could be built into and fixed in new varieties of wheat in a matter of two or three years. The field demonstrations were spectacular and colourful. So bad was the Rust at Cambridge that the susceptible plants were yellow with its spores, while the resistant plants were green. The plots in which the progeny of a cross between American Club and Michigan Bronze was being sorted out made a draughtboard pattern, a living illustration of the Mendelian rules of inheritance in yellow Rust and healthy green.

The theory advanced to explain the phenomena of Mendelism was all ultimately based on a belief in certain small fairies, called 'determinants' or 'genes'. Mendel's idea was that the determinants were just somewhere in the germ-cells, but in the twentieth century they were soon much more confidently located. Genes were fairies that sat upon chromosomes. The nucleus within any ordinary growing cell of a wheat plant contained a number of stainable filaments in its make-up, the material, and observable, chromosomes. It also contained a goodly company of the little fairies or genes which were *not* observable, being of the stuff of inference. Each of these fairies had her own proper place somewhere on one or other of the chromosomes – or, with less likelihood, cramped up *within* it – and each brought with her a different gift, which was one of the observable characteristics of the plant. There was one little gene, for example, which gave the red seed-coats to the grain, another who conferred upon the plant power to resist *Puccinia glumarum*, and so forth. Each gene in the company had either a double or an opposite number, and this was why Mendelian characteristics always went in pairs. The genes were not all equally powerful, the one with the red seed-coats in her gift always dominated over her partner who made the seed-coats white. If the red gene and the white gene were both present in the same company, then the seed-coats were red, and there was no argument about it. The white gene had a recessive disposition. Different varieties of wheat had, of course, different companies of genes located on their chromosomes, that was why they *were* different varieties. When the nucleus of an ordinary growing cell divided to produce an ovule or a pollen grain, only half of its chromosomes went into the germ-cell, so that naturally each germ-cell had only half a company of genes. Each gene was separated from her double or her opposite number, and it was a matter of luck which went over. When the half companies in the two germ-cells were united in the sweet course of fertilization following pollination, the nuclei in the fertile seeds contained full companies of genes again. But they were not the same companies. In the nuclei of a pure red wheat there were two red fairies, in those of a pure white wheat, two white ones. When the red was crossed with the white (by the hand of Man) all the nuclei of the offspring had one white fairy and one red. When these offspring in turn split some of their nuclei in halves for ovules and pollen grains, and were *self*-fertilized, there were equal chances of four things happening. A white fairy in the ovule might get a red companion from the pollen, or she might get a red one; a red fairy in the ovule might get a red companion from the pollen, or she might get a white one. Red and white was the same as white and red, hence the 1:2:1 proportion between the numbers of pure white, mixed, and pure red plants in the experimental plot. It was all due to the breaking-up and reuniting of the pairs of genes according to the rules of chance. The venerable men of science had not the slightest idea how their 'determinants', 'genes' or genii worked all the acts of magic attributed to them. Despite the famous question in Barrie's *Peter Pan* – first produced in London in 1904 – the scientists continued to protest that they did not believe in fairies; they would not dream of postulating their existence to explain *any* observable phenomena; but fairies by any other name were just as useful.

The study of heredity had its attractions for its own sake: it involved everything from genes to the will of God, and it was not for nothing that men of leisured culture called it the Queen of Sciences. But it had also its very practical side, and the work of the Cambridge school on the application of Mendel's laws of inheritance to breeding problems gave a new impetus to wheat-breeding everywhere. Great hopes were aroused of solving the Rust problem by the breeding of resistant varieties; and it seemed almost that before long it would be possible to write a prescription for any desired kind of Rust-resistant wheat, in terms of Mendelian characteristics, and then to make it to order, by picking one character, or gene, from one variety, and another from another, and linking them all up together according to the rules of the Mendelian game.

All this, of course, was sanguine. Great and unexpected difficulties were yet to be encountered, and some researches by Harry Marshall Ward on host and parasite relationships between the Brome grasses and their Brown Rust already clouded the horizon. Ward's work appeared to show that a Rust fungus which could live on a host-plant variety A, but not on variety C, could progress from A to C by accustoming itself to life for a time on an intermediate or 'bridge-variety', B. A little later, Professor Salmon of Wye College traced out what appeared to be the same behaviour on the part of some of the Powdery Mildews. Thus it seemed to those who were cautious-in-hope that varieties of wheat might well be obtained that would be Rust-resistant *for a time*, but which would suffer as severely as ever after some years, when the fungus had completed its education on intermediate varieties and adapted itself for life on the new ones. The 'bridge-theory' was challenged, and shaken, if not shattered, a decade or two later, but it led up to the recognition of even more formidable difficulties in the way of obtaining *permanently* disease-resistant varieties.

Meanwhile, the great value of Mendelian theory as a guide in plant breeding, which would always remain more of an art than a science, was illustrated by some of the immediate results of Biffen's work. When he started wheat-breeding at Cambridge, not only had competition from overseas reduced the area under wheat in Great Britain by two million acres, but it had also sadly reduced the quality of what was left. The farmers had been forced to sacrifice the quality of the English grain to obtain high yields; the better varieties were driven out of cultivation by those giving slightly more grain and straw. As a result, the English grain was very inferior for bread-making, much of it was fit only for feeding to stock, and it fetched 28s. 6d. a quarter on the market when Manitoba Hard was 35s. The task before the English wheat breeders was to obtain wheats with high yield *plus* quality for bread-making *plus* resistance to the prevailing Yellow Rust *plus* strength of straw to stand up to forcing with artificial fertilizers. The measure of success, by 1939, was very great indeed; the average yield over the whole country was further raised to some 32 bushels per acre, and the English grain would make as good bread as all but the very finest of the Canadian. The Yellow Rust was not vanquished, for it was to be seen on the wheat all over East Anglia in 1939; it was still causing far more loss than was generally supposed. Without the Rust the yield might be higher still, but the degree of Rust-resistance already attained was none the less a most significant factor in the improvement. The best of new varieties produced was only a step in the way, but Biffen would always be remembered for his Little Joss. It was a direct outcome of the Mendelian experiments on the inheritance of Rust-resistance. It was obtained from the progeny of a cross between Square Head's Master and a Rust-resistant Ghurka wheat from Russia. On an average over a seven-year period of trial it gave 40 bushels of grain per acre against 36 from the Square Head's Master, and much of this gain was unquestionably attributable to the inheritance of the quality of Rust-resistance from the Russian wheat. By 1919, Little Joss was one of the chief wheats grown in the Eastern counties.

Meanwhile, in the first decade of the twentieth century, attempts to overcome the devastating Black Stem Rust in Canada, Australia and the United States, by breeding for Rust-resistance, with or without the assistance of the Mendelian theory, were only just beginning. No one yet knew whether they would prove successful. The most encouraging news about disease resistance did not come from the Stations where the experiments on the wheat were being made, but from the cotton fields of South Carolina. It was there that the first outstanding and almost complete victory over a serious plant disease was won, by the recognition, the selection and the breeding of disease-resistant varieties.

The cotton in the south was afflicted with a Wilt-disease, due, not to a Rust-fungus, but to a species of Fusarium, which lived in the soil. It obtained entry through the roots and grew rapidly, plugging up the channels of both roots and stems with masses of its spawn. The effect was to cut off supplies of water and mineral salts from the soil and to cause much the same damage as prolonged drought. The leaves wilted, hung dejectedly, yellowed, dried, and fell. Species of this vein-plugging Fusarium were the cause of Wilt-diseases in many cultivated plants, and towards the end of the nineties, Erwin F. Smith, acting as Special Agent for the Department, had occasion to investigate such diseases, not only of the cotton, but also of the watermelons and the cowpeas. The fungus was very well provided with different forms of spores to ensure its survival and dissemination in the soil, and the alarming prevalence of the Wilt Disease was one of the consequences of growing cotton year after year on the same land. Where a rotation of crops was practised, most of the spores of the fungus in the soil died before cotton was planted again – but they did not all die, for some of them could remain viable for many years. The application of chemicals to the soil in sufficient quantity to protect the plants was impracticable. Some other method had to be found, and quickly at that, for one-third of the land in the sea-island district of Carolina was already affected and the disease was spreading in Alabama. Where the Wilt was severe the cotton fields were bare: there was scarcely a green leaf, only miserable rows of dead and barren stems.

The success of the campaign to conquer the Wilt disease owed much to the work of W. A. Orton, a man of great practical sense and organizing ability. As a young graduate from Vermont, when only twenty-two, on his first job with the U.S. Department of Agriculture, he went to live for a year among the planters to size up the trouble. He soon observed that some varieties of cotton were less affected by the Wilt than others, and that in the stricken fields there were usually some plants which withstood the disease to a certain extent while their neighbours, of the same variety, went down. The first step was to get the planters themselves to select their seed from the more resistant plants. The next was to grow different varieties of cotton experimentally in land thoroughly impregnated with the fungus, to test the degree of resistance exhibited by them. Certain Egyptian cottons introduced for trial by the Department were almost unaffected. Outstanding among these was a variety called Jannovitch. In 1899, its seed was distributed widely among the planters for commercial trial, and they found that even where the Wilt made a clean sweep through the ordinary cotton, killing ninety-five plants in a hundred, the Jannovitch stood proud and scarcely a single plant was lost. The quality of the cotton was good, but not good enough. Cotton breeding was then begun at the Experiment Stations in the States concerned to combine the Wilt-resistance of such varieties as the Jannovitch with the productivity and quality of the best of the other varieties. By these three means, the Wilt Disease of the Cotton, was already substantially defeated by 1909.

CHAPTER XXIII

MICROBES AND MOLECROBES

THE disease of peach trees in the United States, which went by the name of 'Peach Yellows', revealed itself in a premature ripening of the fruit. The peaches were yellow, unnaturally splashed with crimson, and apparently fully ripe on the trees some fourteen to forty days before time. Their flesh was insipid and quite unlike that of the normal peach. Branches which had borne such fruit were visibly diseased in the following spring: they put forth feeble, branched shoots on which the foliage was willow-like, stunted and curled; and later on the winter-buds for the next season broke prematurely, giving rise to tufted and broom-like growths of many yellowish shoots. This diseased condition spread progressively to all the branches, the fruit failed to set, and the tree declined and died in a few years. The trouble had been known in the peach orchards since about 1807, and by 1880 it was destroying thousands of trees, notably in the Delaware and Chesapeake regions. It was not known in California or in Europe. The only known remedy was to dig up the affected trees and burn them, in the hope of checking the spread. Laws were passed in several States between 1875 and 1891, to the effect that peach trees afflicted with the Yellows should be held to be without pecuniary value, and their fruit unfit for food; making it unlawful to sell or to keep either the infected fruit or the trees, and providing for the destruction of both, as public nuisances, without liability for damages. These laws, of which the Michigan Yellows Laws were the most famous, followed the long-forgotten laws in Massachusetts for the Eradication of the Barberry and marked the beginning of the modern legislative measures for the control of plant diseases in the United States. And this was not the only notable development in plant pathology which arose out of work for the good of the peach trees. One of the first important investigations of a so-called 'virus' disease in plants was that by Erwin F. Smith, between 1888 and 1895, on the Peach Yellows; and it was for the control of certain fungus diseases of peach trees that the use of the very important fungicide, lime-sulphur, was introduced into orchard practice in 1907. The green guinea pigs of the plant doctors certainly included the peach trees of the United States.

As it happened, the first scientific Bulletin, issued in 1891, by the new

Division of Vegetable Pathology in the U.S. Department of Agriculture, was not about the Apple Scab, or any of the fungus diseases of the Vines; it was on the Communicability of the Peach Yellows. Erwin Smith studied the disease in all its stages, and was able to prove that a single diseased bud, grafted on to a healthy peach tree, would cause that tree to bear the hectic-coloured premature fruits, to put forth the tufted broom-like growths of shoots, and ultimately to languish and die. But nowhere could he find any fungus or bacteria in causal association with the disease. This negative result of a prolonged and careful search, though it seemed disappointing, was in fact of the very greatest importance, for it pointed to the presence of some as yet undiscovered kind of living organism, ultramicroscopic in size, or some non-living regenerative toxic principle, which passed from the diseased bud into the healthy tree, and there multiplied or increased, to give rise to the visible symptoms of the disease after a period of some months for 'incubation'.

Erwin Smith might well have called that which passed from the disease bud into the healthy tree a 'virus'. But he preferred to be more specific. The word 'virus', meaning in Latin simply a poison, had been used in the English language for a very long time to denote any kind of poisonous, loathsome, morbid or deadly principle – material or moral. The nature of the causal agent of the Peach Yellows was obscure, but it was not quite so obscure as all that. One thing *was* known about it – the disease it caused was *contagious*; so Erwin Smith called it, not a 'virus', but a 'contagium'. It was strictly correct to speak of snake-venom as a 'virus', but a man bitten by a poisonous snake was not thereby infected with any contagious disease. The Peach Yellows investigations led to the discovery of no remedy, beyond the continued use of the axe and of fire, but they served to erect two question marks. What could be the nature of the contagium that was neither bacterial nor fungal? And how was it conveyed in nature from tree to tree?

By 1896, Erwin Smith had made the passing remark that the mysterious contagium might be of the same kind as those which caused mottling and variegation of foliage in certain other plants – disorders which were also communicable by grafting or the inoculation of sap. And there was a serious leaf-disease of the vines in California, which had a suspicious resemblance to the Peach Yellows ... Meanwhile, a highly interesting paper by Adolph Mayer, of the Wageningen Research Station in Holland, published in 1886, had not yet received the attention it deserved. The paper concerned the Mosaic Disease of the tobacco-plant, which was responsible for much loss, not only to the Dutch growers, but also to those of Virginia and elsewhere. The characteristic symptom of the Mosaic – or of the Calico Disease, as one form of it was called – was an alternation of light and dark areas on the tobacco leaves. The lighter-coloured parts of the leaves which were quite yellow when the disease was acute, grew slowly owing to a lack of chlorophyll, while the surrounding, greener, parts grew more rapidly, with the result that the leaves became puckered, crinkled, twisted, and variously distorted. The plants were sometimes completely deformed and became a total loss; while even when the mottling of the leaves was slight they were spoilt as wrappers for cigars, and when cured for pipe-tobacco they had an inferior 'burn' and aroma. The Mosaic was an extraordinarily contagious disease: it was necessary only to bruise an infected leaf between finger and thumb and then to touch a bud on a healthy plant, for that plant to become infected in turn. The contagium was not destroyed by the curing process, and even the expectoration of juice, by those chewing tobacco while at work in the tobacco-fields, would spread the disease. There was no growth of any parasitic fungus to be found on the affected leaves, and, as with the Peach Yellows, the contagium appeared to be in the sap.

Mayer expressed the sap from infected leaves and filtered it through a single thickness of ordinary filter-paper. He then injected the slightly turbid fluid into the leaf-veins of healthy plants by means of a small glass capillary tube. The typical symptoms of the Mosaic very soon appeared. It seemed to Mayer that the disease must have been caused by some unknown kind of bacteria in the filtered sap, which were small enough to pass through a single thickness of filter-paper. He therefore filtered some more sap through *two* thickness of filter-paper. The fluid was perfectly clear, and, for some reason or other, it did *not* induce the Mosaic when he injected it into the leaf-veins of healthy plants. He supposed that the disease was caused by bacteria which would pass through one layer of filter-paper but not through two. Six years later, i.e. in 1892, a Russian worker, Iwanowski, sent a short communication to the Imperial Academy of Sciences in St. Petersburg, challenging Mayer's results. He pointed out that there were several known species of bacteria small enough to pass through two layers of filter-paper, and he had gone one better than Mayer, by filtering the sap of tobacco-leaves affected with the Mosaic, through a Chamberland filter of fine unglazed porcelain, the pores of which were so small that no bacteria of any known kind could possibly pass through them. He found that even after such filtration the fluid part of the sap still, in fact, retained its virulence unimpaired. In his experiments it always induced the Mosaic when injected into healthy tobacco-plants.

What did this mean? Were there inanimate substances in nature, yet undreamed-of by the chemists, of which an infinitesimally small amount would cause the disease of an entire living plant, *regenerating themselves and increasing in quantity thereby?* If indeed the Peach Yellows was a disease of the same kind as the Tobacco Mosaic, then a single drop of sap in an infected bud, would not only kill the whole tree on which the bud was grafted, but in the process it would produce pints of sap, every drop of which was as highly charged with the 'virus' or the 'contagium' as that in the original bud. Could there be inanimate substances with such powers of regeneration and increase? Or did the clear fluid which passed through the filter contain some kind of living organism, smaller than the spores of any mould or mildew, smaller even than the smallest known bacteria – some ultramicroscopic form of life?

In 1898, Loeffler and Frosch discovered that the foot-and-mouth disease of cattle also had a filter-passing infective principle, and in that same year Beijerinck, in Holland, published an account of researches, which went to confirm the work of Iwanowski on the Tobacco Mosaic, and in which he postulated the existence of 'living fluid contagiums', as distinct from the unspecified 'contagium' to which Erwin Smith had attributed the communicability of the Peach Yellows. A living fluid contagium was very difficult to imagine. It was easy enough to think of jelly-fish in the sea, but liquid fish . . .? Living liquids were something new.

There were two kinds of solutions that would pass through the pores of the finest porcelain filter. One was an ordinary, or molecular, solution, such as that of salt in water, the other was a colloidal solution, such as that of a gum, in which the 'dissolved' substance was really present in the form of extraordinarily minute suspended particles. Such particles in a filter-passing virus might be of the nature of living bacteria – very small microbes. Or they might be non-living – very large molecules. To take the liberty of coining a neutral word, giving equal weight to both possibilities and anything in between, it could fairly be said that they were 'molecrobes'. If these molecrobes were particles of chemical substances, not endowed with life, then it would be for the chemists to extract them in the pure state by crystallization or otherwise, to analyse them and determine their constitution, and ultimately, perhaps, to synthesize them in the laboratory. If they were indeed living things, then it would be for the biologists to study the habits, the life-histories and the food requirements of a world of pathogens on the extreme border line of life, and of an ultramicroscopic order of size. Ultimately, perhaps, they would classify the invisible into genera and species. And just as in the sixties there were those who believed that germs or microbes might be of spontaneous generation, so now there was the alluring possibility that the chemists and the biologists might meet half-way, with the synthesis in the laboratory of molecrobes in the form of filter-passing viruses having the attributes of life.

By 1939 it was to be discovered that molecrobes were the causal agents of many of the commonest diseases of man and other animals: mumps, bovine pleuro-pneumonia, smallpox, influenza and the common cold. And at the same time the virus diseases of plants would be uppermost in the minds of many plant pathologists. But to anticipate all this would be to leap ahead too fast. The first text-book on the virus diseases of plants was not published until 1937; nearly a quarter of a century was to pass before they began to receive widespread attention. During the nineties it was not admitted that even microbes could cause plant disease, much less molecrobes. Historically, the exploration of the bacterial diseases of plants was a necessary and logical step towards the understanding of those caused by the yet smaller pathogens. This step was delayed by a copy-book idea that fungi caused diseases of plants, bacteria diseases of animals. Although bacteria themselves were generally regarded as *fungi* – unicellular fungi multiplying by fission – they were not supposed to be able to parasitize green plants as did some of the other kinds. Bacteria had become the pet concern of the bacteriologists and the medical profession; the plant pathologists could mind their own business.

There were two age-old tendencies towards stagnation in scientific thought which those of youthful spirit had always to resist. One was the human weakness of accepting the uncorroborated say-so of eminent authorities, and the other was the human stupidity of regarding natural science as something divisible into water-tight compartments. Of course it was contended that such compartments, labelled Chemistry, Mycology, Bacteriology, Etcetera, were never really fish-tanks for myopic specialists to swim about in, but merely convenient *de*partments in one splendid and sunlit edifice of science, separated at the most by glass walls, decorated with the flags of all nations, and provided with innumerable intercommunicating doors. If so many stacks of old scientific papers got piled up on each side of the glass partititions that in the end no one could see through them, that was certainly regrettable; and if some of the doors were locked for periods ranging from a decade to a century, well, that also was a pity – but who wanted to work in a draught?

A little interdepartmental trespassing and determined window-cleaning, on the part of Erwin F. Smith, towards the close of the century, assisted everyone to perceive at last that there *were* some bacterial diseases of plants. It seemed to Erwin Smith, who with the Peach Yellows had been tackling something far more difficult to diagnose than any bacterial disease, that Burrill had been perfectly right in 1878, when he attributed the Fire Blight of pears to the parasitism of a bacillus. The blighted tissues swarmed with it, experimental inoculations with pure cultures caused the disease to appear, and some later work by Waite had shown how honey-bees carried the bacilli from tree to tree, depositing them within the nectaries of the flowers, by which route they obtained entry. There was also a bacterial disease of hyacinths reported by Wakker from Holland – a yellow bacterial slime in the bulbs associated with a gradual decay of the foliage. Indeed a careful search of the literature showed that there were quite a number of rots, wilts, blights and slimy afflictions of plants which had been attributed by one worker or another to direct bacterial agency. Erwin Smith took courses in Bacteriology from the best teachers he could find in America, familiarized himself with their precious technique, studied the life of Pasteur, and then started upon a thorough investigation of some of the bacterial diseases of plants which were not supposed to be caused by bacteria.

His own first discovery in this field was a disease of cucumbers, which he observed near Washington in 1893. The leaves hung limp and collapsed on their stalks; no growth of mould or mildew was present; the plants were dying for no apparent reason. But when he cut through the stalks he found that their vessels were full of a tacky white ooze, which could be drawn out when touched with the finger like strands of well-mouthed chewing gum. This ooze, when examined under the microscope, was revealed as one dense and quivering mass of living bacteria, blocking up the sap-conducting vessels. He made a pure culture of the organism, dipped the point of a needle in it, and then, with this needle, he made one prick in a perfectly healthy cucumber plant. The plant wilted, sickened and was dead in three weeks. Guinea pigs were not more susceptible to Anthrax than were cucumber plants to this bacterial disease. He repeated his experiments again and again, always with the same result, and published a careful account of his work in 1895, naming the organism *Bacillus tracheiphilus*, because of its fondness for living in the tracheae or sap-conducting vessels of the plants. He next studied the Black Rot of Cabbages, which an American worker, Pammell, in 1893, had already found to be caused by a bacillus, and to which he had given the name of *B. campestris*. Erwin Smith pointed out one way by which the bacilli could easily obtain entry into healthy cabbage-leaves. Small drops of moisture were exuded at certain times from the water-pores at the leaf-edges. Bacilli reaching these drops could easily swim through the water-pores into the leaf-veins; they did not have to bore through the skin of the leaves, nor did they necessarily have to enter by way of the stomata or breathing pores, though they could do that also. He went on to confirm Wakker's work on the Yellow disease of hyacinths, and in 1896 published an important paper on a bacterial disease of tomatoes, egg-plants and the potato, which he showed to be due to the parasitism of a bacillus, to which he gave the name of *B. solanacearum*. Once again the bacillus lived and multiplied in the veins or fibro-vascular system of the plants, much as other pathogenic bacilli lived in the veins of animals.

In 1897, Erwin F. Smith, who was certainly no amateur in the investigation of plant diseases, but, by then, one of the chief plant pathologists of the U.S. Department of Agriculture, was more than a little taken aback to find the whole of his work apparently set at naught by one Alfred Fischer, eminent Professor of Bacteriology at Leipzig. In an important text-book on his subject, which was supposed to be comprehensive, and which would be read the world over, Fischer dismissed bacterial diseases of plants in about three-quarters of a page, stating categorically that bacteria had no way of insinuating themselves into the tissue of living plants, and that even when they got in by wounds their progress was stopped by the growth of protective barriers of cork. There were no bacterial diseases of plants. 'New descriptions kept cropping up, but – what worthless descriptions and what uncritical experiments!' In diseased plants bacteria were often to be found in great numbers it was true, but they lived only as saprophytes on tissue broken down and destroyed by genuine fungi . . . Fischer implied that those who had published papers on bacterial diseases of plants were all grossly incompetent; misled by faulty experiments and dirty technique.

Erwin F. Smith was a kindly man; he inspired sentiments of respect and the warmest affection among all his colleagues, he had very frank and pleasant eyes, but – this was more than he could stand. Fischer had previously distinguished himself by telling American students, who went all the way to Leipzig to hear his lectures, that he never read American scientific publications, nor did he give them shelf-room in his library, as there was so rarely anything in them to make it worth his while. Erwin F. Smith replied courteously enough in the circumstances, pointing out that Fischer had never examined any bacterial diseases of plants for himself, that he had not even bothered to read the literature about them, and that his *ex cathedra* pronouncements about what bacteria could or could not do to living plants were based wholly on supposition, and were wrong from beginning to end. 'Never had so much ignorance been concentrated into so few words.'

The formation of protective barriers of cork was precisely what did *no* happen, in the case of Pear Blight, Cucumber Wilt, Brown Rot of Potatoes, Black Rot of Cabbages, the Yellow Disease of Hyacinths, Bacteriosis of Beans, and all the other bacterial diseases, which he, Erwin F. Smith, had investigated. There were, moreover, quite a number of known ways by which bacteria could and did obtain entry into healthy plants. In order that Dr. Fischer might make good some of the deficiencies in his knowledge, Erwin Smith provided him with an imposing list of references to scientific papers, many of them from German sources, which set forth incontrovertible evidence for the existence of *some* truly bacterial diseases of plants. Further search would probably reveal that there were just as many as there were of animals, and in the interests of science and of the health of the crops, it was imperative that they should be recognized. To deny their existence without making experiments was to revert to the scholasticism of the Middle Ages. 'Complaint has sometimes been made', he said, 'that Englishmen and Americans publish without knowing what has been done in Germany. In so far as this has occurred it is always a matter for regret, since Germany is the leader of the world in botanical and bacteriological investigation. Here, however, is a counter-case of a professor in one of the most renowned of German universities, who does not think it necessary to read English, and still worse, who writes dogmatically on a subject without exact knowledge, and is not familiar even with the readily accessible literature in his own language.'

It was very much to the credit of the German scientific fraternity that this rebuke of one of their number who had made a mistake was published in full in the *Centralblatt für Bakteriologie* for 1899. Fischer replied, retracting nothing. Erwin Smith countered with an article entitled: 'Dr. Alfred Fischer in the rôle of a Pathologist'. The polemic was conducted with sarcasm and open indignation on both sides. Indeed, the row was not seemly, and Erwin Smith regretted to the end of his life that Fischer never forgave him, but the battle for the recognition of bacteria as causative agents of disease in plants was decisively won, and thus a new province of investigation was opened up.

It was found that some of the bacterial diseases of plants were of great economic significance, those of the pear, sugar-cane, potato, beet, for examples; but many did not matter very much except to nurserymen, market-gardeners and flower-growers here and there. Great epidemics of bacterial plant disease were comparatively rare, chiefly for the reason that the bacteria were not so well provided with means for dispersal as some of the higher pathogenic fungi. They did not release clouds of spores to be sown by the winds, and indeed the bacteria pathogenic to plants were not spore-formers at all. Their cells lived submerged in fluid within the plants or in exudations from them. They had to be picked up and *carried* from plant to plant — on the mandibles of leaf-eating beetles, or on the proboscides of bees and leaf-sucking flies. Alternatively they had to be carried over to the next generation of their host-plant, in tubers or cuttings or seeds. To prevent the spread of these diseases it was necessary to ensure that cuttings and tubers were not taken from infected plants; and it was necessary to attack not so much the bacteria themselves, as *the insects that carried them from plant to plant.* These were vital realizations, for if insects served to spread bacteria still large enough to be seen under the microscope, how much more readily could they spread filter-passing viruses, or molecrobes? It was many years before this hint was taken, but it was made, plain enough, in the work on the bacterial diseases of plants, and, of course, in the work by Ross and others on the part played by the mosquito in spreading malaria.

Perhaps it was a good thing that bacteria did cause some plant diseases, for it meant that there was one region in which plant pathology and animal pathology could not help but overlap. The two departments of applied science had far too much in common for any arbitrary division to stand between them. Any significant advance on the one side was now extremely likely to point the way to some corresponding advance on the other. It was by trying formalin throat tablets on seed-wheat that Bolley of the North Dakota Experimental Station discovered the very important formaldehyde treatment for seed-disinfection in 1897; and Ehrlich's discovery of salvarsan, in the next decade, for the treatment of syphilis, led directly to the discovery of some of the most potent chemical therapeutants ever known for the treatment of plant disease. The plant pathologists could make very good use of the special methods developed by the bacteriologists, and, on the other hand, it was well that the medical profession should be reminded from time to time that one of the commonest diseases of wheat was attributed to the parasitism of a living organism over a hundred years before Pasteur. Many doctors during the nineteenth century had been moved to seek illumination about the nature of disease by studying the maladies of plants; and the curious might notice, from the gossip columns of the newspapers in 1939, that the King's Physician, Lord Horder, was very keenly interested in the diseases of flowers.

Erwin Smith and his co-worker, Townsend, started seeking in 1904 for the cause of certain tumour-like growths often to be found at the junction of the stem and roots of fruit-trees and other plants. These growths were called

Crown-galls; they often caused the death of the plants on which they grew and always interfered with the normal functioning of the affected parts. On young herbaceous plants they were soft and succulent, rotting away at the end of the season; on apple trees they grew hard and woody with age, and were sometimes as large as cricket balls or even footballs. Some workers had supposed that they were attributable to the parasitism of a slime-mould, similar to that which caused the Club Root of the cabbages. By 1906, however, Smith and Townsend had found that they were in fact caused by a species of bacterium, to which they gave the name of *Pseudomonas tumefaciens*. These bacteria were elusive and hard to find, for they were very small, and there were surprisingly few of them in the affected tissues. They were first isolated from tumours on the roots of the Paris Daisy. By experimental inoculations with pure cultures of them, it was found that they were capable of exciting the growth of tumours on a number of different plants. They caused the plant-cells to proliferate abnormally, and the appearance of the diseased tissue, when sections of the galls were cut and examined under the microscope, bore so much resemblance to that of sarcomous growths in man, that Erwin Smith began to wonder whether he had indeed stumbled upon the track of that most terrible of all afflictions of ageing humanity — Cancer.

At least, the derangement of living vegetable tissue caused by the Pseudomonas merited the thoughtful attention of the medical profession, and, in 1912, Bulletin No. 255 of the Bureau of Plant Industry provided a hundred photomicrographic plates beautifully revealing the structure and development of Crown Gall, for the research workers on cancer to make of them what they could or would. The Bulletin was sent with the compliments of the U.S. Department of Agriculture to all the Institutions in the world dealing with cancer research. Erwin Smith never claimed that *Pseudomonas tumefaciens was* the causal agent of cancer in man; he was always sceptical about it. But it was of interest that by 1925 Dr. F. Blementhal of the Cancer Research Laboratory in the University of Dresden, did claim to have isolated in pure culture, several times, from the human breast, carcinomous fission-fungi with which he had been able to produce malignant transplantable tumours in white rats. One form, he said, was indistinguishable from *Pseudomonas tumefaciens*, and with it he had repeatedly produced tumours on plants indistinguishable from Crown Gall. In 1913, Erwin Smith received an Award of Honour for his work on 'Cancer in Plants', and in 1925 he was elected to the Presidency of the American Association for Cancer Research.

After the polemic with Alfred Fischer, which not only won recognition for the bacterial diseases of plants, but reminded the world how rapidly science was moving west, Erwin F. Smith was acclaimed as something of a hero in the United States. Between 1905 and 1914 his writings on bacteria in relation to plant disease were published by the Carnegie Institution of Washington in three imposing volumes which, in point of bulk, at least, would not have been unworthy of the collected works of Pasteur. But Erwin F. Smith was, above all, a most beloved personality, cautious, wise and fair, and when he died, in 1927, the plant pathologists of the United States called him: 'Pioneer, Prophet, Exemplar, Dean of our Science'.

CHAPTER XXIV

CALLING THE CHEMICAL INDUSTRY

THE peach trees of the United States, like the apple and also the citrus trees, were terribly infested by San José Scale insects. These creatures, rather like minute limpets, an eighth of an inch in diameter, clung fast in great numbers to the twigs and branches, whose juices they sucked. The pest had first claimed attention in the Santa Clara valley, about 1870, and it had spread throughout California and into the eastern States until thousands of orchards were alive with it. Various control measures were tried with greater or lesser success, and some enterprising growers in California had taken to spraying their trees in the winter with a sheep-dip, of which a sample had been sent to one of their number by a friend in Australia, *circa* 1881. The sheep-dip was made by boiling sulphur with lime, and so effective was it against the Scale insects on peach trees that it was already in common use in California by 1885. There were some who noticed that this sulphur wash, applied just before flowering when the trees were still bare of foliage, also had a beneficial effect in suppressing a common fungus disease of the peaches – the Peach Leaf Curl.

The disease was caused by an ascomycete, called *Exoascus deformans*, which had first been described by the Rev. M. J. Berkeley. The fungus survived the winter on the bare shoots, and it attacked the expanding young leaves at an early stage, causing them to thicken and develop a conspicuous 'bloom' on their upper surface – the sporulating stage of the parasite. The thickened leaves puckered and curled up, assumed a red tint and finally fell from the trees, which thus were sometimes entirely defoliated by mid-summer. The disease was widespread, and it could cause just as much loss as the Peach Yellows, but, fortunately, it was about the very easiest of all fungus diseases to control by spraying. A single application of Bordeaux mixture, at the right time – which was just before the buds began to expand in the spring – would almost completely suppress the disease for the year. So also would the lime, sulphur and salt wash, which was the Californian improvement on the original sheep-dip. Although primarily an insecticide, this *sulphur* preparation was also effective against the Leaf Curl – it killed two birds with one stone.

By 1890, some of the peach-growers in California were manufacturing their lime-sulphur-salt wash on a very large scale. At the Rio Bonito Ranch there was an installation like a rudimentary chemical works. It comprised a great water tank on top of a wooden staging, a vat for cooking up nine hundred gallons of the wash at a time, and a vertical boiler to provide the necessary live steam. The sulphur, salt and lime were shovelled into the vat, stirred with the water, and boiled by blowing in steam until all the sulphur and lime had gone into solution. The purpose of the salt was a little dubious unless it was to raise the boiling point of the mix and so expedite the cooking, or unless it was thought that it ought to make the wash even more nasty for the insects. The product was an evil-smelling, amber-coloured solution containing calcium polysulphides and other soluble compounds of sulphur and lime.

East of the Rockies, the California Wash was little used, the commoner winter washes being kerosene emulsions, as employed in the apple orchards, and nauseous mixtures made by boiling together fish-oils with resin and caustic alkalies. Coal-oil emulsions were sometimes employed. These sprays – like the lime-sulphur wash – were only *partially* effective against the Scale insects, and some of them injured the dormant buds of the peach trees. It was of interest that a one-hundred-per-cent-effective weapon against the Scale insects, which was at the same time quite harmless to the trees, was just coming into use by 1900 – and this was Poison Gas. Tents were made of gas-proof fabric, large enough to erect over the peach or other trees and to enclose them completely. Hydrogen cyanide was then generated inside the sealed tents by tipping sulphuric acid on to potassium cyanide, and in the course of a few hours *every* insect within the tent was dead. The trees were completely de-infested. The tents were then opened gingerly to allow the gas to blow away, after which they were taken down and erected over another batch of trees – the fumigation-squads working steadily in this way through the orchards. It was a slow, tedious and rather dangerous job; all this business of putting up and taking down tents over trees, dodging whiffs of instantly deadly prussic acid gas. It had, moreover, to be done in the depths of winter, often when there was a foot of snow on the ground. But it was the only really infallible method of ridding the trees of Scale insects, and it came to be adopted in many countries, especially in the citrus groves.

Cyanide fumigation had no effect on parasitic fungi, but when, in the peach-orchards, it was followed by a single spraying with Bordeaux mixture or California Wash before the buds opened, both the San José Scale and the Peach Leaf Curl were vanquished. It was otherwise with the Scab and the Brown Rot, which were two more fungus diseases of the unfortunate peach trees, not so common as the Leaf Curl, but nevertheless great spoilers of the fruit. To combat these diseases it was necessary to spray the trees when they were in leaf, and so far this did more harm than good. The peach leaves were very sensitive, and copper sprays injured them far too severely. As for the caustic California Wash, no one would dream of using it on peach trees, except during the winter. Until about 1907 no fungicide was known that could safely be used on peach trees in leaf.

There were also some varieties of apples and pears whose fruit and foliage suffered by far too much from russetting and chemical burns following the use of copper sprays. This drawback had yet to be overcome, and a lively reminder that copper compounds could have a destructive as well as a therapeutic effect on plant foliage was provided by the discovery in France, in 1897, that spraying with a plain 2 per cent solution of copper sulphate in the wheatfields would destroy the charlock without harming the wheat. The ingenuity of the French turned to good account the cause of failure when the Americans tried to control the Rust of the wheat by spraying, some years before. The drops of copper sulphate solution in the spray ran straight off the glossy leaf-blades of the wheat, and therefore did them no harm; but they rested and spread on the rough surface of broad-leaved weeds which were thus burnt up and destroyed. It was true that the copper sprays used on fruit trees were carefully 'neutralized' with lime or soda or ammonia, but their effect on fungus spores depended none the less on the liberation of a certain amount of copper in soluble form, and the difference between copper fungus-killers and copper weed-killers was only one of degree. The unfortunate fact was that on peaches and some varieties of apples and pears the traces of soluble copper compounds sufficient to kill the fungus spores were also sufficient to injure the leaves and fruit.

A different and milder fungicide was required for use on such copper-sensitive foliage. In 1907, W. M. Scott, Pathologist in charge of Orchard Spraying Demonstrations for the U.S. Department of Agriculture, hit upon what he called a 'self-boiled lime-sulphur wash'. He put 15 lb. of quicklime into a 50-gallon barrel, and poured over it 3 gallons of boiling water. Then he added 10 lb. of flowers of sulphur and another bucketful of boiling water. The heat generated by the slaking of the quicklime caused the hot mixture to boil violently for a few minutes and kept it simmering afterwards for about half an hour. Hence the expression 'self-boiled'. When the reaction was over the barrel was filled up with cold water, and the wash – which had a large proportion of unaffected sulphur and lime suspended in it – was then strained to remove lumps and used for spraying the trees. It caused no injury even to peach foliage and it effectively checked both the Scab and the Brown Rot.

This lime-sulphur wash was hailed both in the United States and in England as about the most important advance in the preparation of materials for the control of plant diseases by spraying since the discovery of Bordeaux mixture. It was tried out in the American apple orchards during the seasons of 1908, 1909, and 1910, and found to be exactly what was required for the control of the Apple Scab on copper-sensitive varieties. The papers by Scott and others were abstracted, within a month or so of their publication, in the Journal of the Board of Agriculture in England. Those whose job it was to teach the English fruit-growers how best to take advantage of the methods of their commercial rivals for suppressing pests and diseases, were now following up all American innovations promptly and almost automatically. Professor E. S. Salmon of Wye College in Kent tried the 'new' fungicide, as he called it, first on hops and then on a great many varieties of apples and pears. By 1910, official recommendations for its use as an alternative to Bordeaux mixture on some of these varieties were issued by the Board.

Before this time, however, it had been realized, both in the United States and in England, that Scott's gentle lime-sulphur was not so much 'self-boiled' as 'half-boiled'. It was an ingenious idea to use the heat from the slaking of the lime to boil the mixture – incidentally it was the way in which the early balloonists were said to have boiled eggs without setting their balloons on fire – but exactly the same result could be obtained by boiling the mixture *for the same time* in any other way. The self-boiled lime-sulphur was merely a weak solution of ordinary lime-sulphur, as already in use as an insecticide, mixed with uncooked sulphur and lime. The two latter could be dispensed with. While Scott was working on his self-boiled mixture, two other American workers, Cordley of Oregon and Piper of Washington, were already trying much-diluted 'home-boiled' or 'factory-boiled' material on the apple trees. But it was undoubtedly the novelty in Scott's way of preparing his stuff – the fascination of a schoolboy-trick – which drew attention to the fungicidal properties of lime-sulphur and hastened the realization that though it burnt the foliage of both apple trees and peach trees when used too strong, it was an admirably effective, cheap, non-poisonous, and safe fungicide when appropriately diluted.

The roundabout way in which this realization came to be made was all the more remarkable as lime-sulphur was not a new fungicide at all, but one of the very oldest. Under the name of sulphuret of calcium it had been used against the Oidium or Powdery Mildew of the Vine as far back as 1852 (*vide* p. 51 herein), and it had also been used about that time against the Hop Mould. Peach trees were no strangers to it, for the mixture of sulphur and lime which the immortal Mr. Tucker used successfully against the Oidium of the vine, on its very first outbreak in Europe, was one that he had long been accustomed to use against the mildew, also an Oidium, on peach trees. The French chemists during the fifties had indeed carried experiments with lime-sulphur much further in some directions than it occurred to anyone to do, for some years after its revival in 1908. They had tried the boiled wash; they had added soap, casein and other substances to it, for improving the 'wetting' of the foliage; and they had made a form of colloidal sulphur from it, by treating it with acid. There were plenty of references to these experiments in the gardening and viticultural journals of 1850 to 1855. In those days no convenient spraying machines had yet been invented for applying wet mixtures, the use of sulphur dust had proved more convenient, and the fungicidal properties of lime-sulphur thus came to be virtually forgotten or ignored for over sixty years.

Lime-sulphur was to prove a chemical weapon of very general utility in the war against plant disease. It had not quite so many applications as Bordeaux mixture; it was of little or no use against the Potato Blight or the Peronospora of the Vine, but it was effective against most of the Powdery Mildews, and against many other fungus diseases of fruit-trees and vegetables, including some of the Rusts. Significantly for those nations which from time to time would have to conserve limited supplies of copper for the all-important business of destroying each other, lime sulphur would do some of the work of Bordeaux mixture. It was made from sulphur and lime, of which the world's reserves were very large, and even in peace-time its use, wherever possible, would reduce the wasteful dispersal of copper irrecoverably over the land, in spray residues. As more and more millions of acres of crops came to be sprayed with copper mixtures every year, this dispersal of copper was by no means inconsiderable, and sooner or later, it would have to be taken into consideration.

At first the fruit-growers boiled their own lime-sulphur, but this was a job that could be done better and more cheaply in chemical works than on the farm. By 1911 in England, and some years before that in the States, factory-boiled lime-sulphur was available on the market. It was a little more concentrated than the home-boiled, having a specific gravity of 1.30. It saved much time, for the fruit-growers had merely to dilute it with water for use – usually at 1 in 30 before the trees were in blossom, and at 1 in 60 afterwards. The best compound of arsenic to be mixed with the wash for the simultaneous control of caterpillars and fungus diseases was found to be not Paris Green, as used with the copper mixtures, but arsenate of lead. This innovation dated back to about 1897, when lead arsenate was successfully employed to combat the Gipsy Moth, in the State of Massachusetts. It was white, it showed where it had been applied to the foliage, it caused less chemical injury to the leaves than Paris Green and it was compatible with lime-sulphur. At first, in 1902, the Board of Agriculture recommended the English growers to make their own arsenate of lead – by dissolving one ounce of arsenate of soda in warm water, adding sixteen gallons of rainwater, and then a solution of 3 ounces of lead acetate. But, here again, arsenate of lead was best made in a chemical works and not on the farm. The business of the farmers was farming, for that they had the knowledge and the skill; where they had to set up as manufacturing chemists in their spare time they were at a disadvantage, they had not the necessary plant, they knew nothing about chemistry, and they had no time to spare.

By 1911, with all the copper mixtures, the lime-sulphur and sulphur dusts, the arsenic compounds, the cyanides for fumigation, the oil-emulsions, the special kinds of soaps, nicotine and so forth, there was a veritable pharmacopoeia-full of chemical insecticides and fungicides used in the defence of the crops. And in that year just such a pharmacopoeia was indeed published for the first time. It was called *Les Maladies des Plantes* – the original French edition of Bourcart's well-known *Insecticides, Fungicides and Weedkillers*. A glance through the pages of that work, with its thousand and one receipts and formulae, most of which had been proposed or put to use only during the previous twenty-five years, was sufficient to make it quite clear that the chemical warfare already being waged on the insects and the fungi was providing an important new source of business for the chemical dealers and manufacturers, and calling unmistakably upon the great chemical industry for plant-protection materials a little more worthy of the chemist's art.

Bordeaux mixture and lime sulphur were made by the chemistry of the kitchen and the barn. And so far all the formulae of the sprays and dusts and steeps and fumigatants were empirical. They had been discovered more or less by chance, and modified in practice by the occasional exercise of common-sense – that was all. To call them chemical therapeutants would be to pay them a compliment they did not deserve. All too little was known of their intimate physical and chemical action on foliage and on the organisms they were used to destroy. The resources of modern chemical science, the knowledge of those who could synthesize indigo or extract a milligram of radium out of a mountain of ore had so far hardly been tapped at all for the provision of safer, cheaper, and more effective prophylactics for use on the crops. Even the chemical constitution of the active compound in Bordeaux mixture, the most widely used spray material of all, was still an unsolved mystery.

As far back as 1894, Fairchild in the United States had perceived that at least three different compounds could be produced by adding lime to a solution of copper sulphate. The first, with only three-quarters of the lime required according to the schoolboy's chemical equation put forward by Millardet and Gayon,[1] was a sea-green compound which settled rapidly in water; the next, with the amount of lime generally used in practice, was gelatinous and sky-blue, settling quite slowly; and the last, with still more lime, had a deep, artificial-looking purplish tinge. No one even knew with any certainty what these three conspicuously different compounds were, or what was the difference in their fungicidal properties. Fairchild thought that basic sulphates of copper were produced first, and then the hydroxide of copper when lime was added to excess. Further evidence in support of this view was obtained later on, in 1932, when Dr. Hubert Martin studied the reaction using a new method of analysis called electrometric titration. But this did not go far enough; the question was which of the various compounds obtainable by mixing copper sulphate with lime was the best fungicide for use on plants and why. S. U. Pickering, in England, had published some original work on basic salts of copper, and he had long studied them for their purely chemical interest. About 1908, when he was co-operating with the Duke of Bedford in running an experimental fruit-farm at Woburn, he turned his chemical knowledge of basic salts of copper to account in attempts to elucidate the chemistry of Bordeaux mixture and to improve upon it. He covered a page with the complicated structural formulae of all the basic or oxy-sulphates which might be produced in copper sulphate and lime mixtures, and advanced the theory that when the carbon dioxide of the atmosphere acted upon them on the leaf-surface, they would release different amounts of copper in toxic form for killing the fungus spores.[2] According to this theory, most of the copper in Bordeaux mixture as usually made (with a large excess of lime) was wasted, as it was, so to speak, locked up, and never rendered available for doing the job required of it.

By adding reduced amounts of lime to copper sulphate solution, Pickering obtained two different basic compounds of copper which were of very

[1] $CuSO_4 + Ca(OH)_2 = Cu(OH)_2 + CaSO_4$.
[2] $xCuO.ySo_3 + (x\text{-}y)CO_2 = (x\text{-}y)CuCO_3 + yCuSO_4$

considerable interest. The first was the same as Fairchild's sea-green compound, made with three-quarters of the lime chemically equivalent to the copper, known as the trioxysulphate, and having the definite formula, $4CuO.SO_3$. The second, made with nine-tenths of the equivalent lime, and best known as 'the Pickering compound' for convenience of reference, was supposed to have the formula, $10CuO.SO_3$. For a given weight of copper sulphate used, the trioxysulphate compound would liberate two-and-a-half times as much copper in soluble form as the Pickering compound when acted upon by carbon dioxide. It might appear therefore that it would be two-and-a-half times as potent as fungicide. For several reasons, however, Pickering declared that the trioxysulphate was unsuitable for use in spraying, and he campaigned for the adoption of his $10CuO.SO_3$. Direct experiments showed that even from this compound carbon dioxide liberated nearly twenty times as much copper in soluble form as it did from ordinary Bordeaux mixture, and in practice, claimed Pickering, it was necessary to use only one-sixth as much of it – a very important economy indeed.

Apart altogether from the saving of copper, the Pickering compound could be made up in the form of a paste at chemical works, so that the farmer would only have to dilute it with water for use, thus saving much of his time. To make Bordeaux mixture the farmer had to suspend a bag of copper sulphate crystals in one vat or barrel to dissolve in water overnight; then in another vat or barrel he had to prepare milk of lime; and immediately before he was ready to do his spraying he had to mix the two solutions in exactly the right proportions, testing the result by such rough and ready means as that of dipping a bright steel knife in the mixture to see whether it came out coated with copper or not. The operations were not difficult, but they took up precious time, and once again, if equally good ready-made preparations could be produced, it was clearly better for them to be performed by chemists in a chemical factory than on the farm.

The Pickering compound, accurately made according to his directions, was in fact put on the English market about 1909, under the name of the Woburn Bordeaux Paste. Unhappily it was not found in practice to be as good as freshly made Bordeaux mixture, and it caused more injury to foliage. Why? The causes of the failure were insufficiently investigated. Pickering's theories were challenged by other workers, who, however, put forward nothing very convincing in their stead. Pickering, himself, by adopting a most pontifical attitude, did not help matters; and the very sensible attempts to improve on the empirical and now traditional mixture were, for the time being, abandoned. The workers at the research stations, particularly in

England, became settled in an idolatrous belief that there was not, and probably never would be, anything quite so good as freshly-prepared home-made Bordeaux mixture. It was the same with most of the other fungicides and insecticides; once the formulae had the prestige of recommendation in France or America, and they had been sanctioned by adoption for a few years, they were all too readily considered fixed for all time. The entomologist, Maxwell Lefroy, was one of those who challenged this attitude of mind among English workers, just before the first of the twentieth century's great European wars.

The real challenge came, however, from all those enterprising chemical manufacturers and middlemen who were setting themselves up in the spray-material business. The margin of profit on the sale of such staple commodities as copper sulphate, lime, soap, oil, nicotine and the like was relatively small. It paid both dealers and manufacturers much better to sell the farmers compounded products, such as lime-sulphur, and even better to sell them mixtures under fancy trade-names and of undisclosed composition. The Board of Agriculture and the professors at the agricultural colleges had to warn the farmers against buying such secret and branded mixtures, and thus there began a most interesting game of devils and angels. The very enterprising but at best commercially-honest spray-manufacturers played the darker part; while the much less enterprising but impeccably veracious professors and lecturers in the University Departments flapped their indignant wings in pure white light.

Historians, who were, so to speak, neutral, could give the devils their due. The agents and commercial travellers for the spray-manufacturers talked the farmers into spraying their crops. Educational facilities for farmers at agricultural colleges in England were static and few and far between. There was nothing static about commercial travellers; they pursued the farmers round the dairy, lay in wait for them on market days, bribed them with bread-and-cheese and beer, made demonstrations on their farms, and told the tale about the advantages of spraying, with an optimistic enthusiasm that made the angels blush for shame. The farmers had no appreciation of the 'culture' that the university workers put on; all the careful aspirations of the aitches in the 'wheat' and the 'wheres' and the 'whens' was wasted upon them; they liked the travellers better, for they talked to them in their own language; they 'put it over' with a healthy and understandable profit motive behind their endeavours. The farmers sometimes paid rather dearly for this form of education, but education it was, and it was certainly taken to them — they did not have to go to school to fetch it. This was very much to the credit of the devils. The professors then did their best to convince the farmers that the stuffs they had been cajoled into buying were of less value than the orthodox spray mixtures. This could be chalked up to the angels, for it kept things lively and the farmers heard both sides. Then the devils, having once secured a customer, were usually out to sell him spraying materials, not for one year, but year after year, and that would not happen if their dealings were seriously fraudulent. The best of the manufacturers were not above charging the farmers as much as possible for some mythical and especial goodness in their particular preparations, but there had to be something in these stuffs besides water and 'goodness' – they had to do the job. The concern of the manufacturers was to find the cheapest possible ingredients that would do what was required, or, alternatively, to find new materials that would do it better, and for which they could charge their own price. The results of this particular devilry were often of the greatest value to science, especially as the best-kept of trade-secrets had a way of leaking out in time, and patents granted monopolies for only fourteen years.

Two most valuable insecticides were brought into use in England, one before the War, the other just after, purely as the result of commercial enterprise. One was a preparation of certain cheap oils obtained from the distillation of tar – tar oil emulsion – which was much more effective than the caustic alkalies for the winter-washing of fruit-trees; the other was Derris, an insecticide non-poisonous to man, that could be used instead of arsenic for destroying caterpillars and other pests on fruit and vegetables. Derris was the powdered root of a tropical plant called *Derris elliptica*. The Chinese had used it for centuries as a fish-poison, having discovered that a very little of the juice of the bruised roots would poison all the fish in a stream without spoiling them for eating. It was not a kind of fishing that would appeal to British ideas of sportsmanship. There was no dalliance with death. It killed both young and old, both trout and minnows, but it was one way of getting fish if you just wanted to eat them and not to play with them or hurt them. Minute amounts of the drug in the water paralysed their nervous systems, brought them floating to the surface, where they had merely to be picked up. The juice of the roots was also used by the savages of Malay for painting the tips of their arrows. The poison was deadly to cold-blooded animals, fish and insects – but harmful to warm-blooded animals only when it was introduced directly into the blood-stream. It was singularly innocuous to man and beast when it was not on the tip of an arrow, but merely on food passing through the digestive system. The idea of using Derris as an insecticide occurred to Professor William McDougall while working with

Dr. Hose in the tropics, and the first patent for a Derris insecticide was taken out in 1911 by the firm of McDougall and Yalding, in Kent. Their products, Pulvo and Katakilla, put Derris to good use, and one of the most outstanding pieces of purely scientific work on plant-protection materials between 1920 and 1940 was to be the determination of the constitution of rotenone and certain other active principles in Derris root, by Dr. Tattersfield and his colleagues at Rothamsted.

While Derris preparations and some of the other proprietary materials put on the market before the war were of unquestionable value and usefulness, it was a regrettable fact that many of the products sold to the farmers by the less reputable firms contained no ingredient of unique value, and were merely very expensive ways of buying ordinary materials of commerce, diluted, adulterated and variously disguised. There were the same swindles as when artificial fertilizers first came into widespread use, some fifty or sixty years before. The abuses were greatest in the United States, where the number of proprietary stuffs on the market was already legion. In 1910 a Federal Insecticides and Fungicides Act was passed for the protection of the farmers. After that the manufacturers could offer anything they liked for sale, but – the nature and percentage of the active ingredients in it had to be plainly stated on the label, and any claim made for it had to be reasonable. 'Shot-gun' remedies, offered for the treatment of too many pests and diseases at one go, came in for a particularly bad time. If any firm put on the market a compound called, say, COPPER CATASTROPHOSAN, and claimed in the usual light-hearted commercial way that it would cure and prevent all Blights, Mildews, Blotches, Rusts, Caterpillars, Scabs, Spots and Cankers on all plants whatsoever, then that firm would promptly find itself up to its neck in an action brought by the U.S. Department of Agriculture. The experts of the Department would make a careful list of all the Blights, Rusts, Spots, Blotches and so forth, which could not be (*a*) cured, or (*b*) prevented by any of the materials in the mixture, and the transgressors would be brought to book accordingly for an amazingly long string of fraudulent misrepresentations. In Germany after the War a voluntary scheme was set up which went one better. Under this scheme no proprietary *Pflanzenschutzmittel*, whether fungicide or insecticide, had any chance of sale unless its trade-name appeared in an official Register, copies of which were made available to the growers. The Register did not give away any of the manufacturer's trade-secrets, it merely stated which particular pests or diseases the material would control, and the strengths at which it had to be used. Before any product was admitted to the Register, its composition had first to be disclosed to the authorities and it then had to pass a series of extremely well-organized tests at the official German agricultural research stations, which extended over a period of three years. The charges for this testing were not exorbitant, and while the scheme was of the very greatest assistance to the German chemical industry in the evolution of improved materials, it also safeguarded the farmers, for there was no doubt that those products entered on the Register would do the job for which they were intended. In England the chemical manufacturers were not so far-sighted, they did not seek any such assistance, and the farmers never had any such protection. A set of specifications for a few of the standard insecticides and fungicides was agreed between the Ministry of Agriculture and the more influential of the manufacturers in 1934, and farmers were advised to demand a guarantee that the materials they purchased were in conformity with these specifications – but that was all. The further advice to farmers that they should buy products of unspecified composition only from 'reputable British manufacturers' would be hardly worth mentioning, except for the sake of a gentle and understanding smile. The laws of libel in England actually operated to protect all secret and proprietary remedies, for any scientific worker daring to denounce those which happened to be worthless exposed himself and his publishers and printers to the risk of incurring very heavy damages. As for new fungicides and insecticides which promised to be of real value it certainly was possible for chemical firms to get them tested, and very carefully tested, at the English research stations, but not as a simple matter of business, or on payment of a fee. It was necessary for the representative of the firm concerned to ascertain the special interests and prejudices of individual workers, and then to do some very tactful wooing of those who could put up with his personality – in short, it was a labour of love, fraught with some snubs but many delightful surprises.

The development of an altogether new type of therapeutant for the control of seed-borne diseases of plants had its origin in 1909 in the work of Ehrlich and Bertheim on Salvarsan for the treatment of syphilis. The problem which they confronted was that of killing the curly fission-fungus or spirochaete of syphilis, by introducing a chemical fungicide or bactericide into the blood of living animals. So far the fission-fungicides, if one might be permitted to call them that, used for injection into living animals, were natural products, like the anti-toxin of diphtheria prepared from the blood of horses which had recovered from the disease. Such serums were of unknown chemical composition, and they relieved suffering in one kind of animal at the cost of deliberately inflicting it upon another. The new cure for syphilis was essentially to inject into the veins of the syphilitic man or woman some half a pint of a dilute solution of dihydroxy-diamino-arsenobenzene – a pure chemical compound of exactly-known composition synthesized in the laboratory from arsenic and derivatives of coal tar. Salvarsan, the familiar '606' of army life during the 1914–18 war, was not only the most effective prophylactic ever discovered against that ghastly leprosy of the west which since the fifteenth century had always followed the armies; it was in certain other and more subtle respects a victory for the human intellect over cruelty, messiness and ignorance. How Ehrlich, eccentric Jewish worker of Frankfort, followed up the clues, got the chemists to make him over six hundred compounds of arsenic for trial, and by a process of elimination picked out the one which he called Salvarsan from among them – all this was a long story. It was well and dramatically told later on, for all to read, in Paul de Kruif's *Microbe Hunters*, under the title of 'The Magic Bullet'. Briefly, it arose out of the differential staining of tissues with aniline dyes, and the observation of the toxic effect of the dye Trypan Red upon the trypanosomes of sleeping sickness. The difficulty was not in finding some chemical compound that would kill the causal organism of syphilis — there were thousands that would do so – it was to find the one that would kill the organism without injuring the animal within whose warm and sensitive tissues it lived. In this the refinements were extreme, but the problem was the same in principle as that of finding a fungicide that could be used with safety on the delicate foliage of peach trees.

Ehrlich thought in terms of what he called the *Dosis tolerata* and the *Dosis curativa*. The *Dosis tolerata* was the amount, per unit body weight, of any chemical therapeutant that the host organism would tolerate without sustaining injury; the *Dosis curativa* was the amount that would kill the parasite, and so effect a cure of the disease. When Salvarsan was at last found, the amount that would kill the spirochaetes in a syphilitic rabbit was less than one-seventh of that which the rabbit could tolerate without harm. The ratio of *Dosis tolerata* to *Dosis curativa*, the factor of safety, for rabbits, was seven.

The high factor of safety of Salvarsan was attributable to the combination of arsenic in a very special way with dyestuff intermediates – with synthetic derivates of benzene and the like. The dodge was of extreme interest to the plant pathologists, for they, too, wanted chemical therapeutants with a high factor of safety. The seed-steeps, used for the treatment of the Bunt of the wheat, for example, killed the Bunt spores effectively enough, but they also destroyed the germinative power of a certain proportion of the seed. More seed had to be sown per acre than would have been necessary, but for this loss. Following Ehrlich's discovery the German workers began to try steeping wheat and other seeds, not in solutions of copper sulphate and mercuric chloride, but of so-called 'organic' compounds – pure aniline dyes, and compounds of benzene with metals which had fungicidal properties. In 1912, Dr. Riehm, of the German agricultural research service, tried Safranin, Methyl Blue, Bismarck Brown, Congo Red and other synthetic dyes. None of these was successful, but he also tried a new compound of mercury, chlorine and phenol, called Chlorphenol Mercury, and submitted by the Bayer Company of Elberfeld. When treated with a little alkali to render it soluble, this compound proved an effective seed-steep for the treatment of the Bunt of the wheat at a concentration of only one part in a thousand of water. This was the first of the 'organic mercurials' which twenty-five years later would be replacing most other materials for the treatment of seed-grain.

CHAPTER XXV

LEGISLATIVE MEASURES

'Unless the prevalence of the insect and fungoid pests of fruit trees and bushes has greatly increased it is difficult to imagine how any success could have been obtained in fruit-growing before spraying came into use ... Nowadays it is only by a rare chance that an uninjured crop of fruit can be obtained otherwise.' So wrote one of the contributors to the Journal of the Board of Agriculture in England in the year 1905. And thus it was, not only with fruit-growing in England, but in most other countries and with nearly every crop. Success depended upon the effective *defence* of the crops, not only by spraying, which was a measure of limited application, but by all available and appropriate means. It was true that the damage caused by insects and parasitic fungi was coming to be more widely recognized than it had ever been in the past, but with all due allowance for this, it was indeed hard to imagine how the apparently greater prevalence of pests and diseases could be accounted for, otherwise than by their absolute increase. With the specialized and expanding cultivations of the modern world there was a veritable advance of the insects and the fungi. In the field of plant pathology alone, it was not only that many of the old and long-familiar maladies of the crops became more serious – the Rust epidemic in North America in 1904 was one of the worst in history – but in the first decades of the twentieth century there was outbreak after outbreak of 'new' plant diseases reaching epidemic distribution in regions where they had never been known, or had never been of any particular economic significance, before.

The American Gooseberry Mildew, very destructive in the United States, was observed for the first time on bushes in County Antrim in the summer of 1900; by 1906 it was in the Evesham district, and very soon thereafter all the gooseberry bushes in the British Isles were endangered. In 1902 the presence of a new and very serious fungus disease of the potatoes, first called the Black Scab and later the Wart Disease, was reported in Cheshire. In 1902, also, the Silver Leaf Disease of the plum trees began to call attention to itself and by 1906 it was found to be widespread. In 1905 yet another disease of the potatoes, the Leaf Roll, caused great loss in the Rhine provinces of Germany, and by the beginning of 1908 it had given rise to a panic among the German potato growers. It was feared that in the whole of Germany there was not one sound potato for seed, and there were some who cried out that the potato-culture of Europe was once again at stake. When search was made for the disease in Great Britain, Canada and the United States, it was found to be in truth most insidiously destructive. In 1904 the Bark Disease was first noticed on sweet chestnut trees in Long Island, New York. By 1908 it was reported in Connecticut, Massachusetts and Vermont, and it was recognized that 'unless something unforeseen happened to check its spread the complete destruction of all the chestnut orchards and forests of the Atlantic States was only a matter of time'. In 1906 the Blister Rust of the White Pine was found at Geneva, New York, where it had been introduced on nursery stock from Europe; it spread northwards and westwards into Canada, and across Michigan and Minnesota, menacing the great white-pine forests of the Rockies. Meanwhile, to mention but one small excursion of the insect pests, the dreaded Colorado Beetle was found in every stage of its development – adult insects, larvae, eggs and all – in some potato fields near Tilbury in 1901. By isolation and fire and the ploughing of gas-lime into the soil that colony of the beetles was destroyed, but only just in time.

It was significant that of all the plant diseases which became epidemic and gave rise to new alarms during the first decade of the century only one, and that the least of them, could be combated by the method of spraying. The American Gooseberry Mildew, caused by a fungus which grew on the surface of the shoots, berries and leaves, called *Sphaerotheca mors-uvae*, and resembling the other Powdery Mildews long-since studied by the brothers Tulasne (see Plate I, opposite p. 60), could be kept in check by laborious and repeated treatment with liver of sulphur. But the other plant diseases causing the greatest anxiety over this period: the Wart Disease and Leaf Roll of the potatoes, the Chestnut Bark Disease, the Silver Leaf, and the Blister Rust of the Pines, were, as it happened, of such kinds that they did not lend themselves to control by any chemical means. Their historic part in the story was to awaken Departments, Boards and Ministries of Agriculture in every country of the world to the necessity of adopting Legislative measures against the introduction and spread of plant disease.

In 1907 the Destructive Insects and Pests Act was passed in Great Britain. It extended the powers which had been exercised by the Board of Agriculture since 1877 in relation to the Colorado beetle, to *all* insect pests, and also to all fungus diseases of crops, trees or bushes. It armed the Board with wide powers to prohibit or regulate the importation of any vegetable substance or other article likely to introduce foreign fungus diseases, and to order the destruction of such articles landed in contravention of any quarantine in force. It further invested the Board with power to appoint crop-inspectors, to enter upon private land, and to direct the removal or destruction of any crop, tree or bush in the kingdom on which notifiable diseases or pests were established, although, unfortunately, the provisions made for the compensation of farmers, where necessary, were somewhat parsimoniously curtailed. The first Orders under this Act concerned the American Gooseberry Mildew and the Wart Disease of potatoes. A small company of crop-inspectors was duly appointed, and their first exercise in mapping out the geographical distribution and spread of a plant disease, as the American workers were doing for all the major diseases of the crops throughout the vast territories of the United States, was in tracking down the comparatively trifling murrain of the gooseberry bushes in the British Isles. An ingenious use was made of the Workhouses. There were Workhouses in every part of the country, and most of them had bits of land on which some gooseberries were grown. By preparing a large map of the country showing all the Workhouses and then marking the dots in red or green according to whether their gooseberry bushes were mildewed or not, a most useful chart of the spread of the disease could be obtained. Far more alarming than the American Gooseberry Mildew was the Wart Disease of the potatoes; and it was through the exercise of its new powers under the Act of 1907 that the Board averted what might well have been a disaster for the potato growing industry, and fostered such excellent work on the improvement of the potato stocks in connection with it, that in the end the Wart Disease did more good than harm.

Legislative measures designed to prevent the introduction of plant diseases with imported produce were already in force in most European countries in 1907. They were tightened up; similar measures were taken in the several British Dominions and Crown Colonies, and in 1912 the United States, which up to that time had only such laws as the 'Michigan Yellows Laws' in individual States here and there, took federal action and set up a Federal Horticultural Board under a Quarantine Act, whose first Orders were made to check the spread of the White Pine Blister Rust and to prevent the introduction of the Wart Disease with potatoes from Great Britain.

The new and stringent Quarantine restrictions were greeted with opposition and complaint in most countries, on the ground that they were in restraint of trade. There was quite an outcry in the American press over the supposedly high-handed action of the Department of Agriculture in destroying a shipment of flowering-cherries from Tokyo which had been sent as a gift to the wife of the President. But Tokyo just sent another lot which were free from the unwanted pest; the Department demonstrated that it meant business; the cherries bloomed happily thereafter; and the introduction of yet another plague into the American orchards was quite probably averted.

The Quarantine measures, long overdue, were of extreme importance in the control of plant disease, but they were capable of abuse, and as competition for trade of every kind on the world's markets became more and more cut-throat, they were often twisted by dishonest politicans to bar imports of agricultural produce from this country or from that, for quite other than phytopathological reasons. The progress of agricultural science would suffer materially if these embargoes to keep out plant disease were allowed to get under the control of the bureaucrats and commercial wire-pullers. As W. A. Orton pointed out, in the United States a great part of the Department's work for the improvement of that country's agriculture was still the introduction of plants and seeds from every part of the world for acclimatization. Neither the United States nor any other country could afford to close its ports at all indiscriminately to foreign plants. For the intelligent exclusion of alien pests and parasites without unreasonable interference with the desirable and necessary commerce in nursery stock and seeds, some measure of international co-operation and good faith was required. Ideally, the inspection and certification of shipments of plant produce should be done in the country of origin. There should be a Plant-Pest-and-Disease Inspection Service in each country, run by competent plant-doctors of such scientific integrity that their word could be trusted by all the others. For example, if the honourable Plant-Pest-and-Disease Inspectorate in Japan were prepared to certify that a particular lot of flowering cherries were free from all pests and diseases on the honourable U.S. prohibited list, and as far as it was humanly possible to say otherwise perfectly healthy, then, and only then, should they be shipped across the ocean for admittance into the United States. Here evidently was a fine opportunity for the exchange of scientific workers, and for the setting up of services of common benefit to all nations. But what a change there would have to be in international relationships before any such sensible arrangements would ever be possible throughout the world! If the nations could only resolve their political and economic differences, just sufficiently to enable them to do that – to set up an uncorrupted and world-wide organization to fight the real common enemies of all Mankind: the destructive insects and the pathogenic fungi, bacteria and filter-passing viruses – then there would be a new page to turn over in the history of civilization. But what a dream! The first International Phytopathological Conference was held in Rome in May 1914.

While movements towards such international action were fated to encounter many set-backs, to flounder in seas of words, and to reach firm ground only here and there for a long time to come, *national* groupings of phytopathological workers, professional, and in the service of individual Governments, did begin to take shape and grow during those years 1900 to 1914. In the United States, the publications on plant diseases which had previously been issued by the Division of Vegetable [Physiology and] Pathology of the U.S. Department of Agriculture were continued in the Bulletins of the Bureau of Plant Industry. There was more in this than a mere change of name, it was symptomatic of the realization that the control of plant disease had an important and integral part in the development of all the plant industries of the nation. The magnitude of that part might be judged by the fact that of the 285 Bulletins published in the series between 1901 and 1913, 58 were exclusively devoted to plant pathological subjects, while in most of the others considerations of plant disease had some greater or lesser part. They were not little folders, these Bulletins, with three pages of letterpress and a picture on the back; they were fat wads of anything from forty to three hundred pages, a little prosy sometimes, but each one of them a detailed record of some long and business-like investigation – the eager exploitation of scientific knowledge for the betterment of an agricultural industry. The United States was still primarily an agricultural country.

In England, for all the technical efforts of the Board of Agriculture, the agricultural industries were dwindling and not expanding. There was a sinking in the heart of things, and the scientific workers could not but be affected despite themselves. To labour for the improvement of the stocks and the suppression of plant pests and diseases while the very land was being abandoned at such a rate was like caulking the deck while the ship went down. Much of the English work on plant disease tended to be museum-like – the serene presentation of hundreds of maladies, as it were pickled in glass jars, each with a page or two of fair description – as in the works of George Massee of Kew; or, it tended to be academic, philosophic and fundamental, as that of the workers of the Cambridge School. But the amount of 'economic' or 'applied' biological research, which in practice meant chiefly applied entomology and mycology, was increasing under pressure of advice given to the authorities by the first workers in the field, who could see more clearly than anybody else the economic and commercial importance of what they were doing. In 1904 the small company of these workers in the British Isles formed themselves into a scientific association, with the entomologist Dr. Theobald as their first president, 'to discuss new discoveries, to exchange experiences and carefully to consider the best methods of work'. *The Association of Applied Biologists* had, in the beginning, only twenty-six members. Some years later there were about ninety. Until 1914, when part 1, volume 1 of the important *Annals of Applied Biology* was issued, the association had only a semi-official journal for the publication of its proceedings and papers, owned privately by one of its members (*The Journal of Economic Biology*). But, from the first, scientific meetings were held up and down the country, and when a Development Commission was set up in 1910 in connection with the Board of Agriculture and Fisheries, the members of the Association were largely responsible for shaping its policy for the furtherance of agricultural research. The Commission was entrusted with the distribution of a fund of some £2,900,000 for the development of agriculture, forestry, harbours, inland navigation, fisheries and certain other oddments. Some of the money was ear-marked for the setting-up of Farm Institutes and the promotion of elementary agricultural education, and further sums were reserved for research. By 1911 a complete scheme was drawn up which defined the organization of agricultural research in England, very much as it was to be by the year 1940. Provision was made in the scheme for the setting-up of several research institutes one of which, at least, would work on the problems of plant disease. The realization of these schemes was delayed, first by red tape and then by the war, but the Colleges of University rank, in which there was provision for higher instruction in agricultural science, were already making good headway, a certain amount of research was being done at all of them, and an important part of their function was to train workers for overseas. Following the victorious outcome of the Boer War, and other political developments of the period, the Professors at the Agricultural Colleges could console themselves with the reflection that though home agriculture was diminishing, the cultivations of the Empire were expanding, and for them many entomologists, many plant doctors, would be needed. In part this consolation was illusory, for in work on the practical control of plant pests and diseases, at any rate, the Departments of Agriculture in both Canada and Australia had already left the Mother Country, God Bless her, some way behind. It was a fact, however, that many workers were needed to join the few who had already been sent out to South Africa, to India and to the Crown Colonies; in those territories the pests and the diseases of the crops were being surveyed, as they had never been before. The Cambridge *Journal of Agricultural Science*, here already referred to, did not confine itself to the publication of papers from workers of the Cambridge School, and of other University Departments in the United Kingdom; it extended a most cordial welcome to any papers which its referees considered worth publishing from those who had taken out their microscopes after the unfurling flag.

In the United States many of the Agricultural Experiment Stations were now responsible for research work of equal standing to that of the federal Department of Agriculture. Investigations on pests and diseases of the crops were going on at all of them, and in 1913, the Washington *Journal of Agricultural Research*, for scientific papers from both the Experiment Stations and the Department, was added to the massive publications into which the student of plant pathology would now have to delve. In 1908 the teachers, research workers and others directly concerned with plant diseases in the United States formed the American Phytopathological Society, and, in 1911, when their membership had reached about two hundred, they started their own journal, *Phytopathology*. At first the journal was intended to be an informal and friendly vehicle for the exchange of news and views, and for the discussion of all topics of interest to plant doctors in connection with their work. There were biographical notices and other personalities, some most welcome essays on the progress of the science as a whole and on its relation to national and world affairs, many interesting portraits and sketches of leading workers in the present and the past. But when the American plant pathologists got down, as they did most of the time, to accounts of their own researches, then their informal and conversational style was quite sufficiently technical, not to say abstruse. In fact *Phytopathology* was soon to become the principal journal in the world exclusively devoted to plant diseases, and the abstractors, trying to keep pace with the world literature on the subject after the war, would have to record more important papers in *Phytopathology* than in any other single periodical whatsoever.

The formation of new scientific societies, the issue of new Journals, the increasing participation of governments in the promotion of research, the setting up of quarantines and official phytopathological services – all these things marked the gathering of forces to combat the advance of the fungi. Such mobilizations for the defence of the crops were going on not in the United States and the British Empire alone, but with greater or lesser acceleration in every country. Germany, in particular, had her fine agricultural research organization, her journals on plant diseases dating back to the early nineties. Most of the best systematic text-books were still in the German language or translated from it. But in 1913 quite a crop of original books on the subject were published, in English. There was Grove's *British Rust Fungi*, and Massee's *Mildews, Rusts and Smuts*; Stevens' *Fungi which cause Plant Disease*, and Cook's *Diseases of Tropical Plants*. The two first from England, the two latter from America. Such books for students, which would still be among the standard works in 1940, marked a stage reached in the diffusion of knowledge. The outreaching work, of course, was still to be sought, not in text-books but in the original scientific papers. Holland and Denmark were making great contributions; research stations were starting in Japan. More was being written about the diseases of the crops now, than any single book could ever possibly survey. But the great bulk of this work represented a lateral extension of the science, the application of knowledge already won and the filling in of blanks. The advance into the unknown, the thin thread of human understanding of the nature of disease in plants, as in animals, crept ahead as slowly as ever. Genius for original discovery was not distributed any more liberally among the workers of the twentieth century than among those of the nineteenth. If one would know how the plant doctors were getting on at the leading edge of their science – the *diagnosis* of plant diseases – and with how much or how little savvy they seemed to be adding to their fathers' and their grandfathers' discoveries, it would be necessary to follow their adventures in just one or two fields. Undoubtedly the new or prevailing epidemics of plant disease were still setting the course of research. But even the new epidemics were very numerous. Which were the most instructive investigations on plant diseases during the first forty years of the twentieth century? In which did most of the fundamental ideas crop up? In 1939 that was a question that no one would care to have to answer. At a hazard, the researches into the ailments of the long-suffering potato and into the Rust diseases of cereals were easily at the forefront of the advance. But what of all the work on the Rusted Pines, the stricken Chestnut trees, the Wilted Cotton, the Streaked and Smutted Sugar-canes, the Mosaic'd Tobacco, the Blighted Tea bushes, the Sleepy Tomatoes, the Sooted Oranges, and all those other afflicted crops on which a growing army of plant doctors were busy? It would be necessary to look to right and to left, but in the papers on the diseases of the potato and on the Rust of the wheat there would be found most of the ideas energizing plant pathology as a whole. There were several main types of plant disease, and it was not far wrong to say that the potato had them all.

CHAPTER XXVI

BLIGHT, WART DISEASE, LEAF-ROLL

ONE discovery that had evaded every worker for over sixty years was made at last by Clinton, of the Agricultural Experiment Station in Connecticut, in 1910. He obtained the missing winter spores of *Phytophthora infestans*, the Potato Blight fungus, in artificial culture. And now that these long-sought spores were at last veritably found, there was no such excitement in the scientific world as there had been over Worthington G. Smith's doubtful-to-dubious discovery of 1875. Science had moved on, but, as always in discoveries concerning diseases of the ill-starred potato, there was something queer about what was found, something at the very leading edge of pathological investigation at the time. Many attempts had been made to cultivate the Potato Blight fungus on artificial media. But it had proved difficult to find just the right kind of nutrient jelly. The first workers to be rewarded with some slight success were Hecke in 1898 and Matruchot and Molliard in 1903. Clinton made his first attempts to obtain pure cultures in 1904 and after two or three years' work he found that the fungus would grow well on agar jelly containing Lima-bean juice. He grew one particular strain of the fungus, obtained from Holland, for two years on this medium, raising at least twenty-two generations from the summer spores. Only these conidia, these asexual summer spores were produced; so far there was no sign of the missing winter spores, or oospores, arising from a sexual process.

After still another year or two Clinton tried cultivating the fungus on jelly made up with oats or with oat-juice. This time the fungus not only grew profusely in its summer stage, but it *did* produce female and male organs – oogonia and antheridia. Some few of the oogonia were fertilized by the antheridia and one or two perfect oospores were to be found. There they were at last, embedded in the jelly, and perfectly plain to be seen under the microscope. There was no question of their belonging to any other organism, the most elaborate precautions had been taken and this time the cultures were pure. The oogonia were comparatively large, as microscopic objects went; they were about forty microns, one twenty-fifth of a millimetre, in diameter. There were not, however, very many perfect fruits, or oospores; most of the female organs were imperfect and only very rarely were they fertilized, as the corresponding male organs were either absent or small and deficient. In further experiments on other nutritive jellies it was found that the female organs were produced frequently enough, but it was only when the fungus was nourished with oat-juice that it produced any perfect male organs to fertilize the oospheres. The fungus, like many varieties of the potato itself, was male-sterile, and Clinton's interesting theory was that it required an old man's aphrodisiac – a little Spanish Fly, as it were – to revive its male vigour. The oat-juice contained a substance called lecithin, a phosphorized fat, which was of value in cases of nervous debility in man and was known to be a prominent constituent of nerve-tissue and spermatazoa. Perhaps it was the lecithin in the oat-juice which stimulated the Potato Blight fungus to sexual reproduction.

Clinton next proceeded to *mate* the Potato Blight fungus with another species of *Phytophthora* – found on Lima beans – which developed much more vigorous male organs when cultivated on oat-jelly. The Potato Blight fungus was grown at one place on the jelly, and the Bean Blight fungus in another place nearby. At the junction of the two mycelia large and well-formed oospores were produced. In this experiment it appeared that a *hybrid parasitic fungus* had been obtained by the deliberate crossing of *P. infestans* with *P. Phaseoli*.

These researches of Clinton's did not provide any direct answer to the old riddle: where does the Blight go in the winter-time? The oospores had still been found only in artificial cultures. But the suggestiveness of Clinton's little batch of discoveries was immense. First they showed that the old contention that the Blight fungus could grow only on the living tissues of its host was palpable nonsense. It could live as a saprophyte on dead material – for there it was doing so, for anybody to see, on oat-agar jelly which was as dead as boiling could make it. Those who continued to suppose that Nature could not and did not manage to provide the fungus with anything corresponding to the oat-jelly, in all the complex stuffs existing in decayed potato tubers or in the humus of the soil, were simply deficient in imagination. Then the crossing of one species of parasitic fungus with another – that also was significant. It might not happen in nature between the particular Blight fungi which grew respectively on the potato and on the bean; but that it might happen between other nearly related species or sub-species of fungi was all too probable—between the sub-species, or biological strains of the Rust fungi on different cereals, for example. Hybridization might be one of the means by which parasitic fungi could adapt themselves to new hybrid host plants. While man was busy with a chart of the Mendelian system on the blackboard, making elaborate crossings and back-crossings between different varieties of wheat in the attempt to produce Rust-resistant varieties, the Rust-fungi themselves might be going in for inter-marriage on their own account, and this would vastly complicate the situation.

Clinton did not draw attention to all these possibilities, in so many words, in 1910; it was another twenty years before they came into prominence, but the clues were there. Clinton was puzzled about another matter: the Potato Blight fungus would grow on jelly made with oats or beans or peanuts or maize or wheat with the agar-agar, but it would not grow on jelly made with the stuff of its natural host, *videlicet* potatoes. It happened that while Clinton was working on the Potato Blight in Connecticut a rival team, L. R. Jones with Giddings and Lutman, were tackling the same subject at the Agricultural Experiment Station in Vermont. Clinton anticipated them in the discovery of the oospores, but they had the satisfaction of telling him just why he had been unable to grow the Potato Blight fungus on potato jelly. He *cooked* the potatoes first. The fungus would grow fast enough on jelly made with raw potato, but when the potato was cooked the starch grains were disrupted, and perhaps the resulting jelly was too sticky for the mycelium of the fungus to penetrate with ease.

The Jones, Giddings and Lutman Bulletin of 1912 was long and comprehensive. It purported to set forth practically everything that was known about the Potato Blight up to that time; there were some serious errors in the part about the early history of the disease, but the bibliography appended was as valuable as that in Wallace's key-paper on the Apple Scab of the following year, while some of the new and original matter in the paper concerned the scientific testing of potato varieties for Blight-resistance. The method adopted by Jones and his team was to cut small blocks out of raw potato tubers with a sterile knife and to drop them into test-tubes with some damp, sterile cotton-wool in the bottom. A little pure culture of the Blight fungus – a morsel of the jelly on which it was growing – was then introduced into each tube and the growth was left to spread over the block of potato, other organisms being excluded in the usual way. After ten days, at 15°-16° C., the tubes were examined and the extent of the growth of the fungus on each block of potato gave an indication of the susceptibility of that particular variety to the Blight. Three thousand cultures were made on seventy-six varieties, and the results were in fairly good agreement with observations made on the same varieties in the field during severe Blight attacks, and with the rate of spread of the Blight over artificially inoculated leaves. The potato varieties in cultivation could be sorted into five classes ranging from those which were 'Highly Resistant' to the Blight at one end of the scale, to those which were 'Very Susceptible' at the other. The designation 'Highly Resistant' was optimistic, as some of the varieties assigned to that category, Magnum Bonum and Up-to-Date among them, were certainly stricken down in the field when the Blight was at all severe; but there was some real difference in the susceptibility of the different varieties, and this appeared to be due not so much to anatomical differences as to differences in the very protoplasm of the plants.

While this work was going on in the States, the diseases of the potato were being tackled at home, which was to say in Ireland, as they had never been tackled before. The Irish Department of Agriculture and Technical Instruction was not only making good headway with its campaign for the adoption of potato spraying, but, in 1909, in response to insistent reports that the potatoes in the west were stricken with a variety of diseases other than the Blight, it set up a temporary field station at Clifden in County Galway where these troubles could be studied at their worst. The station was not exactly elaborate: it comprised a small laboratory hut, built of corrugated iron, out on a stretch of reclaimed bog-land on which experimental potato crops could be grown. But, above all, it was exactly what had so long been needed: a *field* station. Dr. G. H. Pethybridge, later Mycologist to the English Ministry of Agriculture, was head of the Irish Department's Seeds and Plant Disease Division; he migrated from Dublin to the field station in May each year and stayed there until October; he was at the bedside of the sick potatoes over their whole growing period. The reports of his investigations, some of the most varied and interesting ever made on potato diseases, were published annually in the Department's Journal. And this continued from 1909 until 1916, when the demand of the aircraft industry for more and more flax was responsible for the diversion of his interests to the diseases of that crop.

For a couple of years after 1910, Dr. Pethybridge had assisting him at the field station a former student of his at the Royal College of Science, Dublin, a young pathologist of great promise who hailed from County Kilkenny, and whose name was Paul Murphy. When Clinton's queer discoveries about the development of the Potato Blight fungus were published in 1911, Pethybridge and Murphy set to work to obtain if possible the necessary corroboration of them. They, too, found that oat-juice stimulated the fungus to something approaching sexual reproduction. They confirmed Clinton's results and amplified them by tracing out the course of development of the resting-spores, of which Clinton had described only a part. Indeed Pethybridge discovered something that was even more remarkable about the sex-life of one of these fungi in the genus to which de Bary had given the name Phytophthora. The female organ was not penetrated by the male, but *the male was penetrated by the female*, an entirely novel arrangement – later found by other workers to prevail in several other species of the genus.

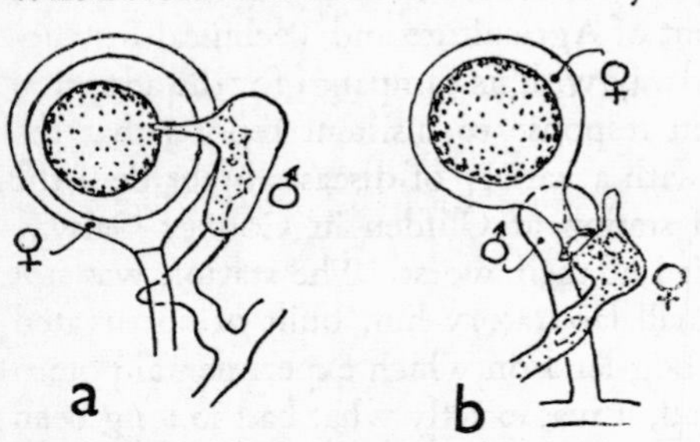

FIG. 53. Reversal of the role of the sexual organs in Phytophthora. (*a*) The usual arrangement: a fertilization tube from the antheridium penetrates the oogonium. *Peronospora Alsinearum*, after de Bary, 1866. (*b*) The oogonium traverses the antheridium. *Phytophthora erythroseptica*, after Pethybridge, 1913

The Potato Blight fungus, *Phytophthora infestans*, caused rotting of the potato tubers in Galway as it did elsewhere, but Pethybridge observed that the potatoes in that region were also subject to another kind of rot, different from that caused by the Blight, which had never before been described. When the affected tubers were cut by the spade or with a knife, the surfaces exposed to the air quickly assumed a deep salmon-pink colour, finally turning black. This 'Pink Rot' was found upon investigation to be caused by a species of *Phytophthora* which closely resembled but was not the same as the Blight fungus. The new species was isolated, cultivated on nutrient jelly, and named *Phytophthora erythroseptica*. It was in this species, and not in the Potato Blight fungus itself that the inverted sexual behaviour in Phytophthora was first observed. Appropriately enough, it generally happened at night; the fungus, growing on nutrient jelly, although encouraged with a little oat-juice, had a pronounced disinclination to copulate in the day-time, and Dr. Pethybridge had to sit up all night with his eye glued to the microscope, watching and drawing the process. What he saw is here illustrated in Fig. 54. Some time in the late evening an enterprising young female organ, or oogonial incept, protruding from one of the tangled spawn threads of the fungus, pushed its tip into a male swelling, or antheridium, borne on an adjacent thread (stage (*a*) in the figure). The tip of the oogonial incept then began to swell within the antheridium, and presently burst out at the top (*b*). Thirty minutes later the developing oogonium had increased considerably in size (*c*). After a further 2 hours and 20 minutes it was as (*d*), and some 15 hours later still it had attained full-size (*e*). The plasm it contained was then beginning to gather together to form the oosphere or unfertilized egg of the fungus. At this stage the funnel-shaped stalk or base passing through the antheridium was plainly to be seen, and in the original paper, in the Proceedings of the Royal Dublin Society for 1913, it was beautifully shown by a photomicrograph taken directly from nature. It was not certain at that time exactly when the true process of fertilization – that was to say nuclear fusion – took place, but the formation of the fertilized egg-cell, the thick-walled oospore, invariably followed. Later, detailed cytological studies by Paul Murphy proved that the actual fusion of the two sexual nuclei occurred

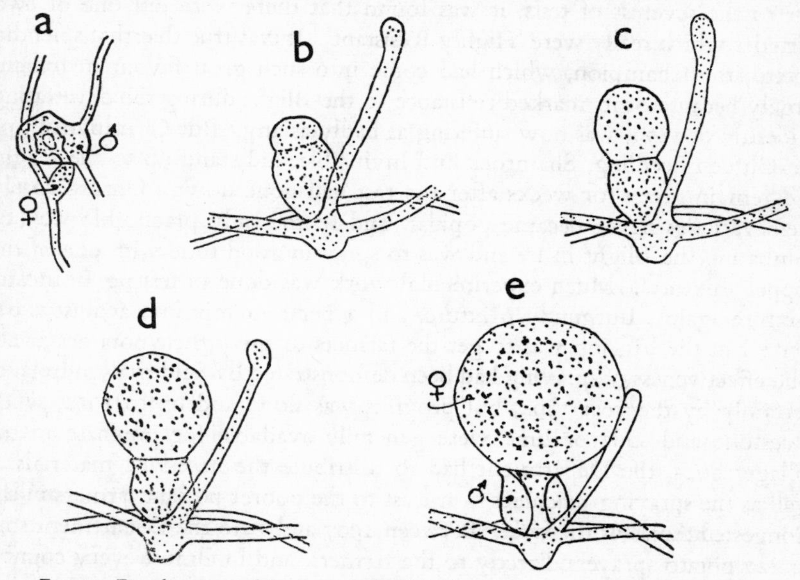

FIG. 54. Development of the oogonium of the fungus causing Pink Rot of potato tubers – *Phytophthora erythroseptica.* ♂ male organ or antheridium. ♀ female organ or oogonium. After Pethybridge, 1913

when the thick wall of the oospore was mature, the male nucleus having reached the unfertilized egg-cell at a somewhat earlier stage.

The parts of the sexual organs of the Potato Blight fungus were not so easy to distinguish as those of the Pink-Rot species of Phytophthora, but Pethybridge and Murphy obtained evidence which left no doubt but that they were of the same character. And that was about as far as fundamental work on the Potato Blight had progressed by 1914. The winter spores which might even yet be found to occur in nature and to have some part in starting the Blight each year, had been seen in artificial culture, and the way in which they developed was known. A beginning had been made in the building up of a technique for the scientific testing for Blight-resistance of commercial varieties produced by the potato breeders' art. Some workers – and among these was Dr. R. N. Salaman of Cambridge with his experiments on *Solanum edinense* – were already beginning to look towards the new scientific plant breeding for a possible ultimate solution of the Blight problem, just as the cerealists were looking that way for the possible ultimate defeat of the Rusts. Even in the west of Ireland where supposedly Blight-resistant potatoes were put to the severest of tests, it was found that there were just one or two varieties which really were 'Highly Resistant'. It was true that that splendid potato, the Champion, which had come into such great favour in Ireland largely because of its marked resistance to the Blight during the devastating epidemic of 1879, was now suffering as badly as any. But Champion II, or the Clifden Seedling, Shamrock and Invincible, did stand up to the Blight and remain green for weeks after the rest had gone down. Unfortunately these varieties never became popular, and so the only practicable way of combating the Blight in Ireland was to spray in good time with one of the copper mixtures. Much experimental work was done in testing Bordeaux mixture against Burgundy mixture, and 1 per cent mixtures against 2 per cent. But the big job was to get the farmers to spray their potatoes at all. The effectiveness of spraying had been demonstrated by field trials in Ireland, certainly by the year 1894, but progress was slow, and up to 1912, when bluestone and soda or lime were generally available for purchase in the village shops, the Department had to distribute the necessary materials as well as the spraying machines – at least to the poorer peasant farmers in the Congested Areas of the west. Between 1907 and 1916 the Department sold 14,827 potato sprayers directly to the farmers, and in almost every county, in addition to permanent Agricultural Instructors, Temporary Spraying Demonstrators, usually third-year students in Agriculture, were appointed each season to give instruction in the use of the machines and to attend to their repair.

The Wart Disease of potatoes was a malady entirely distinct and different from the Blight. First known as the Black Scab, it was also entirely different from the old and well-known Common and Powdery Scabs, which were fungus diseases more or less superficially affecting the skins of the potatoes, especially when they were grown in gravelly, alkaline soil. The Black Scab had a somewhat closer resemblance to the Club Root of the cabbages. It was characterized by warty, tuberous and cauliflower-like proliferations of abnormal tissue on the tubers and lower parts of the stems. The warty growths rotted and released multitudes of thick-walled, persistent, viable sporangia into the soil, which was thereby contaminated for succeeding potato crops. In England, the disease was first reported, simultaneously by Professor M. C. Potter of Durham University and George Massee of Kew, in the *Journal of the Board of Agriculture* for 1902. The diseased specimens which they had examined came from Cheshire and the Liverpool area; the

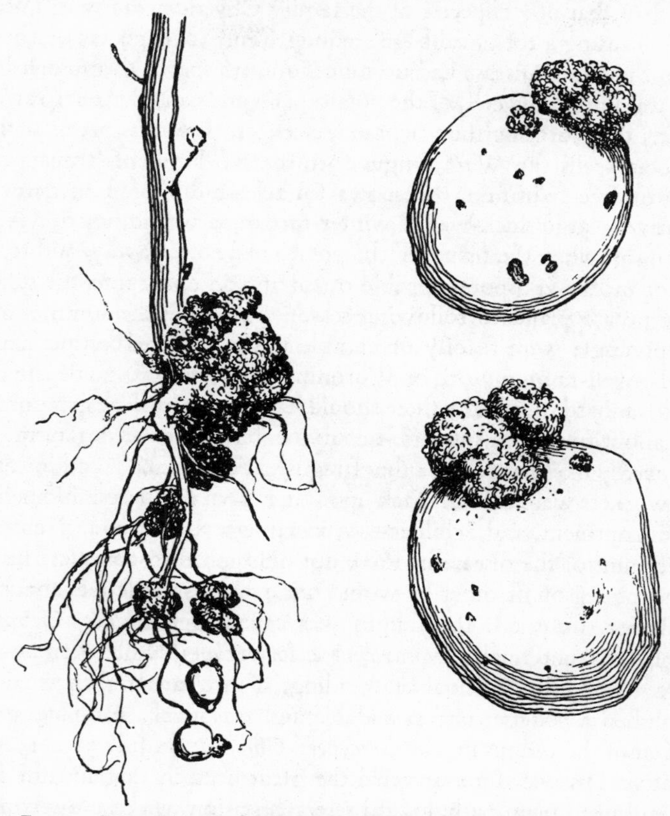

FIG. 55. Wart Disease of Potatoes. Line drawing by Dr. E. S. Gyngell, from photographs

disease at first appeared to be confined to that region, but it was immediately apparent that if it was allowed to spread it would endanger all the potato cultivations of the British Isles. The need for prompt diagnosis and search for control measures was plain enough, but there was much dispute and confusion about the identity of the causal fungus between 1902 and 1909, and there were attempts to sustain claims for priority of discovery, based on scrappy and partial descriptions, which added no lustre at all to the science of mycology which the twentieth century had inherited from the nineteenth.

The fungus was one of the most primitive algal-fungi or Phycomycetes. It was adapted for life under water or in wet soil, and it was even simpler in its parts than that other species of the family Chytridiaceae which Woronin had found causing a rot of cabbage seedlings (Fig. 32, page 179). The causal fungus of the Wart Disease had no mycelium, no spawn threads. It lived as naked plasm within the cells of the potato plant and caused them to swell and proliferate, thus forming the warty excrescences. From its plasm within the living potato-cells the Wart fungus formed two kinds of 'fruits': delicate sacs of little free-swimming zoospores for release during the summer, and comparatively large thick-walled winter-sporangia whose function it was to rest in the soil when the tissues of the potato had rotted away, and to release swarms of motile zoospores capable of forcing an entry into the stems and tubers of potato plants in following seasons. As both the summer and the winter sporangia were readily observable under the microscope, and there was all the well-known work of Woronin and de Bary to guide the investigators, it was hard to see why there should have been any very great difficulty, in 1902, about tracing out the life-history of this particular organism. But it was not *exactly* like that of any other fungus so far described, and for once the English workers were thrown back upon their own resources. No help came from the Continent, and Schilberszky, in Hungary, who had given the first partial account of the disease in 1896, not only failed to complete his work, but for some reason or other he would not even answer letters about it. So the confusion went on: the fungus was called Oedomyces, Urophlyctis, Chrysophlyctis, and finally *Synchytrium endobioticum* (Schilb.) Perc. — 'Perc.' being Professor John Percival of Reading, who cleared up the main facts, and published a concise, understandable and reasonably complete working description of the fungus in *The Gardeners' Chronicle* on July 31st, 1909. The delay before this was done revealed the great need in England for an adequately endowed plant pathological research station where a few competent scientific workers would have a fair chance of investigating new plant diseases which came to threaten the crops of the country, promptly on their outbreak, and of pursuing their work steadily to some degree of completion, undistracted by teaching, administrative or museum duties. In fact this lesson from the Wart Disease was not missed, and provisions for such research were included in the schemes of the Development Commission in 1911. The first really classical study of the life-history and cytology of *Synchytrium endobioticum* was that by Miss K. M. Curtis, published in 1921.

If the diagnosis of the Wart Disease was tardy, the measures taken by the Board of Agriculture for its control, after the passing of the Destructive Insects and Pests Act of 1907, were tolerably prompt and energetic. The Board tackled this disease of the potatoes very much as it tackled the Foot and Mouth disease of cattle. The disease was made notifiable, all reported cases of its occurrence were mapped out, inspectors were sent around to enforce control measures on the spot, the sale of seed-potatoes from the infected areas for planting elsewhere was prohibited, and, in general, everything possible was done to confine the trouble to the few districts in which it was already established. Truck loads of seed which got away from infected areas by negligence or design were tracked down as assiduously as though they had contained spirits stolen out of bond.

In 1908 one of the Board's inspectors, George Gough, was appointed to inquire into the prevalence of the Wart Disease. He interviewed most of those from whom reports were received – gardeners, scientific workers, farmers, allotment-holders – and pieced together the facts. He soon found that in parts of Lancashire and Cheshire the disease was of long standing. It was most prevalent in gardens and allotments where potatoes were grown again and again on the same plot of ground, but it had also made its way on to some of the farms, where rotation of crops was practised. The resting sporangia of the fungus seemed to be almost indestructible. They passed through animals unharmed and were spread with the manure; they were carried from infected to clean land not only on warted seed-potatoes but on boots and cartwheels, and, as it was subsequently found, they resisted all practicable applications of sulphur and other fungicides to the soil. Most of the farmers scoffed at the danger of the disease getting into their potato-land and refused to believe it serious. But it was a farmer, Mr. H. S. Daine of Mouldsworth in Cheshire, who first put Gough on the track of a most important discovery.

'I'm feared of this Black Scab', said Mr. Daine, in effect, 'it's bad in some of the cottage gardens round my land; it's bound to spread; and folk are saying the only kind of potato they can grow is Snowdrop.' 'Snowdrop?' said Mr. Gough, 'you mean that they have actually found in Snowdrop a potato variety which is immune from Wart Disease?' 'Have it any way you like', said Mr. Daine, 'but that's what they say. Go and ask Mr. Swindell and Mr. Derry for yourself. I'll show you where they live . . .'

Mr. Swindell, when he was found, said that as far back as 1894 he had scarcely a sound root in his garden. He grassed down the plot for five years, and then found the Black Scab was in it as badly as ever when he planted potatoes again. Both he and his neighbour had found that they could get a clean crop with Snowdrop, so that was what they grew. Gough now pursued his inquiries with a new interest, and he soon heard from the farmers of several other varieties of potato which were either wholly unaffected or nearly so. Gough reported this matter to the Board of Agriculture with some very practical recommendations, and in 1909 arrangements were made for most of the principal varieties of potato then in cultivation to be grown experimentally on thoroughly infected soil to determine which of them really took the disease and which did not. The first trials were made by the Harper Adams Agricultural College in Shropshire, the Holmes Chapel College in Cheshire, and by the Lancashire County Council at Ormskirk and Manchester. Most of the popular varieties were found to be susceptible, but it was confirmed that there were a few — Golden Wonder, Langworthy, Conquest, Abundance and Snowdrop among them — which grew away clean. For some unknown reason they resisted the Wart Disease, and there was nothing equivocal or partial about this resistance. They were immune, even when grown in the most heavily-infected land. It was about the first time that any such complete resistance to a fungus disease had ever been found among the better economic varieties of a cultivated plant.

Langworthy and Abundance were excellent potatoes, and Golden Wonder indeed, though not a very heavy cropper, was often considered to be the choicest potato known. Many farmers grew other sorts of potatoes for the market but took care to plant some Golden Wonders for themselves. Given the existence of a few immune varieties of first-class quality to start with, it must have been apparent to those who were following the developments abroad with any imagination at all that there was a good chance of defeating the Wart Disease in England even more successfully than that other soil-infecting plant disease, the Fusarium Wilt of the cotton, had been defeated in the United States. But G. C. Gough, unlike W. A. Orton, had not the great organization of the U.S. Department of Agriculture behind him. He persuaded the Board of Agriculture to distribute some seed-potatoes of the immune varieties in 1910 to cottagers and small-holders in the infected areas; informative leaflets were issued to the farmers; but no organized work on potato breeding for Wart disease resistance was then undertaken by the Board. Its direct interest, even in varietal trials, languished after 1910, and was not revived until 1915 under stress of war. Only the negative, or, rather, 'police' measures for Wart Disease control — the restrictions on the sale of infected seed-potatoes and so forth — were officially maintained. The demand for better immune varieties did, however, give rise to new efforts on the part of potato breeders, most of them Scottish, who were commercially interested in the seed-potato trade.

Meanwhile, the Wart disease was not the only new murrain of the potato crops that was causing grave anxiety. And some of these 'new' diseases which rose to prominence between 1900 and 1914 were indeed straining the diagnostic abilities of the plant doctors to the limit of human knowledge. There were several *bacterial* diseases of the potato, causing rotting of the tubers in the ground or in the clamps, and one, which rotted and blackened the base of the stalks, known in Germany as *Schwarzbeinigkeit*, and in England as Black Leg, occasionally caused serious losses. There was sufficient dispute over the identity and the names to be given to the species of bacteria responsible for these troubles, but when once it had been established by Erwin F. Smith that bacteria could live as true parasites on plants, the investigation of the bacterial diseases of the potato was fairly plain sailing. The organisms were isolated, grown in pure culture, and their causal relation to the respective diseases was confirmed by experimental inoculations. The potato diseases which had the most expert of plant pathologists groping in the dark, and which could cause even greater losses of produce than the Potato Blight itself, were those which could not be attributed with certainty to the parasitism of any kind of living organism at all.

In Germany there was the *Blattrollkrankheit*, an epidemic disease or group of diseases of the potato, characterized by a rolling up of the leaves, or rather of the individual leaflets which made up the large compound leaves of the plant. The leaflets assumed curious tubular or trumpet-shaped forms, like brandy-snaps. On close examination it became apparent that on some of the affected plants the rolled-up leaflets were thickened and brittle; when brushed with the hand they produced a dry, rustling sound. In the first year of attack such symptoms appeared about July, and the crop was not greatly affected. If however the tubers were planted for seed in the following year, they gave rise to plants which were more or less stunted, and on which the leaf-rolling began earlier, starting with the leaves which were nearest the ground. Throughout the whole season there was no rotting, either of the haulms or of the tubers, only a little browning at the tips of the curled leaves, but the crop was often reduced to a half or a third of normal. Such tubers as there were sometimes grew even larger than usual, but frequently they were no bigger than walnuts. Nothing reduced the yield from a potato crop so much as the *Blattrollkrankheit*.

This obscure, complex and insidious sickness of the potatoes was found to be widespread in Westphalia and the Rhine provinces in 1905, and Dr. Otto

Appel, of the Imperial Biological Establishment for Agriculture and Forestry at Berlin-Dahlem, was among the first to attempt its investigation. He gave it the name '*Blattrollkrankheit*', and at first attributed it to a parasitic fungus, some species of Fusarium, which invaded the lower parts of the stems through small wounds, and then made its way through the sap-conducting vessels of the plants up to the leaves and down to the tubers. The disease was passed on from one year to another by way of such infected tubers, and in that sense the disease was hereditary. Other investigators, however, examined plants which were unquestionably suffering from the abnormal leaf-rolling, and reported that they could find no parasitic fungus in them or about them. Thus there arose a great argument over the *Blattrollkrankheit*, some saying, in a couple of million words or so, that it was a fungus disease, others with equal brevity that it was nothing of the kind, but merely a most unwelcome revival of some form of the old 'Curl', or *Kräuselkrankheit*, which in greater or lesser degree had been afflicting the potato crops in Europe since the eighteenth century. No, it was not a fungus disease, but a physiological disorder – whatever that might mean – and it had something to do with the still-unexplained Degeneration of potato varieties in cultivation. Indeed as early as 1905 Schultz-Soest took it to be a mark of Degeneration in Magnum Bonum, then extensively grown in Westphalia.

Whatever the cause of the *Blattrollkrankheit* it was certainly spreading; in 1908 Count Arnim-Schlagenthin, one of Germany's most important potato growers, examined seed-potatoes from all parts of that country, and found the disease in all of them. He published an article in which he expressed the fear that in the whole of Germany there was scarcely a healthy potato available for seed and foretold early ruin for the whole potato growing industry. Fortunately his fears proved exaggerated, but the alarm roused attention to the very real losses that leaf-curling diseases were causing in Germany and elsewhere. Commissions of Inquiry were set up in Germany and Austria, many reports were published, and workers in Holland, Ireland and the United States began to look about them. Very slowly, out of the general confusion of conflicting theories, there emerged the simple fact that the potatoes were suffering not from one, but from two distinct and very different kinds of leaf-rolling disease. There was the fungus disease, caused by a species of Fusarium, as Appel had truly said; and there was the non-parasitic disease which was almost certainly one of the forms of the old 'Curl'. This latter of the two diseases covered by the German term '*Blattrollkrankheit*' came to be known in English-speaking countries as the Leaf Roll, and it was one of the most serious of all diseases of the potato.

If the Leaf Roll was not caused by a parasitic organism, what *was* it caused by? Some claimed that it was due to planting immature potatoes for seed. Others attributed it variously to specified and unspecified abnormalities in soil and weather conditions. But none of these proferred explanations stood the test of comparative experiments, or of experience. Then one school of natural philosophers, forgetful that conditions were not causes, began to say that the disease was due to 'enzymatic disturbances', which was particularly interesting as it was a revival in a new form of the old theory, prevalent in 1846, that 'fermentation' could be the cause of plant disease. The chemists had now discovered that the chemical changes in fermentation were brought about by 'enzymes', which was to say by non-living digestive or excretory substances produced by living organisms as a result of their life processes. 'Enzymatic disturbances' implied some sort of abnormal fermentation – though why the potato plants should start fermenting in an abnormal way was something that the modern exponents of the theory could explain no more satisfactorily than could Dr. Lyon Playfair in his day. It was found by chemical tests that there was an accumulation of starch in the rolled and thickened leaves. There was an enzyme in the potato plant which normally digested the starch formed in the leaves and converted it into soluble sugars for transference to the tubers by way of the sap. If this enzymatic mechanism failed, then the starch might well accumulate in the leaves, causing them to swell on the underside and thus curl up – but why should the mechanism fail? What caused it to do so.

One important contribution to the understanding of the way in which the Leaf Roll disease affected the potato plants, though not of its causation, was made by Quanjer of the increasingly famous Wageningen Research Station in Holland, during 1913. He found that certain of the phloem strands – channels in the leaf-stalks and stems down which the food materials elaborated in the leaves passed to the tubers – were shrunken and lignified. They exhibited the condition of necrosis, or of being dead. This went a long way to explain why the tubers were few and the leaves were thickened – the 'pipes' connecting them were restricted or blocked. Quanjer proposed that the disease should be called Phloem Necrosis, and pointed out that the rolling of the leaves was only a secondary effect. He was however unable to say what caused the necrosis of the phloem, and he had not yet discovered any means by which the disease might spread from one plant to another otherwise than through infected tubers planted for seed.

In 1911 there was a serious outbreak of a disease which appeared to have some resemblance to the European Leaf Roll, among the potatoes in

Colorado and Nebraska. It happened that there was also a definite Fusarium Wilt of the potatoes in the United States, resembling the Wilt diseases of the cotton, watermelons and cowpeas. W. A. Orton, who had made the conquest of these particular plant diseases his own, set himself to find out whether there was any connection between the American Fusarium Wilt and the European troubles. For this purpose he sailed to Europe, studied the European potatoes at home, asked innumerable questions, and finally, with characteristic enterprise, induced Dr. Wollenweber, who was the world's leading expert on Fusariums, to leave Berlin-Dahlem and pursue his peculiar labours for some years in the United States. The Leaf Roll was in fact found to be almost the direct opposite of the Fusarium Wilt, for it stopped the food-materials from going *down* from the leaves, while the easily-observable blocking mycelium of the Wilt fungus stopped the water and mineral salts from going *up* from the roots. Orton was mistaken in supposing that the Leaf Roll had anything to do with the Fusarium – which was the cause of the other half of the German *Blattrollkrankheit*. But this did not greatly disturb Orton's peace of mind; he took back with him an invaluable mass of information about all the 'new' potato diseases, and got research started upon them in the States. The 'exchange' of leading workers between Germany and the United States was also in itself a move towards the internationalization of plant pathology, which Orton always did his best to bring about. A little later even Dr. Otto Appel found himself working in America. No great interest in the Leaf Roll was yet aroused in the British Isles, chiefly for the reason that the potatoes in *Ireland* happened to be almost entirely free from it; but the transatlantic stream of scientific and cultural relations did not entirely pass our islands by. Orton turned up at Dr. Pethybridge's humble lodging in Clifden, County Galway, about five o'clock one morning, and sat below, smoking a powerful cigar, until his delighted host was ready to answer questions. More significantly, perhaps, the Irish worker, Paul Murphy, who was to take a leading part in the investigation of potato diseases after the war, received a scholarship under the Development Scheme set up in 1911, which enabled him to study first in South Kensington, then in Berlin-Dahlem, and later in the United States before settling down to work in Ireland again, after a spell in Canada.

W. A. Orton, while he was in Germany in 1911, made one most important observation. He noticed that some potatoes at Gressi were suffering from a Mosaic disease of the same kind as that which affected tobacco plants. It seemed that this Mosaic disease, which caused mottling of the leaves and stunting of the plants, was, like the Leaf Roll, in some way to be associated with degeneration. But no certain reference to this Mosaic of potatoes had been made anywhere in the scientific literature, before Orton's key paper on 'Potato Wilt, Leaf Roll and related Diseases' was published as a Bulletin by the U.S. Department of Agriculture in February, 1914. The Mosaic disease of the tobacco was known to be caused by a filter-passing virus.

That, then, was the situation in 1914. The Leaf Roll, the Degeneration of potato varieties, filter-passing viruses, Mosaic, phloem-necrosis – all these yet doubtfully related subjects were just beginning to be discussed in the same papers and in the same breath. How were the so-called degenerative diseases of the potato conveyed in nature from plant to plant? The direct hint from the known transmission of bacterial plant diseases by insects was not taken. Nor did the hints come from any work on the Tobacco Mosaic or on the several obscure diseases of the potato – it would seem, rather, that they came from observations on the stunted rice in Japan, and the unhealthy curling of beet-foliage in North America. A Japanese farmer, Hashimoto, had found by experiment in 1895 that the attack of leaf-hoppers was followed by the Stunting Disease of the rice. Other Japanese workers followed up this observation, and by 1906, it had been proven at the Imperial Agricultural Experiment Station in Tokyo that the leaf-hopping insects were not the cause of the disease but the carriers of it. Meanwhile, Townsend, Adams, Shaw, Ball and others studying the Curly Leaf disease of the beet were slowly reaching the same conclusion about the leaf-hoppers which they found in association with that disease in the States. It was Ball who was the first to say: 'The punctures of the beet leaf-hopper (*Eutetix tenella*, Baker) cause a specific disease of sugar beets called Curly Leaf.'

In 1914 the part of insects in spreading disease in the potato fields was not yet perceived. But one thing at least was known: the 'new' diseases of the potato, the Leaf Roll, no less than the bacterial Black Leg and the fungal Wart Disease, were all transmissible by way of infected seed-potatoes. 'It would be well', said W. A. Orton in February 1914, 'to follow the example of Germany, where a system of official inspection is being inaugurated through which growers and purchasers may be assured that the crop from a given estate is free from Leaf Roll. Such a certificate can be granted only after the inspection of the growing crop. It is entirely impossible to determine the vigour and freedom from Leaf Roll of a stock of potatoes *after* the harvest.'

CHAPTER XXVII

FUNGI AND THE GREAT WAR

THE crucial importance of maintaining food supplies during the later part of the war of 1914-18 gave point to the provisions for organized agricultural research which were being made in Great Britain under the Development Scheme of 1911, and led to the adoption of many emergency measures, in Great Britain as in other belligerent countries, which were of much significance in the history of plant pathology. But to speak of war measures against the fungi would be to speak of measures which were only *begun* towards the end of the period of hostilities, and which continued long into the ensuing period of troubled peace. One effect of the war was to bring the national health services for the crops in Great Britain more nearly up to the level of those already existent in the United States and in Germany.

When, by 1916, a virtual deadlock had been reached on the western front and both sides were resorting to the weapons of blockade to force a decision, there was a phase of biologic or total warfare. The issue of defeat or victory turned less upon the valour of the forces assembled in the battlefields than upon the power of the populations behind them to obtain provender and to maintain their war efforts in despite of under-nourishment, deficiency diseases and nervous exhaustion. Considered dispassionately and externally, from the point of view of the naturalist, as a happening among the human species on earth, the war first presented the spectacle of younger adult males killing off each other with heroic determination in combats promoted by certain of the older males for the increase of their own power and advantage in the herds. As man had become so largely monogamous the ultimate social benefit to be derived from this drastic thinning-out of the younger males was not apparent; but no doubt it had its roots in the savage ancestry of the species. Its principal observable effect was to check the increase in numbers of the belligerent peoples, and to bring about some degree of racial deterioration as the losses were among the very finest of the male parent stock for the next generation. So long as war was thus confined, as it had been in the past, to this thinning-out process, the older males, females and young already living escaped immediate and obvious physical hurt, and it was all too easy to forget that in war as in peace, man was still engaged in a life and death struggle, not only with wind and weather, but with the multitudinous forces of the insects, the fungi, the bacteria and the viruses, for survival and increase. In the later phases of the war of 1914-18 and in the years of misery that followed it, there were good reasons for this realization to become at least locally acute. Frail humanity was indeed beset by too many natural enemies to have time to destroy its own kind. Total war, continuing after the cessation of hostilities in no less vicious economic strife, went far beyond the mere thinning-out of young males; it gave rise to such living conditions that the very mating instincts of the survivors were affected. In some nations families with a single child became almost the rule; the schools were progressively depleted, and the populations grew 'old'. This was but one consequence of total war; another arose out of the bacterial and virus warfare inherent in the blockading of food supplies. The wispy conscience of man still rebelled at the idea of spreading disease germs among the enemy, even if technical means could be found of making such mass-inoculation effective. To spread disease would be to release forces of destruction, beyond human control, which would make no distinction between friend and foe. How naive and childish was this thought! How little understanding it revealed of the nature of disease! There was no necessity for either side to spread disease germs among the enemy – they were there in plenty already. It was necessary only to lower the natural powers of disease-resistance by partial starvation and nervous strain, when an ever-attendant host of pathogenic lower organisms would accomplish as much and more of evil than the most sinister maniac could desire. The starvation would give rise to deficiency diseases often obscure to medical science, the pathogens would increase in all too obvious epidemics sweeping over the earth. In total war human defences were thrown down, and all the multitudes of smaller living species attacked man in two ways: directly by causing diseases of his enfeebled body, and indirectly by diminishing food supplies. The story of the direct attack, of the dysentery, the syphilis, the tuberculosis, the wound-infections, the typhoid, the famine-fever and the influenza, belonged to the history of medicine; that of the no less significant indirect attack was a part of the history of phytopathology. It was necessary to carry total warfare by blockade only a little further and a condition would arise in which the mute fungi and the bacteria would be charged with the final arbitrament of human disputes. In 1916, not only in Germany but also in Great Britain, there already loomed the dread of that ancient judgment of Jerusalem: 'when I shall send upon *them* the evil arrows of famine, which shall be for *their* destruction, and which I will send to destroy *you*: and I will increase the famine upon you, and will break your staff of bread.'

'For various reasons the cereal year 1916–17 was the most difficult in regard to the maintenance of food supplies which the nation had to face during the war, and the bad harvest of 1916 was a material factor in the situation. The conjunction of a low yield of wheat with one of the worst potato crops on record was especially unfortunate . . . A production of staple crops less by one and a half million tons than the average at a time when reduction of imports was imperatively necessary led to a stringency of supplies.'

This guarded statement was made in the report accompanying the Agricultural Statistics for the United Kingdom in 1918, published during the following year. The war was then over, and no desire was felt to stress past anxieties. In fact the bad harvest of 1916 in a country committed to total war, with four million acres of its arable land out of cultivation, and its livestock so largely dependent on imported food-stuffs was one of the most alarming of reverses. It had a great part in energizing a belated campaign to 'Save the Crops' and 'Speed the Plough'.

In each of the years 1914 and 1915 the United Kingdom, which then included the whole of Ireland, produced some six and a quarter million tons of grain – wheat, oats and barley – and some seven and a half million tons of potatoes. Those were the staple food crops: the potatoes and the grain. In 1916 the grain production was down by half a million tons, and the potatoes by no less than two million. The bad harvest was not to be attributed wholly, or even in the main, to abnormal losses through plant disease. There was a shortage of phosphates and other fertilizers, the weather was unfavourable over the whole growing period, the crops were weeks late. But, as it was realized later, losses loosely attributed simply to 'bad harvests' were always found on sufficiently careful analysis to comprise severe losses from plant diseases of one kind or another. It was very largely through favouring the development of parasitic fungi that bad weather caused bad harvests. Certainly the country's dangerously restricted food supplies were robbed of hundreds of thousands of bushels of grain and many hundreds of thousands of tons of potatoes, by plant diseases during the most critical period of the war. The particular fungus disease which played the chief part in blasting the war provender in the wheatfields of North America during 1916 was known – in that year there was one of the worst Rust epidemics in history. But it was impossible to say exactly which fungus and other diseases were responsible for making the lean crops of the British Isles leaner still. Some of the diseases causing most serious reduction of yield from the potato crop, for example, were as yet unrecognized, and it was a remarkable fact that nothing resembling an official census or adequate survey of the pests and diseases affecting the crops of the country as a whole was ever attempted before 1917. This work of reconnaissance was one fundamental part of the national health services for the crops which began during the war.

In 1917 a sub-committee of the country's leading mycologists and entomologists was set up to advise the Food Production Department. They made arrangements for obtaining reports on the insect and fungus pests of the crops from every agricultural district in England and Wales, and the first survey (Board of Agriculture Miscellaneous Publications No. 21) was published in 1917. It revealed, among other things, that the grain crops in that year suffered much from Smut diseases, little from Rusts, but much also from fungi which were neither Smuts nor Rusts. A common Powdery Mildew, the *Erysiphe graminis* of Tulasne, was bad on the wheat, and a Leaf Stripe disease (*Helminthosporium*), which so far had received all too little attention, was seriously destructive of the barley. After the war the reporting of plant diseases, season by season, and the occasional publication of national surveys, became a part of the work of the Ministry of Agriculture. At the same time the British Mycological Society, which included among its members a small company of people who still studied and loved the fungi for their own sake, joined hands with the economic mycologists, and its Transactions, which had been thin prior to the war and chiefly devoted to pure mycology and to accounts of fungus forays in pleasant parts of the country, now came to include many important research papers on fungi causative of diseases of the crops. The British Mycological Society was to be thought of in conjunction with the department of cryptogamic botany up among the gargoyles under the roof of the Natural History Museum in South Kensington. The Society started a Plant Pathological Committee in 1919, and one of its labours was to compile a standard list of the Common Names of Plant Diseases, with the international scientific names of the organisms which caused them, thus clearing up much confusion. By the united labours of the Ministry's reporters and of the forayers of the Mycological Society the surveying of the parasitic fungus flora of the British Isles had become fairly full and comprehensive by the thirties. How well this part of the job came to be done in the end could be appreciated by turning over the pages of the Ministry's Report on Fungus, Bacterial and other Diseases of Crops, for the period 1928-32, published in 1934. While for guidance to the principal research papers on these diseases there was an invaluable annotated bibliography, called *The Plant Diseases of Great Britain*, compiled by Dr. G. C. Ainsworth, and published in 1937.

The principal immediate result of the 'stringency of supplies' in the cereal year 1916-17, apart from the introduction of the convoy system and the strengthening of other anti-submarine defences on the high seas, was, however, the belated passing of the Corn Production Act. There was almost a revival of home agriculture. A million acres of grassland were ploughed up and sown with grain for 1918. The effect of the ploughing-up campaign on the acreage of various crops under cultivation is shown clearly on the chart already referred to in Chapter XIX, page 249. The decline was arrested and there was a little peak.

In the late thirties, when 'millions' became meaningless, and the expenditure of so-and-so many millions of pounds, marks, dollars, francs and lire, on armaments, was a part of the monotony of every day's news, no idea of the wastage caused by plant diseases could any longer be conveyed by speaking of millions of bushels or tons. But the back-ache and toil of the ploughing-up campaign in Great Britain in 1917-18 was real enough; it would long be remembered, and it could, perhaps, be used as a unit of human effort. How much extra grain did it produce, and how did that grain compare with the loss caused by the Rust epidemic in North America during the year 1916? There were three-quarters of a million more acres under wheat in Great Britain during 1918 than there had been in 1916. The yield was greater by thirty million bushels. But the harvest in 1918 was exceptionally good, weather conditions were propitious over the whole growing season, and the average yield was 33.2 bushels per acre – 2.5 bushels above the average for the previous ten years, and 4.4 bushels above that for 1916. The best crops, which brought up the average, were not obtained on the newly-broken land, and at a most generous estimate the whole emergency campaign did not put more than an extra twenty-five million bushels of wheat into the nation's granaries in 1918. The Rust epidemic during the single year 1916 was estimated to have caused the loss of *two hundred* million bushels of wheat in the United States and *one hundred* million in Canada. Three hundred million bushels in all. That loss was twelve times as great as the gain from the whole of the ploughing-up campaign in Great Britain during the war. True, a bushel of wheat on a blockaded island was worth many bushels in Manitoba or North Dakota – but that was the absolute magnitude of the loss.

The occurrence of so devastating an epidemic revealed how little progress had yet been made in combating the Rust diseases of cereals. The breeding and selection of resistant varieties, particularly needed in the spring wheat regions, had not proceeded far. The work of obtaining such varieties would necessarily be slow. But meanwhile, in 1917, the United States was at war.

The vital grain surplus required to supply the needs of the Allies should not be exposed to the hazard of another great Rust epidemic if any human action could be taken that would prevent it. Was there anything that could be done?

There was just one measure, long discussed but never yet put into practice except locally now and then and here and there: the eradication of the common barberry. It was now known that *Puccinia graminis* in fact rarely over-wintered by way of its summer or uredo-spores except, perhaps, as far south as Mexico, and it was certain that the fungus, all the several biologic strains of it on the different kinds of cereals, did have a stage on the barberry. The eradication of the barberry, in the States where the bushes were numerous, would remove *one* important source of infection. Was it worth while? Just look at the map! At the vast area of the thirteen States of the upper Mississippi valley alone! Certainly it could be done. If it was necessary for the effective pursuance of the war, the U.S. Department of Agriculture, acting in conjunction with the agricultural authorities in the States concerned, was prepared to outlaw the barberry over the entire area, to launch a campaign for seeking out and destroying every bush. Even for this stupendous undertaking the Department had now the necessary organization. But *was* it worth while? Would the cost be justified by the resulting decrease in the loss of grain?

Probably it was the well-documented history of barberry-eradication in Denmark which did more than anything else to help the Department to make up its mind. Denmark was a small country, its area was comparatively speaking minute; but in American eyes the whole of Denmark was just about big enough for a trial plot. There had been six severe epidemics of the Black Stem Rust in Denmark between 1894 and 1901, and the Rust had cost that country some ten million Kroner annually. Professor Rostrup of the Danish agricultural research service had been untiring in collecting data concerning the effect of rusted barberry bushes on the prevalence of Rust in the wheat, and in 1903, he was at last successful in getting a law passed which prohibited all cultivation of the common barberry in Denmark outside of botanical gardens. By 1917 the barberry had been almost completely exterminated from the Kingdom and severe attacks of the Black Stem Rust had ceased.

The U.S. Department decided that the barberry should be no less thoroughly exterminated from the whole of Colorado, Illinois, Indiana, Iowa, Michigan, Minnesota, Montana, Nebraska, Ohio, North and South Dakota, Wisconsin and Wyoming. The campaign was organized by the Bureau of Plant Industry in February and March 1918, and the survey and eradication work began in April of that year. The method of combating the Rust to which Anton de Bary's researches had pointed in 1865 was adopted on a continental scale in North America fifty-three years later, under stress of war. Even in the first year a vast number of bushes were destroyed, and had the war continued the immediate saving of grain would have made some appreciable difference, but the clearing of the barberries over the whole area did not approach completion until 1927, when a second combing began for those bushes which had been missed in the first round. Vigorous barberry bushes, with their roots extended for yards under the hedgerows, were not at all easy to kill in their entirety, and late into the thirties the work of eradication was still going on.

When the war was over, the great Barberry Eradication Campaign was continued with no less determination but in a lighter mood. It was important work for the great benefit of the agricultural community, but that was no reason why it should be done with a face as long as a fiddle. The American workers on the assignment made a first class technological picnic of it all. They went up in aeroplanes and caught Rust spores – chiefly uredospores from the south – at a height of 12,000 feet. They calculated how many æcidiospores were released from a single average-sized rusted barberry bush in Minnesota and made the number thirty-eight times that of the human population of the world. They traced the rate at which the Rust spread from barberry bushes over the grain. By May 26th, in one instance, all the wheat was rusted within a radius of a hundred feet to leeward of a clump of the bushes; by June 6th it had progressed one and a half miles; by June 17th four miles, and by the time of harvest no less than ten miles. The spores from the rusted barberry bushes started the Rust over the wheat much as sparks from locomotives started prairie fires. Some of the large old bushes were almost worth the damage they caused as object-lessons for the farmers. There was one near Alert in Decatur County, destroyed in 1922. More than fifty acres of wheat in its immediate vicinity had not even been cut, and the grain from two hundred acres in more distant fields was so badly shrivelled that it turned out to be unsaleable after threshing. In fields farther away still a prospective yield of 22 bushels per acre was reduced over an area of fifty square miles to 8.8 bushels. The loss from that one bush amounted to over $50,000 in one season.

All the resources of the press, the agricultural colleges, and later of the radio, were pressed into service to bring the significance of the campaign home to the farmers and to enlist their co-operation. It was not mere static education that was required; the bulletins, leaflets and circulars, distributed by the million, had to grip the imagination of those for whom they were intended and to move them to the point of action. The workers of the Department and of the State Experiment Stations who wrote these bulletins exhibited talents for illustration and exposition of no mean order. Cryptogamic botanists in the past had often been fine scholars and sometimes excellent artists as well, masters of the copperplate and the wood-block. Now applied cryptogamic botany was calling to its service not the linguistic and graphic arts of leisured culture, but the living folk-arts of a people as they were to be found in the best of popular journalism and the strip-cartoon. Many and ingenious were the illustrations and the similes used to make the phenomena of 'heteroecism' and all the complex life-history of *Puccinia graminis* — with its succession of teleutospores, sporidia, pycnidia, æcidiospores and uredospores — perfectly understandable to any ordinarily intelligent human being, who had never seen a parasitic fungus or indeed anything else under the microscope, and who did not know a word of Latin or Greek. The academic botanists in other countries looked on with an indulgent smile, but the young American workers of the twentieth century were none the less scientific when they told their story in pictures and in homely words.

The campaign was successful. In the course of twelve years some eighteen-and-a-half million barberry bushes were destroyed, and the average annual loss of grain owing to the Rust in the thirteen barberry-eradication States, which had been 57 million bushels in 1916-20 was reduced to 9 million bushels in the period 1926-30. Some disappointment was, however, in store. Despite the destruction of the barberry bushes there was nevertheless a bad Rust epidemic in the Dakotas during 1935. Owing to that unfortunate 'inner-loop' in the life-cycle of *Puccinia graminis*, no single control measure, except perhaps the substitution of Rust-resistant varieties for the susceptible wheats in cultivation, could be completely effective. But the difficulty of obtaining truly Rust-resistant varieties was seen to be even greater than had previously been anticipated when Stakman and his co-workers in Minnesota discovered that there were not only biological strains of the fungus differing in their capacity to infect different kinds of cereals, but also many strains of *P. graminis tritici* itself which differed in their capacity to infect different varieties of wheat. The first of these specialized strains was distinguished by Stakman in 1917, and by 1922 he had found that there were at least thirty-seven of them. This meant that though it might be fairly easy to breed varieties of wheat resistant to some of the strains of the fungus, to obtain good economic wheats resistant to all of them was fated to be a most pernickety and exasperating business. It was a great help, meanwhile, to have the barberry bushes cleared out of the way. In Rust control, as in most other things, part of a loaf was better than no bread. And, as it was soon to be found, the barberry not only provided winter quarters for the fungus, but it also served as a breeding-ground on which all the different strains could restore their vitality by sexual reproduction and indeed mate with each other to produce new hybrid strains of almost unlimited versatility in their capacity to parasitize different varieties of wheat.

The barberry-eradication was not the only campaign in the United States for controlling plant disease by the method of destroying wild alternative host plants. The Blister Rust of the white pine had a stage on wild currant bushes, and to save the pines the wild currants were hunted down and destroyed over an enormous territory in the north.

Nothing comparable with the great American eradication campaigns had ever been known in the British Isles. The Yellow Rusts were the most prevalent on the English grain and these had no stage on the barberry. The common barberry was comparatively rare in England – the smooth-leaved ornamental kinds, so popular in suburban gardens, were not susceptible to the Rust, and they did no harm. The plant disease surveys started during the war, however, did reveal that there was one corner of the country where the Black Stem Rust associated with the common barberry was causing considerable loss – and that was in the extreme south-west of Wales, in Carmarthen, Cardigan and Pembroke. An interesting little barberry-eradication survey was made there in the summer of 1920. The surveyors drove along the roads in a car, noting the barberries in the hedges and stopping to interview the Welsh farmers. Although the district was mountainous a good deal of wheat was grown, some 22,000 acres of it in the three counties. Seventy-four cases of Black Stem Rust were noted, and all in the vicinity of barberry bushes. The farmers were entirely unaware that the barberry had anything to do with the disease, which like their fathers and their grandfathers before them they attributed solely to the weather. They regarded the life-history of the Rust fungus as a fairy tale – and no doubt found other names for it when the gentlemen had gone off in their car. Especially in Cardigan. It was sometimes said, even by other Welshmen, that the 'Cardies' were so peculiar that they were often to be seen on dark nights crawling sideways like crabs into the sea. They agreed with the surveyors that a good crop of wheat could not be grown near the bushes, but none of them acted on the advice to destroy the bushes at once. Some of them still used the yellow juice of the barberry as a cure for jaundice. The survey indicated that the prevalence of the Black Stem Rust was one of the main causes of unprofitable wheat crops in the region, and that were it not for the barberry bushes much more wheat would be sown.

Where the American plant pathologists were up against the Black Stem Rust the British workers were up against the diseases of the potato, nowhere more severe than in the wetter parts of the British Isles. There was much to be told about potato diseases and the war. In the first place the Blight was being actively combated in Ireland; the wartime potato spraying campaign over there was not left until 1917, it was organized at once and carried out most energetically from the outbreak of hostilities; it did not prevent the disaster to the potato crops in 1916, which was due to other things besides the Blight, but it must have saved over a million tons of stable food-stuffs over the whole war period, and it at last made the practice of potato spraying universal in Ireland. And what of the Wart Disease? Following the failure of the crop in 1916, and the consequent shortage, all too many diseased potatoes were planted for seed. Hundreds of individual cases of Wart Disease were reported from districts where it had not been seen before, and many more counties had to be shaded as 'threatened' on the map.

In 1915, John Snell, an Inspector for the Board of Agriculture, working in conjunction with the Lancashire Farmers' Association, started field trials of potato varieties again, for Wart-Disease resistance, from the point at which they had been left some years previously by Gough. Infected land belonging to the Ormskirk Poor Law Institution was once again used for the trial plots. Snell's work was systematic and thorough, and it led to the reliable sorting of all the potato varieties in the country into two groups according as they were immune from or susceptible to wart disease. The work of classification raised the very important question – what constituted a potato variety? Hundreds of so-called varieties were on the market under as many different names. When these were grown side by side on the trial plots it became apparent that many of them were identical. The seed-potato merchants were passing off well-known varieties under fancy names of their own, often enough as something new and wonderful at an elevated price. Much to the annoyance of the trade, Snell not only reported truthfully on the susceptibility of the varieties to Wart Disease, but he began assigning them to type and calling them by their right names. He started a much-disliked little register of Synonyms for the information of all and sundry. There was more in this than a mere de-bunking of the sham varieties; there was a clearing of the ground. It was obviously impossible to do much honest work for the improvement of the potato stocks in *any* direction until it was known what genuinely distinct and different varieties there were to start from.

In 1919 Snell's fine work was taken under the wing of the newly inaugurated National Institute of Agricultural Botany. A farm of forty acres was purchased at Ormskirk for the continuation of the trials on a more extensive scale. Unhappily Snell died just then, but he had a successor after his own heart in his former assistant, Mr. H. Bryan, and at long last the Station for the independent and scientific testing of potato varieties, advocated in 1880, came into being. It was the Wart Disease and not the Blight or the mysterious Degeneration of the potatoes which called it forth in the end. But that did not matter, the main point was that the country at last had an official Potato Testing Station. It would get around to work for the suppression of other potato diseases, all in good time.

During the war the Scotch potato-breeders had been busy and already by 1920 the list of good economic potatoes immune from Wart Disease and 'tested at Ormskirk' included such well-known varieties as Majestic, King George, Kerr's Pink, Great Scot, Arran Victory and Abundance. The work of the potato-breeders was made easier by the trial facilities at Ormskirk. They could submit their new potatoes for trial in the seedling stage, and obtain preliminary reports on them which often cut out years of work on varieties unlikely to be any good. Bryan and MacDermott at Ormskirk not only observed the vigour, yield, vegetative characteristics and disease-resistance of the new varieties, but often took very dubious potatoes home and tried them for supper. Thus voluntarily joining the company of unsung martyrs of science.

The beginnings of a much-needed scheme for the inspection and certification of seed-potatoes were made in Great Britain just after the War. Seed-potato crops were inspected *while growing*, and certificates were issued only when the inspectors were satisfied that the potatoes were true to name of variety or grown on land where Wart Disease had never occurred. In 1920 a list of British growers of certified immune varieties was published for the first time, and the farmers throughout the country who bought certificated seed had only to turn up a reference number to find the proper name of the variety, where it had been grown, and by whom. They knew exactly what they were buying. This control measure, first adopted for the suppression of the Wart Disease, became of paramount importance several years later in the attack upon the last great murrains of the potato crops, the Leaf Roll and the various Mosaic diseases. But it was early yet to speak of these; although they were robbing the British Isles alone of nearly a million tons of potatoes every year, in 1920 their depredations were scarcely perceived.

The fundamental scientific research into the etiology, or causation, of these obscure diseases, like so much other work in the van of civilization, was halted in all belligerent countries during the war. Hands which could divide the micron were called to haul cannon and many were stilled in the mud. The scientific societies were only just able to preserve the continuity of their Annals, Berichten and Mémoires. The volumes were thin on the shelves. But in neutral Holland, home of Beijerinck, great pioneer in the study of filter-passing viruses, the work on the Leaf Roll, now suspected of complicity in the degeneration of potato varieties, went steadily on. In 1916, Quanjer, working with van der Lek and Oortwijn Botjes at Wageningen, established the fact that the 'phloem necrosis', as he called it, was communicable by grafting parts of the affected plants on to the healthy, and that healthy plants became affected when they were grown near others suffering from the Leaf Roll. These discoveries pointed to some unknown living organism, contagium or virus as the cause of the trouble, and brought the understanding of the Potato Leaf Roll about up to the level of that of the Peach Yellows after the publication of Erwin Smith's paper of 1891. Support for the view that there was some agency spreading the contagium from plant to plant in the field came from the work of Paul Murphy on Prince Edward Island in Canada, and Wortley in Bermuda. M. J. Berkeley had referred to the prevalence of the 'Curl' among the potatoes of Bermuda in 1847, and in 1918 it was a great scourge. Attempts to clear the potato stocks of this Leaf Roll, by the method of selecting seed-potatoes from healthy plants alone, failed in both Bermuda and Nova Scotia. There was evidently something carrying the virus from infected to healthy plants during growth. Sucking insects, small aphides or leaf-hoppers, were suspected, and the first definite proof came from Oortwijn Botjes in Holland in 1920. With this, and many contributions by the American workers, Allard, Schultz and others on the Mosaic diseases of tobacco and potatoes, the long period of preliminary skirmishing with the virus diseases of plants was over. When the companies of the research workers in the war-stricken countries had licked their wounds and filled the empty places a new and vastly interesting field of phytopathological investigation awaited their attention. And in the name of pure science there was a whole Kingdom of living or 'half-living' things yet to be explored, the 'molecrobes', the filter-passing viruses, or as some, in 1939, would like them to be called, the *VIRA*.

In Great Britain facilities for fundamental research in all the departments of plant pathology were greatly extended in the years immediately following the war. New laboratories, or extensions to existing ones towards the building of which grants had already been made in 1914, were completed, equipped and staffed. The reasons for the new interest in the promotion and support of agricultural research on the part of the Government were complex. On the one hand there was the wish that the country should never again be exposed to such danger as it had been by the state of home agriculture in 1916; on the other hand there was a perfectly deliberate intention to jettison the country's agriculture yet further, and to cover this crime by grants for research which were really in the nature of conscience-money. The conflicts of wish and intention, the muddled, unclear policies, heaved to and fro. Several parts of the emergency organization created to stimulate food-production during the war were given permanency, and indeed it was as a side-consequence of a Bill to extend the wartime County Agricultural Committees in Statutory form that the old Board of Agriculture was dissolved and a *Ministry* of Agriculture (and Fisheries) was at last set up, in 1919. This promised well – but did it mean that the scientific men who would compose so small a part of the staff of the new Ministry as of the old Board were going to be assisted at last by a little real statesmanship above? The first test came over the question of what to do about those million and a half acres of the former arable land which had been reclaimed by the ploughing-up campaign. Was the gain to be held, or was all that land to go down again to grass? Those who were most competent to give advice – such men as Sir Daniel Hall and Sir Thomas Middleton – did not mince words either during the war or after it, about the consummate economic folly of allowing so much of the country's agricultural land to be two-thirds wasted as indifferent pasture. In 1916, Middleton in the Journal of the Board of Agriculture, had quoted and vindicated Lord Selbourne's statement that 'if agriculture had made no more progress in Germany than it had in the United Kingdom during the period 1895 to 1915 the German Empire would have been at the end of its food resources long before the second year of the war'. Despite less favourable soil and climate the German farmers were feeding 70 to 75 persons per hundred acres of agricultural land, where the British were feeding only 45 to 50. To raise cattle and to produce milk was all very well, but even if that was the objective three times as much food for cattle was produced on the arable than on the pasture. A hundred acres of pasture would provide food-units – in the form of meat and milk – sufficient to maintain at the most twenty persons. The same area of arable would maintain four times as many, and the crowning, culpable absurdity of letting the reclaimed arable slip back to grass after the war was that dairy farming and stock-raising (so largely on imported feeding stuffs) employed less workers on the land. Every hundred acres of arable put down to pasture would throw three men out of employment, and this in a country where the post-war slump, already anticipated in 1919, was going to provide such a wealth of available labour and so many hungry mouths. Unhappily, the wise and far-sighted counsels of scientific men were ignored; the whole acreage reclaimed during the war was lost by 1924, and between that year and 1939 a further two million acres in Great Britain, a territory greater in extent than the whole of Kent and Sussex, was added to that already forsaken by the plough. With the repeal of the Corn Production Act in 1921 a stop-gag of £850,000 was provided, to be spread over five years, for the promotion of more agricultural education and research. The formula was much the same as when the *Board* of Agriculture was formed in 1889. If Science wanted something to do it could help the farmers to help themselves – and, strictly by way of experiment, it could try making one acre grow what two had grown before.

Until the world economic collapse at the end of the twenties, with the subsequent rise of the N.R.A. in the United States, the National Government in England, and National Socialism in Germany, the old system of *Fais ce que vouldras*, for the industrialists and the money-changers, persisted substantially unchanged. Tariffs here and there perpetuated the blockade measures of open war in the field of economic strife, but in the main British agriculture had to survive, if it was to survive at all, wholly unprotected from that merciless buying-in-the-cheapest-market which was called 'foreign competition'. In substance, the only interest that the industrialists and the financiers, through their successive puppet governments, had in British agriculture was the market it provided for manufactured and imported commodities, oil-cake, maize, labour-saving machinery, artificial fertilizers, insecticides and fungicides. *After* the world economic collapse the situation deteriorated still further.

In 1919 the country had a Ministry of Agriculture. But what could the Ministry do? Subsidies? Subsidies to particular agricultural industries, as for the development of sugar-beet growing, were only a dabbing at the economic paintwork, and, human nature being what it was, they often found their way into the wrong people's pockets – back to the Treasury in Excise duty, or into nice bonuses for sugar-extracting shareholders. On occasion they could even operate to encourage deliberately *in*efficient cultivation. Subsidies, even where they could be wheedled out of the Exchequer, had to be administered with extreme care. And the greater part of the assistance which the Ministry was able to render – whether the farmers considered it schoolmarmish eyewash or not – was still to find ways of making the various cultivations yet more economical and efficient, down to the last detail every one of them. Even the design of the small chip-baskets in which strawberries were packed in the summer was to receive most careful official consideration. Research was required not only on the big cultivations – the wheat, oats, barley, swedes, potatoes, grasses and clovers – but on a number of specialized cultivations, occupying very small parts of the total area of agricultural land, which were nevertheless of considerable importance as they might with sufficient technical assistance be made little strongholds of tolerable prosperity for those with sufficient capital to run them. Where, even after 1924, the wheat would still account for about one and a half million acres, there was the fruit-growing, about one-third of a million, the sugar-beet to become about the same; all the different kinds of green vegetables, a fifth of a million; down to the little hop-growing industry, only a fiftieth of a million acres, to provide flavouring for beer; some ten thousand acres of flowers for banquets, funerals, weddings and table decorations; and two thousand acres of tomatoes and other crops under glass. All these industries, great and small, would have to be rationalized and brought to the highest pitch of efficiency if they were to survive. This involved not only the closest attention to marketing, the choice of stocks and fertilizers and methods of machine-cultivation, but also to plant pests and diseases. There had to be a nation-wide and efficiently organized health service for the crops.

The first necessity was to recruit and train a considerable number of able research workers. This was accomplished in the main by means of Development Commission Scholarships. The next need, evident enough when one considered the history of plant pathology in Great Britain, was the provision of some liaison service which would assist the British workers to keep abreast of developments in other countries. This linkage was effected by the establishment in 1918 of the Imperial Bureau of Mycology at Kew. This was a war measure. There were then about a hundred mycologists, or plant pathologists, at work overseas in different parts of the Empire. Many of them, especially in the tropics, were far removed from access to good libraries and herbaria; it was necessary for them to refer to centres of botanical learning in Europe for the identification of the thousand and one species of parasitic fungi which they were encountering in their explorations. Until the outbreak of the war most of the help in this particular work of colonization had come from Germany; the loss, when communications were broken off, was very great indeed, and in 1918 no less a body than the Imperial War Council had to take the fungi directly into consideration. It was decided to provide a British clearing-house for world mycological intelligence, somewhat on the pattern of the successful Imperial Bureau of Entomology founded five years before. The new Bureau gathered financial and other support from the Dominion and Colonial Governments and began work in September 1920. Dr. E. J. Butler, one of the pioneers in the investigation of Indian plant diseases, was the Director, and he assembled about him a staff of other experienced plant pathologists who between them were able to abstract the essential information from the current scientific literature in almost every language. They issued the first number of their *Review of Applied Mycology* in 1922, and it appeared monthly thereafter, providing both home and overseas workers with news *in English* from all the principal publications on plant diseases throughout the world.

The abstracts were often sufficiently detailed for workers to dispense with reading the original papers altogether, even when they were easily available. In an imperfect world there was no good thing that was wholly to the good. Complete text-books could be put together from material culled in the main from these abstracts, and too much reading of abstracts was not good for the souls of those engaged in original research. It was true that in most of the original papers there was a tremendous amount of verbiage and repetition, and that the real additions to knowledge made by their authors could quite often be set down in half a page – or even a couple of lines. But when this was done much of the 'life' in the paper was necessarily left behind. Even in the twentieth century disciplined scientific thought was still hardening out of a free play of speculation and dream. It was, as ever, an intensely human product, and in the original papers the writers affected their readers in other ways than through the communication of facts or abstractable hypotheses. Mere asides made in the course of the author's statement of his problem or discussion of his results, caught by a receptive ear, could start new trains of thought, and always there were internal clues in every scrap of writing, scientific or literary, to the quality and mind of its author. He might be a man of acute perception whose every word was worth reading again; he might be a careerist, out for a professorial chair – often enough he was both, but from the abstracts 'you never could tell'.

The proper function of the abstracts in the whole organization of health services for the crops was to serve as a guide, and only as a guide, to the research work going on throughout the world. In addition to issuing its *Review*, the Imperial Bureau of Mycology did much work on the identification of fungi found on the crops at home and overseas, and it put workers on special problems in touch with one another. Some of those quiet students of the fungi who were as allergic to Imperialism and Bureaucracy in all their manifestations as were the fungi themselves to taints of sulphur and copper, steered shy of the Bureau because of its name. But this was a mistake. The unpretentious Institute was down one of the lanes leading to the river at Kew; one could read at ease in its excellent library, and it kept open house to students of every nation as did that mother of botanical institutions, 'Kew', itself, next door.

So much for communications, and the liaison with workers in other countries. Meanwhile at home, in the United Kingdom, in accordance with the plans of the Development Commission, the more fundamental agricultural research was assigned subject by subject to a number of Research Institutes in various parts of the country, some of which were financed from funds administered by the Ministry of Agriculture, others jointly by the Ministry, private donors, and agricultural trade associations likely to derive most benefit from the work.

Of the Institutes forming part of the health services for the crops, there was the Ministry's own Plant Pathological Laboratory at Harpenden, to advise on the administration of the Destructive Pests and Insects Acts, and to make investigations in connection with the *legislative measures* for plant disease control. Then there was the laboratory for *basic research* in plant pathology, started at Kew, and transferred to a new Institute at Rothamsted in 1919. The Rothamsted Station as a whole, traditionally devoted to the investigation of soil problems, dealt with another part of the work for the health of the crops – all that concerned their *nutrition*. The Rothamsted Station had a Director, four trained workers and only sixty acres of land in 1910; after the war it had fine new laboratory buildings, the experimental farm was increased to three hundred acres and thirty or more scientific workers were on its staff. The National Institute of Agricultural Botany arose at Cambridge in 1919 for the testing of improved varieties of cereals and other agricultural plants, and to house the Ministry's official *seed-testing station*. The work of the Institute served the health of the crops in so far as it was concerned with *enhanced vigour and disease-resistance* obtainable by methods of breeding and selection. The Seed Testing Station had an important part in the *suppression of seed-borne diseases*, such as the Bunt of the wheat, the Leaf Stripe of the barley and the destructive Septoria Blight of the celery. The Ormskirk Potato Testing Station, with its varietal trials, was to vanquish the Wart Disease and to bring about a vast improvement of the country's potato stocks by practical work for the suppression of the *degenerative diseases* of the potato. The Cheshunt Research Station, started by the Market Gardeners' Development Association in 1914, became the centre for the investigation of *diseases of crops under glass*. And as in glass-houses the soil could be sterilized, the amount of light reaching the plants could be varied, and the temperature, humidity and even the carbon-dioxide content of the air could be exactly controlled, the opportunity was taken, at Cheshunt, of studying the influence of *environmental factors on the incidence of plant diseases*. The tomatoes, cucumbers, chrysanthemums and roses, between them, suffered severely from every type of plant disease when forced under glass. Serving the fruit-growing industry there was the new East Malling Station in Kent, well provided in the end with laboratory buildings and land for experimental orchards, and specializing on the *influence of the root-stocks*. Researches on the insect pests and *fungus diseases of fruit trees and of hops* continued at Wye College, now a veteran of English agricultural research stations, which had been at work since 1896, while in the west there was the Long Ashton Station at Bristol, originally established to work on the improvement of cider, but provided with mycological and entomological departments in 1914. Fundamental research on plant physiology, a somewhat wide subject, concerning the *functioning of plant organs in sickness and in health*, was allocated to the Imperial College of Science in London. Provisions for field and laboratory work on plant diseases in general were extended at many of the provincial universities, notably at Reading, and the official centre for the work on *clovers and grasses* was at Aberystwith. In the Royal Horticultural Society's gardens at Wisley there were laboratories for the study of *diseases of all kinds of garden plants*, while the John Innes Institution at Merton, the Kirton Farm Institute in Lincolnshire and Seale-Hayne College in Devon worked, *inter alia*, on the diseases of tulips, daffodils and narcissi — the principal commercial spring-flowers. Some of the stations where plant pathological work was done were dignified with the title of Research Institutes and they were supposed to tackle the more fundamental problems; but such paper distinctions dissolved in practice, and it was invidious to draw any distinctions of rank between different kinds of research. The Research Institutes had no privilege of discovery, and the most valuable work was done just where there happened to be men of ideas. Many of the most important contributions in the post-war years were made by workers at the Albert Agricultural College near Dublin, Queen's University in Belfast, the University College of North Wales at Bangor, and at the East, West and Aberdeen Colleges in Scotland. Work on the control of plant diseases by *spraying, dusting and seed-disinfection*, for example, was done at practically all of the Research institutes and stations, while the country's leading worker specializing more particularly in the chemistry of insecticides was Dr. F. Tattersfield of Rothamsted, and in the chemistry of fungicides, Dr. Hubert Martin of Wye, and later of Long Ashton.

The research organization would be of very restricted practical value in the total scheme of health services for the crops without provisions for bringing the findings of the research workers home to the farmers – and the problems of the farmers home to the research workers. The latter being quite as important as the former, if only for the reason that a good half of the greatest fundamental discoveries in science had arisen out of attempts to solve immediate practical problems, including those of how to make or save money. The indispensable go-betweens were some very hard-working functionaries called Advisory Officers and County Agricultural Organizers. The former acted, incidentally, as intelligence-men for the Ministry, and among their duties was that of reporting any unusual outbreak of plant disease. They were usually on the staffs of the Agricultural Colleges; they were in communication with all the Research Stations, and they spent most of their time out among the growers or answering their inquiries. Along with the County Agricultural Organizers they had a fairly full life. They were, in effect, the general practitioners of the health service for the crops. By 1927 fourteen Advisory Centres were established in England and Wales with sixty-four Advisory Officers, some of them dealing with veterinary matters, some with the fungus diseases and insect pests, others with 'agricultural economics'.

The new provisions for the diffusion of information about plant diseases and other subjects of agricultural research did not by any means displace the old. The object of the Ministry was not to control but to reinforce the efforts of the Universities, County Councils, Agricultural Societies, Trade Associations and other bodies which in one way or another contributed to agricultural education in the country. There were, for example, several hundred agricultural shows, great and small, organized by agricultural societies up and down the country, every year. The Ministry was represented at all these shows and its Advisory Officers helped to stage educational exhibits. The *Journals* of the Royal Agricultural and Royal Horticultural Societies, and *The Gardeners' Chronicle*, which in 1939 had already reached or were fast approaching their centenaries, continued their long and honourable work for the linkage of science with practice. News of discoveries still usually appeared first in *Nature* and then in *The Gardeners' Chronicle*. *The Fruit Grower*, a trade journal notable for the integrity of its editorial policy, faithfully served the fruit growers, much as *The Farmer and Stock-breeder* and *The Scottish Farmer* served the surviving high-farmers and the dairy farmers. One sign of the times, however, was the issue by the Royal Agricultural Society in 1925 of its first annual *Farmers' Guide to Agricultural Research*. The 'research' here referred to being chiefly organized research at Government-assisted stations throughout the world, and not the research or experimentation by private enterprise with which the Society had been primarily concerned in the past. The *Guide* was later incorporated in the Society's *Journal* of which it made up about a third of the matter for each year. It was hoped that the *Guide*, by providing news of progress in tolerably simple language, would give the general press something really interesting to sprighten-up and dilute. The 'general press', however, was far too busy 'collecting the words of persons in authority, or in noting and subtly explaining the acts of kings, even the smallest and those of no importance', to take much notice of agricultural research. It was remarkable, also, how very little about modern agriculture filtered into the novels and romances and scrap-books of science on which the man in the street fed his capacity for wonder. The imagination of the people did not turn towards the land or the things of the land. The mathematical and mechanical sciences were more popular, and, as for the 'intelligentzia', they lapped up fantasies about that third-rate planet, Mars, and stood star-gazing while the thistles grew around their feet.

With so much yet unknown about many plant diseases, and with only partially effective means of combating all but a few of them, no one would suggest that the health services for the crops, as they took shape in Great Britain following the war, left nothing to be desired. There were some gaps which remained, as for example the lack of provision for the official testing and registration of insecticides and fungicides, and some important extensions were made a little later, as by the setting up of the Potato Virus Research Station at Cambridge in 1926. The services needed above all a change in the country's agricultural policy, a drive to increase the home production of food-stuffs, to give them a breath of life. But it was doubtful whether any other country in the whole world had so good a cover of plant pathological services for the acreage served.

In some respects at least these services were actually better than the medical services for the human population. If your tomatoes were suffering from the Spotted Wilt you could write to the Advisory Officer in your district, or directly to the Ministry of Agriculture in Whitehall, and you would receive by return and free of charge a well-illustrated leaflet setting forth briefly all that was really known for certain about the Spotted Wilt of tomatoes, what the symptoms were, what caused it, and the best way to prevent it. If, however, you happened to suffer much from the common cold, and you wrote to the Ministry of Health for corresponding information about *that* disease, you would be disappointed. You would be referred to your medical advisor, and he, being a member of a closed profession or Worshipful Mystery, would treat you to the best of his ability, but as to the nature of your malady and the principles of treatment, he would give you no information, nor would he tell you where to find it. If he gave you a prescription it would be written in an alchemical scrawl expressly designed to prevent you from knowing what it meant. The medical profession did their best to keep their knowledge to themselves, thereby leaving a clear field for all the proprietary and patent medicine racketeers, and perpetuating all kinds of mental suffering based upon ignorance and fear, from which they further profited by the administration of reassurance. The policy of the plant doctors was the direct opposite of that of the doctors of medicine. From the leading research workers down to the junior assistants of the advisory officers, they sought to dispel ignorance and not to encourage it. They wanted farmers and allotment holders and gardeners to share as much as possible of their knowledge of the diseases of plants, and to act on that knowledge like rational beings.

With plant pathological services, more or less well-adapted to local needs, set up and working not only in Great Britain and throughout the British Empire, but in practically every country or province in the world from Latvia to Mauritius, the infant science which the Rev. M. J. Berkeley had attempted to christen in 1854, could be said to have grown up. There was still no name for it in the English language; 'phytopathology' was not English—,it was a mouthful of shunt-Greek. But, name or no name, the science which was concerned with the diseases of the crops, was now to be reckoned among the greatest of the applied sciences, and one sign of its coming of age was a certain consciousness of its history and interest in the records of its childhood. In 1918, the first outline of the history of phytopathology was published. It was written by H. H. Whetzel, Professor of Plant Pathology at Cornell. A little later, the American Phytopathological Society began to publish one by one English translations of the great historic papers which were the foundations of the science: its *Phytopathological Classics*. By 1939 the papers thus made available for easy reference and study included the most important works of Fabricus, Fontana, Millardet, Woronin, Tillet and Prévost. It was to be hoped that if *The Gardeners' Chronicle* did not happen to do it in their centenary year, the American Phytopathological Society would one day publish in convenient book-form the collected writings on Vegetable Pathology of that great English pioneer, Miles Joseph Berkeley. Of all the directions of search and research now open to the plant pathologists, that back into the past, into the history of the science was as likely as any to lead to new fields of discovery. Such looking back was not to be confused with the sentimental and personal recollections in which scientific workers sometimes indulged at the close of their useful life. It was research within the strict meaning of the word, leading to the reconsideration of many facts and hypotheses whose full significance could not be seen at the time they were set down. And it was of great service to the science to give a new currency to some of the older works. One outstanding example of this was the fine translation of Tulasne's *Selecta Fungorum Carpologia* by the English worker, W. B. Grove, and its publication with reproductions of all the magnificent plates by the Clarendon Press in 1931. Other forms of practical work in the historical field were those which facilitated search, such as the check list of all the publications of the U.S. Department of Agriculture on the subject of plant pathology from 1837 to 1918, published in 1919; and the well-documented histories of agricultural education and research in the U.S.A. by A. C. True, published in 1929 and 1937 respectively.

CHAPTER XXVIII

DUSTING AND SEED-DISINFECTION

JUST after the War, three treatments were in common use in the United States for the control of seed-borne diseases of cereals. The first was the very old one, dating back to Prévost, of steeping or sprinkling the seed with copper sulphate solution and then drying it, with or without lime. The second was the Jensen Hot-Water Treatment; and the third was the treatment of the seed with formaldehyde. The formaldehyde method, discovered in 1897, had been developed during the war, particularly in Germany where there was a shortage of copper. The seed was piled in heaps, sprinkled with a dilution of '40 per cent formaldehyde' – the commercial concentrated solution of the gas in water – the heaps were then covered with sacks or tarpaulins so that the gas liberated from the solution was more or less confined within the heap, where it permeated between the husks of the grains, killing fungus spores both on the surface and between the husk and the kernel. By the use of one or other of the three treatments all of the Loose and Covered Smut diseases of cereals were preventable. But all the treatments involved wetting the seed grain, which had to be dried before sowing; they all injured a certain proportion of the seed; and they all involved a considerable amount of labour, especially where large quantities of seed had to be treated. Much floor space was required for the sprinkling or steeping and subsequent drying, and there was no fun at all in manipulating tons of wet or damp grain.

A very much more convenient treatment, effective against some of the Covered Smuts such as the Bunt of the wheat, was introduced into the United States, following a suggestion made by Darnell Smith in Australia during 1917. This was to coat the seed grain with blue carbonate of copper in the form of a fine dry powder. The grain was run into a drum mounted on a spindle, and 'churned' with the copper powder, at the rate of about four ounces per bushel, for a few minutes until every grain was uniformly blued over. Nothing further had to be done. The treated seed could be stored in sacks for months before sowing, without risk of its sustaining any injury, as the copper powder was quite inert when dry. After the seed was sown some slow chemical action took place between the nearly insoluble copper carbonate and the water and dissolved substances in the soil, or between the copper compound and something excreted by the fungus itself.

which liberated just sufficient copper in soluble form to kill the germinating spores on the surface of the seed without adversely affecting the growth of the seedling. This dry treatment which saved so much time and trouble soon became very popular, and by 1925 one-tenth of all the wheat sown in the United States was treated with the dry copper carbonate powder for the control of the Bunt. Attempts were then made to get other seed-disinfectants into powder-form. Even the gas, formaldehyde, was tried, absorbed in chalk or talc powder for churning with the seed – but this was not so successful.

Meanwhile several of the German chemical manufacturing firms were at work on attempts to improve upon the 'Chlorphenol Mercury' which had been tested by Riehm in 1912. When this first 'organic mercurial' was mixed with the necessary alkali to dissolve it, and put on the market by the Bayer Company under the trade-name of Uspulun in 1915, it contained 18.8 per cent of mercury in chemical combination, and it was intended for use in water for the wet treatment of seed wheat against the Bunt. It proved so successful for this purpose that it was tried against a great many other fungus diseases of plants, including the Wart Disease of potatoes (1916), and Vine Mildew and Pear Scab (1919). It caused too much burning of foliage to be useful as a spray fluid in competition with lime-sulphur or Bordeaux mixture, but it was quite apparent to the German workers that they had a new type of fungicide of the greatest potential value for seed-treatment. It remained to try other chemical combinations of mercury with dyestuff intermediates, and to pick out those which were most toxic to particular fungi and least toxic to the seeds or seedlings affected. It might be possible to obtain a very safe and economical general seed-disinfectant, or, failing that, a whole series of special products for specific uses.

The German dye patents were revoked in Great Britain during the war, the processes disclosed under promise of protection by the Crown were exploited by the British industrialists to their own great advantage, and when the war was over the German dyestuff monopoly was lost. All the more easily manufactured dyes were being made in England and other consuming countries, and the only hope of recovery for the German dye industry was to specialize in those dyes and allied products which required the highest chemical knowledge and skill in manufacture. Moreover, in the 'swords to ploughshares' mood which was real enough in disarmed Germany for some time after the war, the manufacture of fine chemical therapeutants and of materials for the better protection of the crops, was not only commercially but also idealistically attractive. There was in it some expression of a nation's legitimate pride in the unbeaten and still unsurpassed abilities of its scientists and technical workers. Among the new products of German research to which they turned their hands were the organic mercurials for the prevention of the smutting and corruption of the grain in the ear.

It was hardly to be expected, however, that the German firms would now disclose, in patent specifications or otherwise, exactly what their new products were or how they could be made. But 'Germisan', marketed by the Saccharin Fabrik A.G., in 1920, was stated to contain cresyl mercuric cyanide, and one of the products put out by the pioneering Bayer Company itself, 'Tillantin R' in 1924, was said to have for its active ingredient a nitro phenol mercury derivative. At first, the new mercurial compounds, of which there were a considerable number, were all intended for use dissolved in water as seed-steeps, but when the advantages of dry seed-treatment had been demonstrated in the United States, by the success of the copper carbonate dusts, organic mercurials were made in that form also. Talc powder or some other inert carrier was soaked with a solution of the active material and then dried and ground for churning with the seed. Although a short wet-process was subsequently developed in Germany, which had its advantages, the production of the mercurials in the form of dusting-powders was a decisive step towards their perfection for widespread use. The first of these mercurial dusts was the Tillantin R.

By 1925 it had been found in the United States that while copper carbonate gave a splendid control of the Bunt of the wheat, for the Covered Smut diseases of oats and barley it left much to be desired, Tisdale, Leukel and others had tried the (liquid) mercurial treatments for the oats and the barley. The German products, Uspulun and Germisan, and already the rival products of American manufacture, Chlorophol and Semesan, were among those tried. In experiments on Wisconsin winter barley, treatment of the seed with Semesan reduced the percentage of smutted ears in the crop from 21.7 to nil, and increased the yield from 31.10 to 40.75 bushels per acre. Then by 1927, Leukel and his associates had tried a number of the organic mercurials, in dry form now, against another and most intractable disease of the barley, caused by a fungus whose living spawn was ensconced within the coat of the seed kernel – the Leaf Stripe, or Helminthosporium disease. In each of the trial plots there should have been about 2,500 plants. Where the seed was untreated some five hundred of the plants failed to come up, and over four hundred of the rest were diseased. Where the seed was treated with the best of the mercurials, all the 2,500 plants came up, and only one, single, diseased plant was to be found among them. It was much the same in trials by Reddy and Burnett in Iowa during 1929, when the latest Bayer dust, Ceresan, effectively controlled the Leaf Stripe, and gave a mean increase of yield from a number of different commercial varieties of barley, amounting to 2.77 bushels per acre.

In practice it seemed that the treatment of the seed with these new compounds of mercury actually brought about a greater increase in the yield of barley than could be accounted for by the freedom of the plants from Smut and Leaf Stripe diseases. It seemed that the compounds had some positive invigorating effect on the barley itself, for it came greener, thicker and stronger – there was a far better stand of young barley – where the seed was treated than where it was not. The difference in the appearance of the fields was perceptible from an aeroplane or from a hill-top half a mile away. And by those not in the secret it might well have been attributed to some marked difference in the fertility of the soil. It was thought that the better 'stand' might in fact be due to the protection of the seedlings not only from the Smut and Leaf Stripe fungi, but from a miscellaneous host of pathogenic bacteria and fungi in the soil. This idea was not new: way back at the beginning of the eighteenth century Jethro Tull had held the view that the steeping of seed-wheat – in ineffectual sea-salt in those days – would afford some general protection to the seed against all the surrounding processes of decay while it lay in the ground. Now that so many kinds of fungi were known which could attack seedlings in the soil, the idea of general protectives for the seed was coming back again. Further investigations indicated, however, that it was not necessary to postulate a vague host of miscellaneous parasites attacking the barley – the Leaf Stripe fungus, when its ways were more closely considered, was seen to be quite capable of causing the damage. The full extent of the losses due to the Leaf Stripe was not realized until the use of the organic mercurials gave healthy crops for comparison. The observation of the notably better stand of barley and also of oats through the suppression of Leaf Stripe diseases, circa 1930, was one of the pleasant surprises, the memorable happenings, in the history of plant pathology. No! They did not cease with Prévost's discovery of the fungicidal effect of the water from his copper alembic, or with Millardet's observation that the bespattered vines by the wayside were free from the Mildew, or with Biffen's alternating green and yellow-rusted plots of wheat, the evidence that Rust-resistance was an inheritable Mendelian characteristic . . . Yesterday is also the past.

The Leaf Stripe fungi did the half of their damage before ever the plants appeared above the ground. When the infected seed germinated, the fungus quickened also, extending its hyphae to attack the young seedling in its earliest stages of growth. Many were killed outright and thus there were gaps in the farmer's rows; many of the rest were sapped and weakened, coming up weedy and thin. The first leaves of the barley plants were striped with lesions in which the fungus fructified, producing spores which blew about, spreading the infection in the field. As the plants grew up the leaves were successively infected as they broke from their wrappings, and the young ears were 'blind' or distorted. The grain was poorly developed and the leaves split. The treated seed, however, had a film of mercurial dust on its surface which in contact with the moist soil provided an enveloping taint of curiously persistent fungus-poison. This lay in wait against the time when the hyphae of the fungus would reach out to attack the seedling. It then withered the fungus, and the barley or the oats grew away unharmed. The remarkable delayed action of mercurial fungicides on seeds was studied in Germany during 1915 by Hiltner, in connection with some other fungi, species of Fusarium attacking the wheat and the rye.

The mercurial dusts controlled the Leaf Stripe diseases, and *also* the Covered Smuts – where they had only to kill spores on the surface of the seed. By the end of the twenties they were already in extensive use in the United States and in Germany, and following some excellent results published by O'Brien and Prentice, of the West of Scotland College of Agriculture, in 1930, there were soon very few farmers in the British Isles who had not heard of 'Ceresan'. The Leaf Stripe was by far the most destructive disease of the oats in Scotland. It thinned out the stand to such an extent that it was often necessary to sow at the rate of eight to ten bushes of seed to the acre, and, even so, twenty-five per cent of the plants which did come up would be infected and set little or no grain. Ceresan was found to give an effective control of the disease. It was used at the rate of two ounces only for each bushel of seed, the average cost was eightpence per acre, and the net profit was about fifteen shillings per acre, half of which was due to saving of seed and half to augmented yield.

In the beginning, the chief disadvantage of the organic mercurials had been their high cost, which was partly due to the fact that mercury cost money. The research chemists employed by the manufacturers sought for more and more potent compounds of mercury effective at smaller and smaller dosage. One of their happiest ideas was to combine the mercury with 'unsubstituted hydrocarbon' instead of 'substituted phenolic' groups, and by 1933, when references to a British product, Agrosan G, manufactured by the I.C.I., began to appear in the literature, the Bayer product, Ceresan, was reported to contain only 1.5 per cent of mercury in the form of phenyl mercuric acetate. The Agrosan G was reported to contain 1.5 per cent of mercury also, but in the form of the tolyl mercury salt.

This, then, was the point of technical efficiency to which the control of the principal seed-borne diseases of cereals had been pushed by 1933. The materials as used by the farmers now contained over ninety per cent of inert diluent which served to spread an extremely small amount of active substance over the surface of the seed. At the generally recommended rate of sowing – three to four bushels of seed per acre – it meant, when you worked it out, that the chemists had found a way of making a globule of mercury weighing about a tenth of an ounce and no larger than a small haricot bean, protect every plant in a whole acre of barley or oats from the Leaf Stripe fungus, or every plant in a whole acre of wheat from the old blackening and corruption of the grain in the ear.

It was hard to see how any more perfect method of preventing these particular diseases of the crops could ever be devised by man. The materials cost the farmer round about a shilling an acre, and the labour involved in treating the seed was very small indeed. Certainly, there was another line of attack on the Smut diseases: about 1925, it began to be apparent that there was a possibility of obtaining not only Rust-resistant varieties of cereals, but Smut-resistant varieties also. There were some who saw in this the perfect solution. But would it ever be the perfect solution? If the Smut-resistant varieties turned out to be in the least degree inferior in yield or quality of grain – or in *Rust*-resistance – to the old, then it might well pay the farmer best to ignore them, and to spend even as much as a shilling per acre for a couple of handfuls of mercurized french chalk. To prevent some of the seed-borne diseases it was not necessary to spend by half so much; some copper carbonate powders, very much cheaper than the mercurial dusts, would also effectively control the Bunt of the wheat when used at the rate of two ounces per bushel of seed.

So valuable, however, were the mercurial dusts for the control of Leaf Stripe diseases, that the manufacturers were able to effect what they evidently regarded as a sufficient volume of sales, while maintaining their price at about two shillings per pound. The dusts contained two or three per cent of mercury compound, the rest being mostly french chalk with a little colouring matter. The value of the french chalk was at most twopence, and, allowing another twopence for the packing, the *active compound* was really being sold at about 1s. 8d. for a third of an ounce. True, the stuff had to be manufactured and distributed, but, even so, £8,960 per ton, for such products as ethyl or tolyl or phenyl mercuric acetate, was not at all bad.

Before 1925, the price of such things as the new mercurial dusts would have been lowered almost automatically by competition between rival manufacturers, and with the increasing demand. The very best of the seed-dressings that science could produce would thus have become economically available for the protection of the grain crops everywhere. About 1925, however, profound changes in the economic as in the political systems of all the industrial countries were ushered in by the formation of such combines as the I.G. Farbenindustrie in Germany and the I.C.I. in England. Firms which had once competed with each other now bound themselves together for greater strength, like fasces in a bundle. They were aligned on profit-axes and tied with price-regulating agreements. The erstwhile 'laws' of supply and demand became increasingly inoperative, Free Trade was a thing of the past, and with the extending fasciculation of shareholders' interests in all the principal industries, Britain, Germany, France, Italy, the United States and Japan, for all the different names which they gave to their systems of government, had really become, by the thirties, industrial-corporate states, with political arrangements which increasingly served and reflected their economic structure. The 'cornering' of commodities which had once been abhorred as a crime against society, was now no longer the exception but the rule. By 1939 it was hardly possible to find a single important commodity that was not under the monopoly control of one ring or another. The consequences of these changes were far-reaching, they affected every activity of man. In agriculture, Marketing Boards were set up which controlled the prices that farmers should receive for their produce while giving the distributive combines a free hand to charge the consumers what they pleased for it. In international affairs, re-armament campaigns begun as measures of industrial pump-priming headed the nations once again towards the holocaust of war. It was in this kind of world that the work in plant pathology, as in the other sciences, was now going on. With the rise of the new industrial hegemonies, and the associated decline of all liberal and democratic institutions everywhere, science suffered no less than did literature and the arts. The maintenance of the price of organical mercurials, limiting the use in practice of new products of scientific discovery, was one small instance of what was happening; another, affecting pure science rather than its application, was the withholding of knowledge concerning the chemical constitution of the new products.

When some synthetic compounds of mercury were found to be so much safer, and so much more toxic to parasitic fungi than others, it was of the highest importance to science to know *why* this should be so — to correlate the intimate chemical constitution of the compounds, the grouping of atoms in their molecules, with their fungicidal effect. But most of the ablest research chemists working upon the new compounds were employed by the industrial combines; the results of their researches were not published. When they *were* allowed to write anything about their work it was impossible to tell where truth ended and commercial propaganda began. In consequence of this, their fellow scientists at the plant pathological research stations were obliged to make experiments on plants with materials the exact composition of which was withheld from them. Such experiments served the combines as advertisements but they were of little scientific value. Science was divided against itself. By 1934 workers who still retained their independence in some of the institutions for fundamental research were forced to waste their time, seeking, not for new knowledge, but for that which was being withheld. Their task was often difficult, for in the small chemical laboratories of the research stations there were not the resources of the great chemical works, and products made in bulk could not always be reproduced in flasks and test-tubes. Information which went a long way towards de-bunking the proprietary organic mercurials was however provided by the researches of Dillon Weston, Hanley, and Booer, at Cambridge, beginning in 1935. They synthesized a number of the mercury compounds which various of the commercial products were stated to contain — along with some others which they thought of for themselves — mixed them with the usual amount and kind of talc powder, and tried them on seeds. Some of their mixtures, containing organic mercury compounds of comparatively simple constitution appeared to be about as effective as 'Anyoldsan' under the conditions of the experiments. But with compounds of the types investigated at Cambridge the quest had by no means reached finality. In those countries which were shaping their internal economies in preparation for another war, there was the consideration that supplies of mercury might become very limited at times when it would be most vital to protect the grain crops. Already in 1937, in connection with a Four Year Plan for self-sufficiency, Germany was taking stock of her needs. The annual consumption of mercurial dusts in Germany for seed treatment was then estimated at 800 tons, and of mercurials for liquid treatments, 180 tons. The chemists were urged, if only for political reasons, to reduce the mercury in these compounds to the very minimum. There were references in the literature to a yet further improved 'Ceresan', which was reported to contain ethyl mercury phosphate and to be effective at only half an ounce per bushel of seed. Attempts were also being made to produce non-poisonous mercurial dusts, for there was just a possibility of accident with the highly-poisonous dusts in use, if stock should happen to be fed on treated seed-corn by mistake; while in the British product, 'Harvesan', manufactured by Boots Pure Drug Company of Nottingham, and put on the market in 1939, opportunity was taken of incorporating certain of the newly-discovered growth-promoting hormones, so that the seed treatment would not only protect, but also positively invigorate the young seedlings.

The story of two hundred years of search for materials with which to treat the seed-grain could be brought to a close in 1939 with the organic mercurials. There was as yet no more to tell, but leave could not be taken of the ancient Bunt of the wheat without some reference to the beautiful researches on the Bunt fungus itself, made between 1920 and 1940, by Professor A. H. Reginald Buller of the University of Manitoba. These researches did not directly concern control measures, they formed part of a lifetime's study more particularly concerning the dispersal of fungus spores and the remarkable natural mechanisms by which they were projected from the spicules or other organs which bore them. There were six rich volumes of Buller's researches by 1934; they were of about the same classical scientific standing as Oscar Brefeld's *Untersuchungen über Schimmelpilze*, but for those acquainted with the technical terms employed, they were at the same time about as fascinating as the writings of Jean Henri Fabre on the lives of insects. Such observations as those on the projection of spore-missiles by the Sphaerobolus and Pilobolus 'fungus-guns' might well inspire new works of imagination, new plays, even new fairy-tales, as Fabre's observations inspired works by Maeterlinck and Karel Capek. In the particular section dealing with the Bunt fungus, in Volume v, 1933, Buller put forward further evidence to show how closely the promycelium of the fungus (Fig. 10, p. 84, herein) with its four sporidia borne on four little spicules, resembled the four-spore-bearing basidium characteristic of the Basidiomycetes. This realization did not invalidate the drawings and descriptions of the fungus left by the brothers Tulasne, it added a little, and that chiefly of taxonomical significance, after eighty years. The Smut fungi were very closely related botanically to the common mushroom.

As during the post-war years there was a great development in the treatment of seeds not with liquid steeps but with dry dusts, so also there was a great increase in the use of fungicidal and insecticidal dusts for application to foliage. Practically every material formerly used for spraying – with the exception of oil sprays – was made available for alternative use in the form of dry dust. The careful spraying of crops with fluid mixtures or solutions generally gave a better control both of insect pests and of fungus diseases than did dry dusting. But it took a considerable time, it involved the cartage of water, it was difficult in districts where water was scarce, and it was impracticable for the treatment of grain-crops and forest trees. By grinding the solid materials very finely, and 'diluting' them where necessary with equally finely ground chalk or talc or dried clay, they could be produced in suitable form for blowing on to the plants by machines which incorporated some powerful kind of fan. If the particles were made small enough – and if they did not clog together – the plants could be swathed in clouds of imponderable fungicidal or insecticidal dust. Much of this always settled on the ground where it served no useful purpose, but the foliage was also fairly well covered, especially if the dusting was done when the plants were moist with dew. Large areas could be treated rapidly, and a timely if not altogether perfect protection was afforded to crops where the slower spraying might be too late. The control of insects and fungi obtainable by dusting was on the whole remarkably good, and because of its greater convenience dusting actually came to supersede spraying in many localities and for many crops, even where ample supplies of water were available. The wind often took part in the game, and swathed the operators as well as the plants in toxic dust, but when this happened they turned the machines about and drove the other way, or sat under the hedge until things had quietened down. They used their intelligence. It was not advisable to smoke on the job when arsenical powders were being applied, as the arsenic was volatilized at the hot end of the cigarette and it tended to be licked off the damp end, but, apart from this, dusting was a simple and safe farm operation even when arsenicals were employed.

The dusting methods were worked out chiefly in the United States, Canada, and Soviet Russia. Blodgett, in New York State, used a mixed dust of sulphur and lead arsenate with success in apple orchards about 1914, and by 1921, Saunders and Kelsall in Nova Scotia had hit upon the ingenious dodge of producing Bordeaux mixture *in situ* on damp foliage by dusting it with a mixture of roasted, anhydrous, copper sulphate and dry slaked lime. Dusting with arsenical powders against the cotton boll-weevil was much practised in the south, and by about 1930 improved sulphur dusts and new ways of applying them made the chemical control of even the Black Stem Rust of the wheat a practicable possibility.

The light internal combustion engines, working on petrol or paraffin, which had been developed since the beginning of the century, were as handy for driving the fans on the dusting machines as they were for working the pumps on some of the modern sprayers. Large power-driven machines which would dust a dozen rows of potatoes at a time became available for use on the ground, while in 1921 an aeroplane was tried for the first time, by workers of the Agricultural Experiment Station in Ohio, for dusting from the air. By 1939 the amount of crop dusting done by aeroplanes was altogether trifling compared with that done by machines on the ground, but it caught the popular imagination, which accepted the aeroplane as a symbol of Progress, and it was made a-much of from time to time in the press.

There was one thing, however, about the air-currents set up by an aeroplane in flight, which, as it happened, *did* make the aeroplane a very efficient crop-dusting machine. The dust, running through a Venturi tube from a hopper in the cockpit, did not merely trail behind the plane. It was caught by the 'slip-stream' – the air-blast from the propeller – and projected rearwards and downwards at a velocity greatly exceeding the forward velocity of the craft. The dust cloud assumed the form of a spirally rotating column, and it could be laid on the fields in comparatively narrow and manageable swathes. The dust swirled about the plants and covered them well. But the aeroplane had to fly very low, only fifteen to forty feet above the ground, and as its speed was about a hundred miles an hour, much strain was imposed on the pilots' nerves and skill. It was rather like hedge-hopping and sky-writing at the same time. Where the fields were of only moderate size, and there were buildings, trees, and other obstructions, then dusting by aeroplane was not practicable. A flying-machine was required that could be driven about, just off the ground, as easily as a small car.

The collective management of farms in the Soviet Republics facilitated the employment of aeroplanes for dusting field crops, but their first successful use was for such purposes as dusting Paris Green over the open swamps of Louisiana to destroy mosquito larvae, the spreading of poison bait over the breeding grounds of locusts, and the bathing of forests with insecticides, to destroy caterpillars. The German workers were not quite so enthusiastic as the Americans and the Russians about the aerial application of *arsenical* dusts. In 1926 they treated 3,460 acres of oak forest at Haste, and on going round afterwards, they found that besides the pest (*Teras ferrugana*), the casualty list included nineteen roe deer, two hares, four rabbits, two birds, and innumerable honey-bees. Dusting with innocuous sulphur powders to control the Rust of the wheat was another matter. The area that could be treated by a single aeroplane was very large. Morrill estimated, in 1926, that as much as a thousand acres of cotton could be dusted by an aeroplane in an hour, while only thirty acres could be covered by a machine on the ground in an eight-hour day. The aerial dusting was two hundred and fifty times as fast, but the cost per acre was about the same.

More interesting perhaps than the trial use of aeroplanes – an obvious development once aeroplanes were available – was the work on the dusts to be applied. Particles of sulphur dust, for example, readily acquired charges of frictional electricity. The charged particles would be held apart by mutual repulsion in the dust-cloud, and if the charge was of opposite polarity to that on the plants, the dust would be attracted and caused to adhere to the foliage. Unfortunately, however, the electrical properties of sulphur were also sometimes responsible for a very troublesome 'balling' or cohesion of the dust particles together in masses. The electro-statics of the dusts had to be studied. Again, particles of pure sulphur were not easily wetted by water; means had to be found of making the particles 'take' to the moisture on the foliage. And there was a world of significance in the particle size.

About 1924 uses were being found for a peculiarly absorptive and water-loving clay, which was mined from the 'soap-holes' of Wyoming, and known as 'bentonite'. This sodium clay was composed of mineral particles much smaller than any that could be obtained by mechanical grinding, and when mixed with water it formed a kind of jelly. A unique *mineral* jelly. The stuff could be dried down to dust without losing this capacity to form a jelly when again suspended in water, supplies were plentiful, and it was not expensive. It could be bought in England a little later for about £10 a ton. One of the uses that had already been found for it was the removal of printers' ink from old newspapers so that the paper could be used over again. It seized on the particles of ink when the old newsprint was pulped and held them in suspension in the water, which was then drained off and washed away, leaving the pulp clean. It occurred to an American inventor, Henry Banks, to use this bentonite to make an improved sulphur dust for combating the Rust of the wheat.

He fused sulphur and bentonite together and then ground the dry mass. When the fused sulphur solidified on cooling it coalesced about the infinitesimally small bentonite particles. Every grain of the powdered mass, as dusted on the plants, was composed of large numbers of these bentonite-sulphur particles. In contact with moisture the grains broke down and there were drops of milk-white colloidal sulphur. A fraction of one per cent of the fused material, mixed with an inert dust as a 'carrier', was sufficient to prevent the germination of the uredospores of *Puccinia graminis*. By mixing a proportion of his bentonite-sulphur with plain wind-blown sulphur powder, Banks obtained a very potent and fine dust for practical use, which did not 'ball' when dry, but which adhered well to the smoothest foliage owing to the stickiness of the bentonite in it, when wet. This product was called 'Kolodust' (U.S. Patent No. 1,550,650, of 1925), Banks' bentonite-sulphur was of particular interest as it was a new departure, but other sulphur dusts, dependent for their high activity on very fine mechanical grinding, were also successful. The best of these dusts were so fine that they would pass a sieve having three hundred meshes to the inch. Potassium permanganate was sometimes added to the sulphur, with the object of increasing its fungicidal activity by accelerating oxidation – a dodge which was also under trial in Germany in attempts to make sulphur do the work of copper in potato spraying.

The Dominion Rust Laboratory at Winnipeg was under way in 1925 with a programme of investigations covering every aspect of the Rust problem in Canada. Greaney at this institution and Stakman in Minnesota were among those who did the pioneering work, between 1925 and 1931, on the control of the Rust of the wheat by the new dusting methods. In trials with a horse-drawn dusting machine on Marquis wheat during 1930, Greaney applied 30 lb. of Kolodust per acre at five day intervals from July 16th to August 1st – 120 lb. of the dust per acre, in all. The Rust was severe in the locality, and the dusted fields yielded 16 more bushels of wheat per acre than those left untreated, and the grade was improved from No. 3 to No. 1 Northern. To dust the wheat from the ground in July and Augu t, however, would seem liable to cause considerable mechanical damage unless alley-ways could be left through the wheatfields for the passage of the machines. Trials of dusting by aeroplane were made by the staff of the Dominion Rust Laboratory in conjunction with the Canadian Civil Air Service. Again, excellent results were obtained. But to fight the Rust of the wheat by sulphur dusting, with aeroplanes or otherwise, was neither technically nor economically a very good method. It was going to war against the fungus when its spores were most multitudinous, and it was no *substitute* for barberry-eradication (where barberry-bushes were present), or for the sowing of Rust-resistant varieties (where such were available). It could not be recommended as general farm practice, but, having regard to the increasing difficulties which were now seen to stand in the way of obtaining resistant varieties, sulphur-dusting was of very great importance indeed *as an emergency measure*. Now, even as late as July, when a Rust epidemic was seen to be impending, it would be humanly possible to call out the planes, *and save the wheat.*

CHAPTER XXIX

NEW SPRAYS FOR OLD

WHILE a great number and variety of chemical compounds, from simple metallic salts to the most complex of alkaloids, were being utilized during the period 1920-40 for the destruction of the insect pests of the crops, the materials used for the chemical control of parasitic fungi were almost wholly confined to preparations or compounds of sulphur, copper and mercury. It was true that there were several other elements besides these three whose compounds were highly toxic to the fungi, but they were expensive, difficult to combine in suitable ways for practical use, or available only in very small quantities. During the thirties, McCallan and Wilcoxon, of the Boyce Thompson Institute for Plant Research, in New York State, carried out a long series of laboratory researches to ascertain the fungicidal properties of most of the elements in the chemists' periodic classification, which was to say of most of the elementary stuffs of which the universe was composed. They found that the remarkable fungicidal activity of *copper* salts, which would inhibit the germination of some fungus spores when present at a fraction of one part in a million of water, was by no means unique. The lethal dosages of salts of cerium, cadmium and uranium were of about the same order, while salts of osmium, silver and mercury were deadly to fungus spores in even smaller amount. Precious therapeutants containing osmium or silver could well be used in medicine, but hardly in the large-scale operations of agriculture. Osmium was a metal rather more expensive than gold, it cost about 160s. per fine ounce; and even silver, at about 1s. 9d. per fine ounce, was about fifty times as expensive as copper. There were several elements whose fungicidal properties were of a lower order than those of copper — arsenic and zinc amongst others — which were nevertheless deserving of further consideration, and a very satisfactory control of the Leaf Mould of tomatoes was actually obtained in practice with salicyl anilide, an organic fungicide — discovered at the Shirley Institute in England — containing no metal at all. By 1939 the field of search for possible new fungicides could not be said to have been at all thoroughly explored, let alone exhausted, but it was plain that the three elements of greatest use to man for the defence of his crops against fungus diseases were sulphur, copper and mercury. Of these, the use of mercury was confined to seed and seedling disinfection, where very small quantities were effective. The compounds of mercury were, in general, too expensive, too poisonous, and too injurious to leaves to be utilized in sprays or dusts for the protection of foliage. Thus the attempts to improve upon this most important practical method of plant-disease control, during the twenties and the thirties, amounted in the main to search for more convenient and more economical ways of utilizing the two old specifics: sulphur and copper.

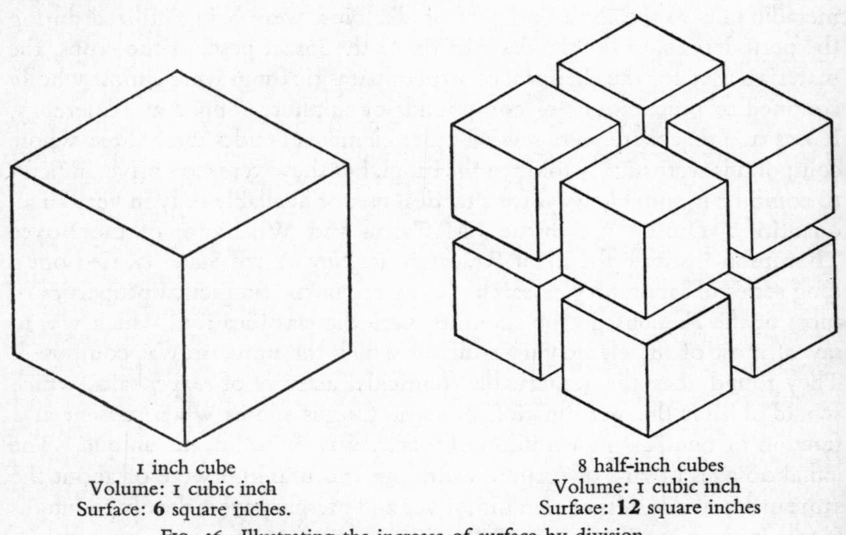

FIG. 56. Illustrating the increase of surface by division.

All the work on sulphur dusts and mercurial seed-disinfectants showed that there were two ways of utilizing to the best advantage those elements which had inherent fungicidal properties. One way was chemical, the other physical. A little mercury could be made to go further, while causing the minimum of injury to seed-grain, by combining it not with chlorine as in corrosive sublimate, but with organic radicals – groups of carbon, oxygen and hydrogen atoms – as in ethyl mercury acetate. *That* was a *chemical* way of increasing the factor of safety and conserving the precious element. A little sulphur dust could be made to go further by grinding it finer. And that was a *physical* method. Not only did the finer dust cover a greater area of foliage, per pound of sulphur applied, but a greater surface of sulphur was exposed, and the rate at which the sulphur gave off the fumes or soluble compounds which actually killed the fungal growth on the leaves was thereby increased. If the average diameter of the sulphur particles in a dust was halved, the surface of sulphur exposed was doubled. Hence one way of increasing the activity of fungicidal substances was to produce them in forms in which the particles were exceedingly small.

The smallest particles of any chemical compound or element which could exist as such in nature were its individual molecules, or constituent ions, and it was very easy to reduce most substances to this state of division. It was necessary only to vaporize the substance or to dissolve it in water or some other solvent and the job was done. But it was not in this extreme state of division, of molecular or ionic solution, that fungicidal substances were best applied to the foliage of plants. Like copper sulphate solutions without lime they were then generally *too* active and would injure the leaves as well as the organs of the fungi. Moreover, they would have no persisting effect. It was a case for compromise, the desideratum being an intermediate state of division in which the particles, still comprising myriads of ultimate molecules, would be small enough to avoid waste and to expose an extensive reactive surface, but still large enough to release toxic substance in solution at a gentle rate over a period of some weeks when deposited on leaves.

The sulphur powders generally used for dusting foliage would just pass through a sieve having two hundred meshes to the inch, the best of them would pass a three-hundred mesh. Thus the maximum diameter of their particles was about 60 or about 40 microns, respectively. Such particles made up dusts which seemed impalpably fine to the touch, but their size was in reality quite gross in comparison with that of the fungus spores they had to destroy – they looked like great stones or boulders under the microscope (Fig. 57). Banks had found a way of reducing solid sulphur to particles of an altogether lower order of size by his dodge of fusing it with bentonite. Other methods were available for producing very fine suspensions of sulphur for application to foliage in the form of wet sprays.

When sulphur was precipitated from solutions of its compounds, as by adding acid to the liquid lime-sulphur of the fruit-growers, the resulting particles began as molecules and grew to the point of visibility under the microscope. By suitably arresting their growth, and adding substances which had the effect of holding them apart in the liquid as they were formed, suspensions could be obtained in which the bulk of the sulphur was in the form of particles only about a single micron in diameter. Sixty thousand of these would not make up the bulk of a single particle of the 300-mesh sulphur dust. They were so small that the irregular bombardment of the water molecules kept them in perpetual motion, and the yellow colour of the sulphur was lost owing to an optical effect. Such suspensions of sulphur in water were as white and as liquid as milk. They contained, moreover, multitudes of sulphur particles which were much smaller than one micron in diameter, particles of the same order of size as those of filter-passing viruses, particles which were truly colloidal and which betrayed their presence only by causing sparklings of light in the dark field of the ultramicroscope.

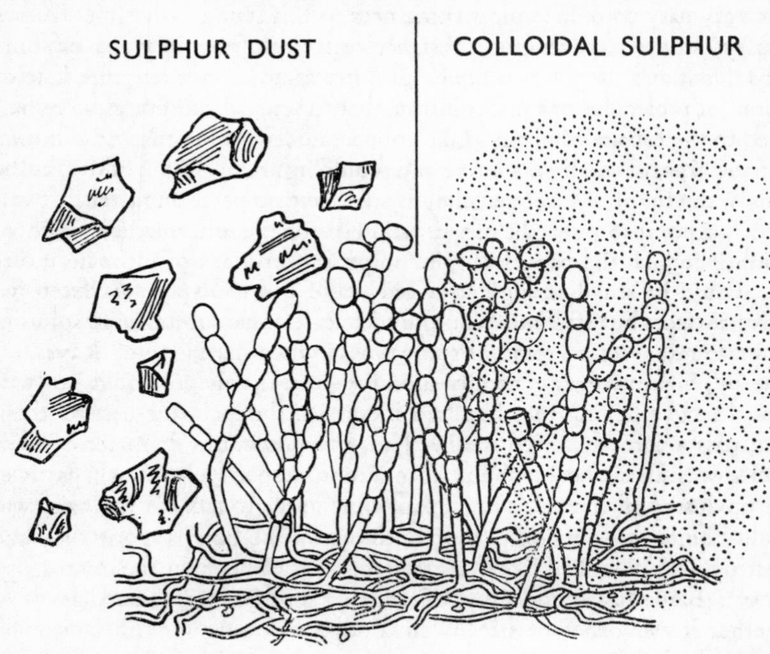

FIG. 57. The relation in size between particles of dusting sulphur (200 mesh), colloidal sulphur, and the conidia of a Powdery Mildew (× 200).

The first good commercial preparation of colloidal sulphur, of British manufacture, to be made available for use in horticultural sprays at an economic cost, was produced by a chemical precipitation process, and sold under the trade-name of 'Ialine'. This was followed, in 1930, by a rival commercial product called 'Sulsol', which was manufactured by a mechanical process. A paste of sulphur, water and gum was passed through roll mills similar to those used in the refining of chocolate or soap. The brittle grains of sulphur were sheared and torn apart as the ribbon of paste passed between the rolls, the minute colloidal particles were coated with a film of soluble protective material as they broke away, and were so prevented from cohering together. The ground paste was stirred up with water in large vats, the coarser particles were removed by sedimentation over a period of some weeks, and the white suspension of colloidal sulphur was drawn off after concentration by a method of battery working.

Such colloidal sulphurs represented the principal advance in sulphur sprays since the reintroduction of lime-sulphur *circa* 1908. Owing to the manufacturing processes involved, they were rather more expensive than lime-sulphur, and they did not by any means supersede it in general use. They gave a most excellent control, however, of all those pests and diseases against which sulphur was effective, notably Apple Scab, Red-Spider mites, Apple Mildew, Hop Mould and Powdery Mildews generally, as well as some of the Rusts, and they were of the greatest value for the protection of delicate fruit and foliage, which was injured or marked by the more caustic lime-sulphur. Colloidal sulphur was about the safest spray material ever produced. In this respect it was much superior to the mildest of Scott's historic 'self-boiled' lime-sulphurs, which first enabled peach trees to be sprayed when in leaf. As it was also odourless and perfectly innocuous on food-stuffs, it became very popular amongst gardeners for the spraying of greenhouse and garden plants.

The minuteness of the particles in colloidal sulphur rendered it an ideal material for the treatment of some plant diseases caused by fungi which grew in close tufts on the leaves, such as *Cladosporium fulvum*, the common Leaf Mould of the tomatoes. The particles were small enough to penetrate into the very midst of such growth; ceaselessly knocked about by the water molecules, they would reach every part of the fungus wetted by the spray. But here there was another difficulty. Unless special substances were added to cause them to spread, the drops of liquid projected on to the leaves by the spraying machines remained poised there as small rounded globules. They did not spread in a film over the leaf and they did not flood the growth of parasitic fungus. This was a difficulty with all fungicides and insecticides applied to foliage in the form of liquid sprays, and from about 1912 onwards the physics of liquid drops and films on leaves had been recognized as a very necessary subject of study in connection with the improvement of spraying operations.

The globular form of water-drops was due to tension between the water molecules at the surface, operating to make that surface as small as possible. The geometrical form having the smallest surface for a given volume was a sphere; hence the tiny drops of spray on the leaves were spherical, except so far as their shape was distorted by their weight, or by the leaf-surface on which they were resting. The objective of those seeking to control plant diseases by spraying was the direct opposite of that of the outer molecules in the spray-drops. It was necessary that those drops should assume shapes, not with the smallest, but with the greatest surface for their volume – they were required to spread over fungus and leaf in a thin film.

One way of reducing the surface-tension of the drops was to put a little soap in the water. Drops of soapy water on the leaves instantly collapsed and spread in a film; hence the old expedient of using soft-soap with nicotine washes to make them wet both the leaves and the bodies of the insects. With colloidal sulphur washes soft-soap could also be used. But soft-soap formed curds with the lime in hard water, and it was altogether incompatible with lime-sulphur and Bordeaux mixtures. Even where it could be used – with the nicotine for hop-washing against aphides, for example – most of it was wasted. Five pounds of soft-soap were commonly required for a hundred gallons of wash. Of these five pounds of good soap about four-and-a half merely formed curds with the lime in the water, while the other half-pound did the job. In short ninety per cent of the soap was used up in softening the water. And as a water-softener, soft-soap was about the messiest and most expensive reagent conceivable. The insoluble lime-soap curds produced served no useful purpose and they tended to block up the machinery with sticky scum. It was the same in the use of soap for domestic purposes – most of all the soap used in the world was wasted in softening water.

One of the most memorable achievements in the industrial arts during the reign of George V was the obtaining of soaps that did *not* form curds with hard water. It was an achievement as noteworthy as the realization of the ancient dream of making unbreakable glass. In 1939, the new soaps were still being withheld from the labouring housewife for reasons best known to the soap combines, but they formed ingredients of sundry shampoo powders, they were used to make foam-baths for film-stars, they had a most important industrial application in wool-scouring and wetting-out textiles for dyeing, and they had solved the difficulty in getting globules of spray-fluids to spread over the leaves of plants.

It all began in 1846 when John Mercer patented a process for making sulphonated olive oil for use in dyeing. Instead of boiling olive oil with caustic potash or soda to make soap in the usual way, he treated it with sulphuric acid. This also converted the oil into a substance which was soluble in water and which had the properties of a soap. By about 1875 sulphonated castor oil, made in much the same way, had been adopted by the dyers and calico printers, notably for use in the dyeing of cotton with Turkey Red. When the oil was well and thoroughly 'sulphonated' the resulting 'soap' formed comparatively little scum or curd with hard water. By 1930 sulphonated castor oil, or Turkey Red Oils as they were called, had been plain articles of commerce for fifty years or more, they cost fourpence or fivepence a pound in hundredweight lots, and some of them, the Monopole Soaps or Oils, for example, were not only useful for making up tar-oil and other emulsions for the winter spraying of fruit trees, they also made good insecticidal washes with Derris, nicotine, etc. They were little used for this latter purpose, however, except in proprietary preparations.

During the nineteen-twenties a variety of new synthetic detergents, greatly superior to the old Turkey Red Oils, began to come into use in the textile industry, and shortly afterwards, in proprietary mixtures, as 'wetters' for use with horticultural sprays. Agral I, an I.C.I. product, was one of these, and sulphonated Lorol, manufactured by the Deutsche Hydrierwerke A.G., was another. Happily no mystery was made about the composition of the Lorol stuff, so that those experimenting with it knew something about its chemical nature. It was sulphonated lauryl alcohol, made by the hydrogenation of coconut oil to produce lauryl alcohol, which was then treated with sulphuric acid and neutralized with soda. It was sold as a white powder, containing 50 per cent of the new soap or wetter, at about 1s. 10d. per pound. It was unaffected by the hardest water, even by sea-water, and it could be used with lime-sulphur, Bordeaux mixture, nicotine, colloidal sulphur, lead arsenate, oil emulsions and most of the other materials employed in spraying. As little as four to eight ounces of it in a hundred gallons served to make the sprays wet foliage, insects and fungi most efficiently. It had long been known that one way of wetting a duck's back was to put the bird in soapy water; some of these new synthetic soaps dissolved in the water would not only wet the unfortunate bird but they would very nearly submerge it. They caused the water to penetrate all the minute interstices of the greasy plumage and flood the air-padding on which the bird depended for warmth and buoyancy. It was this penetrative action which made the new products so extremely valuable for wetting-out close-woven greasy fabrics and the felted patches of fungal growth on leaves.

For some years there was a belief, fostered by the spray-material merchants and commercial travellers, that these new wetters could be added with advantage to every kind of spray, whatever its function and purpose. By 1936, however, when the second edition of Dr. Hubert Martin's *Scientific Principles of Plant Protection* was published, this excessive enthusiasm was cooling down.

The new wetters not only helped the spray fluid to run over the leaves, they also helped it to run off them, or to collect at the leaf-tips and so cause 'tip-burn'. When wetters were used the amount of protective material that could be deposited on the leaves was reduced. The new wetters were of most value in those sprays which were designed to kill insects or fungi by immediate contact. To penetrate the close 'pile' of such fungi as the Leaf Mould on tomatoes they were practically indispensable. But for those sprays which were required to exert a persisting protective action, such as Bordeaux mixture, Millardet's original theory still held. Little deposits of the mixture, closely dotted about the leaves but not altogether covering them, were quite sufficient to charge all the moisture falling on the leaf with the necessary taint of copper. If anything was to be added to these protective sprays it should be something fixative or strongly adhesive, such as bentonite or a drying-oil or gelatine, which would prevent the deposits from being washed away over a period of weeks. A 'sticker' rather than a 'wetter'. A certain limited amount of wetter assisted the distribution, but to cover the leaves with a multitude of small individual drops, by using a misty spray with a high pressure behind the nozzle, was as good a method as any where protective fungicides were being applied. The advantages of using a wetter were somewhat dubious in potato spraying.

Potato spraying! It was remarkable how little was done in fifty years to improve the art of potato spraying, which with the mere variant of potato dusting, was still the only really practical method yet available for combating the historic Potato Blight. The long-sought overwintering spores of the Blight fungus were found again, this time in somewhat less artificial culture, by Professor Paul Murphy of the Albert Agricultural College near Dublin, in the year 1927. They were *not* found within the tissues of blighted leaves, nor indeed within any part of the potato plant. They were found among the external growth of the fungus from the cut surface of an infected tuber resting on sterilized soil in a flower pot. Sterilized soil was 'dead' soil; in nature the soil was very much 'alive', populated by innumerable protozoa and bacteria; it constituted an entirely different milieu. But if the Blight fungus could produce oospores in sterilized soil, it was at least arguable that it might also produce them in the same way in nature, not *on* but *near* the blighted potatoes in the ground. Perhaps that was where they had been all the time during one of the longest games of hide-and-seek in natural history. But up to 1939 the find had still not been made. It was a little difficult to understand why no one undertook the search for these historic oospores in the unsterilized soil of a potato field. In 1926, Helena de Bruyn, of Wageningen, showed that the Blight fungus could live not only as a parasite on potato plants, but also as a saprophyte on wheat, oat and rye straw, and also on the remains of plants gathered at random from the side of a ditch. The fungus grew on this dead stuff, and it produced oospores in abundance. But, in these experiments also, the plant remains were first sterilized in the laboratory. The resting spores found by Murphy and de Bruyn were some of them formed parthenogenetically, others had perfect male organs attached, but whether the spores were fertilized or not, nobody had ever succeeded in getting them to germinate, so that there was still no evidence that they had any part in the propagation of the Blight. Perhaps the living spawn of the fungus did survive the winter in the soil, but even if this were so, no new way of preventing the Blight was indicated. Up hill and down dale for the better part of a century the Blight had attacked potatoes grown in every kind of soil, and in soil which had received every known kind of treatment. The Blight had survived many changes in farm practice, from the days of the old self-sufficient high-farming in England, when nothing was put on the land but its own straw and farmyard manure, down to the times of synthetic nitrates and manurial residues of imported feeding-stuffs, and it went on attacking the potatoes just the same. Paul Murphy further devoted much study to the viability of the summer spores of the fungus in the soil, but in the main he merely confirmed the importance of the protective methods of lifting, advocated before him by Jens Ludwig Jensen. There was nothing for it but to spray the potatoes every year.

One important advance in the organization of spraying arose out of the development of a new science which the Americans had to call 'epiphytotiology'. The study of the weather conditions associated with epidemics – or epi*phyto*tics of *plant* diseases – enabled outbreaks to be forecast with a certain amount of accuracy. Meteorologists associated with regional plant pathological services were able to give the farmers warning, some days in advance, of the time to spray their potatoes or their apple trees. By 1926, Professor van Everdingen in Holland had defined with considerable exactitude the meteorological conditions which usually preceded severe attacks of Potato Blight. There was dew for at least four hours during the night, the minimum of night temperature was not less than 10 degrees Centigrade, the mean cloudiness of the day following the dew was not less than 0.8, and the rainfall on that day was at least one-tenth of a millimetre. Naturally other meteorologists found in such criteria a great deal to argue about, but between them, by rule or by judgment, they were quite often able to give fair warning to the farmers, thus saving much waste of materials and labour through spraying too early, and much loss of produce through spraying too late. Spray warning services, utilizing the broadcasting stations, and based either on meteorological observations or on the earliest reports of the appearance of the disease, were adopted with much success in Holland, the British Isles, various parts of the United States, and elsewhere.

The copper mixtures officially recommended in 1939 for the spraying of potatoes and so many other crops had undergone no improvement since about 1890. Some of the plant pathologists who had reason to bless these old mixtures in the days of their youth were still maintaining that nothing could ever be quite so good as home-made Burgundy mixture – unless it was home-made Bordeaux mixture, which was even more of a nuisance to prepare. This nostalgic idea, in itself no more worthy of respect than a romantic pining for home-made soap, suited the big suppliers of copper sulphate and washing soda very well. The farmer was even encouraged to believe that in making up his own mixtures he was keeping money in his pocket and preserving some degree of independence of the industrialists, although in point of fact the price of copper sulphate was controlled by one ring, and that of washing soda by another, so that he was merely paying maintained prices for two products of the chemical industry instead of one. There were, however, valid reasons for the continued recommendation of the old mixtures until new ones had proved their superiority in use and under stringent official test. Bordeaux and Burgundy mixtures when correctly and freshly prepared had their active substances in a gelatinous state which was not reproducible by diluting any ready-made mixtures of the same formulae which had been dried during manufacture. Ready-made Bordeaux and Burgundy mixtures, in paste or powder form had all consistently failed on test; they had neither the adhesiveness nor quite the same fungicidal properties as the troublesome two-solution mixtures made on the farm.

There were a number of chemists, however, who tried again to storm the citadels of Burgundy and Bordeaux. With all the resources of their art they were not obliged to confine themselves to attempts to imitate the old mixtures with manufactured preparations. As fungicidal activity was an intrinsic property of copper, they could break new ground and try to get other compounds of copper into suitable form for use in spraying. The old mixtures were unquestionably effective, but they had their disadvantages, and the point about them which struck the chemists' imagination was that they were apparently very wasteful of precious copper metal.

In Ireland, where the Blight was ever most severe, the potato grower was advised to spray three times, with 2 per cent Burgundy mixture, using 80-100 gallons per acre for the first application, and 120 gallons per acre for the second and third. This meant using some 64 lb. of copper sulphate crystals and 80 lb. of washing soda per acre of potatoes per season. In Great Britain, where the rainfall was not so high, and in Ireland where considerations of economy had to be put before getting the very best results, the use of 1 per cent mixture was advised, and thus the quantities used per acre were halved, but they were still very considerable. Copper sulphate would certainly kill the spores of the Potato Blight fungus at a concentration of five parts in a million of water. As the total rain falling in a very wet season on an acre of potatoes in central Ireland during July, August and September was about 10 inches, or 227,000 gallons, it followed by a simple calculation that the amount of copper sulphate being used there was six times as much as that necessary to make all the rain which fell from heaven over the period completely toxic to Blight spores. It was true that so far as the Blight was concerned dew mattered more than rain, but the actual precipitation in the form of dew was small and much of it evaporated off the foliage again, leaving the copper where it was. Whether the water in which the Blight spores germinated came from the dew or the rain, it was fairly evident that attempts to find more economical ways of using copper in potato spraying were very well justified. And this was the case in the spraying of other crops also.

One expedient was to modify the home-made copper mixtures by adding substances to enhance the adhesion of the spray deposits on the leaves – to minimize the loss due to the washing off of toxic substance by the rain. Dr. Hubert Martin emulsified cotton-seed oil in ordinary Bordeaux mixture, and by this means he was able to reduce the amount of copper required for the successful control of Apple Scab, by one-half. This was an important advance, but the cotton-seed oil cost money, and the addition had the disadvantage that it made the preparation of the mixture more rather than less troublesome on the farm. In fruit-growing this did not matter so much. The highly-skilled fruit-growers, with elaborate 'Spray Calendars' on their walls, were now spraying against one pest or another almost the whole year round. They were accustomed to making up even more complicated mixed sprays; many of them had specially-constructed tanks for the purpose, beside central pumping stations which delivered the spray-fluids through permanent mains to convenient points amongst the trees. Some of them did so much spraying that they could well afford to keep a young chemist on the premises. But the potato-growers and the vine-growers – to say nothing of allotment-holders and gardeners – needed some economical ready-made preparation of copper, which they could just dilute in water as required, and so get ahead with their job.

In British Patent specification, No. 321,260 of 1929, the Dr. A. Wacker Company of Munich disclosed an inexpensive process for manufacturing a basic chloride, or oxychloride, of copper in form suitable for use as a fungicide. This basic chloride had about the same fungicidal potency, for the weight of copper it contained, as the other basic copper compounds which were the active materials in Bordeaux and Burgundy mixtures. But a noteworthy point about the Wacker process was that it entirely eliminated the use of soda or other alkali, both in the field and during manufacture. One hundred lb. of copper sulphate crystals and 60 lb. of common salt were first crushed together with a little water, to produce copper chloride. Three hundred lb. of scrap copper metal were then mixed in, and the mass, which was raked over occasionally, was exposed to the air in shallow tanks for three weeks or more. The necessary oxygen was absorbed from the air – which cost nothing – and a very fine-grained mass of copper oxychloride was produced. This was separated and dried, as an apple-green powder to which a little powdered gum was then added. For use in spraying, this product was simply stirred up with the necessary amount of water, and no addition of lime or soda was required.

The green copper oxychloride could also be manufactured by letting a solution of cupric chloride trickle over a heap of scrap copper metal exposed to the air. The stuff was really a marine 'rust' of copper, a product of atmospheric corrosion, a kind of verdigris except that it contained chlorine instead of the acetic acid radicle. It was formed on the copper roofs of buildings exposed to spray from the sea, and on the hulls of ships, which were treated with copper paint to prevent growths of marine algae upon them.

The new 'Kupferkalk Wacker' was being used with conspicuous success in place of Bordeaux mixture on thousands of acres of vines in the Rhine and Moselle valleys by 1932. And along with other copper oxychloride fungicides of a like nature, at first identified by manufacturers' code numbers and later by trade-names, it was being tried in all countries, and on all kinds of crops, including potatoes, during the thirties.

Meanwhile, in London, Mr. Emil Hatschek, one of the world's leading colloid chemists, tackled the problem of copper sprays from another side. As it was apparent that the fungicidal activity of sulphur could be increased by reducing it to the colloidal condition, there was good reason for attempts to obtain basic salts of copper in that form also. In 1923, H. D. Hooker in the United States had obtained a colloidal solution of copper hydroxide and found that it adhered well to foliage and was deadly to the Apple Scab fungus at about one part in five thousand of water. The difficulty was, however, that this and other known colloidal solutions of copper salts were excessively dilute, and the cost of manufacture put them out of court for agricultural use. By the Hatschek process, British Patent No. 392,556 of 1931, a practical and inexpensive colloidal copper fungicide was obtained. The starting point was copper oxychloride, precipitated in the form of minute particles by the carefully controlled addition of caustic soda solution to cupric chloride solution in large vats fitted with agitators. The particles after formation adhered together in flocculent masses, so that they could be separated from the liquid by filtration and washed to produce a moist 'cake' of the pure material. The particles adhering together in the cake were then further reduced, chemically, and caused to disperse in a *small* quantity of fluid medium – thus giving a *liquid* product of high concentration – by a process known to colloid chemists as 'pectization'. Every drop of the heavy olive-green liquid contained millions of minute particles of active copper compound in stable suspension. The product was put on the market with tentative recommendations for use in 1931 under the trade name of 'Bouisol' – a copper *bouillie* in the form of a sol. This refined colloidal preparation proved its worth; it won an established place among the really scientific chemical therapeutants for use on plants, by 1939 it was being sold to gardeners over the counters of chemists' shops, and the price to the potato growers, who bought it in barrels by the ton, had been reduced to about sixpence halfpenny per lb.

With Bouisol, one of the disadvantages of the traditional Bordeaux and Burgundy mixtures was at once overcome: the requisite quantity of the liquid had merely to be run out of a barrel and poured into the water in the spraying machine; all the labour and delay involved in preparing copper mixtures on the farm was eliminated. But several other points of fundamental interest in the whole practice of spraying were brought to light in the course of adventures with this new fungicide in the field. The strengths at which Bordeaux and Burgundy mixtures were used provided no guide to the strength at which it would be necessary to employ a colloidal solution of partially-reduced copper oxychloride. All that had to be determined *de novo*, and after some seven years of use and trial it was found that 5 lb. or less of the product, containing on ultimate chemical analysis 15 per cent of copper, would go as far against most of the fungus diseases of horticultural and garden plants as 10 lb. of copper sulphate (containing 25 per cent of copper) and 10 lb. of lime made up into Bordeaux mixture. By modifying the chemical and physical condition of the copper compound, a great saving in the amount of copper used in spraying *was* therefore possible But not necessarily on every crop or under all conditions of incidence of plant disease. In England and Scotland satisfactory control of the Potato Blight was obtained year after year, and over thousands of acres, when Bouisol was used at about 8 lb. per hundred gallons, but trials by Professor Paul Murphy showed that to be on the safe side, in Ireland, in bad years, it would be advisable to raise the dosage of copper, in colloidal form, to equality with that in 1 per cent Bordeaux mixture, i.e. to use the Bouisol at about 16 lb. per hundred gallons. At the Ormskirk Potato Testing Station in 1933 an even higher dosage was employed. Here, a *single application* of the colloidal copper product, at 28 lb. per hundred gallons, kept the potato foliage green from July right through to September, while plants in surrounding plots, which had received several applications of Bordeaux mixture, were almost completely destroyed by the Blight before the end of August.

But other phenomena encountered in spraying with colloidal copper, which pointed to directions in which spray materials might be improved, were those concerning the physiological effects of the spray on plants. Owing to the minuteness of the colloidal particles and their dispersion, the spray deposits on foliage were practically invisible, while those of Bordeaux mixture looked like a coating of bluish lime-wash. The vine-growers objected that now they could not see where the plants had been sprayed, while the gardeners rejoiced that the appearance of their plants was not spoiled. In the potato fields the mere appearance of the plants did not matter much one way or another, except that freedom from disfiguring spray deposits facilitated the examination of the foliage for virus diseases. But opaque spray deposits had a shading effect on the leaves, and to some extent they slowed down the processes of photosynthesis by which starch was manufactured in the leaves for ultimate storage in the tubers. It could be seen by direct experiment that in the course of the day the amount of starch formed in a potato leaf under a thick deposit of Bordeaux mixture was less than where the leaf was unshaded. Leaves decolorized with alcohol in the evening and then tested with iodine showed a fainter blue where the spray deposits had been. By how much this shading over a period of months might reduce the yield of a potato crop was difficult to say. But the effect was there. When the sun was strong some shading was perhaps desirable – photosynthesis was fastest in a moderate light. But when the light was weak . . .?

Then again, one of the objections raised to the spraying of potatoes by the illustrious Dr. Sorauer, back in the early nineties, was that Bordeaux mixture while checking the Blight also checked the growth of the potato plants. This had been observed again and again in forty years, but little attention was paid to the consequent effect on the crop, and sometimes it was even claimed to be positively advantageous. The spray hardened the leaves, reduced the amount of new foliage to be attacked by the Blight, and was supposed in some mysterious way to drive the 'strength' of the plant down to the tubers. When the potatoes were sprayed not with Bordeaux mixture but with colloidal copper it was found that the check to growth of the plants did not occur, the leaves remained soft and green, and there was good reason to believe that the crop was sometimes increased by as much as a ton an acre, solely by the avoidance of the check to growth, in the middle of the growing period, when the tubers were normally putting on weight most rapidly. It was arguable that spraying with Bordeaux mixture retarded the coming to maturity of the potato plants, and therefore the onset of the Blight – apart altogether from its direct fungicidal action – but there was certainly also something to be said for the contention, that, other things being equal, those sprays were best which interfered least with the normal functioning of the plants.

One of the materials used in the manufacture of the Hatschek copper colloid, to 'pectize' the cake of copper oxychloride, to disperse the particles in a liquid medium, to modify them chemically and ultimately to assist their spread over foliage, was a substance known as sulphite cellulose extract or Sulphite Lye. Its composition was complex, for it contained all the materials extracted from wood when it was 'cooked' in the bisulphite process to obtain pulp for paper-making. As concentrated for sale it was a treacly liquid, with a pleasant caramel odour, containing much reducing-sugar and gums. Among other stuffs in it were some rather indeterminate compounds, known as lignin-sulphonic acids, derived from the lignin in the wood. While Mr. Hatschek was experimenting with this prize-packet of stuffs useful to colloid chemists, Dr. Hubert Martin, then at Wye College, was trying the material for another purpose, having conceived the idea that the lignin-sulphonic acids in it might function in somewhat the same way as the new synthetic wetters which were then being put on the market. He found that although the sulphite lye caused no appreciable lowering of the surface tension of water, it was nevertheless an efficient wetter when used in sufficient quantity – about six pints per hundred gallons of spray mixture. It was unaffected by hard water and it was compatible with practically every material used in the spraying of plants. It made an excellent emulsifying agent for oil-sprays in place of soaps or casein and of itself it caused no injury to foliage even in very high dosage. Thus the sulphite lye which had once been allowed to run to waste from the pulp works into the rivers of Canada and Sweden, found an important use during the thirties in materials for the prevention of plant diseases. It had the great merit of being very cheap – only a halfpenny to three farthings a pound in ton lots.

The sodium clay, bentonite, as used by Banks for the improvement of sulphur dusts, could also be used with much advantage in the preparation of new copper fungicides. The clay had remarkable adhesive properties and dry manufactured products containing it would form flocculent and gelatinous precipitates in water, very closely resembling those in freshly-made Bordeaux and Burgundy mixtures. The present writer obtained a dry bentonite-copper-oxychloride fungicide, which could be used either as a dust, or for spraying, merely by heating together a mixture of bentonite with copper sulphate, common salt and washing soda crystals in the theoretically correct proportions (British Patent No. 493,148 of 1938). The reaction took place in the water of crystallization of the copper sulphate and soda, and the mass rose like a dough with the carbon dioxide evolved. Copper oxychloride was produced in the form of very fine particles in association with the bentonite, and the dried powder, to which a small quantity of sodium pyrophosphate could be added with advantage, dispersed readily when stirred up in water for use as a spray. The manufacturing process was so simple that small quantities for trial could readily be made in an old enamel plate heated over a saucepan of water.

Indeed the necessary materials could be purchased from any chemical dealers and there was no reason why 'home-made' copper oxychloride sprays should not be freshly prepared as required for use in the garden. Quite a good one, incorporating several refinements, could be made by first mixing together 10 ounces of crushed copper sulphate crystals, 8½ ounces of crushed washing soda, 1½ ounces of common salt, ¼ ounce of neutral sodium pyrophosphate and 1¼ ounces of bentonite; then pouring a kettleful of boiling water over these mixed materials, stirring for a minute or two, until the effervescence was over, and finally adding cold water to make 6½ gallons. This spray, which contained the same amount of copper as 1 per cent Bordeaux mixture, would be suitable for spraying potatoes; for spraying flowers and fruit trees the strength could well be reduced by half. If the spray was prepared exactly as above, but without the pyrophosphate and the bentonite, it would be found that the green copper oxychloride flocculated and settled rapidly, necessitating frequent agitation of the mixture in the pail or spraying machine during use. The pyrophosphate had the effect of preventing the flocculation; and the purpose of the bentonite was to get the active material into a more finely-divided and gelatinous condition, and very greatly to enhance its adhesiveness to foliage, so that it would long resist washing off by the rain.

By 1939, it was all the more interesting to try home-made copper oxychloride sprays occasionally, as manufactured products of one kind and another, containing this material, were then emerging from their experimental stage, and they appeared perhaps the most likely to displace the old Bordeaux and Burgundy mixtures at last. But many other compounds of copper beside the oxychloride were under trial. The red cuprous oxide for example. This had been in use in America as a soil fungicide for some years before Dr. Martin brought to light the interesting fact that it had general fungicidal possibilities rivalling those of the basic copper salts. With red cuprous oxide sprays there might well be a revival, in new guise, of Michael Perret's copper sucrates, which were tried and too soon abandoned in the early nineties. Cuprous oxide was the copper compound formed when Perret's Bordeaux mixtures containing molasses were allowed to stand some while before use, and there was no doubt that the product Bouisol owed some part of its success to the partial reduction of the copper oxychloride particles in it by the reducing-sugars in the sulphite lye. Another compound of copper whose use had been proposed in the past, but which had fallen into the background, was black copper sulphide. When experiments were being made with lime-sulphur as though it were a new charm, *circa* 1910, several workers tried adding copper sulphate solution to it. Black copper sulphide was precipitated in more or less colloidal form, and it was found to be extraordinarily adhesive to foliage. There were some who claimed that it was also the safest compound of copper known. This latter notion appeared to be mistaken, for other workers found that the copper sulphide caused severe burning of the leaves, and rejected its use on that account. But one fact remained: the whole of the copper in copper sulphide was 'available'. The compound, as such, was inert and insoluble but when exposed to air and moisture on leaves the whole of it would gradually oxidize to soluble copper sulphate. The trouble was that in the crude form in which it was tried the stuff no doubt oxidized too fast, liberating the soluble copper compound at such a rate that it injured the leaves as well as the fungus spores. But what of that? It might well be possible to alter the physical condition of the substance so that when applied to the leaves it dissolved very slowly.

Oxychloride or suboxide or sulphide of copper, as you pleased, the rational course which remained to be pursued was to produce the actual compounds of copper required by the farmer for spraying his plants as directly as possible from the copper ore. It was irrational to produce refined copper sulphate for agricultural use when the kind of copper compound that the farmer wanted was not the sulphate at all. Some 300,000 tons of copper sulphate were produced annually, nearly the whole of which was used in the war against plant diseases. Farmers and manufacturers and middlemen were transforming this copper sulphate, generally by the addition of alkali, into the insoluble or very slowly soluble basic copper compounds used in spraying. Unless the copper producing companies were in cahoots with the alkali manufacturers it was passing strange that they were not more enterprising in attempts to produce the copper products actually needed in agriculture directly from their raw materials – the oxide and sulphide ores. The Wacker process by which copper oxychloride was obtained from the metal seemed a step in the right direction. But was it really necessary to go to the cost of extracting the metal, only to corrode it away again into marine copper rust?

CHAPTER XXX

DEGENERATION AND VIRUS DISEASES

AFTER 1920, when the researches of a small and scattered company of pioneers had fairly opened up the subject, more and more attention came to be given to the so-called 'virus' diseases of the crops. The number of scientific papers about them increased year by year, until in 1939 it was very easy for the inquiring onlooker to fall into the error of imagining that the virus diseases were not only the worst murrains of the crops in the twentieth century, but that they were of recent beginning, and that the fungi had somehow given place to them as prime agencies of agricultural waste. Such imaginings were illusions of the lamp; they came of judging the economic significance of the virus diseases by the amount of space devoted to them in the current phytopathological literature. The truth was that they now happened to provide one of the most attractive fields of research for those who hoped to make discoveries. Viruses, like vitamins, were all lit up on the altars of high science during the nineteen-thirties. It was their turn.

Certainly the plant virus diseases appeared to have spread alarmingly, and to have become much more prevalent since the beginning of the century. One might speak of 'the advance of the viruses' as of 'the advance of the fungi', and fairly attribute it to the same world causes; but the virus diseases of plants were new in nothing but name. The Leaf Roll of the potatoes, when it was at last disentangled from the other diseases to which it had a most misleading partial resemblance, could be taken as one of the very best examples of a modern virus disease; but as the chief part of the trouble once known as the 'Curl' it had ravaged the potato crops in England during the eighteenth century – long before the Blight was ever heard of; the Peach Yellows had a long history in the United States; the Tobacco Mosaic had been recognized as a destructive disease for over fifty years; and the 'breaking' and streaking of tulips, found during the twenties to be a consequence of virus disease, had been depicted in the paintings of old masters of the Dutch school.

The virus diseases of plants were numerous; they deserved every one of the thousands of modern scientific papers devoted to them, and many more again; but in comparison with all that had been written about the fungi, the entire literature on plant viruses was still very small. By no means all the fungi caused plant diseases, but a great number of them did so, and by 1931 Saccardo's *Sylloge fungorum omnium hucusque cognitorum* had run into twenty-five volumes and about as many thousands of pages. Yet unreported species of fungi were still being discovered by the score every year, and hardly a decade passed without some new and serious epidemic of fungus disease among the crops. 'Virology', if that was what it was going to be called, was more of a swirl than a science in 1939. Each new text-book classified the viruses in a different way, and even the book by Bawden of Rothamsted, which was then one of the latest and best, was still only a non-committal discussion of the subject. The young science was in much the same highly interesting but turbulent state that mycology had been in, *circa* 1850. There were not many people who would care to say that it had yet reached the state of systematization represented by de Bary's *Morphologie und Physiologie der Pilze* of 1866. It was not yet known for certain whether the viruses were mice or cheese – living organisms or inanimate proteins.

For this, if for no other reason, it would be a strategic mistake for the practical man to seek enlightenment about virus diseases by way of all the conflicting theories about the nature of viruses themselves. There was nothing more enjoyable than a good long wrangle about plant viruses and what was meant by 'life'. But that wrangling was best left till after; until evening, when with a little alcohol to help things along, one could have a very good time, agreeing or disagreeing with each theory in turn. In the morning there was work to do. Some of these virus diseases were causing great losses of agricultural produce, and it was work of prime social importance to examine how those losses could be reduced in practice. It was a mistake to let the obscurity about the nature of viruses blur the realization that some of the very worst of the plant virus diseases could be avoided, and that without any overwhelming difficulty. For instances of this there were the several virus diseases of the potato.

In 1913, W. A. Orton, of the United States Department of Agriculture, began saying that as far as he could see, the ancient and mysterious Degeneration or 'running out' of potatoes, was really brought about by three kinds of disease to which the potato was subject: Mosaic, resembling that of the tobacco, and characterized by mottling or crinkling of the foliage and dwarfing of the whole plant; Leaf Roll, characterized by rolling of the leaves, progressive falling off of the crop and Quanjer's 'phloem necrosis'; and Streak, which was manifest as a streaky decay and drooping of the leaves. No one knew what caused these diseases; no bacteria or fungi were to be found in causal association with them; and so far they were distinguishable only by their symptoms. Then, in 1916, came Quanjer's discovery that the Leaf Roll was an *infectious* disease, and in 1920 the proof by Oortwijn Botjes that it was spread by insects from plant to plant. The contagium was presumably something in the sap of the infected plants: the 'virus' of the disease.

After this, many workers contributed in the teazing out of the several virus diseases of the potato, and the determination of their part in causing the running out of different varieties in different regions. It was the time of teamwork, and often the string of names on the scientific papers was as long as the chorus of *Widecombe Fair*. There was E. S. Schultz of the Bureau of Plant Industry, working in collaboration with D. Folsom and others at the Orono Experiment Station, in the great potato-growing State of Maine — the Scotland of the U.S.A. In the Irish Free State there was Paul Murphy, often collaborating with Robert McKay. Quanjer and his associates in Holland continued their pioneering work. At the University College of North Wales, at Bangor, there were T. Whitehead and W. Maldwyn Davies; at the Potato Virus Research Station in Cambridge, set up in 1926, Drs. Redcliffe N. Salaman and Kenneth M. Smith, with F. C. Bawden, who went later to Rothamsted. These were among the leading workers on the virus diseases of the *potato*, but, of course, much of the work on the virus diseases of other crops, notably tobacco and tomatoes, was contributory to that on potatoes. Many of the methods used in all plant virus research were worked out in connection with the Tobacco Mosaic, and for these methods, as well as for the determination of many of the properties of viruses, the whole science was very largely indebted to the American workers, Johnson, Holmes, Price, Kunkel, Stanley and the rest. It was noteworthy that the German workers took very little interest in plant virus research: it was in the main a Dutch-Anglo-American pursuit; it had not been started by German initiative, and the Germans were as reluctant to embrace it, as they were to avail themselves of the copper fungicides of French invention a generation before. More work was done on virus diseases in Japan than in Germany.

The result of much intensive research was to bring about a great itemization of the degenerative diseases of the potato, between 1920 and 1940, but so far as finding means of preventing or avoiding losses from this group of diseases went, the effect was not so much to discover anything new, as to sort out the valid from the false notions long held by practical potato growers and to show how the empirical measures, which they had found out for themselves during the nineteenth century, and had to some extent adopted, could be developed and utilized rationally and deliberately. To conquer the Leaf Roll would be half the battle, and as the control measures for that disease would cover most of the other virus diseases of the potato as well, it was convenient to consider the Leaf Roll first. The workers after 1920 had the great advantage of knowing that the Leaf Roll was an infectious disease, and that it was spread by aphides. But there were some who would date this knowledge right back to 1778, when the Agricultural Society of Manchester offered a prize for the best essay on the 'Curl', and one of the competitors expressed his view, in so many words that it was (*a*) a disease, and (*b*) spread by aphides. To say that these things were really known at that time, however, would be like saying that the effect of copper in preventing the Potato Blight was really known in 1846, when a contributor to the Cambrian newspaper pointed out that potatoes in the vicinity of the copper-smelting works at Swansea were healthy, while others a little further off were all decayed. It was but one of a hundred and one theories and observations put forward but lost among the crowd. By 1855, however, the notion that aphides had some part in spreading the Curl was quite common. The Rev. M. J. Berkeley said at that time that the very name 'Curl' was often applied to potatoes affected by aphides, that a few individuals about the plants were quite sufficient to affect the foliage, though they were most injurious where they multiplied to excess. As so very often happened, that extraordinarily prescient and reverend gentleman was later found to be right. Then the reality of the degeneration of potato varieties had been insistently stressed by John Lindley. It was true that some other botanists attempted to dismiss it as a chimera, but the farmers knew very well that they had to cope with it in practice. They did this, with some partial success, by substituting new potato varieties for old ones that seemed to have 'worn out', and by 'change of seed'. They had a theory that the degeneration was associated with the longevity of the potato, constantly propagated by tubers and denied the rejuvenation of sexual reproduction. In this they were not wrong: degeneration was not caused by old age, but it was a concomitant of it, when the potatoes were grown in districts infested by greenflies. The farmers knew that, except in one or two strangely favoured localities, the yield fell off when they saved seed-potatoes from their own crops, for planting year after year. In England the farmers took to sending to Scotland for their seed, and thus the Scottish seed-potato trade had developed, a long time before the word 'virus' came to have any specialized meaning. Was there any real reason why Scottish seed-potatoes should do any better than those grown elsewhere? The farmers thought so, and they backed their conviction with cash.

After 1920 the entomologists at last realized that it would be worth their while to help the plant pathologists, and they began studying the habits of the aphides infesting the potato crops. They found that the Peach Aphis, *Myzus persicae*, was the one chiefly responsible for spreading the Leaf Roll. The number of peach trees in England, however, was insufficient to account for the prevalence of the Peach Aphis on the potatoes, and one exceedingly important discovery was made by Maldwyn Davies of Bangor during the winter of 1931. He found the greenfly, in its wingless stage, in great abundance on savoys at a provincial market. He then went out with his specimen bottle into the market gardens, and at thirty-six places visited in North Wales he found savoys harbouring *Myzus persicae* over the winter. The insects found shelter in the wrinkled leaves. Like the Black Stem Rust of the Wheat, these aphides had more than one host plant, they hibernated on savoys – and on cabbages and brussels sprouts, which were also green over the winter – and they migrated to the potatoes from May onwards. Thus the aphides which spread virus disease among the potatoes were most prevalent in the vicinity of market gardens.

Then there was the question of the dispersal of the aphides by wind. It might appear at first sight that a high wind would blow them all over the country. But here another piece of Maldwyn Davies's work was very instructive. He collected some of the live aphides and attempted to blow them off glass surfaces in the laboratory with a 'high wind' generated by a hair-dryer. He found that the insects were very reluctant to take to wing when the wind velocity exceeded three to four miles an hour, and that when it reached six to seven miles an hour they just hung on where they were for dear life. Their natural provisions for holding fast in a wind that might smash them to pieces could be seen through the glass with the aid of a microscope. Thus, and by field experiments made by Maldwyn Davies and a number of other workers, it was established that the spread of the aphides was favoured only by very gentle movements of air, and that in localities where the wind velocity commonly exceeded five or six miles an hour very few aphides were to be found on the potato crops. High atmospheric humidity also inhibited the insects' flight, and they did not like the cold; they would not multiply below about 55 degrees Fahrenheit.

Many puzzling phenomena were now explained, and the distribution of the Leaf Roll and sundry other virus diseases of the potato which were spread by aphides, was now stripped of half its mystery. In a sense these diseases were a special consequence of an insect plague; of infestation by insects relatively harmless in themselves, but pestilent in fact, because they sucked the juices of diseased potato plants and then flew off to feed on the healthy, which they injected with the viruses they had picked up. This plague of virus-disseminating insects was still sweeping the potato crops of the British Isles in 1939, as surely as the Phylloxera was sweeping the vines of France during the seventies and eighties. The aphides on the potatoes and the plant-lice on the vines were not, indeed, unrelated. The aphides did not form galls, they did not infest the roots of the potato plants, and their virgin wingless females brought forth swarms of living young instead of laying eggs, but otherwise their life-cycle was much the same as that of the Phylloxera (Fig. 26, p. 155).

In sheltered warm localities, and in the proximity of towns and market gardens, as over much of the south of England, the potatoes were greatly infested by the aphides and they degenerated rapidly – which was to say that the yield of tubers fell off when the locally-grown seed of one year was used for planting in the next. In parts of Scotland, where seed-potato crops were grown away from other cultivations, especially in bare, exposed, or windy places near the sea, the aphides found conditions unfavourable, and healthy potato crops could be grown year after year from local seed without exhibiting any appreciable degeneration. By roguing out the few affected plants found in the fields here and there the seed stocks could be kept fairly free from virus disease. Thus the deservedly high repute of Scotch seed-potatoes was attributable, not only to the great skill and business acumen of the Scotch, but to the fact that much of Scotland was too wet and cold and windswept to be any sort of paradise for greenflies.

During the nineteen-thirties, however, when the reasons for the superiority of the Scotch seed came to be understood, the canny Scottish potato men were in for some competition. They had a succession of very mild seasons, when the aphides were more prevalent than usual, and there was a good deal of Leaf Roll and other virus disease in the Scotch seed. It came to be realized that there was nothing magical about the mere name 'Scotch' as applied to seed-potatoes. There were many ideal places for seed-potato growing in the Irish Free State and in Northern Ireland; Whitehead and Maldwyn Davies found several on the north coast of Wales; and a pioneering co-operative scheme was set up there, between the farmers and the College, which was successful, and which showed the way to produce good seed potatoes in *any* exposed locality, suitable for potato growing, where aphides were absent or not at all numerous. Similar schemes were later started in Cumberland and Pembroke, and the possibilities of Dartmoor and Bodmin Moor were being explored.

Healthy potato plants, inoculated with the virus of Leaf Roll by aphides

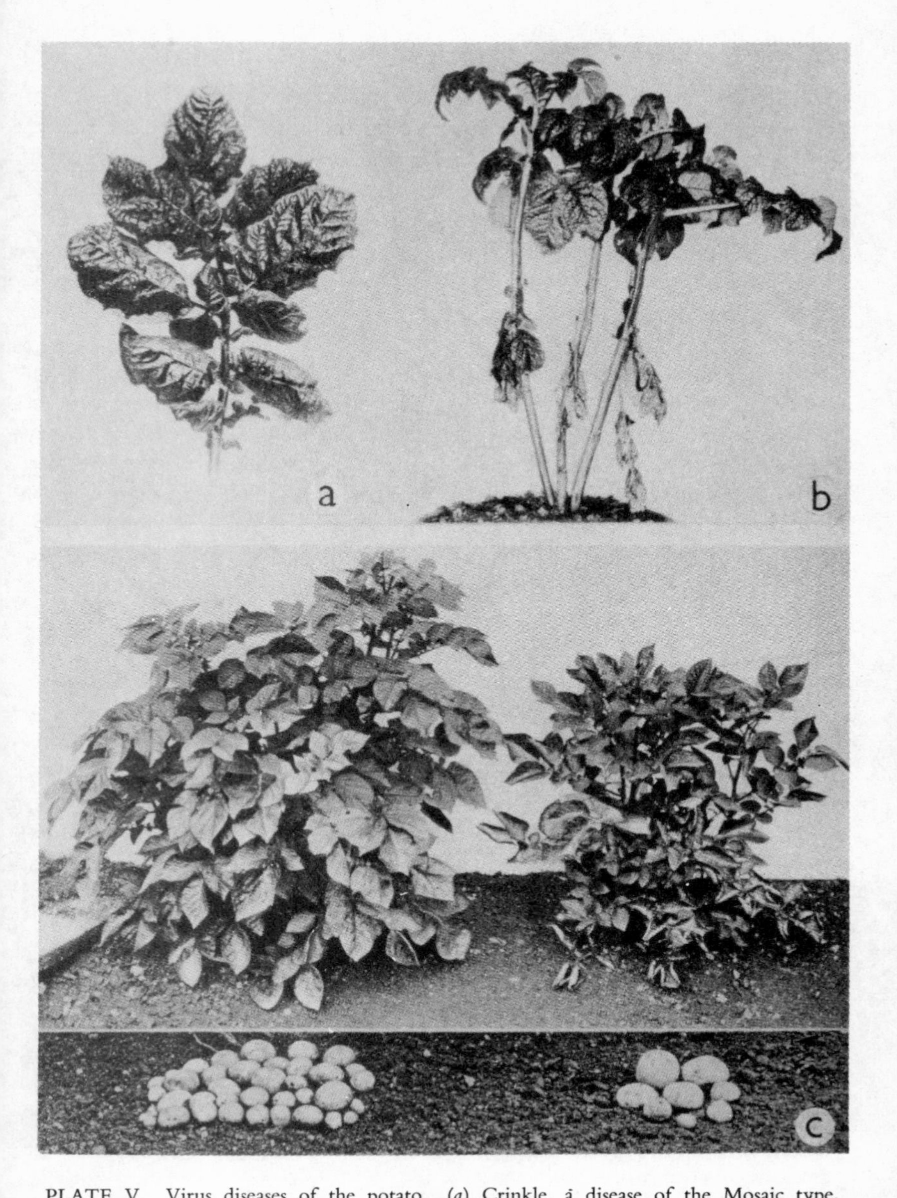

PLATE V. Virus diseases of the potato. (*a*) Crinkle, a disease of the Mosaic type. (*b*) Leaf-drop Streak. (*c*) Leaf Roll, illustrating the reduction in yield. A healthy plant with its produce is shown on the left for comparison.
(*a*) and (*b*) by courtesy of Dr. G. H. Pethybridge. (*c*) From the Ministry of Agriculture and Fisheries' Advisory Leaflet No. 278, by permission of the Controller of H.M. Stationery Office.

which had been feeding on diseased plants, became infected in all their parts, with the single exception of their true seeds, but including their tubers. By planting infected tubers the disease was perpetuated. The plants were stunted, their leaves rolled up in trumpet shapes, and the next crop of tubers was small (Plate V, *c*). No practicable way was known of ridding the potato fields of aphides where the climatic conditions favoured them; all the varieties of potato in cultivation were susceptible to Leaf Roll in greater or lesser degree; the obtaining of resistant or tolerant varieties was yet no more than a possibility; and the one and only, practical and effective method of combating the disease was to plant healthy seed-potatoes — to raise these seed-potatoes from the best available stocks in naturally aphis-free reservations in Scotland or elsewhere, and to make the best use of them. The more of this 'clean seed' there was planted in the aphis-ridden areas, the fewer diseased plants the aphides would have to feed on, and thus by concerted action on a national scale extending over a period of years it would be possible to rid the country's potato crops of Leaf Roll almost entirely. Failing such co-operation, which was perhaps too much to hope for in Great Britain, the method amounted to planting healthy potatoes, letting them run the gauntlet of infection from neighbouring crops for one year or two, but obtaining clean seed from the aphis-free reservations again before the yield had fallen off to any very serious extent. Co-operation or no co-operation, every bag of clean seed planted meant an increased crop for the individual farmer concerned, and a small contribution towards the eradication of the Leaf Roll, *and all the other virus diseases of the potato*, over the whole countryside.

The Leaf Roll was not the only virus disease of the potato causing degeneration or progressive diminution of yield. There were also a number of diseases of the Mosaic type, including Crinkle. There was Curly-Dwarf, Paracrinkle, Leaf-drop Streak . . . In Kenneth M. Smith's *Text-book* of 1937 no less than eighteen virus diseases of the potato were described. The etiology of most of these diseases, other than the Leaf Roll, was extraordinarily complex. They were caused by a collection of viruses, acting severally, or in all sorts of combinations of two or more at a time. They ran into one another. In the early thirties only four principal potato viruses, other than that of the Leaf Roll, had been distinguished, namely viruses A, F, X and Y. And perhaps most people not absolutely obliged to study potato virus diseases in detail, would be content to glance at the situation as it was then, bearing in mind that later it became much worse. There were a number of strains of each of the four viruses, differing in their virulence to each of several hundred different varieties of potato. X viruses, which like that of the Tobacco Mosaic were *not* known to be carried by insects, revealed their presence by causing a simple Mosaic or mottling of the potato leaves, but they were often carried passively, causing no marked symptoms of disease. Nearly all of the potato varieties were said to carry some strain of the virus; most of them without suffering much harm, and some—such as Epicure, Arran Crest, King Edward and Great Scot—were so hypersensitive to virus X that it could not multiply in them and they were field immune. The Y virus alone caused severe mosaic and Leaf-Drop Streak (Plate V, *b*), probably the most serious virus disease of potatoes in Great Britain, after Leaf Roll. X plus Y, together, caused Rugose Mosaic; X plus A caused Crinkle (Plate V, *a*). And so it went on.

When the alphabetical set of potato viruses was broken up and the diseases they caused were considered in their dubious individuality, it was discovered that there were several possible means of combating some of them. The tolerance of King Edward to the E virus, for example, pointed to the fact that a variety that would carry and tolerate a virus without suffering any ill-effect was as good as a resistant variety, so far as that particular virus (alone) was concerned. Many of the potatoes which the farmers had chosen for cultivation in the past owed a part of their practical superiority over others to the fact they were good carriers of some of the viruses. The selection of such tolerant varieties could continue. Then it was found that if some kinds of potato were inoculated with a certain mild strain of virus X, inoculation with a virulent strain of the same virus, ten days later, produced no ill-effect. The vaccination, or preventive inoculation of potatoes could be thought of as a possibility. There was a certain hope that means might some day be found of raising stocks of seed-potatoes ready vaccinated against the deadly virus Y, which, either alone, or completing the work of others, was about the worst of the whole alphabet in the field. But with all due respect for such possibilities, the one simple and practical control measure for all the potato virus diseases, Leaf Roll *and* the rest of them, was, and would always be, to PLANT CLEAN SEED. And here it was clearly up to the Ministry of Agriculture to help by overriding short-sighted commercial opposition and issuing straightforward Health Certificates for seed-potatoes. It took an expert to understand the significance of the certificates issued during the thirties, which, contrary to popular belief, were still generally concerned rather with trueness to name of variety, or with locality of origin, than with freedom from disease. Surely there should be a category of 'Healthy' Certificated seed-potatoes, in which the humblest grower could invest, with full confidence that they had been examined for *all* kinds of tuber-borne diseases (virus, fungus and bacterial) and found as healthy as it is possible in practice for them to be. Such Healthy seed-potatoes would be well worth the little extra they would cost.

There was scarcely a potato in Great Britain that was not carrying one or more crop-diminishing viruses, and, now that the Potato Blight could be fairly well controlled by spraying, they were the principal cause of the miserably low average yield of potatoes over the whole country, which was only six-and-a-half tons per acre. All the indications went to show that if only a determined effort were made to get the potato stocks reasonably free from virus diseases this average yield could be raised by about two tons. It was even easily within the bounds of possibility to make a clean sweep. At the Potato Virus Research Station at Cambridge in 1939, there were aphis-screened stocks of potato plants of the very best economic varieties, which, by every *laboratory* test, were completely free from all virus diseases. They grew with such apparent health and vigour that they scarcely seemed to belong to the same family as the virus-ridden potatoes in general cultivation. The small stock of seed-tubers from these isolated plants could be multiplied, as Robinson Crusoe multiplied his few grains of seed-barley, by planting it away from other potato crops, in some aphis-free region, keeping it there, using none of the produce for ware for some years, and then progressively utilizing the bulk supplies of healthy seed-tubers as they became available, to replace all the virus-ridden or but partially healthy potato stocks in the land. This was the vision of Dr. Redcliffe N. Salaman, who had spent years and gone to infinite trouble to obtain the first few eugenically healthy plants. But he had much to do before his vision would come near to fulfilment; he would first have to get some philanthropist to buy him an island in the Hebrides, or to find some other place where the potatoes could be multiplied apart; then, when he had enough of them, he would need to convince other scientists that his virus-free potatoes remained virus-free, and to convince the farmers that it paid better to grow them than the kind they had already. In all this he would not find everybody ready 'to help him plant his corn'. To start a campaign with the object of *increasing* the yield of potatoes was considered all the wrong way about in the demented thirties; it was hardly consistent with the policy or the operations of the Potato Marketing Board, and at best it could lead only to a further restriction of the potato acreage. It could never be allowed to put more potatoes into Mrs. Brown's pot. The virus-free stocks at Cambridge were tended very carefully none the less, for apart from their great value from comparative scientific experiments, it was felt that the country might be glad of them, quite soon.

Meanwhile, with a little of the day's work done, as far as willing scientific workers were allowed to do it, there remained the evening's intellectual pleasure of discussing the nature of plant viruses themselves. And this could be opened by dropping the casual remark that, all present company excepted, the virologists had a most extraordinary way of defining the *size* of the organisms, or non-living infective particles, with which they were concerned. They said that they would pass through such-and-such filters and that they were below the limit of visibility by white light in the ordinary microscope. This was rather like defining sheep as entities capable of passing through such-and-such gaps in a hedge but invisible through a particular kind of telescope at a distance of two-and-a-half miles on a moonlit night. The definition was not perhaps quite so bad as all that, since invisibility in the microscope did imply a definite upper limit of size, no matter how good the microscope might be. It was approximately half the wave-length of the light employed. With ordinary white light it was about one quarter of a micron. But, that being so, why should the microscope be dragged into the definition at all? Why not say the things were not more than a quarter of a micron, or 250 millimicrons, in diameter, and be done with it?

In 1933, W. J. Elford provided a table of the probable particle sizes of a number of viruses as revealed by his experiments using the method of ultra-filtration. And in 1936 K. M. Smith, adding a few items and omitting others, put the table into an interesting pictorial form, somewhat as shown here (Fig. 58). The table indicated the estimated diameter in millimicrons of several representative plant and animal viruses, in relation to the cross-sectional diameter of a typical bacillus, or 'microbe', at one end of the scale and the estimated diameter of a *molecule* of oxyhaemoglobin at the other. The viruses, or 'molecrobes' as they have hereinbefore been called, ranged in size from those of the Parrot Disease, Psittacosis, 275 millimicrons, down through those of Rabies or Hydrophobia, 125, to those of the Tobacco Mosaic, 30, and below that still, to the virus of the Foot and Mouth Disease of cattle, only 10 millimicrons in diameter and actually smaller than the molecules of haemocyanin. The particles with which all colloid chemists had long been familiar, those of the purple and red gold sols, were at about the middle of the scale. The particles of the purple sol a trifle larger than those of the Potato Virus X; the particles of the red sol a little larger than those of the Tobacco Mosaic. It was apparent that whether the virus particles were living or not, they had the same size range as those occurring in colloidal solutions; so that the workers on the viruses had for their guidance the whole highly developed science of colloidal chemistry, which had been slowly built up since the classical researches of Thomas Graham in 1849. Many of the properties of viruses followed at once from their colloidal condition; they would pass through ordinary filters but were held back by the membranes of parchment or collodion which the colloid chemists used for dialysis; the larger ones revealed their presence by the Tyndall effect, the scattering of a cross-beam of light in a microscope fitted with a dark-ground condenser; their size could be estimated according to Stokes' Law by the rate at which they sedimented out when solutions containing them were spun in a centrifuge; they could be caused to disperse or to flock together by adding known dispersing or flocculating agents to their solutions, and, on the whole, so much was already known about the colloidal state of matter, that the long-continued marvelling at the mere smallness of virus particles was more than a little naive.

Much more perplexing was the question whether or not such colloidal particles could be endowed with life. Although the atomic physicists were now saying that every single atom was a little universe of flying electrons with the will of God at its core, the biologists were inclined to speak as though life could

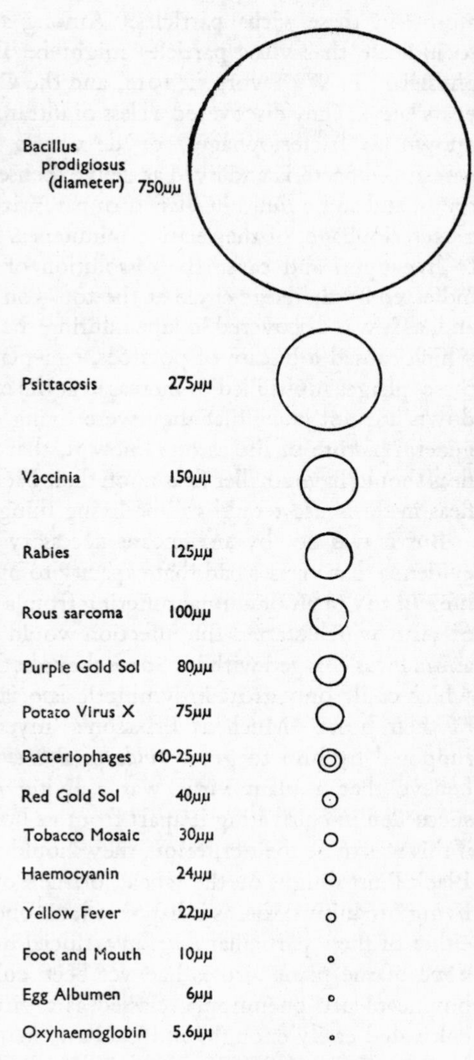

FIG. 58. Estimated particle diameters of some representative viruses compared with those of certain bacteria, colloids, and protein molecules. 1$\mu\mu$, or millimicron, equals one millionth of a millimetre.

After W. J. Elford, 1933 and K. M. Smith, 1936

not be a sub-atomic phenomenon, and there were not so very many atoms in these virus particles. Among the observations which seemed to indicate that virus particles might be alive, were those of the English physician, F. W. Twort, in 1914, and the Canadian, d'Hérelle, two or three years later. They discovered a class of ultramicroscopic organisms or 'things', known as bacteriophages, or devourers of bacteria, which apparently parasitized bacteria and lived at their expense, just as some bacteria parasitized fungi, and some fungi in their turn parasitized the higher plants. Swarms of a bacteriophage, of the relative minuteness indicated in Fig. 58, were found to live upon and cause the dissolution of bacilli of the relative hugeness indicated by the large circle at the top—on the bacilli of dysentery in man, and, as it was discovered in Japan during the thirties, on *Bacillus solanacearum*, which caused a disease of potatoes, egg-plants and tomatoes. The fact that these 'phages multiplied or increased at the expense of the bacteria they broke down did not *prove* that they were living organisms; but it fitted into the general picture of life as one knew it, that right down to the bacteria little fleas should have smaller fleas upon their backs to bite them. And the smallest fleas in this sense would still be living things.

But it was not by any means necessary to go to the bacteriophages for evidence that viruses had that capacity to increase, which was an attribute of life. In any plant or animal suffering from a virus disease the minute quantity of virus which started the infection would increase until the whole plant or animal was charged with it. Some thought that viruses were living organisms which could only grow in symbiotic association with the other living matter of their hosts. Much as Eriksson's 'mycoplasm' of the Rust fungi was supposed by him to grow (*vide* p. 298 *et seq.*). Others said they would believe that a plant virus was a living organism when somebody had succeeded in cultivating it apart from its host, in sterile nutrient media. But if this was to be their criterion, they should still be in doubt as to whether the Black Rust fungus on the wheat, or the Powdery Mildew of the vine, were living organisms, for, as it happened, no one had yet succeeded in cultivating either of these particular *fungi* in artificial media. Up to 1939 it seemed that none of the plant viruses had yet been cultivated; but the causal agent of bovine pleuro-pneumonia, classed as a virus on the basis of size, could be cultivated easily enough, and Laidlaw, in 1936, found what appeared to be non-parasitic viruses growing vigorously in London sewage. But even if some plant virus *was* found to increase on some non-living matter in a Petri dish, that would still not *prove* that it was a living organism. It might still be some queer kind of catalytic agent initiating progressive chemical change in a substance that was its own precursor. The chemists might yet have to consider chemical phenomena closely parallel with those of crystallization in physics, where a minute crystal of a salt, introduced as 'seed' into a supersaturated solution of the same salt, would promote the growth of a large crop of crystals of the same kind as itself.

The vitalists among those working on plant virus diseases said: here is a tobacco plant, and the particulate virus of Tobacco Mosaic multiplies in it pretty nearly as fast as the bacillus of Anthrax multiplies in a guinea-pig; for tobacco plants it's as contagious as the plague; it must be a living germ, as other germs, for all that it is so minute. We had all this out in the time of Pasteur. The workers of the other persuasion, however, said: No! It isn't any kind of a living germ, it's an enzyme. Then, retorted the vitalists, you'd better extract some of your hypothecated enzyme out of the plant sap, crystallize it, purify it, make sure it's dead, and then demonstrate that it causes the disease.

And this, surprisingly enough, was exactly what the chemists did. They availed themselves of the dodge, long known to colloid chemists, of 'salting out' organic colloids with concentrated ammonium sulphate solution. A method was first worked out for the extraction of certain of the proteins found in living substance, and, as it was hoped, of isolating and purifying them. W. M. Stanley, of the Rockefeller Institute for Medical Research, made use of these methods, and in 1935 he was able to report the successful isolation from diseased Turkish tobacco plants of a crystalline protein possessing the properties of the Tobacco Mosaic virus. The protein would induce the Mosaic when injected into healthy tobacco plants in doses amounting to about one thousandth-millionth part of a gram. Earlier extractions of crystalline substances alleged to be the toxic principle of the Tobacco Mosaic had been criticized by J. Caldwell at Rothamsted and others, on the ground that they might be contaminated still with an ultramicroscopic living virus, and that this and not the crystalline material, might render the preparations infective. Stanley's extracts, however, were purified by no less than ten successive 'recrystallizations' and it was hard to believe that they could still contain any living thing – unless the 'crystals' themselves were alive. Thus the Tobacco Mosaic virus, exemplar of all plant viruses, appeared to be an autocatalytic protein, non-living, but requiring the presence of living cells for its increase. The theory then being that there were proteins forming part of the normal substance of healthy tobacco plants which were the precursors of the virus, and that a little of this, introduced into the plant, initiated some process whereby the normal protein was progressively transformed into virus and the whole plant became diseased.

Stanley's discovery – which constituted another signal event in the history of plant pathology – was immediately seized upon and very eagerly followed up by a group of English workers, F. C. Bawden at Rothamsted, N. W. Pirie and J. D. Bernal at Cambridge, amongst others. They turned all the instruments of modern scientific investigation: X-rays, polarized light, fine chemical analysis, on to Stanley's preparations, and found that they were perfectly all right, except that the crystals weren't true crystals, and that the 'pure' virus wasn't pure. The stuff was, however, an extremely concentrated preparation of something that caused the disease, and the active material in it was, so to speak, crystalline in one plane; its particles, which were not spherical but rod-shaped, were all oriented the same way in solution. One pretty experiment of Bawden's was to put a goldfish into a solution of Tobacco Mosaic virus, and then observe the spectacle by polarized light. The wake of the fish appeared luminous, as the agitation of the water disturbed the shoal-like layering of the virus particles, allowing the light to pass through. Elsewhere the scene was dark. Stanley's views about the nature of the virus extracts had to be modified, but his main contention held. Extracts of other plant viruses were made, Potato Virus X and Tomato Bushy Stunt, and for all that it was possible to prove to the contrary, the active principles in them were non-living proteins of one kind or another.

As these fibroid or liquid-crystalline proteins were certainly 'nitrogenous substances', evidently delicately constituted and 'unstable', the latest theory about the causation of the Tobacco Mosaic and other virus diseases was practically identical with that put forward by the chemists of Liebig's school, in 1845, to account for the supposed Disease of the potatoes preceding the growth upon them of the Blight fungus. It was then said that unstable azotic (or 'nitrogenous') substances, derived from the gluten and albumen of the plant, were carried round it as a 'ferment', causing a struggle between the plant's vital force and the forces of chemical fermentation. If 'catalysis' was read for 'chemical fermentation', in the old sense of that term, before Pasteur – where was the difference? It was chiefly in the circumstance that the chemists in 1939 now had some of the pathogenic chemical ferments, very highly concentrated, in bottles.

If the old theory of the chemical origin of plant diseases was revived in the nineteen-thirties, in connection with plant viruses, so also was the ancient and somewhat tattered theory of heterogenesis. The determinants of plant growth, the small fairies that made a King Edward potato a King Edward potato, or a Cox's Orange Pippin a Cox's Orange Pippin, were not always visualized, as they have been herein, as sitting dangling their legs, in allotted places along the chromosomes. Usually, in the more profound works on genetics, they were spoken of as 'specialized' groups of molecules, forming part of the material substance of the chromosomes, and arranged within them in chains. Presumably they were living, as they were parts of the most vital living substance in the cell, and they were called 'genes'. One of the current hypotheses about plant viruses was that they were nothing other than individual genes, broken loose from the chromosomes and drifting about at large in the plant sap. The following out of this hypothesis led to two different logical results, according to whether you believed the viruses to be living organisms or you did not. If you did not, then the stuffs which Stanley and others had extracted were bottled and semi-crystallized genes. If you did believe that the viruses were living organisms, capable of growth and increase, then you had one of the prettiest examples of heterogenesis on record.

The American worker, F. O. Holmes, who was one of the vitalists, proposed in 1939 that the Linnean, or binomial, nomenclature should be extended to the viruses, and with the help of a lexicon he sketched out the way it might go. The Potato Virus X, for example, should be called *Marmor dubium*, of the family Marmoraceae, of the class Spermatophytophagi, of the division Phytophagi, of the natural kingdom of the Vira. So far so good – and those who hastened to say that 'Vira' was illiterate were on very dangerous ground – but if the X virus of potatoes was in reality broken away from the chromosomes of that plant, then *Marmor dubium* was a living species which had its origin in fragments of vital matter which had once been a part of *Solanum tuberosum*. As the X virus certainly had the power of perpetuating itself when injected into a potato plant, science in its forward march had now come full circle, and was back again with Robert Hooke in 1667, proclaiming:

'So, though the seminal principles from which this minute plant on rose leaves (virus in potatoes) did spring, were, before the corruption caused by the Mill-dew (environmental conditions or the virus itself), a component part of the leaf on which it grew, and did serve as a coagent in the production of it, yet might it be so consummate, as to produce a seed (more virus) which might have the power of perpetuating the same species.'

If the attempt to classify the plant viruses into species and families involved the taxonomists in profound philosophic difficulties, so also did the attempts to classify the things in any other way. The viruses could be distinguished from one another, to some extent, by the 'symptom pictures' of the diseases they caused. The term Mosaic, calling up a vision of mottled leaves, was descriptive of a symptom picture. There were viruses causing leaf-rolling, yellowing, ring-spotting, streaking, stunting, crinkling, witches-brooming, and sundry other conspicuous and nameable disorders of plants. But there were many additional, and often more reliable, criteria by which different viruses could be distinguished. Some were carried by insects, others not; some were merely transferred by insects, others seemed to undergo some necessary kind of incubation in their insides. Some viruses were killed, or rendered innocuous, at a very slightly elevated temperature, others were not destroyed at 90 degrees Centigrade. They differed in their 'thermal death-points'. Kunkel, in America, adapting Jensen's heat-treatment against a virus disease, actually cured young peach trees of the Peach Yellows by growing them for some time in a room at 35 degrees Centigrade. Some viruses produced X bodies, or crystalline inclusions, in the cells of the affected plants; and the confusion caused by these X bodies until Henderson Smith and his team threw a little cold light on them, was a story in itself. Then there were all the marvels of the 'serological technique'. A virus from a potato or a tobacco plant was injected into a living rabbit. The rabbit retaliated by producing in its blood stream substances which would precipitate the particular virus injected, and no other. Some of the rabbit's blood was therefore drawn off, the clear serum was separated from the blood clot, and used as a laboratory reagent for testing viruses in test tubes. If the virus added to the serum was the same as that previously injected into the rabbit, it would be precipitated, if it was a different virus it would not be. Then, again, some viruses were more virulent than others; sometimes, as F. O. Holmes discovered, the strength of a virus could be estimated by counting the number of spots produced when a particular dose of it was injected in a particular way into a particular sort of tobacco plant. The accumulation of unrelated facts about the properties of viruses was stupendous, and for the time being most virologists preferred to give their viruses alphabetical appelations or to refer to them as so-and-so's Potato (or Solanum) Virus No. 1, 2, 3 . . . 16, 17, 18, etc. This did not spoil the pitch for workers of a later generation who would no doubt name the viruses properly when the true bases of their science had been found, but there were some who said it was a great present nuisance, and merely a repetition of the mistake that had been made in naming vitamins. No one except the specialist could ever for the life of him remember the differences between vitamins A, B, B_1, C, D, and the rest. They just meant something to do with cod-liver oil, bran, tomato juice, white rats, and casuistry over food-values. It was difficult to get on any sort of familiar terms with a numeral or a letter of the alphabet.

One thing at least was in favour of the binomial plan for naming viruses – the stimulus it would give to collectors. Although there were more or less serious virus diseases of nearly every agricultural plant, and gardens and greenhouses were veritable virus museums, no one had yet really begun to collect the 'vira' of wild plants and the herbs of the field. Scientific folk were great magpies; they would collect anything, even bibliographical references, if they could lay their hands on nothing better. The 'Spermatophytophagi' would certainly be collected. If they could only be given such wonderful botanical names – at least until the chemists could find *their* names for them – it would not be long before new companies of enthusiasts would be going out into the country at week-ends and holidays on plant virus forays – all for no other reward than to write *Marmor viridens* (Bloggs) Fanny, or some such thing, on another crowded page of the book of nature.

CHAPTER XXXI

TOWARDS IMMUNITY

So much spraying and dusting of the crops with chemical mixtures! So much particularized research into the ways of destructive insects and parasitic fungi and nameless viruses! So much elaborate crossing and back-crossing between strains of agricultural plants in attempts to breed varieties that might escape some, but never all, of the parasites that lie in wait for them! Infinite patience for every small achievement; control measures that were often costly, or that demanded closely-knit collaboration between farmers, research workers and governments to make them effective! Was there no simpler and more direct way of raising healthy crops? No general safeguard or panacea against all the murraines to which they were heir?

In every generation since the Potato Blight first swept across Europe, and at all times before that, wherever the Rust shrivelled the wheat, or pestilence followed the eating of ergoted rye, there were men of platonic or wishful mind who saw in the last-to-be-advocated reform in the practice of agriculture, a hope of lifting Disease from the crops as by the waving of a wand. There were always some ready to dream of a return to Eden, and despite all critical judgment and experience, fond to perceive in the plants of the farm a provision of inherent perfection for the nourishment of man, ailing only in consequence of some human sinfulness or folly.

In the eighteenth century it was 'inclosure', 'horse-hoeing husbandry' and the cultivation of turnips for feeding the stock and cleaning the land: the great reform of 'rotation'. Then it was 'drainage'. In 1846, there were many who asserted that there would be but little trouble with the Potato Blight if only the land were properly drained in accordance with their proposals. Then it was the use of mineral fertilizers: in turn imported nitrates, superphosphates from bones and basic slag, then sulphate of ammonia, and potash salts. John Lawes, improving upon the ideas of the great Justus von Liebig, was of the opinion that the Yellow Rust of the wheat in East Anglia, and indeed all plant diseases, would recede before the use as recommended of his nitrogen (N), phosphorus (P) and potash (K). The universal formula for health, as of abundance, bore the cryptic letters 'N.P.K.'. In 1939, in some quarters, 'accessory mineral constituents' were the white hope, as were vitamins in human nutrition: the plants, for health, needed traces in the soil of practically every element, and indeed it was found that the making good of a *boron*-deficiency would prevent a common disease of swedes, and the application of *copper* to the soil, in Germany and Denmark, was the recognized cure for the reclamation-disease of oats. In 1939, in yet another quarter, 'humus' was the magic word and all synthetic fertilizers were anathema. If only town-refuse and sewage, along with all vegetable wastes and animal excrements of the farm, were appropriately pre-rotted and returned to increase the amount of humus in the soil, then, with good cultivation, the crops would have strength to resist insects and fungi, and radiant health would come not only to them, but to the animals and the communities nourished on their produce.

Sir Albert Howard was one of the most redoubtable champions of 'humus'. He had worked as a mycologist at Wye College in its early days, and when out in India he had perfected a process for manufacturing humus, or pre-rotted manure, by stacking vegetable rubbish layered with dung in well-aerated compost heaps. From the vegetable wastes and the dung and urine of the oxen on three hundred acres of land belonging to the Institute of Plant Industry at Indore, he obtained some thousand cart-loads of valuable manure to put back on the land each year, and in consequence it stood out like a green oasis in a locality where vegetable refuse was generally burnt and all except its ash was wasted. Howard conserved the soil humus but used no insecticides or fungicides either at Pusa or at Indore; he burnt no infested or diseased vegetable refuse but put it back on the compost heaps with the rest. He then tried out what happened when the insects and the fungi were left entirely alone and unchecked. In twenty years he found that varieties of agricultural plants *which suited the local conditions* remained, in fact, practically free from diseases.

Later in his life, when the green fields at Indore shone for him in the sweet provinces of reminiscence, Howard sought to convince a sceptical world that the labours of so many generations of workers to find means of *protecting* plants from the insects and the fungi were misconceived. The true role of the insects and the fungi, he said, was that of censors, provided to point out to erring humanity those crops which were being wrongly cultivated or improperly nourished. Only those insects and fungi and bacteria and viruses which happened to be benign could find sustenance on properly nourished plants with plenty of humus at their roots. No diseased wastes should be destroyed, no barberry bushes or other wild host plants should be eradicated, no attempts should be made to keep out foreign pests and parasites, artificial fertilizers if they had to be used at all should be added only in small quantities to the compost heaps to assist in the making of humus, and all insecticides and fungicides should be relegated to the museum. Green-flies on roses could be made to disappear merely by aerating the soil – an indication that the magical humus would even dispel the principal carriers of plant virus diseases. And cattle, well-fed on the produce of land rich in humus, would enjoy immunity even to such highly contagious plagues as the Rinderpest and the Foot and Mouth Disease.

'Sanguine', said Sir Daniel Hall to this last. 'Reminiscent of notions that a diet of nuts or shedding of clothes will dispel human ills', said Dr. Hubert Martin, to that part of the theory which concerned plant diseases, 'and like those crankish beliefs it contains enough truth to convert the credulous'. Sir Albert was trailing his coat, and he must have been gratified when it was so firmly trodden upon by his peers. 'We have been using Sir Albert's process, more or less, for a very long time', went on Sir Daniel. 'Before the introduction of artificial fertilizers the skilful use of farmyard manure and legumes brought the level of productiveness of our English soil up to twenty bushels of wheat per acre – the use of artificial fertilizers then raised it to thirty bushels.' But to this, at least, Sir Albert had his devastating return ready. 'In their one-sided chase after quantity', he said, 'the experiment station workers are not only misleading practice, but are doing the greatest possible disservice to the true cause of agricultural research. They have failed to insist on the effective return to the soil of the waste products contributed by the plant, the animal, and the community . . . There is no need to trouble so much about yield. It is surely unnecessary to lumber up still further the world's congested markets with produce that none can buy.'

There was much in Sir Albert Howard's thesis that was indisputably sane. In many parts of the world vast tracts of agricultural land had been reduced to desert through loss of humus and surface cover. Where there had once been wheat or cotton now there was bare and gullied waste, and the sandstorms drove over forsaken homesteads. For several of the world's Departments of Agriculture, and especially that of the United States, how best to check and repair the havoc of soil-erosion, was one of the most acute problems of the time. And apart from soil-erosion the burning of town-refuse, and the outpouring of sewage into the seas from centres of urban population, was constantly and wantonly draining away the substance from the land. It was estimated that the habitation-wastes, per head of the population per annum, amounted to some 200 lb. of organic matter, containing not only the stuff of invaluable humus, but 15 lb. of combined nitrogen, 4 lb. of potash, and over 5 lb. of phosphoric acid. The continuance of such waste, multiplied by the million-fold over the earth, was not only present bad-management, it was emptying the cupboards for posterity.

And then again, after the Great Slump, at the beginning of the nineteen-thirties, when the majority of people went insufficiently nourished, poorly clad and housed, shabbily entertained, and either over-worked or unemployed, there was a cry of 'Overproduction!' The failure of Governments to govern those autonomous minorities which controlled the economic and financial affairs of the nations, and the subsequent failure to solve the problems of distribution, left the farmers ruined by fictitious 'gluts' of produce of which communities were in need. It was even announced by many of the tamed or paid mouthpieces of the powerful that the problems of agricultural production had been solved, and that now it was necessary to go into reverse. In the United States the plant pathologists were somewhat bitterly reflecting that there might still be a job for them – in pointing out the best land on which *not* to grow crops. In Great Britain there were the several marketing boards, operating to restrict production and to maintain prices, in part for the producers, but more particularly for the distributors, under thin cover of some real endeavour to improve grades and quality. Every year there was news of foodstuffs being left to rot, or being dumped in the sea, or being burnt for fuel. The forcing of crops for high yields, the leaving behind in the course of scientific plant breeding of too many of the qualities making for disease-resistance among plants in the wild state, the development of intensive as opposed to conservative systems of cultivation, all these things favoured the advance of the fungi. High yields could be obtained only by the continued expenditure of much thought, effort and money in keeping down plant diseases, which were very often factors limiting the possible increase. If to reduce production was the objective then a case could even be made out for reverting to the level of production before artificial fertilizers or 'vegetable pathology' were ever heard of, and letting the insects and the fungi take the somewhat smaller tithe that they most certainly had taken in those days. It would necessitate the employment of more labour on the land, and in all countries it would be a better way of finding unnecessary work for idle hands to do than starting vast re-armament campaigns.

But the idea that the insects and the fungi would be dispelled from the crops if the farmers were content, or could afford, to go back to the lower yields and inferior quality of produce, by humus conservation and good cultivation alone, was hardly supported by the historical evidence. Nor did even Sir Albert Howard really make any such claim. 'Naturally', he said, 'you must grow plants which suit the local conditions. The censors, the insects and the fungi, will show you which those are. Fortunately the protection of any area from imported pests is impossible in the long run, so there will always be plenty of censors. Do not attempt to shut them out, for they are our best teachers: without them I should never have invented the Indore process.'

The postulated restriction of cultivation to those plants which were not only suited to the local conditions, but were also able to survive the attentions of all and sundry pests and parasites that might at any time be imported from other parts of the world, was the nigger in the woodpile, the snag, the hitch in the heresy. In 1920, a Downy Mildew, somewhat similar to the Potato Blight fungus, which was first recorded on wild and cultivated hops in Japan was observed in the experimental hop-garden at Wye College in Kent. Shortly afterwards the same or another strain of the fungus was also found on wild hops in the hedges in various parts of England. In ten years the disease had spread throughout the English hop-growing districts, it attacked the Bramlings, the Mathans, even the Fuggles, and where it was left unchecked it was capable of causing the total loss of the crop in a bad year. The produce from an acre of hops fetched a good deal of money, the cultivation was expensive, and much care and attention was lavished upon it. The bines and the cones were nevertheless marked down in a most spectacular manner by this new censor, the Downy Mildew first found in Japan. Was it to be concluded that the Bramlings and the Mathans and the Fuggles, varieties which had been grown in Kent for so long, were not suited to the local conditions? Or that the hop plant itself was unsuited to English soil, and that beer should be flavoured with wormwood instead? Were the hop growers to forsake their traditional cultivation, already sadly whittled down through the high beer duties and the decline in popularity of beer, just because of this foreign cryptogamic invader? The suggestion that the growers should try getting more humus into the soil, where humus was deficient, was a sensible one. But in doing that, would they be justified for one moment in ignoring the advice of Professor Salmon, one of the most experienced economic mycologists in the country, who taught them to remove and burn the first diseased shoots from which the spores of the fungus blew about, and to spray in good time with Bordeaux mixture? By these means, for all that they were expensive and troublesome, the hops were saved.

And then the Colorado beetle, the most dreaded insect pest of the potato. Had it not, in fact, been kept out of Europe for over forty years after the great scare of 1875? It was discovered in several places near Bordeaux in 1922; it entered France exactly where it had been so long expected, probably at some time during or just after the war. If human vigilance had not then been relaxed, it might have been kept out still. As it was, by 1922 the pest had already established itself over a considerable region, and its eradication was hopeless. It advanced inexorably through province after province of France, and northwards into Belgium and Germany. The old hope that it could not adapt itself to the climatic conditions of these latitudes was belied. It became necessary to spray the potatoes on the Continent not only with copper mixtures against the Blight, but with lead arsenate to destroy the all-devouring beetle. In Jersey they said 'If this grub grows our grub goes'. In England there was an outbreak near Tilbury in 1933; fortunately it was suppressed by the prompt action of the Ministry of Agriculture, and the potato crops of Great Britain were still free of the beetle in 1939. But, with the pest ravaging the potatoes just across the Channel, there was a constant and ever-threatening danger of invasion. Was this particular 'censor' to be welcomed? Would it teach the British potato growers anything that the growers of France and America did not already know, only too well? Should the farmer or the gardener, finding any yellow beetles or reddish grubs on potato plants looking at all like those here shown in Fig. 42, p. 219, be in doubt what to do? He should put them alive with a bit of potato leaf into a tin with a tight-fitting lid and *without* holes in it, and post them at once to the Ministry of Agriculture, stating where the insects were found and his name and address. He should then stand by, and watch what happened, as one who had pulled a fire alarm near a gunpowder dump.

And then again there were the homely snapdragons, old-fashioned flowers, hardy enough in England. They were attacked by a Rust fungus from North America in 1933. For two years this Rust spread like the plague among the snapdragons in private and municipal gardens. It threatened to wipe the snapdragon off the list of showy bedding plants. Over in America there were varieties of snapdragon resistant to the Rust, but of poor colour. Were these dull kinds to be substituted for all the gay and brave ones that happened to be susceptible to the disease? Or were gardeners to say, oh, never mind, and plant more Dahlias or Geraniums instead? The new censor said 'delete the Antirrhinum'. But if there was one thing that all mentally-healthy human beings hated more than anything else it was censorship. That it should be necessary to engage in incessant warfare with the insects and the fungi was bad enough, but that they should be accepted as the proper censors of human whim or endeavour was an intolerable proposition. If *Puccinia Antirrhini* made the growing of snapdragons more difficult, then there would be plenty of people all the more keen to grow them. And they would not be content with the misshapen flower heads and the drab magenta colour of the first resistant varieties. They would have snapdragons shapely and of every satin colour in the colour book – Rust or no Rust. If getting more humus into the flower-beds would help, then, again, it was thanks for the suggestion. If it meant spraying the plants with sulphur or copper fungicides every ten days throughout the summer, then so be it. The only objection to that was that it was troublesome, not that it was in any sense philosophically or morally wrong. Another measure was to dig up and burn *all* snapdragon plants in November, to make sure that they did not carry the Rust over to another year. A little humus would be lost by the burning, but until somebody could prove conclusively that the spores of the fungus were killed in the compost heap, it would be folly to take the risk of perpetuating the Rust for the sake of a few shovelfuls of mould. The Rust, as a censor, did *not* indicate what varieties of snapdragon should be grown, for the simple reason that the desired varieties were not in existence. It was necessary to make them – to filch the genes of Rust-resistance from the dowdy varieties and build them into the gay ones. This was being done, and at the Royal Horticultural Society's gardens at Wisley in 1939, D. E. Green had some good pink and terra-cotta resistant varieties already, and was on the track of others.

Hops and snapdragons were but picking; if major examples were required of continued and successful cultivations in flat defiance of the censors, they were to be found in the history of the vines in France and of the potatoes in the British Isles. Time and time again the censors had pointed out that for all it could be so prolific the potato was only imperfectly adapted to the soil and climatic conditions of Britain. First the Curl and the Scabs and several tuber-rots, then the devastating Blight, and all the time the notorious 'degeneration', found at last to be due to accumulation of numerous viruses, not only that of the Curl; the Wart Disease, the many bacterial and minor fungus diseases – they all indicated something that everybody knew: the potato was a foreign plant, modified by centuries of selection and cultivation, that could be kept reasonably healthy and made to go on yielding heavy crops of tubers, out of all proportion to those of the plant in its wild state, only by the constant exercise of human ingenuity. The domesticated potato was an easy prey for many parasites, but it provided one of the most valuable foodcrops none the less, and even after the tragedy in Ireland during the forties the pessimists had been few who suggested that its cultivation should be abandoned. Progress in a century of endeavour to combat the diseases of the potato had been slow, by 1939 there were still only partial victories, but the story had never been one of retreat.

The censorship of the fungi was not acceptable to man. His intention was to defeat them, and to grow the crops he needed, in districts of *his* choice, in despite of them. But the fungi were formidable enemies, and they were not to be beaten with one hand tied. As the severity of their attack in any locality depended so largely upon the weather they could not be vanquished by attention to the soil alone. That was but a dream. To cheat them or hold them in check, it was necessary to employ with reasoned strategy every means that human wit or science could devise. It was merely ludicrous to suggest that in such inter-special warfare, where the issue was one of survival, man should disarm himself for a sentiment and refrain from using his chemical weapons where they happened to be effective. The protection of plants with a little sulphur or copper or mercury, cunningly employed, often made it possible to raise healthy crops, under adverse conditions, on soils and in localities to which they were not ideally adapted, and from disease-susceptible plants when resistant varieties bearing produce of equal quality were not available.

All agriculture was artificial. There was nothing more artificial in the world than a field of cultivated potatoes. For what was agriculture, after all, but an attempt to strip areas of the earth's surface of its wild mixed flora and fauna, and to reserve such areas exclusively for the growth of plant prodigies, most of them brought from foreign lands, and all of them chosen for abnormalities of special utility to man? This agriculture, this exclusive tending of vegetable freaks and monsters, was necessary if the human species was to survive. But as it was necessary, so there was nowhere at which it was philosophically possible to draw a line, and reasonably say that up to such and such a level in its historical development agriculture was 'natural' and right, while all beyond became 'unnatural' and wrong. No one could say, for example, that it was natural and right and proper to put lime on sour land, as their great-great-grandfathers had done, but wrong to stimulate the growth of plants with synthetic sulphate of ammonia. Both lime and sulphate of ammonia were products of the chemical industry; both were ultimately derived from the waters and rocks of the earth and the constituents of the atmosphere. The best that man could do at any time to defend the health of the hypertrophic agricultural plants that in his cunning he had sought out or made, was to apply to the work of rearing them the *whole* of his experience and the whole of his science. And of this the greatest of individual contributions formed but a small part, and the last proposal would be honoured beyond common fortune if in the works of to-morrow it received mention at all beside others of yesterday.

The day when chemical fungicides and insecticides would be relegated to the museum lay very far ahead, but if there was one line of attack which promised, in time, to outdistance all others, and to have an almost universal application against nearly all plant diseases, it was that of breeding disease-resistant varieties. There were some valid reasons for hope that in time to come so many good disease-resistant kinds of agricultural plants might be in cultivation that the old measure of protecting seeds or foliage with chemical therapeutants might appear to have been a mere temporary expedient, *in the sweep of the centuries*. Taking a somewhat optimistic view of the situation, and including such plants as the early-maturing and therefore partially Rust-escaping Marquis wheat among resistant-varieties, G. H. Coons of the Bureau of Plant Industry estimated that already in 1937 over one-quarter of the total farm acreage of the United States was under disease-resistant agricultural plants of one sort or another. The resulting increase in the real wealth of the nation could be put at about sixty million dollars per annum.

In some instances the success of the resistant varieties already found, selected or bred, was spectacular. In Louisiana, for example, the falling-off in yield and repeated crop-failures of the sugar-cane, between 1923 and 1927, due to sundry virus and fungus diseases, led to the virtual bankruptcy of the historic sugar-industry in that State. In 1924 all the old 'noble' varieties of cane began to be replaced with new and disease-resistant ones. By 1928 the substitution was almost complete and where there had been 6.8 tons of cane per acre in 1926, there were 18.8 tons in 1929. Of course, the greatly increased yields nearly ruined the industry again, after the world economic collapse. The vascular economic system in the organism of society was sodden with profit-viruses and rotten from the roots up – but that was another matter. The *plant* pathologists were more concerned with the fact that the sugar-cane was a plant propagated by cuttings, as the potato was propagated by tubers. Such plants accumulated virus diseases, as they so rarely had the chance of growing away clean from their uncontaminated, true seeds. The success of resistant or virus-tolerant sugar-canes indicated another possible future victory for resistant-varieties – over the degenerative diseases of the potato.

There were great hopes for resistant-varieties in all the agricultural industries of the world, but it would be of the greatest disservice to the true cause of agricultural science to look ahead too fast, to despise good bones for shadows, and to gloss the difficulties that the plant breeders had yet to overcome little by little and one by one. 'At present', said Coons, 'we are dealing with host plants that we know imperfectly, exposing them to pathogens that we also know very imperfectly, expecting to move about genes, which we postulate, and that produce, in some unknown way, effects on some unknown characteristic of protoplasm that imparts disease-resistance.'

If ever success in obtaining disease-resistant varieties should render all other measures virtually obsolete, no one would have the 'censors' to thank for pointing out the way. It would not have come about by growing 'plants that suited the local conditions', but by finding and making the plants first and then trying them, scientifically, under the local conditions—which was a very different matter. To 'make' the plants, and to understand what they were doing, many indefatigable workers would have to delve yet deeper into the mysteries of heredity, the chemical and physical nature of living protoplasm, and the life-histories of hosts and parasites, right down now to the tracing of the dividing and re-uniting nuclei, with their groups of chromosomes, not only from spore to spore but from cell to cell. To see what the study of life-histories of the fungi, in terms of cytology, really meant, in 1939, one could not perhaps do better than to read some of the works by Dame Helen Gwynne-Vaughan or Bessey's *Text-Book of Mycology*, to ease the way, and then to tackle the monumental *Vergleichende Morphologie der Pilze*, by Gäumann, of which there was an English translation by Dodge. Such studies were not to be avoided: there was no short cut. While in the laboratories for fundamental research the 'censors' taught the workers little until they were studied one by one in the most exhaustive detail, in practical plant-breeding it was not so much the many ailing plants that helped, as those rare few which exhibited a natural tolerance or resistance to specific diseases. Often these were not good economic plants: dwarf or trailing potatoes, with small misshapen tubers, little more than weeds, or coarse and tufted semi-wild wheats, like the Einkorn. But from them disease-resistant varieties could sometimes be bred; their value to the plant-breeders was beyond price, and they had to be sought out from the ends of the earth. Man could no more make a 'gene' than he could say what it might be; he could only seek with sharp eyes among the wild and cultivated flora of the world for plants with inheritable qualities that he wanted in his parent stocks. Thus *exploration*, in the noblest and oldest sense of that word, the traversing of far mountains and little-trodden plains, remained an indispensable part of plant pathology.

And here this long book, for all its shortcomings, shall be brought to an end, as at September 3rd, 1939, where it began in 1845, with some more particular reference to the Potato Blight. The idea that Blight-proof potatoes for cultivation might be obtained by crossing domestic varieties with wild potato plants was as old as the very name 'Blight' itself. John Lindley tried a dwarf Mexican potato, which he called *Solanum demissum*, for Blight-resistance in the Chiswick Gardens in 1847. It was then as severely attacked as all the rest, but in Germany, about the same time, wild potatoes sent home from Mexico by the same explorer were *crossed* with domestic sorts, and the hybrids were acclaimed as very promising, though later no more was heard of them. Darwin was interested in the possibility of raising Blight-proof potatoes from crosses with South American species, and after the severe Blight epidemic of 1879, many trials were made by Messrs. Sutton & Sons, with Darwin's *Solanum Maglia*, as found on the Chonos peninsula, and another of the few South American species then known, *Solanum Commersonii*. The trials were continued for twenty years, with little success in the end. But it could not be said that all the early attempts resulted in nothing but failure. The prolific, wildish Maggie Murphies, better known as the variety Evergreen, which were cultivated to some extent in the United States, exhibited a very definite resistance to the Blight, and it seemed that it had first been raised by one of the pioneering American potato-breeders, Goodrich, some time in the early fifties, as a result of deliberate attempts to obtain Blight-proof potatoes at that time by crossing domestic varieties with wild sorts from Mexico. After 1918, attempts to defeat the Blight by the method of plant-breeding, which had by then become more scientific, were taken up again, notably by Professor Donald Reddick at Cornell University, in the United States, by K. O. Müller and R. Schick in Germany, and by Dr. R. N. Salaman at Cambridge. Requests began to be sent about the world for wild or cultivated potatoes, no matter how unprepossessing they might be in themselves, which had the rare quality of Blight-resistance, and might serve as donors of that quality in Mendelian and other breeding experiments.

At first the finds were not numerous: there was the dwarf *Solanum demissum* from Mexico, apparently different from the one to which Lindley gave the name, almost totally immune from the Blight, but bearing its diminutive crop of tubers only when the period during which it was exposed to Blight was reduced to that in its native clime – when it was artificially blacked-out for some fifteen hours out of the twenty-four. It was not only dwarf and difficult to grow, but it had long stolons which reached away for six feet or more under the ground, so that one had to excavate half the garden to find the crop from a single plant. Then there was a weird, scaly-tubered, unappetizing variety, called Ekishirazu, found by Oti in Japan in 1918, almost immune; and Steinthaler and Halbfrüh, found in the Vosges in 1924, highly resistant. With this scanty and unpromising collection the new breeding experiments began. The phenomena of 'photoperiodism', the effects of the length of day upon plant growth, very important in connection with all work on potatoes from the equatorial regions, was the subject of some classical studies by Allard in the States.

Then, in 1925, Soviet Russia took a hand. During the interval between the first war-to-end-war and the next, when the great social test of communism was regarded hopefully by most of the self-styled intelligentzia, many extravagant things were said about Soviet Russia. Her science and her co-operative applications of science were often extolled to the skies, as though there had never been any such thing as the Imperial Academy of Sciences in St. Petersburg in the time of the Czars. But perhaps it was now indeed Russia's turn to import, to forward, and to exploit with a new enthusiasm all the sciences of western Europe, as the United States had done during the seventies and eighties of the previous century. The U.S.A. had now become primarily an industrial country; all the free land had gone, and, as had long been foretold, with it had gone the real basis of that nation's short-lived but abundant prosperity. In Russia, agriculture was expanding and not contracting; the Soviet workers were visibly building a new, and as they still dared to hope, a better world to live in. In agricultural research Russia entered the lead. But money for the purchase of scientific apparatus at first was short; well-equipped laboratories were few, and the Russian botanists in particular turned to those fields of research which demanded great enterprise and patience, but not too much apparatus – notably they turned to exploration and to plant-breeding.

Earl Cathcart, President of the Royal Agricultural Society of England, had called, in 1884, for an expedition to study the potato in its South American home. The suggestion was ignored and forgotten, and it was left to the workers of the Soviet Republics to reap the honours of discovery by doing just this thing at last. In 1925, the Institute of Plant Industry at Leningrad, under the direction of N. I. Vavilov, sent out a three-year expedition to collect and study the distribution of the wild and cultivated potatoes, at first of Mexico, Guatemala and Colombia, later of Peru, Bolivia, Ecuador and the Argentine. The Russian explorers penetrated into many previously unexplored regions and found potatoes growing under a vast range of different climatic conditions, from latitude 40 degrees south to the Tropic of Cancer, and from sea-level to the snow-line of the high Andes. They brought back with them species and varieties of potato, of the very existence of which European science had scarcely dreamed. Potatoes that could be grown in the tropics; frost-resistant potatoes that they grew with success at the Polar Research Station at Hibiny, far north in the Arctic circle; potatoes almost as rich in protein as in starch; and potatoes that amongst them had natural powers of resistance, some to Leaf Roll or to Mosaic, some to Wart Disease, and more than a few to the Potato Blight. The Russian finds, providing work for a whole generation of potato breeders, gave life to all the breeding for Blight-resistance that was already under way, and the Russian expeditions were jealously followed by others, from Germany, from the United States, from Sweden, and even, at long last, from Great Britain.

By 1928, K. O. Müller in Germany had whole races of hybrids from cultivated and wild Mexican potatoes, including *Solanum demissum*, under observation for Blight-resistance and indications of cropping quality. W-races, he called them, and they promised well. He availed himself of the idea that potato plants seemed to exhibit their maximum susceptibility to the Blight when very young; by exposing large numbers of young hybrid seedlings to infection, and then discarding those attacked, an important preliminary selection could be made, with very great saving of time. The method was adopted, with some modification, by Miss O'Connor, then working at the Virus Research Station at Cambridge under the direction of Dr. R. N. Salaman, who had demonstrated, by experiments with *S. demissum* hybrids, that Blight-resistance *was* an inheritable character of the potato plant, as far back as 1911. Meanwhile, Reddick at Cornell, though experimenting still with the Japanese Ekishirazu and the American Maggie Murphies, was also reaching the conclusion that hybrids of the dwarf *S. demissum* showed the greatest promise in the field. Although all the hybrids so far obtained were of scientific interest only, it did appear that by the continuance of patient crossing, backcrossing and selection over a period of years, good Blight-resistant potatoes could be obtained for the farmers, even, perhaps, with less difficulty than Rust-resistant wheats.

The most formidable obstacle in the way of breeding Rust-resistant wheats was the existence of so many different biological strains of the Rust fungus; varieties resistant to some of the strains would fall to others, and so the wheat-breeder's labours were interminable. Fortunately, however, no biological strains of the Potato Blight fungus had yet been found anywhere; and the potato-breeders seemed to have even better reason to congratulate themselves after Craigie's historic discovery of the function of the spermogonia of the Rust fungi in 1927 (*vide* p. 156). Craigie's discovery was followed up by Ruth Allen, Stakman, Levine and others, and it was found and confirmed that the long-mysterious, flask-shaped spermogonia on the barberry leaves were respectively 'plus' and 'minus', and that the mingling of nectar containing minute spermatia from two of these organs was, in effect, the sexual act of *Puccinia graminis*. It was found, furthermore, that if 'plus' spermatia from one biological strain of the fungus were caused, as by the attentions of an insect, to mingle with the 'minus' spermatia of another, then new hybrid strains of the fungus would result from the cross. During the thirties over two hundred biological strains of the Black Stem Rust were distinguished, a great many of which were undoubtedly of hybrid origin. The persistent curiosity of the botanists about the sexual arrangements and sex-life of the fungi had one of its principal modern justifications in this – sexual reproduction was a mechanism for producing new biological strains.

The Potato Blight fungus was not known to mate when it grew on the potato; and although its egg-spores could now be obtained readily enough in various artificial cultivations, no one had ever seen them germinate. Thus it seemed that the mechanism which the organism might once have had for producing new biological strains was now vestigial and inoperative.

Such reflections greatly encouraged all the workers on Blight-resistant potatoes – who had meanwhile been getting varieties nearer and nearer the mark – until the year 1932, when, despite all the prognostications, a new and virulent biological strain of the fungus was reported in Pomerania. In 1933, K. O. Müller found that even his W-races, which so far had been *immune* from the Blight, were quite severely attacked on the Kamekesch Seed Production Farm in Streckenthin; and, in 1933 also, Miss O'Connor, not to be outdone, found two distinct strains of the Blight fungus attacking the potatoes at Cambridge. Her seedlings, which inherited their resistance from *Solanum demissum*, were immune from Strain A, which was the common one, but they all went down before Strain B, which seemed to have the characteristic of attacking potatoes about a month later than usual. It was almost heartbreaking, but, as Müller said, the fight would have to be carried further; the issue was too important to permit surrender just because of this first disillusion.

Already, in 1934, Donald Reddick, discussing the results of *his* experiments in the friendly pages of *Phytopathology*, was asking his fellow plant pathologists of North America whether the complete elimination of the Potato Blight from the whole of that Continent should not now be regarded as within the bounds of practical possibility. He also had crossed the dwarf *Solanum demissum*, as female parent, with domestic varieties. Ninety per cent of the first hybrid generation – which resembled their wild parent – were totally immune from the Blight. The plants of this generation were then back-crossed with pollen from a good cultivated variety. The progeny was heterogeneous, some eighty per cent of the plants being immune. Two hundred immune, double-back-crossed plants were raised from seed in 1933, and set out in the fields in June, where an ensuing severe Blight attack put them to test. There was no infection, and from this lot of plants a dozen were selected which had tubers of commercial size. Was it not reasonable to anticipate that in a few more years good new commercial potato varieties would be obtained, if not totally immune from the Blight, at least immune from certain clear-cut biological strains of it? The Americans were immediately concerned only with the strain or strains present in North America. Meanwhile Bukasov and Lechnovitz in Russia were obtaining hybrids from the domestic potato, and another type of wild disease-resister, resembling the tall *Solanum andigenum* from the Andes, which gave over five pounds of tubers per plant. Such possibilities were significant enough in the United States, where despite a great expenditure on spraying, the losses attributable to the Blight had been very heavy indeed in 1927, '28, '32, and again in '36. In 1928 the loss amounted to thirteen million bushels of potatoes in New York State alone. The U.S. Department of Agriculture was now going all out to promote potato breeding for Blight-resistance, and work on the field scale was being done at the Orono Experiment Station in Maine, and elsewhere.

But what of the experiments in the British Isles, where the Potato Blight had once caused such grievous woe and turned the high policy of an empire? The two biological strains, or biotypes, of the fungus, which attacked the new hybrid potatoes at Cambridge in 1933, were isolated by Miss O'Connor, and Petterson, another worker at the Station, raised them from single spore cultures. It was confirmed that the potatoes were immune from Strain A, susceptible to strain B. It became necessary to find some source of resistance to strain B, and happily about that time Professor Knappe in Estonia made the Station a present of a parcel of tubers of another wild potato, believed to have come from Ecuador, which was called 'Aya Papa'. The Aya Papa was found to have just the quality desired; it was crossed with the A-resistant stocks already available; selected plants from the progeny were crossed and variously back-crossed again with good domestic varieties, until, in 1937, new varieties were obtained, with tubers not so very different from those of Great Scot, but immune from *both* strains of the Blight fungus – doubly-resistant Blight-proof potatoes.

At the Royal Horticultural Society's Show at Chelsea in 1939, ninety-four years after the first account of the Blight fungus in the first number of that Society's Journal, these Blight-proof potatoes, with some of the wild potato plants, which had contributed in their making, were exhibited to the public. Many great shades must have haunted that exhibit, staged by Dr. Redcliffe N. Salaman and his assistants of the Potato Virus Research Station in Cambridge. There, in leaf and some of them in flower, presents from scientific workers in many countries, were specimens of the wild potatoes of Central and South America, which Earl Cathcart, and John Lindley before him, had so much wanted to see. And there also was something that until recent years no man had ever seen – a promising new variety for the commercial potato breeders, raised anew from some of these wild parent plants, and, so far as it could be tested in the greenhouse and the laboratory, totally immune from the Potato Blight. It was not very much to look at, the centrepiece of that exhibit – just two young potato plants growing side by side in a large flower pot; but the plant on the left, of an ordinary commercial variety, had already three-parts succumbed to the Blight, while the one on the right, the new immune variety, with its foliage in actual contact with that of the diseased plant and covered with the Blight spores from it, was growing away green and completely unaffected (Plate VI).

There was at least one member of the public who remembered a long story as he stood regarding that unspectacular exhibit at the Chelsea Flower Show in 1939; who seemed to hear coming from out of the past the sad strains of the Famine Song, the endless wranglings of disputative botanists, the tale of the wretched people seated on the fences of their decaying gardens, and the oft-repeated plaint that man had no power to resist the dispensations of Providence. But now, in England, as in America, in Russia, and as in Germany, Blight-proof potatoes of new promise had been obtained at last – and here was one of them. Its greenness, when so patently exposed to the Blight from its diseased neighbour, seemed portentous. Did this mean that by about the year 1950 such Blight-proof potatoes would begin to come into extensive cultivation, and that in the generation thereafter, man could write 'paid' to his account with *Phytophthora infestans*? By death, hunger, and all the cost and labour of potato spraying since that palliative was discovered – 'paid in full'?

The answer was 'Perhaps'. The disputation over the ailing potato had not ceased, and every proposition on which such new hopes could be based was challenged by workers of another mind, by men of great experience whose objections were not lightly to be set aside. The experts did not agree. The efforts of potato-breeders, juggling with inheritable characters and mutations occurring among varieties of the domesticated potato alone, had produced many fine sorts in the past, and during the nineteen-thirties such varieties as Kerr's Pink, Great Scot, and the famous Arran series, raised by Mr. Donald

McKelvie in the Isle of Arran off the Clyde, were indeed magnificent potatoes. Clean, heavy-cropping and shapely, suited according to their class to the requirements for early, mid-early and main crops, and of excellent quality for the market and the table. But fine as these potatoes were, they fell very far short of perfection; they were all of them susceptible to the Blight, to frost-injury and to virus disease. Attempts to breed equally good potatoes without these drawbacks made but little progress, and in 1932, the Russian worker, S. M. Bukasov, with so much new solanaceous treasure from the Americas about him, seemed to have put his finger upon the reason. 'Potato breeding', he said, 'is stewing in its own juice, using for the introduction of new varieties always the same old parents in innumerable combinations. A cul-de-sac had been reached.' In 1937 Dr. R. N. Salaman planked his double-resistant hybrids down on the table, and amplified Bukasov's remarks with reference to recent tendencies in British commercial potato-breeding. This breeding, he said, was not only confined to ringing the changes among the genes in the old potato varieties but in the process many of the genes were being left behind and lost altogether. 'We eliminate, let us say, deep eyes, long stolons and highly-coloured skins. How do we know that the genes reponsible for these are not also of material importance in the maintenance of a successful symbiosis or tolerance towards the active agents of virus disease? We eliminate late maturity, numerous and upstanding stems, fibrous roots and long stolons; are we sure that much of the plant's vigour or its resistance to frost may not have gone with them? While, as for resistance to the Potato Blight, it may be that our European stocks never possessed the genes necessary to establish a degree of resistance of any value; if they did, they are certainly completely lost, and lost beyond all hope of recovery, so long as we confine our breeding to the use of existing domestic parental stocks.'

It sounded reasonable enough, to go to wild plants for the qualities of disease-resistance, to try re-introducing a little savage blood. It also seemed plausible that the native South American potatoes, with the Blight always amongst them, had undergone some natural selection in the course of centuries, so that only those having sufficient resistance to the Blight survived. But against this, the heretic Donald Reddick, who in all things concerning the potato had a most disconcerting way of thinking for himself, pointed out that he had never seen a Blight-resistant potato from South America – they all came from Mexico; and there wasn't a ha'p'orth of real evidence that the Blight fungus was a native of South America at all. It seemed to him more probable that it had been introduced into North America, sometime before

PLATE VI. The Reality of Blight-resistance. The plant on the left, typical of the susceptible potato varieties at present in cultivation, has almost succumbed to the Blight; the other plant, touching it, and covered with Blight spores, is totally unaffected. The new resistant variety produces tubers resembling those of Great Scot, but it inherits the Blight-resistance of the dwarf wild potato, *Solanum demissum* (inset).

Photographs of plants at the Potato Virus Research Station, Cambridge, taken by permission of Dr. Redcliffe N. Salaman, F.R.S. 1939

the outbreak of the Blight there in 1842, on another solanaceous plant, the tomato perhaps, or some garden or pharmaceutical novelty; and that on some plant other than the potato the perfect fungus might still be found, reproducing itself both sexually and asexually, still capable of originating new hybrid biological strains. Then for the contention that the 'genes' of Blight-resistance were entirely lost in domestic varieties, Dr. G. H. Pethybridge, *vide* page 349 herein, might well have said: how about those varieties, Champion II, Shamrock and Invincible, which I had out in the natural Blight-bath of County Galway for years before the Great War? Perhaps they were not absolutely immune, but they stood up to the Blight until the very end of the season, and I could have staged an even more impressive exhibit at the Chelsea Flower Show in 1914, than the one they had there in 1939. I could have shown, not experimental seedlings, but varieties already in cultivation, untouched while the other sorts were destroyed. Take a look at some of the photographs in my reports of that time, in the Journal of the Irish Department of Agriculture!

An impartial onlooker might be tempted to exclaim: Well, if there are some sorts of domestic potatoes which are highly resistant, surely it is so much the better? Wild or tame, why don't you go on? Why not try to get these potatoes into cultivation? Why hang about arguing, meeting difficulties half-way? And there was the rub. In the demented thirties the potato industry was not at all sure that it *wanted* Blight-proof potatoes, and indeed anyone introducing them was as likely to be reviled as rewarded. It was the same with Blight-resistant as with virus-free stocks; in the beginning the seed would cost a little more, but, beyond that, such products of scientific research would increase the yield per acre, lower the cost of production, favour the small growers, put too many good and cheap potatoes on the market, and plunge the whole already-restricted industry into hopeless confusion. There would first have to be a change in the agricultural policy of the country. Perhaps it would come, soon enough, after September 3rd, 1939, when the agricultural-production telegraph on the bridge of the crazy ship of state would once again be pushed hard over from Astern to Ahead, and folk would come to think with wonderment of the time, so recently past, when the aim was to restrict home food-production and not to increase it. Perhaps the vital necessity of deflecting supplies of copper from the armament factories for spraying the potatoes during the new 'emergency' would result in some encouragement being given to those undertaking the breeding of Blight-proof varieties – especially to those practical breeders taking the first passably good resistant stocks from the greenhouse and the laboratory, and attempting to raise up from them new and Blight-proof Arran Banners and Abundances, which would require no spraying. It might seem an excess of caution then to inquire if there was any guarantee that the Blight fungus would not adapt itself in time to a new mode of living on the new plants and so continue the Blight as before? But it had to be admitted that to this question the answer was 'None'. Those who waited for a guarantee could have none at all. New biological strains of the Blight fungus might be cheated one after another, but – it was already known that the parasite had a more *flexible* way of adapting itself to modified host-plants. Harry Marshall Ward had pointed to this in 1902, with his theory of 'bridging-species' for the Brown Rust fungus among Brome grasses, and by 1938 Reddick and Mills had shown that a given individual strain of the Potato Blight fungus itself could increase in virulence, by growing on some of the partially-resistant new hybrid potato plants, until it was capable of attacking those previously immune. There was even a certain danger in letting the new hybrid potatoes go out into cultivation too soon, for in severe Blight attacks the fungus would only sharpen its teeth upon them, increasing the difficulties for the breeders, and rendering of less avail the degree of resistance enjoyed by some of the older varieties.

Those who believed in genes postulated the existence of an eternal quality, R, which they could take from wild plants, build into the genetical constitution of cultivated ones, and so make them disease-resistant for ever. Those who thought, not in terms of mathematical abstractions, but of the green flux of ever-changing nature, saw little hope of such permanency, and no end to man's labours in defending the crops upon which he depended for life.

BIBLIOGRAPHY

CHAPTERS I AND II: THE POTATO MURRAIN; FAMINE IN IRELAND

Philosophical Transactions of the Royal Society begin 1665
London. (Philos. Trans.)

HOOKE, R. 1667
Micrographia: or some physiological descriptions of minute bodies made by magnifying glasses. Reprinted: R. T. Gunther, Museum of the History of Science, Oxford, 1938

Annales des Sciences naturelles begin 1824
Paris (Ann. Sci. nat.)

UNGER, F. 1833
Die Exantheme der Pflanzen, und einige mit diesen verwandte Krankheiten der Gewächse. Carl Gerold, Vienna. 422 pages, 7 plates

Comptes rendus hebdomadaires des séances de l'Académie des Sciences begin 1835
Paris. (C. R. Acad. Sci. Paris)

Journal of the Royal Agricultural Society of England begins 1840
London. (J. R. Agric. Soc. England)

HENSLOW, J. S. 1841
Report on the diseases of wheat. J. R. Agric. Soc. England, II: 1–25

The Gardeners' Chronicle and Agricultural Gazette begins 1841
London. (Gdnrs' Chron.)

FOSTER, T. C. 1845
Letters on the Condition of the People in Ireland. *The Times*, 1845. Reprinted with notes, Chapman & Hall, London, 771 pages, 1846

LINDLEY, J. 1845
On the Potato Murrain. Editorials and notes, Aug. 23rd on. Gdnrs' Chron.

Journal of the (Royal) Horticultural Society begins 1845
London. (J. hort. Soc.) (J. R. hort. Soc., after 1866)

BERKELEY, M. J. 1845
Observations, Botanical and Physiological, on the Potato Murrain. J. hort. Soc., I: 9–34. 4 plates

PLAYFAIR, L. 1845
On the nature and causes of the decay in Potatoes. J. R. Agric. Soc. England, VI: 532–65

GRAHAM, F. J., AND OTHERS 1846
Prize Essays on the Nature and Cause of the Potato Disease. J. R. Agric. Soc. England, VII: 300–33, 357–91, 486–98

SOLLY, E. 1846
Chemical Observations on the cause of the Potato Murrain. J. hort. Soc., I: 35–42

LINDLEY, J., AND OTHERS 1846
Influence of copper fumes on Potato Blight. Gdnrs' Chron., Sept. 26th, 1846, p. 643

BERKELEY, M. J. 1847
Observations on the propagation of Bunt, *Uredo Caries* D.C., made with especial reference to the Potato Disease. J. hort. Soc., II: 107–14

GOODIFF, J. M. 1847
The food question in Ireland. Gdnrs' Chron. Nov. 27th, p. 786

TREVELYAN, C. 1848
The Irish Crisis. In *The Edinburgh Review*, CLXXV; reprinted Longman & Co, 16mo, 201 pages, 1848

LINDLEY, J. 1848
Notes on the Wild Potato. J. hort. Soc., III: 65-72

MURRAY, A. 1863
The Book of the Royal Horticultural Society. Bradbury & Evans, London. 225 pages, 4to, with embellishments

O'ROURKE, J. 1875
The History of the Great Irish Famine of 1847, with notices of earlier Irish Famines. M'Glashan & Gill, Dublin. 559 pages

CREIGHTON, C. 1894
History of Epidemics in Great Britain. Cambs. Univ. Press 2 vols. 8vo

O'BRIEN, W. P. 1896
The Great Famine. A retrospect of fifty years: 1845-1895. Downey & Co., London. 340 pages

ROZE, E. 1898
Histoire de la Pomme de Terre. Rothschild, Paris. 464 pages, 4to, 158 figures

REDDICK, D. 1928
The Origin of *Phytophthora infestans*. Phytopathology, XVIII: 494-500

BARGER, G. 1931
Ergot and Ergotism. Gurney & Jackson, London. 279 pages, illustrated

FAY, C. R. 1932
The Corn Laws and Social England. Cambs. Univ. Press. 223 pages

CHAPTERS III AND IV: OIDIUM ON THE VINES; FRUITS OF THE FUNGI

FRIES, E. 1821
Systema mycologicum, sistens fungorum ordines, genera et species huc usque cognitas. E. Mauritius, Gryphiswaldia. I, 1821; II, 1823; III, 1829

SCHWEINITZ, L. D. 1834
Synopsis Fungorum in America Boreali, etc. Trans. Amer. Phil. Soc., IV: 269-70

TUCKER, — 1847
The Grape Disease. The Gardeners' and Farmers' Journal, Oct. 2nd, page 212. M. J. Berkeley on same. Gdnrs' Chron., Nov. 27th, p. 779

LÉVEILLÉ, J. H. 1851
Organisation et disposition méthodique des espèces qui composent le genre Érysiphé. Ann. Sci. nat., 3e sér. Bot., XV: 109-79

LÉVEILLÉ, J. H. 1851
Observations on the Vine Mildew. Trans. with observations by M. J. Berkeley. J. hort. Soc., VI: 284-95

MOHL, H. VON 1852
On the Grape Mildew. Trans. of papers in Botanische Zeitung. J. hort. Soc., VII: 132-8, 1852; IX: 1-10, 1855; IX: 264-72, 1854

AMICI, G. B. 1853

On the Disease of the Vine. Trans. J. hort. Soc., VIII: 231-43

HERAPATH, T. J. 1854

Prevention and Destruction of Vine Mildew [with lime-sulphur, etc.] Gdnrs' Chron., Jan. 28th, p. 55

MONTAGNE, C. 1855

A brief sketch of the present state of the question relative to the Vine Mildew. Trans. J. hort. Soc., IX: 112-28

BERKELEY, M. J. 1855

Botanical notes on the Mildew of the Vine and the Hop. J. hort. Soc., IX: 61-70. Also: Gdnrs' Chron., July 26th, p. 501, and July 19th, p. 485, 1856

HENDERSON, J. 1855

The Chinese Yam, *Dioscorea Batatas*. A pamphlet. London

TULASNE, L. R. AND C. 1861

Selecta Fungorum Carpologia. 3 vols in folio. 772 pages, 61 plates. Imprimerie Impériale, Paris. 1861-5. English trans. by W. B. Grove, edited by A. H. R. Buller and C. L. Shear. Clarendon Press Oxford, 1931

DE BARY, A. H. 1863

Über die Fruchtentwicklung der Ascomyceten. W. Engelmann, Leipzig. 38 pages, 4to, 2 plates

DE BARY, A. 1870

Eurotium, Erysiphe, Cicinnobolus, nebst Bemerkungen über die Geschlectsorgane der Ascomyceten. De Bary & Woronin Beiträge, III. C. Winter, Frankfurt a. M. 95 pages, 6 plates

DE BARY, A. 1888

Biographical particulars. Nature, XXXVII: 297-9, 1888. Phytopathology, I: 1-2, 1911. Zeitschrift für Botanik, XXIV: 1-71, 1930

HARPER, R. A. 1895

Die Entwickelung des Peritheciums bei *Sphaerotheca Castagnei*. Bericht. Deutsch. Botan. Gesell., XIII: 475-81

COUDERC, G. 1893

Sur les périthèces de l'*Uncinula spiralis* en France et l'identification de l'Oidium Américain et de l'Oidium Européen. C. R. Acad. Sci. Paris, CXVI: 210-11

SALMON, E. S. 1900

A Monograph of the Erysiphaceae. Memoirs of the Torrey Botanical Club, New York, IX: 1-292. 9 plates

CHAPTER V: BUNT OF THE WHEAT

TILLET, M. 1755

Dissertation sur la cause qui corrumpt et noircit les grains de bled dans les épis, et sur les moyens de prevenir ces accidens. Bordeaux. 4to. Trans by H. B. Humphrey, Phytopathological Classic, No. 5, 1937. 191 pages.

TESSIER, L'ABBÉ 1783

Traité des maladies des grains. 8vo. Paris. 351 pages. 7 plates

PRÉVOST, B. 1807

Mémoire sur la cause immédiate de la Carie ou Charbon des blés et de plusieurs autres maladies des plantes, et sur les préservatifs de la Carie. Montauban. 80 pages, 4to, 3 plates. Trans. by G. W. Keitt. Phytopathological Classic No. 6, 1939

SINCLAIR, J. 1815

Hints regarding the agricultural state of the Netherlands, with some observations on the means of diminishing the expense of growing corn, etc. London. 8vo.

DOMBASLE, M. DE 1843

Calendrier du Bon Cultivateur, ou Manuel de L'Agriculteur Praticien. Audot. Paris

TULASNE, L. R. AND C. 1847

Mémoire sur les Ustilaginées comparées aux Urédinées. Ann. Sci. nat., 3e sér., Bot., VII: 12-127

DE BARY, A. 1853

Untersuchungen über die Brandpilze, und die durch sie verursachten Krankheiten der Pflanzen, etc. Müller, Berlin. 144 pages, 8 plates

BERKELEY, M. J. 1856

Bunt. Vegetable Pathology CXLIV. Gdnrs' Chron. Nov. 15th, p. 757

CHAPTER VI: 'VEGETABLE PATHOLOGY'

PUSEY, P. 1840

On the present State of Agriculture as a Science in England. J. R. Agric. Soc. England, I: 1-21

Hedwigia. Ein Notizblatt für kryptogamische Studien begins 1852

Dresden. Edited by L. Rabenhorst. (Hedwigia)

PAYEN, A. 1853

Les maladies des Pommes de Terre, des Betteraves, des Blés, et des Vignes, de 1845 à 1853. Avec l'Indication des meilleurs Moyens à employer pour les combattre. Hachette, Paris. 200 pages, 8vo, 5 plates

BERKELEY, M. J. 1854

Vegetable Pathology. In The Gardeners' Chronicle. Begins with Article I on Jan. 7th, 1854, p. 4, and ends with Article CLXXIII and an index on Oct. 3rd, 1857, p. 676

Proceedings of the Royal Society begin 1854

London. (Proc. roy. Soc.)

BERKELEY, M. J. 1857

Introduction to Cryptogamic Botany. Bailliere, London. 604 pages, 127 figures

KÜHN, J. G. 1858

Die Krankheiten der Kulturgewächse, ihre Ursachen und ihre Verhütung. Bessel-mann, Berlin. 312 pages, 7 plates.

Jahrbuch fur Wissenschaftliche Botanik begins 1858

Berlin. Founded by Nathanial Pringsheim. (Jb. wiss. Bot.)

Die Landwirthschaftlichen Versuchsstationen begins 1859

Berlin. (Landw. VerSta.)

GRIFFITH, J. W. AND HENFREY, A. 1856

The Micrographic Dictionary. London. 8vo. 3rd edition with contributions by M. J. Berkeley, 1873. 2 vols, 8vo.

CHAPTER VII: OOSPORES AND ZOOSPORES

SPEERSCHNEIDER, J. 1857

Die Ursache der Erkrankung der Kartoffelknolle durch eine Riehe Experimente bewiesen. Botanische Zeitung, XV: 122-4. Also: Flora, XL, 81-7

DE BARY, A. 1861

Die gegenwärtig herrschende Kartoffelkrankheit, ihre Ursache und ihre Verhütung. Arthur Felix, Leipzig. 75 pages, 1 plate

DE BARY, A. 1863

Recherches sur le développement de quelques Champignons parasites, etc. Ann. Sci. nat. 4e sér. Bot., XX: 1-148

CHAPTER VIII: ENTER LOUIS PASTEUR

APPERT, C. 1810

L'art de conserver pendant plusiers années toutes les substances animales et végétales, etc. Paris. 116 pages, 1 plate. Trans. Black & Co., London, 1811

PASTEUR, L. 1861

Mémoire sur les corpuscules organisés qui existent dans l'atmosphère. Examen de la doctrine des générations spontanées. Ann. Sci. nat., 4e sér. Zoo., XVI: 5-98. 1 plate. Also Ann. Chim. Physiq. 3e sér., LXIV: 5-110. 2 plates. 1862

BASTIAN, H. C. 1871

The modes of origin of lowest organisms, including a discussion of the experiments of M. Pasteur. London. 8vo. Also: The Origin of Life. Watts, London. 74 pages, 10 plates. 1911

VALLERY-RADOT, R. 1900

La Vie de Pasteur. Paris. 692 pages, 8vo, 1900. Trans. by Mrs. R. L. Devonshire. Constable, London. 2 vols, 1902. 1 vol, 484 pages, 1919

PASTEUR, L. 1922

Oeuvres de Pasteur. Réunies par P. Vallery-Radot. Masson, Paris. 7 volumes. 1922-39

CHAPTER IX: THE BARBERRY AND THE WHEAT

FONTANA, F. 1767

Osservazioni sopra la ruggine del Grano. Jacobo Giusti, Lucca. 114 pages, 8vo, 1 plate. Trans. by 'a friend' in Young's Annals of Agriculture, XVII: 232-80, 1792. Another trans. by P. P. Pirone, Phytopathological Classic No. 2, 1932

PERSOON, C. H. 1801

Synopsis methodica fungorum. H. Dieterich, Göttingen. 706 pages, 5 plates

SINCLAIR, J. 1809

Result of an inquiry into the nature and causes of the Blight, the Rust and the Mildew which have particularly affected the crops of wheat on the borders of England and Scotland. Edinburgh. 8vo

PHILLIPAR, F. 1837

Traité Organographique et Physiologico-Agricole sur La Carie, Le Charbon, l'Ergot, La Rouille, et autres Maladies du même genre qui ravagent les Céréales. Versailles. 220 pages, 9 plates

LÉVEILLÉ, J. H. 1846

Considérations Mycologiques, suivies d'une nouvelle classification des Champignons Paris. 136 pages, 16mo

TULASNE, L. R. 1854

Mémoire sur les Urédinées et les Ustilaginées. Ann. Sci. nat., 4e sér, Bot., II: 77-196. Plates VII-XII

DE BARY, A. 1863

Recherches sur le développement de quelques Champignons parasites. Mémoire pour servir de supplément aux Travaux sur la question des Générations dites spontanées. Ann. Sci. nat., 4e sér., Bot., XX: 5-148. 13 plates

DE BARY, A. 1865

Neue Untersuchungen über die Uredineen, inbesondere die Entwicklung der *Puccinia graminis* und den Zusammenhang derselben mit *Aecidium berberidis*. Monatsber. K. Preuss. Acad. Wiss., 1865: 15-49

CHAPTER X: SCHOOL FOR PLANT DOCTORS

DE BARY, A. 1866

Morphologie und Physiologie der Pilze, Flechten und Myxomyceten. W. Hofmeister: Handbuch der physiologischen Botanik, II. Engelmann, Leipzig. 316 pages, 101 woodcuts, 1 plate

SACHS, J. VON 1868

Lehrbuch der Botanik, nach dem gegenwärtigen Stand der Wissenschaft. Engelmann, Leipzig. 632 pages, 358 woodcuts. Trans. by A. W. Bennett, Oxford, 1875

HALLIER, E. 1868

Phytopathologie: die Krankheiten der Culturgewächse. Engelmann, Leipzig. 373 pages, 8vo, 32 woodcuts, 5 plates

The American Naturalist begins 1868

Salem. Mass. (Amer. Nat.)

Nature. A weekly illustrated Journal of Science begins 1869

London. Macmillan. (Nature)

TAYLOR, T. 1871

Reports on fungoid diseases of plants, etc. Ann. Reps. U.S. Dep. Agric., 1871-6

SORAUER, P. 1874

Handbuch der Pflanzenkrankheiten. 1st edition 1874; 2nd, 1886, 4 volumes; and subsequent editions. Paul Parey, Berlin. 3rd edition, 1908, trans. by F. Dorrance

CAIRD, J., VOELCKER, A., AND OTHERS 1878

Memoir on the Agriculture of England and Wales. J. R. Agric. Soc. England, 2nd ser., XIV, 267-644

FRANK, A. B. 1880

Die Krankheiten der Pflanzen. Trewendt, Breslau. 844 pages, 149 woodcuts

SACHS, J. VON 1890

History of Botany: 1530-1860. Trans. by H. E. F. Garnsey. 584 pages. Also continuation of this history: 1860-1901, by J. R. Green, 544 pages. Clarendon Press, Oxford, 1909

KIRKLAND, J. 1917

Three Centuries of Prices of Wheat, Flour and Bread. Kirkland, London. 63 pages, 8vo.

ORR, J. 1922

A short history of British Agriculture. Humphrey Milford, London. 96 pages, 8vo

JOST, L. 1930

Zum hundertsten Geburtstag Anton de Barys. Zeitschrift für Botanik, XXIV: 1-74

BIBLIOGRAPHY

CHAPTER XI: PHYLLOXERA OF THE VINES

PLANCHON, J. É. 1868
Nouvelles observations sur le Puceron de la Vigne, etc. C. R. Acad. Sci. Paris, LXVII: 333-6, 588-94

WESTWOOD, I. O. 1869
New Vine diseases [Phylloxera at Hammersmith]. Gdnrs' Chron., Jan. 30th, p. 109

RILEY, C. V. 1872
On the cause of the deterioration in some of our native grape vines, etc. American Naturalist, VI: 532-44

PLANCHON, J. É. 1872
Sur l'extension actuelle du Phylloxera en Europe. C. R. Acad. Sci. Paris, LXXV: 1007-9. Also: Congrès. Scient. France, XXXV, 505-621

RILEY, C. V. 1874
Les espèces américaines du genre Phylloxera. C. R. Acad. Sci. Paris, LXXIX, 1348-8

BLAKESLEE, A. F. 1904
Sexual reproduction in the Mucorineae. Proc. Amer. Acad. Arts & Sciences, XL: 205-319, 14 plates. Also: Science, n.s. XXIV: 118-22

CHANCRIN, E. 192–
Viticulture Moderne. 6th edition. Hatchette, Paris. 334 pages, 208 figures

CRAIGIE, J. H. 1927
Discovery of the function of the pycnia of the Rust fungi. Nature, CXX: 765-7. 2 figures

CHAPTER XII: THE WATER FUNGI

UNGER, F. 1844
Sur l'*Achlya prolifera*. Ann. Sci. Nat., 3e sér., Bot., II: 5-20

THURET, G. 1850
Recherches sur les zoospores des Algues. Ann. Sci. nat., 3e sér., Bot., XIV: 214-60

PRINGSHEIM, N. 1858
Die Saprolegnieen. Jb. wiss. Bot., I: 284-306, 1858, and III: 205-36, 1860

Grevillea. A monthly record of cryptogamic botany and its literature. Edited by M. C. Cooke. 1872-1894 begins 1872

JENKINS, H. M. 1874
Report on the Cultivation of Potatoes, with special reference to Potato Disease. J. R. Agric. Soc. England, 2nd ser. X: 475-514

HESSE, R. 1874
Pythium de Baryanum, ein endophytischer Schmarotzer. Halle a. S. 76 pages, 29 figures

CARRUTHERS, W. 1875
Report on the results of the Competition of 1874 for the Society's Prizes for potatoes that should be free from disease for three years in succession. J. R. Agric. Soc. England, 2nd ser., XI: 376-95

SMITH, W. G. 1875
Resting spores of the Potato Blight fungus. Nature, XII: 234; Quart J. micr. Sci., XV: 360-3; J. R. Agric. Soc. England, 2nd ser., XI: 396-8; Gdnrs' Chron., July 17th, 24th, 1875

DE BARY, A. 1876
Researches into the Nature of the Potato fungus – *Phytophthora infestans*. J. R. Agric. Soc. England, 2nd ser., XII: 239–69. 8 figures

SMITH, W. G. 1878
The Salmon Disease. Gdnrs' Chron., May 4th, pp. 560–2

BUCKLAND, F. T., AND OTHERS 1880
Report on the Disease which has recently prevailed among the Salmon in the Tweed, Eden and other rivers. G. B. & I. Home Office. Inspectors of Fisheries. (C-2660).

DE BARY, A. 1881
Untersuchungen über die Peronosporeen und Saprologenieen. De Bary & Woronin Beiträge, IV: 1–145. 6 plates. Frankfurt a. M.

HUXLEY, T. H. 1882
A contribution to the Pathology of the Epidemic known as the 'Salmon Disease'. Proc. roy. Soc., XXXIII: 381–9

WARD, H. M. 1883
Observations on the genus Pythium and on Saprolegniae. Quart J. micros. Sci., XXIII: 485–515, 272–91

COOKE, M. C. 1898
Sixty years of British Mycology. The Essex Naturalist, X: 216–23

PATTERSON, J. H. 1903
On the Cause of the Salmon Disease. Report of the Fishery Board for Scotland (C-1544). 52 pages, 10 plates

BUTLER, E. J. 1907
An account of the genus Pythium and some Chytridiaceae. Mem. Dept. Agric. India, Bot. Series, I (5): 1–160. 10 plates

COKER, W. C. 1923
The Saprolegniaceae. Univ. N. Carolina Press. 201 pages, 63 plates

FITZPATRICK, H. M. 1930
The Lower Fungi – Phycomycetes. McGraw-Hill, London and New York. 331 pages, 112 figs.

CHAPTER XIII: CLUB ROOT AND ANTHRAX

VOELCKER, A. 1859
Anbury; and the analysis of diseased turnips. J. R. Agric. Soc. England, XX: 101–5

WORONIN, M. S. 1866
[On the root-nodules of the common garden-lupin, etc.] Mém. Acad. Sci. St. Petersbourg, Sér. VII, Tome X (6): 1–13, 2 plates

LANCEREAUX, E. 1868
A Treatise on Syphilis: Historical and Practical. New Sydenham Society, London. 2 volumes, 784 pages

Beiträge zur Biologie der Pflanzen begins 1870
Breslau. Founded by Ferdinand Cohn. (Beitr. Biol. Pfl.)

COHN, F. J. 1872
Untersuchungen über Bacterien. Beitr. Biol. Pfl., II: 127–222

KOCH, R. 1876
Die Aetiologie der Milzbrand-Krankheit beigründet auf die Entwickelungsgeschicte der Bacillus anthracis. Beitr. Biol. Pfl., II: 277–308

KOCH, R. 1876
Verfahren zur Untersuchung, zum Conserviren und Photographiren der Bacterien. Beitr. Biol. Pfl., II: 399–434. 3 plates

WORONIN, M. S. 1878
Urheber der Kohlpflanzen-Hernie [the causal organism of Club Root] Jb. wiss. Bot., XI: 548–74. 6 plates. Trans. by C. Chupp, Phytopathological Classic No. 4, 1934

BURRILL, T. J. 1880
Anthrax of Fruit Trees, or the so-called Fire-blight of Pear, etc. Proc. Amer. Assoc. Advanc. Sci., XXIX: 583–97

HALSTEAD, B. D. 1893
Club Root of cabbage and its allies. Bull. New Jersey Agric. Exp. Sta. No. 98

LAGRANGE, É. 1938
Robert Koch: Sa vie et son Oeuvre. Brussels. 90 pages, with portraits

BULLOCK, W. 1938
History of Bacteriology. Oxford Univ. Press. 434 pages, illustrated

CHAPTER XIV: CANKER OF THE LARCH

BERKELEY, M. J. 1859
On the Larch Disease. Gdnrs' Chron. Dec. 17th, p. 1015

MACINTOSH, C. 1860
The Larch Disease and the present condition of Larch plantations in Great Britain. Blackwood, Edinburgh. 136 pages, 8vo., no figs.

WILLKOMM, H. M. 1867
Der Rinderkrebs der Lärche, oder die Larchenkrankheit. In Die mikroskopischen Feinde des Waldes, II: 167–218. 4 plates. Dresden

HARTIG, R. 1874
Wichtige Krankheiten der Waldbaume. J. Springer, Berlin. 127 pages, 4to, 160 figs, 6 plates. Trans. by W. Somerville, edited by H. M. Ward, 'Text-book of the Diseases of Trees', Macmillan, London, 1894

HARTIG, R. 1880
Die Larchenkrankheiten, etc. Untersuch. forstbotan. Inst. Munchen, I: 63–87

WARD, H. M. 1901
Disease in Plants. Macmillan, London. 309 pages, no figs.

HILEY, W. E. 1919
Fungal Diseases of the Common Larch. Clarendon Press, Oxford. 204 pages, 8vo, 73 figs.

CHAPTER XV: COFFEE RUST IN CEYLON

NIETNER, J. 1861
Observations on the Enemies of the Coffee tree in Ceylon. Ceylon Times Office, Ceylon. 31 pages

BERKELEY, M. J. 1869
Hemileia vastatrix [first description]. Gdnrs' Chron., Nov. 6th, p. 1157

MORRIS, D. 1879
The Campaign of 1879 against the Coffee-leaf Disease by the coffee planters of Ceylon, assisted and guided by D. Morris, Esq., M.A., F.G.S. Ceylon Observer Press, Colombo. 274 pages. Also: J. linn. Soc., XVII: 512–17

WARD, H. M. 1880
Report on the Coffee-leaf Disease. Colombo Sessional Paper No. XVII, 1880, with continuations, 1881-2

THISELTON-DYER, W. T. 1880
The Coffee-leaf Disease of Ceylon. J. micros. Sci., XX: 119-29

WARD, H. M. 1882
Researches on the life-history of *Hemileia vastatrix*. J. linn. Soc., XIX: 299-335. Also J. micros. Sci., XXII: 1-11

CHAPTER XVI: AFTER FORTY YEARS

BREFELD, O. 1872
Botanische Untersuchungen über Schimmelpilze, etc. A. Felix, Leipzig, later H. Schoningh, Munich. I-IV, 1870-81; V, 1883; VI-XV, 1884-1912. In all over 2500 pages, 110 plates

FARLOW, W. G. 1874
On the American grape-vine Mildew. Bull. Bussey Inst., I: 415. Biographical Memoir by W. A. Setchell. Mem. Nat. Acad. Sci. Washington, XXI

BATES, H. W. 1875
The Colorado Potato-Beetle. J. R. Agric. Soc. England, 2nd ser., XI: 361-75

RILEY, C. V. 1877
The Colorado Beetle. With suggestions for its repression and methods of destruction. Routledge, London. 123 pages, 8vo, and frontispiece

PLANCHON, J. É. 1879
Le Mildew, ou faux Oidium américain dans les vignobles de France. C. R. Acad. Sci. Paris, LXXXIX: 600-3

MILLARDET, P. M. A. 1883
Sur le rôle des spores d'hiver du mildiou (*Peronospora viticola* de By.) dans le réinvasion par ce parasite. Mém. Soc. Sci. phys. nat. Bordeaux, 2e sér., V: xxiv-xxvii

Sylloge fungorum omnium hucusque cognitorum, Saccardo, P. A. begins 1882
25 volumes. I, 1882. XXV, 1931. Pavia. Italy

Zentralblatt für Bakteriologie, Parasitenkunde und Infektionskrankheiten begins 1887
Jena. (Zbl. Bakt.)

MUIR, R., AND RITCHIE, J. 1907
Manual of Bacteriology. 4th edition. Pentland, Edinburgh. 605 pages, 175 figs., extensive bibliography. (1st Edition 1897)

CHAPTER XVII: BORDEAUX MIXTURE

Journal d'agriculture pratique begins 1837
Paris. (J. Agric. prat.)

MILLARDET, P. M. A. 1885
Traitement du Mildiou par le Mélange de Sulfate de Cuivre et de Chaux, etc. J. Agric. prat., 1885 (2): 513-16, 707-10, 801-5. Trans. of these three papers by F. J. Schniederhan, Phytopathological Classic No. 3. 1933

VARIOUS AUTHORS 1886-7
The first knapsack spraying machines. J. Agric. prat., 1886 (1): 329-31, 442-3; 1886 (2): 174, 308; 1887 (1): 453, 529, 573, 709

MASSON, E. 1887
Nouveau Procédé Bourguignon contre le Mildiou. [Burgundy Mixture] J. Agric. prat., 1887 (1): 814-16. Also: Patrigeon, G., ibid.: 879-84

RICAUD, J. 1887
Le traitement du Mildiou. La dissolution cuivreuse comparée aux autres préparations liquides. J. Agric. prat. 1887 (1): 87-92

LAMSON-SCRIBNER, F. AND OTHERS 1888
Report on Experiments made in 1887 in the treatment of the Downy Mildew and the Black Rot of the Grape Vine, with a Supplement by P. Ferrouillat of Montpellier on spraying apparatus. Bull. U.S. Div. Bot. No. 5. 113 pages. Also: Scribner, F. L. and Viala, P. ibid., No. 7. 29 pages

VASEY, G., AND GALLOWAY, B. T. 1889
A record of some of the work of the Division of Botany. Bull. U.S. Div. Bot. No. 8: 45-67

PERRET, M. 1890
L'emploi du sucrate de cuivre contre le Mildew. Bull. Soc. Nat. d'Agric. France, L: 532-4

GIRARD, A. 1890
Du traitement de la Maladie des Pommes de Terre par les sels de cuivre. J. Agric. prat., 1890 (1): 803-6

PRILLIEUX, E. 1895
Maladies des plantes agricoles. Didot, Paris. Vol. I, 421 pages, 190 figs, 1895; Vol. II, 592 pages, 293 figs., 1897

LODEMAN, E. G. 1896
The Spraying of plants. A succinct account of the history, principles and practice of the application of liquids and powders to plants for the purpose of destroying insects and fungi. Macmillan, London and New York. 399 pages

CHAPTER XVIII: DANISH 'HOT WATER'

LANG, J. 1858
The Potato; its culture, production and disease. [Protective cultivation]. Prize Essay. J. R. Agric. Soc. England, XIX, 65-81

JENSEN, J. L. 1882
How to overcome the Potato Disease. A pamphlet. Menzies, Edinburgh. Abs. in Gdnrs' Chron., Sept. 30th, pp. 429-30

PLOWRIGHT, C. B. 1884
Mr. Jensen on the Potato Disease. Gdnrs' Chron. 1884 (1): 152-3, 446-8, 588-9, 615-6

JENSEN, J. L. 1887
Moyens de Combattre et de détruire le Peronospora de la pomme de terre. Mém. Soc. nat. Agric. France, CXXXI: 31-156

JENSEN, J. L. 1888
The propagation and prevention of Smut in Oats and Barley. J. R. Agric. Soc. England, 2nd ser. XXIV: 397-415

SWINGLE, W. T. 1892
Treatment of Smuts of Oats and Wheat. Fmrs' Bull. U.S. Dep. Agric. No. 5

RAVN, F. K. 1917
Jens Ludwig Jensen (1836-1904). Phytopathology, VII: 1-4

CHAPTER XIX: THE LEAD OF THE U.S.A.

DE BARY, A. 1884
Vergleichende Morphologie und Biologie der Pilze, Mycetozoen und Bacterien. Engelmann, Leipzig. 558 pages, 198 woodcuts. Trans. by H. E. F. Garnsey, 'Comparative Morphology and Biology of the Fungi, etc', Clarendon Press, Oxford, 1887

SMITH, W. G. 1884
Diseases of Field and Garden Crops, chiefly such as are caused by fungi. Macmillan, London. 353 pages, 143 woodcuts

Reports on the Experimental Farms, Canada begin 1888
Ottawa. (Rep. exp. Fms. Can.)

Experiment Station Record begins 1889
Washington. (Exp. Sta. Rec.)

Farmers' Bulletins, U.S. Department of Agriculture begin 1889
Washington. (Fmrs' Bull. U.S. Dep. Agric.)

PLOWRIGHT, C. B. 1889
A Monograph of the British Uredineae and Ustilagineae. Kegan Paul, London. 347 pages, 13 figs., 8 plates

CAIRD, J. 1890
Fifty years' progress of British Agriculture. J. R. Agric. Soc. England, 3rd ser., 1: 20–37

Zeitschrift für Pflanzenkrankheiten und Pflanzenschutz begins 1891
Stuttgart. Founded by Paul Sorauer. (Z. PflKrankh.)

Bulletins of the Division of Vegetable [Physiology and] Pathology begin 1891
Washington. (Bull. U.S. Div. Veg. Physiol. Path.)

Rivista di Patologia vegetale begins 1892
Padova. (Riv. Patol. veg.)

CRAIGIE, P. G. 1895
Report on the Agricultural Experiment Stations and Agricultural Colleges of the U.S.A. Board of Agric., G.B. & I. (C-7699)

GREATHOUSE, C. H. 1907
Historical Sketch of the U.S. Department of Agriculture, its objects and organization. Bull. U.S. Div. Pubns. No. 3

FLOUD, L. C. 1927
The Ministry of Agriculture and Fisheries. Putnam's, London. 330 pages, 8vo

TRUE, A. C. 1929
A History of Agricultural Education in the United States, 1785–1925. Misc. Pub. U.S. Dep. Agric. No. 36. 436 pages

TRUE, A. C. 1937
A History of Agricultural Experimentation and Research in the U.S.A., 1607 1925. Misc. Pub. U.S. Dep. Agric. No. 251. 321 pages

CHAPTER XX: POTATO SPRAYING

CATHCART, EARL 1884
On the cultivated Potato. J.R. Agric. Soc. England, 2nd ser., XX: 266–300

GIRARD, A. 1892
Recherches sur l'adhérence aux feuilles des plantes et notamment de la pomme de terre, des composés cuivriques destinés a combattre leurs maladies. J. Agric. prat., 1892 (I): 176–8

VOELCKER, J. A. 1892
The Woburn Experiments on prevention and cure of 'Potato Disease'. J. R. agric. Soc. England, 3rd ser., III: 771–83

GIRARD, A. 1892
La lutte contre la maladie de la pomme de terre, au moyen des composés cuivriques. Mém. Soc. Nat. d'Agric. France, CXXXIV: 691–721

BOARD OF AGRICULTURE, G. B. & I. 1892
Report on recent experiments in checking Potato Disease in the United Kingdom and Abroad. (C-6647). 183 pages. Also: Report on further experiments as above (C-7138) 97 pages, 1893

GIRARD, A. 1893
Rational Potato Culture. Trans. by C. Whitehead in J. R. agric. Soc. England, 3rd ser., IV: 406–11

Journal of the Board of Agriculture begins 1894
London (J. Bd. Agric.)

BOARD OF AGRICULTURE, G. B. & I. 1897
Report of Experiments and Demonstrations conducted by the Irish Land Commission (Agric. Dep.) during 1896, in the prevention of Potato Disease. (C-8505) Abs. J. Bd. Agric., IV: 261–2

CHAPTER XXI: FUNGI IN THE ORCHARDS

COOKE, M. C. 1866
Foliicolous Sphaeriae. Seeman's Journal of Botany, IV: 241–53

MILLARDET, P. M. A. 1886
Note sur le chancre du pommier et du poirier. Mém. Soc. Sci. phys. nat. Bordeaux, 3e sér., II: 83–9

GOETHE, R. 1887
Weitere Beobachtungen über den Apfel-und Birnerost, *Fusicladium dendriticum* (Wallr.) Fuckel. Gartenflora, XXXVI: 293–99, with a double plate No. 1248

WHITEHEAD, C. 1891
Methods of preventing and checking the attacks of insects and fungi. J. R. agric. Soc. England, 3rd. ser., II: 217–56

GALLOWAY, B. T. 1892
Report on the experiments made in 1891 in the treatment of plant diseases. Bull. U.S. Div. Veg. Physiol. Path. No. 3. 76 pages

ANON. 1892
Spraying fruits for insect pests and fungous diseases, with a special consideration of the subject in its relation to the public health. Fmrs' Bull. U.S. Dep. Agric. No. 7

BAILEY, L. H. 1892
Scab-proof Apples. Garden & Forest, New York, V: 442

ADERHOLD, R. 1894
Die perithecienform von *Fusicladium dendriticum*, etc. Ber Deutsch. Bot. Ges., XII: 338–42. Also: Landw. Jahrb., XXV, 875–914, 1896; and Hedwigia, XXXVI: 80–3, 1897

ANON. 1894
Many articles on fruit growing, and on pests and diseases of fruit-trees in J. Bd. Agric., London, 1894 on

Journal of the South-Eastern Agricultural College, Wye begins 1895
Wye, Kent. (J. S-E. agric. Coll. Wye)

Transactions of the British Mycological Society begin 1896
Worcester. (Trans. Brit. mycol. Soc.)

ANON. 1898
English Orchards. J. Bd. Agric., V: 1-10, 145-51

CLINTON, G. P. 1901
Apple Scab. Bull. Illinois Agric. Exp. Sta. No. 67: 109-156

SALMON, E. S. 1907
Apple Scab or 'Black Spot'. J. S-E. agric. Coll. Wye, XVI, 291-6. Also: ibid, XVII: 304-15, and XVIII: 267-70

WALLACE, E. 1913
The Scab Disease of Apples. Bull. Cornell Univ. Agric. Exp. Sta. No. 335: 545-624

HESLER, L. R., AND WHETZEL, H. H. 1917
Manual of Fruit Diseases. Macmillan, New York. 462 pages, 126 figs.

SALMON, E. S., AND WARE, W. M. 1924
Apple and Pear Scab. [Perithecial stage found in Kent] J. Minist. Agric., XXXI, 546-54

WORMALD, H. 1936
Diseases of Fruit and Hops. Crosby Lockwood, London. 290 pages, 24 figs., 40 plates

MINISTRY OF AGRICULTURE AND FISHERIES 1939
Fungus Diseases of Fruit Crops. Collected Leaflets No. 1. Insect Pests of Fruit Crops. Ibid, No. 2. H.M. Stationery Office, London. Each about 150 pages, copiously illustrated, price 1s. 6d.

CHAPTER XXII: WHEAT—SPECIES IN THE MAKING

LITTLE, W. C. 1883
Report on Wheat Mildew [Rust]. J. R. agric. Soc. England, 2nd ser., XIX: 634-93

BARCLAY, A. 1890
On some Rusts and Mildews in India. Journal of Botany, XXVIII: 257-61, 1890; XXX: 1-8, 40-9, 1892

KELLERMAN, W. A. 1891
Spraying to prevent wheat Rust. Bull. Kansas Agric. Exp. Sta. No. 22

GALLOWAY, B. T. 1892
[Spraying] Experiments in the treatment of Rusts affecting Wheat and other cereals. Rep. U.S. Sec. Agric. 1892: 216-24

CARRUTHERS, W. 1892
The Life of the Wheat Plant from Seed to Seed. J. R. agric. Soc. England, 3rd ser., III: 82-99

ERIKSSON, J., AND HENNING, E. 1896
Die Getreideroste. Norstedt, Stockholm. 463 pages, 13 plates

BIBLIOGRAPHY

CROOKES, W. 1898
The Wheat Problem. Presidential Address to B.A. 1898. Amplified: Longmans, London. 100 pages, 8vo, 1917

CARLETON, M. A. 1899
Cereal Rusts of the United States, a physiological investigation. Bull. U.S. Div. Veg. Physiol. Path. No. 16, 74 pages, 4 plates

SMITH, E. F. 1899
Fungous [Fusarium] infestation of agricultural soils in the U.S., Scientific American, Supplement No. 1246, p. 19981

CARLETON, M. A. 1900
The Basis for the improvement of American Wheats. Bull. U.S. Div. Veg. Physiol. Path. No. 24. Also: Bull. U.S. Div. Bot. No. 23

ORTON, W. A. 1900
The Wilt Disease of Cotton and its control. Bull. U.S. Div. Veg. Physiol. Path. No. 27

MENDEL, G. J. 1901
Experiments on Plant Hybridization. Trans. of orig. paper in Abhand. naturforsch. Vereines, Brünn, IV, 1865. J. R. hort. Soc., XXVI: 1-32

WARD, H. M. 1902
On the relations between Host and Parasite in the Bromes and their Brown Rust, *Puccinia dispersa* Erikss. Annals of Botany, XVI: 233-315

WARD, H. M. 1903
On the histology of *Uredo dispersa* Erikss. and the 'Mycoplasm' hypothesis. Philos. Trans. (B), CXCVI: 29-46

BIFFEN, R. H. 1904
Experiments with Wheat and Barley Hybrids illustrating Mendel's Laws of Heredity. J. R. agric. Soc. England, LXV: 337-45. Also: ibid, LXVII: 46-63, 1906

CARLETON, M. A. 1905
Lessons from the Grain-Rust Epidemic of 1904. Fmrs' Bull. U.S. Dep. Agric. No. 219

Journal of Agricultural Science begins 1905
Cambridge. (J. agric. Sci.)

DE VRIES, H. 1905
Species and Varieties, their origin by Mutation. Kegan Paul, New York. 800 pages

BOLLEY, H. L. 1905
Overwintering of Uredospores of *Puccinia graminis* in North Dakota. Science, n.s., XXII: 60-1

BIFFEN, R. H. 1905
Mendel's Law of inheritance and Wheat Breeding. J. agric. Sci., I: 4-48

MCALPINE, D. 1906
The Rusts of Australia. Dep. Agric. Victoria, Melbourne. 349 pages, 55 plates

BIFFEN, R. H. 1907
Studies on the inheritance of Disease-resistance. J. agric. Sci., II: 109-28

WOOD, T. B. 1913
The story of a loaf of bread. Cambs. Univ. Press. 140 pages, 17 figs.

CARLETON, M. A. 1916
The Small Grains. Macmillan, New York, 699 pages, 8vo, 183 figs.

BULLER, A. H. R. 1919
Essays on Wheat. [The story of Marquis wheat] Macmillan, New York. 399 pages, 49 figs.

MAINS, E. B. 1930
Effect of Leaf-Rust, *Puccinia Triticina* Erikss., on yield of wheat. J. agric. Res. Washington, XL: 417-46

LEHMANN, E., KUMMER, H., AND DANNEMANN, H. 1937
Der Schwarzrost, seine Geschichte, seine Biòlogie und seine Bekämpfung in Verbindung mit der Berberitzenfrage. Lehmann, Munich. 584 pages, 88 illustrations

CHAPTER XXIII: MICROBES AND MOLECROBES

MAYER, A. E. 1886
Über die Mosaikkrankheit des Tabaks. Landw. VerSta., XXXII: 450-67. Abs. in Journal of Mycology, VII: 382-5, 1894

SMITH, E. F. 1891
On the Communicability of Peach Yellows, etc. Bull. U.S. Div. Veg. Path. No. 1. 65 pages, 38 plates

IWANOWSKY, D. 1892
Ueber die Mosaikkrankheit der Tabakspflanze. Bull. Acad. Sci. St. Petersbourg, n.s., III, XXV: 67-70. Also: Zbl. Bakt., V: 250-4; VII: 148, 1901

BEIJERINCK, M. W. 1898
Ueber ein Contagium vivum fluidum als Ursache der Fleckenkrankheit der Tabaksblätter. Verh. K. Akad. Wetensch., Amsterdam, II, VI: 1-22. Abs.: Zbl. Bakt. Abt. 2, V: 27-33, 1899

SMITH, E. F. 1899
Are there bacterial diseases of plants? Zbl. Bakt. Abt. 2, V: 271-8. Fischer's reply, ibid: 279-94. Smith's rejoinder, ibid: 810-17

WOODS, A. F. 1902
Observations on the Mosaic Disease of Tobacco. Bull. U.S. Bur. Pl. Ind. No. 18

SMITH, E. F. 1905
Bacteria in relation to Plant Disease. Carnegie Institution, Washington. 3 volumes. I, 1905; II, 1911; III, 1914. In all 962 pages, 4to, profusely illustrated

SMITH, E. F. 1925
Cancer in plants and in Man. Science, n.s., LXI: 419-20

TRUE, R. H. 1927
Erwin F. Smith, 1854-1927. Biography and list of works. Phytopathology, XVII: 675-88

CHAPTER XXIV: CALLING THE CHEMICAL INDUSTRY

FAIRCHILD, D. G. 1894
Bordeaux mixture as a fungicide. Bull. U.S. Div. Veg. Path. No. 6. 55 pages

ANON. 1899
The Eradication of Charlock [by means of copper sulphate solution]. J. Bd. Agric., VI: 17-21

PIERCE, N. B. 1900
Peach Leaf Curl, its nature and treatment. Bull. U.S. Div. Veg. Physiol. Path. No. 20. 204 pages, 30 plates

PICKERING, S. U. 1907
The Chemistry of Bordeaux mixture. J. chem. Soc., XCI (2): 1988-2001. Also: on the carbonates of copper, Trans. chem. Soc., pp. 1409-29, 1909

SCOTT, W. M. 1908
Self-boiled lime-sulphur as a promising fungicide. Circ. U.S. Bur. Pl. Ind. No. 1. Followed up: ibid. No. 27, 1909

BOURCART, E. 1910
Les Maladies des Plantes, leur traitement raisonné et efficace en agriculture et en horticulture. Octave Doin, Paris. 655 pages, 8vo. Trans: 2nd English ed. revised, 'Insecticides, Fungicides & Weedkillers', Benn, London, 1926

WAITE, M. B. 1910
Experiments on the apple with some new and little known fungicides [including copper and iron sulphides]. Circ. U.S. Bur. Pl. Ind. No. 58

PICKERING, S. U. 1910
Researches on copper fungicides. Rep. Woburn. Exp. Fruit Farm, XI: 1.190. Also: J. agric. Sci., IV: 273-81, 1912

SALMON, E. S. 1910
Lime-sulphur washes for use on foliage. J. S-E. agric. Coll. Wye, XIX: 336-50. Also: J. Bd. Agric., XVII: 184-9, 1910, and 881-91, 1911

BROWNING, C. H., AND MACKENZIE, I. 1911
Recent methods in the Diagnosis and Treatment of Syphilis. [Salvarsan, etc.] Constable, London. 303 pages

BARKER, B. T. P., AND GIMINGHAM, C. T. 1911
The fungicidal action of Bordeaux mixture. J. agric. Sci., IV: 76-94

RIEHM, E. 1913
Prüfung einiger Mittel zur Bekampfung des Steinbrandes. [Chlorphenol Mercury for Bunt] Mitt. K. Biol. Anst. Land-u. Forstw., Berlin, XIV: 9

RAMSAY, A. A. 1914
The preparation and composition of lime-sulphur sprays. J. agric. Sci., VI: 194-202, 476-83

DE KRUIF, P. H. 1926
Microbe Hunters. Harcourt Brace, New York. Jonathan Cape, London

MARTIN, H. 1932
The interaction of copper sulphate with calcium hydroxide. Ann. appl. Biol., XIX: 98-120

MINISTRY OF AGRICULTURE AND FISHERIES 1934
Specifications and methods of analysis for certain insecticides and fungicides. Bull. Minist. Agric., No. 82

CHAPTER XXV: LEGISLATIVE MEASURES

TUBEUF, K. F. VON 1895
Pflanzenkrankheiten durch kryptogame Parasiten verursacht. J. Springer, Berlin. 599 pages, 306 figs. Trans. by Wm. G. Smith, 'Diseases of plants induced by cryptogamic parasites', Longmans, London, 1897

SWINGLE, W. T., AND WEBBER, H. J. 1896
The principal diseases of Citrus fruits in Florida. Bull. U.S. Div. Veg. Physiol. Path. No. 8. 40 pages, 8 plates

Bulletins of the U.S. Bureau of Plant Industry begin 1901
Washington. (Bull. U.S. Bur. Pl. Ind.)

Annales Mycologici begin 1903
Berlin. Edited by H. Sydow. (Ann. mycol. Berlin)

SALMON, E. S. 1908
Plant pests and legislation. J. R. agric. Soc. England, LXIX: 122–32

PICKERING, S. U. 1906
Silver-Leaf of Plums. Rep. Woburn Exp. Fruit Farm, VI: 210–24. Also: ibid, XII: 1–34, 1910

FREEMAN, E. M. 1905
Minnesota Plant Diseases. Pioneer Press, St. Paul, 432 pages, 211 figs.

METCALF, H. 1909
The present status of the Chestnut Bark Disease. Bull. U.S. Bur. Pl. Ind. No. 141. Also: ibid., No. 121, 1908

MASSEE, G. 1910
Diseases of Cultivated Plants and Trees. Duckworth, London. 602 pages, 171 figs. Earlier 'Text-books' 1899 and 1903

Phytopathology begins 1911
Ithaca, N.Y. Organ of the American Phytopathological Society

SALMON, E. S. 1911
Economic Mycology and some of its problems. J. S-E. agric. Coll. Wye, XX: 434–51

ERIKSSON, J. 1912
Fungoid Diseases of agricultural Plants. Baillière, Tindall & Cox, London. 208 pages, 117 illusns. 2nd edition, 526 pages, 399 illusns. 1930

ORTON, W. A. 1913
International Phytopathology and Quarantine legislation. Phytopathology, III: 143–51

GROVE, W. B. 1913
British Rust fungi. Cambridge Univ. Press. 412 pages, 290 figs.

STEVENS, F. L. 1913
The Fungi which cause Plant Disease. Macmillan, N.Y. 754 pages, 449 figs.

COOK, M. T. 1913
The Diseases of Tropical Plants. Macmillan, 317 pages, 85 figs.

MASSEE, G. 1913
Mildews, Rusts and Smuts. Dulau, London. 229 pages, 5 plates

Bulletin de la Société de Pathologie Végétale begins 1914
Paris. (Bull. Soc. Path. veg. France)

Annals of Applied Biology begin 1914
London. (Ann. appl. Biol.)

Annual Reports Long Ashton Agric. & Hort. Research Station begin 1913
Bristol. (Rep. Long Ashton Agric. Hort. Res. Sta.)

LINDAU, G., AND SYDOW, P. 1913
Thesaurus litteraturae mycologicae et lichenologicae ratione habita praecique omnium quae adhuc scripta sunt de mycologia applicata [Catalogue of principal papers on applied mycology to 1910] 3 volumes. Borntraeger, Leipzig

BRIERLEY, W. B. 1939
The Association of Applied Biologists and the Annals of Applied Biology. A retrospect, 1904–38. Ann. appl. Biol., XXVI: 178–95, with some portraits

BIBLIOGRAPHY

CHAPTER XXVI: BLIGHT, WART DISEASE, LEAF ROLL

SCHILBERSZKY, K. 1896
Ein neuer Schorfparasit der Kartoffelknollen. Ber. Deutsch bot. Ges., XIV: 36–7

POTTER, M. C. 1902
A new potato disease, *Chrysophlyctis endobiotica.* J. Bd. Agric., IX: 320–3. Also: Massee, G., ibid., 307, on *Oedomyces leproides* Trabut.

PERCIVAL, J. 1909
New facts concerning warty disease of potato. Gdnrs' Chron., July 31st, p. 79

PETHYBRIDGE, G. H. 1910
Investigations on Potato Diseases. Reports I–X, yearly in J. Dep. Agric. Ireland, X–XIX, 1910–19. In all 233 pages, 78 plates

CLINTON, G. P. 1911
Oospores of the Potato Blight fungus. Rep. Connecticut Agric. Exp. Sta. XXXIII–IV: 753–74

APPEL, O., AND SCHLUMBERGER, O. 1911
Die Blattrollkrankheit und unsere Kartoffellernten. Arbeit. Deutsch. Landw. Ges., CXC: 1–102, 3 plates

JONES, L. R., GIDDINGS, N. J., AND LUTMAN, B. F. 1912
Investigations of the Potato Fungus – *Phytophthora infestans.* Bull. U.S. Bur. Pl. Ind. No. 245. 100 pages

PETHYBRIDGE, G. H. 1913
On the rotting of potato tubers by a new species of Phytophthora having a method of sexual reproduction hitherto undescribed. Sci. Proc. R. Dublin Soc., n.s. XIII: 529–65

QUANJER, H. M. 1913
[Phloem necrosis of the potato plant, the cause of Leaf-Roll Disease.] Medel. R. Hoog. Land Tuin-en Boshbouwsch. Wageningen, VI: 41–80

PETHYBRIDGE, G. H., AND MURPHY, P. A. 1913
On pure culture of *P. infestans* de By. and the development of oospores. Sci. Proc. R. Dublin Soc. n.s. XIII: 566–88

ORTON, W. A. 1914
Potato Wilt, Leaf Roll and related diseases. Bull. U.S. Dep. Agric. No. 64

GOUGH, G. C. 1920
Wart Disese of Potatoes. A study of its history, distribution and the discovery of immunity. J. R. hort. Soc., XLV: 301–12

CURTIS, K. M. 1921
The life-history and cytology of *Synchytrium endobioticum* (Schilb.) Perc., the cause of Wart Disease in Potato. Philos. Trans. (B), CCX: 409–78. 4 plates

JONES, L. R. 1931
William Allen Orton. 1877–1930. Biography and list of works. Phytopathology, XXI: 1–9

DAVIDSON, W. D. 1935
History of Potato varieties. J. Irish Free State Dep. Agric., XXXIII: 57–81

KATSURA, S. 1936
The Stunt Disease of Japanese rice, the first plant virosis shown to be transmitted by an insect vector. Phytopathology. XXVI: 887–95

COOK, M. T. 1937
Insect transmission of virus diseases of plants [history of]. The Scientific Monthly, XLIV: 74–177

PETHYBRIDGE, G. H. 1939
History and connotation of the term 'Blattrollkrankheit' (Leaf-roll Disease) as applied to certain potato diseases. Phytopath. Z., XII: 283-91

CHAPTER XXVII: FUNGI AND THE GREAT WAR

MIDDLETON, T. H. 1916
The recent development of German agriculture. Bd. Agric. & Fish., London (C.8305). Abs.: J. Bd. Agric., XXIII: 426-30

QUANJER, H. M., LEK, H. VAN DER, OORTWIJN, B. 1916
[On the nature, mode of dissemination, and control of Phloem Necrosis (Leaf Roll) and allied diseases of the potato.] Medel. R. Hoog. Land Tuin-en Boschbouwsch. Wageningen, X: 1-138. Abs.: Gdnrs' Chron., Sept. 9th, p. 124

BOARD OF AGRICULTURE AND FISHERIES 1917
Report on the occurrence of insect and fungous pests on plants in England and Wales in the year 1917. Bd. Agric. etc., London, Misc. Pub. No. 21. Also: ibid No. 23 for 1918, No. 33 for 1919

STAKMAN, E. C., AND PIEMEISEL, F. J. 1917
Biologic forms of *Puccinia graminis* on cereals & grasses. J. Agric. Res., X: 429-95, with 7 plates

WHETZEL, H. H. 1918
An Outline of the History of Phytopathology. W. B. Saunders & Co. 130 pages, 22 portraits

WORTLEY, E. J. 1918
Potato Leaf Roll, its diagnosis and cause. Phytopathology, VIII: 507-29

U.S. DEPARTMENT OF AGRICULTURE, LIBRARY 1919
A check list of the Publications of the U.S. Dep. Agric. on the subject of Plant Pathology, 1837-1918. Bibl. Cont. No. 1

HALL, D. 1920
Our National Food Supply: Limits of self-support. J. Minist. Agric., XXVII: 133-7

MIDDLETON, T. H. 1920
Farming of the United Kingdom in peace and in war: the Plough Policy and its results. J. Minist. Agric., XXVI: 1192-204

SNELL, J. 1920
Annual Report for 1919 on the Ormskirk trials of varieties of potatoes immune from Wart Disease. Bd. Agric. Misc. Pub. No. 28

BROADBENT, W. H. 1921
Report of the Barberry and the Black Rust of Wheat Survey in S.W. Wales. J. Minist. Agric., XXVIII: 117-23

MURPHY, P. A. 1921
Investigations of Potato Diseases. Dep. Agric., Canada, Div. Bot. Bull. No. 44; 1-88

Review of Applied Mycology begins 1922
Kew. (Rev. appl. Mycol.)

STAKMAN, E. C., AND LEVINE, M. N. 1922
The determination of biologic forms of *Puccinia graminis* in Triticum spp. Tech. Bull. Univ. Minnesota. Agric. Exp. Sta. No. 8

HANSEN, H. R. 1923
Severity of attacks of Black Stem Rust in Denmark, 1884-1921. Phytopathology, XIII: 404-7

ROYAL AGRICULTURAL SOCIETY OF ENGLAND 1925
[Farmers' Guide to] Agricultural Research in 1925. Then annually to 1931, when incorporated in the Society's *Journal*

ROLFE, R. T. AND F. W. 1925
The Romance of the Fungus World: an account of fungus life in its numerous guises, both real and legendary. Chapman & Hall, London. 309 pages, 85 figs.

BUTLER, E. J. 1925
The work of the Imperial Bureau of Mycology. Empire Cotton Growing Review, II, No. 1

AMERICAN PHYTOPATHOLOGICAL SOCIETY 1926
Phytopathological Classics. Translations of historic papers. I. Fabricus on Diseases of Plants (1769) 1926. II. Fontana on Rust of Grain (1767) 1932. III. Millardet on Bordeaux mixture (1885) 1933. IV. Woronin on Club Root (1878) 1934. V. Tillet on Bunt (1755) 1937. VI. Prévost on Bunt (1807) 1939. Edited by H. B. Humphrey. Obtainable from H. H. Whetzel, Cornell Univ. Ithaca, N.Y.

STAKMAN, E. C., AND OTHERS 1927
The Common Barberry and the Black Stem Rust. Fmrs' Bull. U.S. Dep. Agric. No. 1544. Also: ibid., No. 1058

GROVE, W. B. 1931
Trans. from the Latin of the *Selecta Fungorum Carpologia* by L. R. & C. Tulasne. Edited by A. H. R. Buller and C. E. L. Shear. Clarendon Press, Oxford. 3 vols. 864 pages, Imp. 4to, 61 plates

Phytopathologische Zeitschrift begins 1929
Paul Parey, Berlin. [International] (Phytopath. Z.)

BRITISH MYCOLOGICAL SOCIETY 1929
List of Common names of British Plant Diseases. Trans. Brit. mycol. Soc., XIV. Revised and published separately, Clarendon Press, Oxford. 1934. 95 pages, boards, 2s. 6d.

MINISTRY OF AGRICULTURE AND FISHERIES 1934
Report on Fungus, Bacterial and other Diseases of Crops in England and Wales, 1928-32. Bull. Minist. Agric. No. 79. 117 pages, 15 figs, 2s. 0d.

AINSWORTH, G. S. 1937
The Plant Diseases of Great Britain. A bibliography. Chapman & Hall, London. 273 pages

CHAPTER XXVIII: DUSTING AND SEED-DISINFECTION

DARNELL-SMITH, G. P. 1917
The prevention of Bunt [with dry copper carbonate]. Agric. Gaz. New South Wales, XXVIII: 185

Scientific Agriculture 1921
Ottawa. Organ of Canadian Soc. of Technical agriculturalists. (Sci. Agric.)

NEILLIE, C. R., AND HOUSER, J. S. 1922
Fighting insects with airplanes. National Geographic Magazine, Washington, XLI: 333-38, 6 figs.

TISDALE, W. H., AND OTHERS 1925
New seed disinfectants for control of Bunt of wheat and the Smut of oats and barley. Phytopathology, XV: 651-75. Also: Fmrs' Bull. U.S. Dep. Agric. No. 1540, 1927

BAILEY, D. L., AND GREANEY, F. J. 1925
Preliminary experiments on the control of Leaf and Stem Rusts of wheat by sulphur dusts. Sci. Agric., VI: 113-17

SAMPSON, K., AND DAVIES, D. W. 1925
Dry treatment for Smut diseases of cereals. Welsh J. Agric., I: 169-76

MORRILL, A. W. 1926
Airplane Dusting for the control of Vegetable pests on the Mexican West coast. J. Econ. Entomol., XIX: 695-99

GÜSSOW, H. T., AND CONNERS, I. L. 1927
Smut diseases of cultivated plants and their control. Bull. Canadian Dep. Agric. n.s. No. 81. 79 pages, 15 figs.

BAYER COMPANY LTD. 1927
Notes on the history of seed-disinfection, with many refs., in *advertisement* pages of Phytopathology, XVII

O'BRIEN, D. G., AND PRENTICE, E. G. 1930
Leaf Stripe or Yellow Leaf of oats. Scot. J. Agric., XIII: 272-84

REDDY, C. S., AND BURNETT, L. C. 1930
Development of seed treatments for the control of Barley Stripe. Phytopathology, XX: 367-90

HEALD, F. D. 1932
Manual of Plant Diseases. McGraw-Hill. 2nd revised edition. 891 pages, 272 figs. (1st edition, 1926)

BULLER, A. H. R. 1933
Researches on the Fungi. On the Bunt fungus, Vol. V, 1933, but 6 volumes altogether, 1909-1934. Longmans, London. Roy. 8vo

U.S. BUREAU OF ENTOMOLOGY 1934
Annotated bibliography on use of airplanes in insect control, 1922-34

GREANEY, F. J. 1934
The prevention of cereal rusts by the use of fungicidal dusts. Dep. Agric. Canada. Bull. No. 171, New Series. 90 pages, 30 figs., 107 refs.

CUNNINGHAM, G. H. 1935
Plant Protection by the aid of Therapeutants. Published by the author, Palmerston North, N.Z. 243 pages, 8vo, 22 figs., 4 plates, extensive bibliography

DILLON WESTON, W. A. R., HANLEY, F., AND BOOER, J. R. 1935
Outline of an investigation on disinfectant dusts containing mercury. J. agric. Sci., XXV, 628-49. Also: large-scale field trials, *ibid.*, XXVII: 43-52, 1937

MARTIN, H. 1936
The Scientific Principle of Plant Protection, with special reference to chemical control. 2nd edition. Arnolds, London. 379 pages. (1st ed. 1928: 3rd, 1940)

CHAPTER XXIX: NEW SPRAYS FOR OLD

DE BRUYN, HELENA L. G. 1926
The overwintering of *Phytophthora infestans* (Mont.) de Bary. Phytopathology, XVI: 121-40

MURPHY, P. A. 1927
The production of the resting spores of *Phytophthora infestans* on potato tubers. Sci. Proc. R. Dublin Soc., n.s., XVIII: 407-12

WOODMAN, R. M., AND TAYLOR, MCK. 1929
The character, properties and possible uses of Bentonite, a sodium clay. J. Soc. Chem. Ind., XLVIII: 121-4. See also: Anon, Chemical Age, Nov. 9th, 419-20, 1935

WILTSHIRE, S. P. 1931
Correlation of weather conditions with outbreaks of Potato Blight. Quart. J. roy. meterol. Soc., LVII: 304-16

BEWLEY, W. F., AND ORCHARD, O. B. 1932
The Control of Tomato Leaf Mould. Ann. appl. Biol., XIX: 185-9

BRISCOE, M. 1932
The fatty alcohols and their sulphonated products. Ind. Chem., VIII: 67-9

MCCALLAN, S. E. A., AND WILCOXON, F. 1934
Fungicidal action and the periodic system of the elements. Cont. Boyce Thompson Inst., VI: 479-500

YOUNG, H. G., AND BECKENBACH, J. R. 1936
Spreader materials [bentonite] for insoluble copper sprays. Phytopathology, XXVI: 450-5

MARTIN, H., KEARNS, H. G. H., AND MARSH, R. W. 1934
Combined washes [for fruit-trees etc.]. Ann. Rep. Long Ashton Agric. Hort. Res. Stat., 1934: 109-25

CHAPTER XXX: DEGENERATION AND VIRUS DISEASES

MURPHY, P. A., AND WORTLEY, E. J. 1920
Relation of climate to the development and control of Leaf Roll of potato. Phytopathology, X: 407-14

SCHULTZ, E. S., AND FOLSOM, D. 1923
Transmission, variation and control of certain degeneration diseases of the Irish potatoes. J. agric. Res , XXV, 43-117. Followed up: ibid., XXX: 493-528, 1925, and in Bull. Maine Agric. Exp. Sta. No. 316, 1924, and No. 331, 1926

WHITEHEAD, T. 1921
Leaf-Curl and Mosaic of potatoes, and their relation to deterioration in yield. Univ. Coll. N. Wales, Bangor, Rep. agric. Expts. 1920-21: 48-50. Also: Ann. appl. Biol., XI: 31-41, 1924

MURPHY, P. A., AND MCKAY, R. 1925
Investigations on the Leaf-roll and Mosaic diseases of the potato. J. Dep. Agric. & Lands, Ireland, XXV: 138-54, 1925; XXV: 1-8, 1926; XXVI: 295-305, 1927

COONS, G. H., AND KOTILA, J. E. 1925
The transmissible lytic principle (bacteriophage) in relation to plant pathogens. Phytopathology, XV: 357-70

SALAMAN, R. N. 1926
Potato Varieties. Cambs. Univ. Press. 378 pages, 19 figs., 9 plates

RIVERS, T. M. 1928
Filterable Viruses. Baillière, Tindale & Cox, London. 438 pages, 8vo

BROWN, W., AND BLACKMAN, V. H. 1930
Field experiments on the deterioration of the Scotch potato seed in England. Ann. appl. Biol., XVII: 1-27

GARDNER, A. D. 1931
Microbes and Ultramicrobes. An account of bacteria, viruses and the bacteriophage. Methuen Monograph. 128 pages, 21 figs., 3s. 6d.

SALAMAN, R. N. 1932
The analysis and synthesis of some diseases of the Mosaic type; the problems of carriers and auto-infection in the potato. Proc. roy. Soc. B, CX: 186-224

SMITH, K. M. 1933
Recent Advances in the study of plant viruses. Churchill, London. 423 pages, 8vo, 67 text figs., 1 plate

ELFORD, W. J. 1933
The principles of ultrafiltration as applied in biological studies. Proc. roy. Soc. B, CXII: 384-406

SALAMAN, R. N. 1933
Protective inoculation against a plant virus. Nature, CXXXI: 468: Also, Research in relation to the production of 'good' potato seed. Agricultural Progress, XI: 77-86, 1934

CURRIE, J. F. 1934
The production of high-grade seed-potatoes in North Wales. J. Minist. Agric., XL: 316-26

DAVIDSON, W. D. 1933
Potato growing for seed purposes. Irish Free State Dep. Agric., Dublin, 236 pages, 78 illusns.

STANLEY, W. M. 1935
Isolation of a crystalline protein possessing the properties of the tobacco Mosaic virus. Science, LXXXI: 644-5. Also: Phytopathology, XXVI: 305-20, 1936

CALDWELL, J. 1935
On the interactions of two strains of a plant virus: experiments on induced immunity in plants. Proc. roy. Soc. B, CXVII: 120-39

KUNKEL, L. O. 1936
Virus diseases of plants: twenty-five years of progress, 1910-1935. Mem. Bot. Gard. Brooklyn, IV. Also: Heat treatment for the cure of Peach Yellows. Phytopathology, XXVI: 809-30

MURPHY, P. A. 1936
Nature and control of potato virus diseases. Nature, CXXXVIII: 955-6. [succinct]

COOKE, M. T., AND OTERA, J. I. 1936
Partial bibliography of virus diseases of plants. J. Agric., Univ. Puerto Rico, XVIII: 5-410, 1934; XIX: 129-313, 1935; XX: 691-803, 1936

BAWDEN, F. C., PIRIE, N. W., BERNAL, J. D., AND FANKUCHEN, I. 1936
Liquid crystalline substances from virus infected plants. Nature, CXXXVIII: 1051-2

DAVIES, M. W. 1936
Studies on the Aphides affecting the potato crop. Ann. appl. Biol., XXI: 283-99; XXIII, 401-8

SMITH, K. M. 1937
A Textbook of Plant Virus Diseases. Churchill, London. 615 pages, 101 illusns.

COOK, M. T. 1938
Pioneers in the study of virus diseases of plants. The Scientific Monthly, XLVI: 41-6

SMITH, HENDERSON J. 1938
Some recent developments in virus research. Ann. appl. Biol., XXV: 227-243

HOLMES, F. O. 1939
Proposal for extension of the binomial system of nomenclature to include viruses. Phytopathology, XXIX: 431-6. Amplified: Handbook of Phytopathogenic viruses. Burgess, Minneapolis. 221 pages

BAWDEN, F. C. 1939
Plant viruses and virus diseases. Chronica Botanica Co. Leiden, Holland. 272 pages, 36 illusns.

CHAPTER XXXI: TOWARDS IMMUNITY

SALMON, E. S., AND WARE, W. M. 1925
The Downy Mildew of the Hop and its epidemic occurrence in 1924. Ann. appl. Biol., XII: 121-5. Also: Misc. Pub. Minist. Agric. No. 42, 1925

GÄUMANN, E. 1926
Vergleichende Morphologie der Pilze. G. Fischer, Jena. 626 pages, 398 illusns. Trans. by C. W. Dodge, 'Comparative Morphology of the Fungi'. McGraw-Hill, 1928

BROOKS, F. T. 1928
Plant Diseases. Oxford Univ. Press. 386 pages, 62 figs.

GWYNNE-VAUGHAN, H., AND BARNES, B. 1927
The Structure and Development of the Fungi. Cambs. Univ. Press. 384 pages, 285 figs. (2nd edition, 1937)

MÜLLER, K. O. 1928
Über die Züchtung Krautfäuleresistenter Kartoffelsorten. Z. Pflanzenzüchtung, XIII: 143-56

REDDICK, D. 1928
Blight-resistant potatoes. Phytopathology, XVIII: 483-502. Also: *ibid.*, XX: 987-91, 1930

ARTHUR, J. C., AND OTHERS 1929
The Plant Rusts (Uredinales). John Wiley, New York. 446 pages, 186 figs.

ALLEN, RUTH F. 1930
A cytological study of heterothallism in *Puccinia graminis.* J. agric. Res., XL: 585-614

STAKMAN, E. C., LEVINE, M. N., AND COTTER, R. U. 1930
Origin of physiologic forms of *Puccinia graminis* through hybridization and mutation. Sci. Agric., X: 707-20

CRAIGIE, J. H. 1931
An experimental investigation of sex in the Rust fungi. [With historical summary]. Phytopathölgy, XXI: 1001-46

IRISH FREE STATE DEPARTMENT OF AGRICULTURE 1931
Collected Leaflets on all agricultural subjects, Nos. 1 to 104 inclusive. [A modern Hesiod.] Stationery Office, Dublin. About 800 pages, illustrated. Price 1s. 0d.

GREEN, D. E. 1933
A disease of Antirrhinums new to Great Britain. Gdnrs' Chron., Aug. 12th, p. 131. Also: J. hort. Soc., LXIX: 119-26, 1934, and LXII, 530-7, 1937

MÜLLER, K. O. 1933
[On the Biotypes of *Phytophthora infestans* and their geographical distribution in Germany]. Nachr. deutsch. Pflanzenschutzd., XIII: 91-2

O'CONNOR, C. 1933
Potato Breeding and resistance to Blight. Gdnrs' Chron. Feb. 11th, pp. 104-5

REDDICK, D. 1934
Elimination of Potato Late Blight from North America? Phytopathology, XXIV: 555-7

World List of Scientific Periodicals 1934
2nd edition. Oxford Univ. Press. [Reference to this List will indicate at which libraries in Great Britain any periodical mentioned herein may be consulted.]

BESSEY, E. A. 1935
A Text-book of Mycology. Blakiston's, Philadelphia. 495 pages, 136 illusns. [Guide to literature for identification of fungi, pp. 395-468]

MAINS, E. B. 1935
Rust-resistant Snapdragons. Phytopathology, XXV: 977-991

HOWARD, A. 1936
The Rôle of Insects and Fungi in Agriculture. Empire Cotton Growing Review, XIII: 186-92. Also: The Manufacture of Humus by the Indore Process. J. R. Soc. Arts, LXXXIV: 26-59, 1935

BUKASOV, S. M. 1936
The Problems of Potato Breeding. Amer. Potato Journal, XIII: 235-52

FREEMAN, E. M. 1936
Phytopathology – and its future. Phytopathology, XXVI: 76-82

ANON. 1936
The South American Potatoes and their breeding value. Imp. Bur. Plant Genetics, School of Agric., Cambridge. 15 pages. Price 3s. 6d.

HEALD, F. D. 1937
Introduction to Plant Pathology. McGraw-Hill. 591 pages, 200 figs.

COONS, G. H. 1937
Progress in Plant Pathology; Control of diseases by resistant varieties. Phytopathology, XXVII: 622-32

STEVENSON, F. J., AND OTHERS 1937
Breeding for resistance to Late Blight in the Potato. Phytopathology, XXVII: 1059-70

SALAMAN, R. N. 1937
Potato Variety Production: a new departure. Gdnrs' Chron., Oct. 30th, pp 326-7

REDDICK, D., AND MILLS, W. 1938
Building up virulence in *Phytophthora infestans*. Amer. Potato Journal, XV: 29-34. Also: *ibid.*, XVI: 220-4, 1939

BOWER, F. O. 1938
Sixty years of Botany in Britain, 1875-1935. Macmillan. 112 pages, with portraits

WAKSMAN, S. A. 1938
Humus. Origin, chemical composition, and importance in nature. Baillière, Tindall & Cox. London. 526 pages

MARTIN, H. 1939
The Trend of Progress: Fungicides. Chem. & Ind., LVIII: 641-43

MELHUS, I. E., AND KENT, G. C. 1939
Elements of Plant Pathology. Macmillan, New York. 493 pages, 259 figs.

NATIONAL INSTITUTE OF AGRICULTURAL BOTANY 1939
Varieties of Potatoes. The most valuable source of human and animal food in War Time. Nat. Inst. Agric. Bot. Farmers' Leaflet No. 3

REDDICK D. 1939
Whence came *Phytophthora infestans*? Chronica Botanica, V: 410-12

INDEX

INDEX

INDEX

INDEX

CATALOG OF DOVER BOOKS

CHEMISTRY AND PHYSICAL CHEMISTRY

ORGANIC CHEMISTRY, F. C. Whitmore. The entire subject of organic chemistry for the practicing chemist and the advanced student. Storehouse of facts, theories, processes found elsewhere only in specialized journals. Covers aliphatic compounds (500 pages on the properties and synthetic preparation of hydrocarbons, halides, proteins, ketones, etc.), alicyclic compounds, aromatic compounds, heterocyclic compounds, organophosphorus and organometallic compounds. Methods of synthetic preparation analyzed critically throughout. Includes much of biochemical interest. "The scope of this volume is astonishing," INDUSTRIAL AND ENGINEERING CHEMISTRY. 12,000-reference index. 2387-item bibliography. Total of x + 1005pp. 5⅜ x 8. Two volume set.
S700 Vol I Paperbound **$2.00**
S701 Vol II Paperbound **$2.00**
The set **$4.00**

THE PRINCIPLES OF ELECTROCHEMISTRY, D. A. MacInnes. Basic equations for almost every subfield of electrochemistry from first principles, referring at all times to the soundest and most recent theories and results; unusually useful as text or as reference. Covers coulometers and Faraday's Law, electrolytic conductance, the Debye-Hueckel method for the theoretical calculation of activity coefficients, concentration cells, standard electrode potentials, thermodynamic ionization constants, pH, potentiometric titrations, irreversible phenomena, Planck's equation, and much more. "Excellent treatise," AMERICAN CHEMICAL SOCIETY JOURNAL. "Highly recommended," CHEMICAL AND METALLURGICAL ENGINEERING. 2 Indices. Appendix. 585-item bibliography. 137 figures. 94 tables. ii + 478pp. 5⅝ x 8⅜.
S52 Paperbound **$2.35**

THE CHEMISTRY OF URANIUM: THE ELEMENT, ITS BINARY AND RELATED COMPOUNDS, J. J. Katz and E. Rabinowitch. Vast post-World War II collection and correlation of thousands of AEC reports and published papers in a useful and easily accessible form, still the most complete and up-to-date compilation. Treats "dry uranium chemistry," occurrences, preparation, properties, simple compounds, isotopic composition, extraction from ores, spectra, alloys, etc. Much material available only here. Index. Thousands of evaluated bibliographical references. 324 tables, charts, figures. xxi + 609pp. 5⅜ x 8.
S757 Paperbound **$2.95**

KINETIC THEORY OF LIQUIDS, J. Frenkel. Regarding the kinetic theory of liquids as a generalization and extension of the theory of solid bodies, this volume covers all types of arrangements of solids, thermal displacements of atoms, interstitial atoms and ions, orientational and rotational motion of molecules, and transition between states of matter. Mathematical theory is developed close to the physical subject matter. 216 bibliographical footnotes. 55 figures. xi + 485pp. 5⅜ x 8.
S94 Clothbound **$3.95**
S95 Paperbound **$2.45**

POLAR MOLECULES, Pieter Debye. This work by Nobel laureate Debye offers a complete guide to fundamental electrostatic field relations, polarizability, molecular structure. Partial contents: electric intensity, displacement and force, polarization by orientation, molar polarization and molar refraction, halogen-hydrides, polar liquids, ionic saturation, dielectric constant, etc. Special chapter considers quantum theory. Indexed. 172pp. 5⅜ x 8.
S64 Paperbound **$1.50**

ELASTICITY, PLASTICITY AND STRUCTURE OF MATTER, R. Houwink. Standard treatise on rheological aspects of different technically important solids such as crystals, resins, textiles, rubber, clay, many others. Investigates general laws for deformations; determines divergences from these laws for certain substances. Covers general physical and mathematical aspects of plasticity, elasticity, viscosity. Detailed examination of deformations, internal structure of matter in relation to elastic and plastic behavior, formation of solid matter from a fluid, conditions for elastic and plastic behavior of matter. Treats glass, asphalt, gutta percha, balata, proteins, baker's dough, lacquers, sulphur, others. 2nd revised, enlarged edition. Extensive revised bibliography in over 500 footnotes. Index. Table of symbols. 214 figures. xviii + 368pp. 6 x 9¼.
S385 Paperbound **$2.45**

THE PHASE RULE AND ITS APPLICATION, Alexander Findlay. Covering chemical phenomena of 1, 2, 3, 4, and multiple component systems, this "standard work on the subject" (NATURE, London), has been completely revised and brought up to date by A. N. Campbell and N. O. Smith. Brand new material has been added on such matters as binary, tertiary liquid equilibria, solid solutions in ternary systems, quinary systems of salts and water. Completely revised to triangular coordinates in ternary systems, clarified graphic representation, solid models, etc. 9th revised edition. Author, subject indexes. 236 figures. 505 footnotes, mostly bibliographic. xii + 494pp. 5⅜ x 8.
S91 Paperbound **$2.45**

MATHEMATICAL RECREATIONS

MATHEMATICS, MAGIC AND MYSTERY, Martin Gardner. Card tricks, feats of mental mathematics, stage mind-reading, other "magic" explained as applications of probability, sets, theory of numbers, topology, various branches of mathematics. Creative examination of laws and their applications with scores of new tricks and insights. 115 sections discuss tricks wtih cards, dice, coins; geometrical vanishing tricks, dozens of others. No sleight of hand needed; mathematics guarantees success. 115 illustrations. xii + 174pp. 5⅜ x 8.
T335 Paperbound **$1.00**

MATHEMATICAL EXCURSIONS, Helen A. Merrill. Fun, recreation, insights into elementary problem-solving. A mathematical expert guides you along by-paths not generally travelled in elementary math courses—how to divide by inspection, Russian peasant system of multiplication; memory systems for pi; building odd and even magic squares; dyadic systems; facts about 37; square roots by geometry; Tchebichev's machine; drawing five-sided figures; dozens more. Solutions to more difficult ones. 50 illustrations. 145pp. 5⅜ x 8.
T350 Paperbound **$1.00**

CRYPTOGRAPHY, L. D. Smith. Excellent elementary introduction to enciphering, deciphering secret writing. Explains transposition, substitution ciphers; codes; solutions. Geometrical patterns, route transcription, columnar transposition, other methods. Mixed cipher systems; single-alphabet, polyalphabetical substitution; mechanical devices; Vigenere system, etc. Enciphering Japanese; explanation of Baconian Biliteral cipher; frequency tables. More than 150 problems provide practical application. Bibliography. Index. 164pp. 5⅜ x 8.
T247 Paperbound **$1.00**

CRYPTANALYSIS, Helen F. Gaines. (Formerly ELEMENTARY CRYPTANALYSIS.) A standard elementary and intermediate text for serious students. It does not confine itself to old material, but contains much that is not generally known, except to experts. Concealment, Transposition, Substitution ciphers; Vigenere, Kasiski, Playfair, multafid, dozens of other techniques. Appendix with sequence charts, letter frequencies in English, 5 other languages, English word frequencies. Bibliography. 167 codes. New to this edition: solution to codes. vi + 230pp. 5⅜ x 8. T97 Paperbound **$1.95**

MAGIC SQUARES AND CUBES, W. S. Andrews. Only book-length treatment in English, a thorough non-technical description and analysis. Here are nasik, overlapping, pandiagonal, serrated squares; magic circles, cubes, spheres, rhombuses. Try your hand at 4-dimensional magical figures! Much unusual folklore and tradition included. High school algebra is sufficient. 754 diagrams and illustrations. viii + 419pp. 5⅜ x 8. T658 Paperbound **$1.85**

BIOLOGICAL SCIENCES

THE ORIGIN OF LIFE, A. I. Oparin. A classic of biology. This is the first modern statement of the theory of gradual evolution of life from nitrocarbon compounds. A brand-new evaluation of Oparin's theory in light of later research, by Dr. S. Morgulis, University of Nebraska. xxv +270pp. 5⅜ x8. S213 Paperbound **$1.75**

HEREDITY AND YOUR LIFE, A. M. Winchester. Authoritative, concise explanation of human genetics, in non-technical terms. What factors determine characteristics of future generations, how they may be altered; history of genetics, application of knowledge to control health, intelligence, number of entire populations. Physiology of reproduction, chromosomes, genes, blood types, Rh factor, dominant, recessive traits, birth by proxy, sexual abnormalities, radiation, much more. Index. 75 illus. 345pp. 5⅜ x 8. T598 Paperbound **$1.45**

MATHEMATICAL BIOPHYSICS: PHYSICO-MATHEMATICAL FOUNDATIONS OF BIOLOGY, N. Rashevsky. One of most important books in modern biology, now revised, expanded with new chapters, to include most significant recent contributions. Vol. 1: Diffusion phenomena, particularly diffusion drag forces, their effects. Old theory of cell division based on diffusion drag forces, other theoretical approaches, more exhaustively treated than ever. Theories of excitation, conduction in nerves, with formal theories plus physico-chemical theory. Vol. 2: Mathematical theories of various phenomena in central nervous system. New chapters on theory of color vision, of random nets. Principle of optimal design, extended from earlier edition. Principle of relational mapping of organisms, numerous applications. Introduces into mathematical biology such branches of math as topology, theory of sets. Index. 236 illustrations. Total of 988pp. 5⅜ x 8.
S574 Vol. 1 (Books 1, 2) Paperbound **$2.50**
S575 Vol. 2 (Books 3, 4) Paperbound **$2.50**
2 vol. set **$5.00**

ELEMENTS OF MATHEMATICAL BIOLOGY, A. J. Lotka. A pioneer classic, the first major attempt to apply modern mathematical techniques on a large scale to phenomena of biology, biochemistry, psychology, ecology, similar life sciences. Partial Contents: Statistical meaning of irreversibility; Evolution as redistribution; Equations of kinetics of evolving systems; Chemical, inter-species equilibrium; parameters of state; Energy transformers of nature, etc. Can be read with profit even by those having no advanced math; unsurpassed as study-reference. Formerly titled ELEMENTS OF PHYSICAL BIOLOGY. 72 figures. xxx + 460pp. 5⅜ x 8. S346 Paperbound **$2.45**

FRESHWATER MICROSCOPY, W. J. Garnett. Non-technical, practical book for the layman and student. Contains only information directly confirmed by the distinguished British scientist's personal observation. Tells how to collect and examine specimens, describes equipment and accessories, mounting, staining, correct illumination, measuring, the microprojector, etc. Describes hundreds of different plant and animal species, over 200 illustrated by microphotos. Many valuable suggestions on the work amateurs can do to throw new light on the field. Index. 51 full-page plates. 50 diagrams. Bibliography. 2 Appendices. Glossary of scientific terms. xii + 300pp. 6 x 9. S790 Clothbound **$5.95**

CULTURE METHODS FOR INVERTEBRATE ANIMALS, P. S. Galtsoff, F. E. Lutz, P. S. Welch, J. G. Needham, eds. A compendium of practical experience of hundreds of scientists and technicians, covering invertebrates from protozoa to chordata, in 313 articles on 17 phyla. Explains in great detail food, protection, environment, reproduction conditions, rearing methods, embryology, breeding seasons, schedule of development, much more. Includes at least one species of each considerable group. Half the articles are on class insecta. Introduction. 97 illustrations. Bibliography. Index. xxix + 590pp. 5⅜ x 8. S526 Paperbound **$2.75**

THE BIOLOGY OF THE LABORATORY MOUSE, edited by **G. D. Snell.** 1st prepared in 1941 by the staff of the Roscoe B. Jackson Memorial Laboratory, this is still the standard treatise on the mouse, assembling an enormous amount of material for which otherwise you spend hours of research. Embryology, reproduction, histology, spontaneous tumor formation, genetics of tumor transplantation, endocrine secretion & tumor formation, milk, influence & tumor formation, inbred, hybrid animals, parasites, infectious diseases, care & recording. Classified bibliography of 1122 items. 172 figures, including 128 photos. ix + 497pp. 6⅛ x 9¼. S248 Clothbound **$6.00**

THE BIOLOGY OF THE AMPHIBIA, G. K. Noble, Late Curator of Herpetology at the Am. Mus. of Nat. Hist. Probably the most used text on amphibia, unmatched in comprehensiveness, clarity, detail. 19 chapters plus 85-page supplement cover development; heredity; life history; speciation; adaptation; sex, integument, respiratory, circulatory, digestive, muscular, nervous systems; instinct, intelligence, habits, environment, economic value, relationships, classification, etc. "Nothing comparable to it," C. H. Pope, Curator of Amphibia, Chicago Mus. of Nat. Hist. 1047 bibliographic references. 174 illustrations. 600pp. 5⅜ x 8. S206 Paperbound **$2.98**

STUDIES ON THE STRUCTURE AND DEVELOPMENT OF VERTEBRATES, E. S. Goodrich. A definitive study by the greatest modern comparative anatomist. Exceptional in its accounts of the ossicles of the ear, the separate divisions of the coelem and mammalian diaphragm, and the 5 chapters devoted to the head region. Also exhaustive morphological and phylogenetic expositions of skeleton, fins and limbs, skeletal visceral arches and labial cartilages, visceral clefts and gills, vascular, respiratory, excretory, and periphal nervous systems, etc., from fish to the higher mammals. 754 illustrations. 69 page biographical study by C. C. Hardy. Bibliography of 1186 references. "What an undertaking . . . to write a textbook which will summarize adequately and succinctly all that has been done in the realm of Vertebrate Morphology these recent years," Journal of Anatomy. Index. Two volumes. Total 906pp. 5⅜ x 8. Two vol. set S449-50 Paperbound **$5.00**

THE GENETICAL THEORY OF NATURAL SELECTION, R. A. Fisher. 2nd revised edition of a vital reviewing of Darwin's Selection Theory in terms of particulate inheritance, by one of the great authorities on experimental and theoretical genetics. Theory is stated in mathematical form. Special features of particulate inheritance are examined: evolution of dominance, maintenance of specific variability, mimicry and sexual selection, etc. 5 chapters on man and his special circumstances as a social animal. 16 photographs. Bibliography. Index. x + 310pp. 5⅜ x 8. S466 Paperbound **$1.85**

THE AUTOBIOGRAPHY OF CHARLES DARWIN, AND SELECTED LETTERS, edited by **Francis Darwin.** Darwin's own record of his early life; the historic voyage aboard the "Beagle"; the furor surrounding evolution, and his replies; reminiscences of his son. Letters to Henslow, Lyell, Hooker, Huxley, Wallace, Kingsley, etc., and thoughts on religion and vivisection. We see how he revolutionized geology with his concept of ocean subsidence; how his great books on variation of plants and animals, primitive man, the expression of emotion among primates, plant fertilization, carnivorous plants, protective coloration, etc., came into being. Appendix. Index. 365pp. 5⅜ x 8. T479 Paperbound **$1.65**

THE LIFE OF PASTEUR, R. Vallery-Radot. 13th edition of this definitive biography, cited in Encyclopaedia Britannica. Authoritative, scholarly, well-documented with contemporary quotes, observations; gives complete picture of Pasteur's personal life; especially thorough presentation of scientific activities with silkworms, fermentation, hydrophobia, innoculation, etc. Introduction by Sir William Osler. Index. 505pp. 5⅜ x 8. T633 Paperbound **$2.00**

ANTONY VAN LEEUWENHOEK AND HIS "LITTLE ANIMALS," edited by Clifford Dobell. First book to treat extensively, accurately, life and works (relating to protozoology, bacteriology) of first microbiologist, bacteriologist, micrologist. Includes founding papers of protozoology, bacteriology; history of Leeuwenhoek's life; discussions of his microscopes, methods, language. His writing conveys sense of an enthusiastic, naive genius, as he looks at rainwater, pepper water, vinegar, frog's skin, rotifers, etc. Extremely readable, even for non-specialists. "One of the most interesting and enlightening books I have ever read," Dr. C. C. Bass, former Dean, Tulane U. School of Medicine. Only authorized edition. 400-item bibliography. Index. 32 illust. 442pp. 5⅜ x 8. S594 Paperbound **$2.25**

MICROGRAPHIA, Robert Hooke. Hooke, 17th century British universal scientific genius, was a major pioneer in celestial mechanics, optics, gravity, and many other fields, but his greatest contribution was this book, now reprinted entirely from the original 1665 edition, which gave microscopy its first great impetus. With all the freshness of discovery, he describes fully his microscope, and his observations of cork, the edge of a razor, insects' eyes, fabrics, and dozens of other different objects. 38 plates, full-size or larger, contain all the original illustrations. This book is also a fundamental classic in the fields of combustion and heat theory, light and color theory, botany and zoology, hygrometry, and many other fields. It contains such farsighted predictions as the famous anticipation of artificial silk. The final section is concerned with Hooke's observations on the moon and stars. 323pp. 5⅜ x 8. Paperbound **$2.00**

CONDITIONED REFLEXES: AN INVESTIGATION OF THE PHYSIOLOGICAL ACTIVITIES OF THE CEREBRAL CORTEX, I. P. Pavlov. Full, authorized translation of Pavlov's own survey of his work in experimental psychology reviews entire course of experiments, summarizes conclusions, outlines psychological system based on famous "conditioned reflex" concept. Details of technical means used in experiments, observations on formation of conditioned reflexes, function of cerebral hemispheres, results of damage, nature of sleep, typology of nervous system, significance of experiments for human psychology. Trans. by Dr. G. V. Anrep, Cambridge Univ. 235-item bibliography. 18 figures. 445pp. 5⅜ x 8. S614 Paperbound **$2.25**

THE PRINCIPLES OF PSYCHOLOGY, William James. The full long course, unabridged, of one of the great classics of Western science. Wonderfully lucid descriptions of human mental activity, consciousness, emotions, reason, abnormal phenomena, and similar topics. Examines motor zones, sensory aphasia, phosphorus and thought, cerebral thermometry, neural process in perception, ideo-motor action—in short, the entire spectrum of human mental activity. "Standard reading . . . a classic of interpretation," PSYCHIATRIC QUARTERLY. 94 illustrations. Two volume set. Total of 1408pp. 5⅜ x 8. T381 Vol I Paperbound **$2.50**
T382 Vol II Paperbound **$2.50**
The set **$5.00**

THE TRAVELS OF WILLIAM BARTRAM, edited by Mark Van Doren. This famous source-book of American anthropology, natural history, geography is the record kept by Bartram in the 1770's, on travels through the wilderness of Florida, Georgia, the Carolinas. Containing accurate and beautiful descriptions of Indians, settlers, fauna, flora, it is one of the finest pieces of Americana ever written. Introduction by Mark Van Doren. 13 original illustrations. Index. 448pp. 5⅜ x 8. T13 Paperbound **$2.00**

FRUIT KEY AND TWIG KEY TO TREES AND SHRUBS (FRUIT KEY TO NORTHEASTERN TREES, TWIG TREE TO DECIDUOUS WOODY PLANTS OF EASTERN NORTH AMERICA), W. M. Harlow. The only guides with photographs of every twig and fruit described—especially valuable to the novice. The fruit key (both deciduous trees and evergreens) has an introduction explaining seeding, organs involved, fruit types and habits. The twig key introduction treats growth and morphology. In the keys proper, identification is easy and almost automatic. This exceptional work, widely used in university courses, is especially useful for identification in winter, or from the fruit or seed only. Over 350 photos, up to 3 times natural size. Bibliography, glossary, index of common and scientific names, in each key. xvii + 125pp. 5⅝ x 8⅜. T511 Paperbound **$1.25**

TREES OF THE EASTERN AND CENTRAL UNITED STATES AND CANADA, W. M. Harlow, Professor of Wood Technology, College of Forestry, State University of N. Y., Syracuse, N. Y. This middle-level text is a serious work covering more than 140 native trees and important escapes, with information on general appearance, growth habit, leaf forms, flowers, fruit, bark, and other features. Commercial use, distribution, habitat, and woodlore are also given. Keys within the text enable you to locate various species with ease. With this book you can identify at sight almost any tree you are likely to encounter; you will know which trees have edible fruit, which are suitable for house planting, and much other useful and interesting information. More than 600 photographs and figures. xiii + 288pp. 4⅝ x 6½. T395 Paperbound **$1.35**

HOW TO KNOW THE FERNS, F. T. Parsons. Ferns, among our most lovely native plants, are all too little known. This modern classic of nature lore will enable the layman to identify any American fern he is likely to come across. After an introduction on the structure and life of ferns, the 57 most important ferns are fully pictured and described (arranged upon a simple identification key). Index of Latin and English names. 61 illustrations and 42 full-page plates. xiv + 215pp. 5⅜ x 8. T740 Paperbound **$1.25**

INSECT LIFE AND INSECT NATURAL HISTORY, S. W. Frost. Unusual for emphasizing habits, social life, and ecological relations of insects, rather than more academic aspects of classification and morphology. Prof. Frost's enthusiasm and knowledge are everywhere evident as he discusses insect associations, and specialized habits like leaf-mining, leaf-rolling, and case-making, the gall insects, the boring insects, aquatic insects, etc. He examines all sorts of matters not usually covered in general works, such as: insects as human food; insect music and musicians; insect response to electric and radio waves; use of insects in art and literature. The admirably executed purpose of this book, which covers the middle ground between elementary treatment and scholarly monographs, is to excite the reader to observe for himself. Over 700 illustrations. Extensive bibliography. x + 524pp. 5⅜ x 8.
T517 Paperbound **$2.25**

COMMON SPIDERS OF THE UNITED STATES, J. H. Emerton. Only non-technical, but thorough, reliable guide to spiders for the layman. Over 200 spiders from all parts of the country, arranged by scientific classification, are identified by shape and color, number of eyes, habitat and range, habits, etc. Full text, 501 line drawings and photographs, and valuable introduction explain webs, poisons, threads, capturing and preserving spiders, etc. Index. New synoptic key by S. W. Frost. xxiv + 225pp. 5⅜ x 8. T223 Paperbound **$1.35**

BEHAVIOR AND SOCIAL LIFE OF THE HONEYBEE, Ronald Ribbands. Outstanding scientific study; a compendium of practically everything known about social life of the honeybee. Stresses behavior of individual bees in field, hive. Extends Frisch's experiments on communication among bees. Covers perception of temperature, gravity, distance, vibration; sound production; glands; structural differences; wax production; temperature regulation; recognition, communication; drifting, mating behavior, other highly interesting topics. Bibliography of 690 references. Indexes. 127 diagrams, graphs, sections of bee anatomy, fine photographs. 352pp. 5½ x 8½. S410 Clothbound **$4.50**

ANIMALS IN MOTION, Eadweard Muybridge. Largest, most comprehensive selection of Muybridge's famous action photos of animals, from his ANIMAL LOCOMOTION. 3919 high-speed shots of 34 different animals and birds in 123 different types of action: horses, mules, oxen, pigs, goats, camels, elephants, dogs, cats, guanacos, sloths, lions, tigers, jaguars, raccoons, baboons, deer, elk, gnus, kangaroos, many others, in different actions — walking, running, flying, leaping. Horse alone shown in more than 40 different ways. Photos taken against ruled backgrounds; most actions taken from 3 angles at once: 90°, 60°, rear. Most plates original size. Of considerable interest to scientists as a classic of biology, as a record of actual facts of natural history and physiology. "A really marvellous series of plates," NATURE (London). "A monumental work," Waldemar Kaempffert. Photographed by E. Muybridge. Edited by L. S. Brown, American Museum of Natural History. 74-page introduction on mechanics of motion. 340 pages of plates, 3919 photographs. 416pp. Deluxe binding, paper. (Weight 4½ lbs.) 7⅞ x 10⅝. T203 Clothbound **$10.00**

THE HUMAN FIGURE IN MOTION. Eadweard Muybridge. This new edition of a great classic in the history of science and photography is the largest selection ever made from the original Muybridge photos of human action: 4789 photographs, illustrating 163 types of motion: walking, running, lifting, etc. in time-exposure sequence photos of speeds up to 1/6000th of a second. Men, women, children, mostly undraped, showing bone and muscle positions against ruled backgrounds, mostly taken at 3 angles at once. Not only was this a great work of photography, acclaimed by contemporary critics as a work of genius, it was also a great 19th century landmark in biological research. Historical introduction by Prof. Robert Taft, U. of Kansas. Plates original size, full detail. Over 500 action strips. 407pp. 7¾ x 10⅝. Deluxe edition. T204 Clothbound **$10.00**

See also: **ANALYSIS OF SENSATIONS, E. Mach; ON THE SENSATIONS OF TONE, H. Helmholtz; FROM MAGIC TO SCIENCE, C. Singer; A SHORT HISTORY OF ANATOMY AND PHYSIOLOGY FROM THE GREEKS TO HARVEY, C. Singer; ELEMENTARY STATISTICS, WITH APPLICATIONS IN MEDICINE AND THE BIOLOGICAL SCIENCES, F. E. Croxton.**

MEDICINE

CLASSICS OF CARDIOLOGY, F. A. Willius and T. E. Keys. Monumental collection of 52 papers by 51 great researchers and physicians on the anatomy, physiology, and pathology of the heart and the circulation, and the diagnosis and therapy of their diseases. These are the original writings of Harvey, Sénac, Auenbrugger, Withering, Stokes, Einthoven, Osler, and 44 others from 1628 to 1912. 27 of the papers are complete, the rest in major excerpts; all are in English. The biographical notes and introductory essays make this a full history of cardiology —with exclusively first-hand material. 103 portraits, diagrams, and facsimiles of title pages. Chronological table. Total of xx + 858pp. 5⅝ x 8⅜. Two volume set.
T912 Vol I Paperbound **$2.00**
T913 Vol II Paperbound **$2.00**
The set **$4.00**

SOURCE BOOK OF MEDICAL HISTORY, compiled, annotated by Logan Clendening, M.D. Unequalled collection of 139 greatest papers in medical history, by 120 authors, covers almost every area: pathology, asepsis, preventive medicine, bacteriology, physiology, etc. Hippocrates, Gain, Vesalius, Malpighi, Morgagni, Boerhave, Pasteur, Walter Reed, Florence Nightingale, Lavoisier, Claude Bernard, 109 others, give view of medicine unequalled for immediacy. Careful selections give heart of each paper. save you reading time. Selections from non-medical literature show lay-views of medicine: Aristophanes, Plato, Arabian Nights, Chaucer, Molière, Dickens, Thackeray, others. "Notable . . . useful to teacher and student alike," Amer. Historical Review. Bibliography. Index. 699pp. 5⅜ x 8. T621 Paperbound **$2.75**

CLASSICS OF MEDICINE AND SURGERY, edited by C. N. B. Camac. 12 greatest papers in medical history, 11 in full: Lister's "Antiseptic Principle;" Harvey's "Motion in the Heart and Blood;" Auenbrugger's "Percussion of the Chest;" Laënnec's "Auscultation and the Stethoscope;" Jenner's "Inquiry into Smallpox Vaccine," 2 related papers; Morton's "Administering Sulphuric Ether," letters to Warren, "Physiology of Ether;" Simpson's "A New Anaesthetic Agent;" Holmes' "Puerperal Fever." Biographies, portraits of authors, bibliographies. Formerly "Epoch-making Contributions to Medicine, Surgery, and the Allied Sciences." Introduction. 14 illus. 445pp. 5⅜ x 8. S539 Paperbound **$2.25**

FREE! All you do is ask for it!

A WAY OF LIFE, Sir William Osler. The complete essay, stating his philosophy of life, as given at Yale University by this great physician and teacher. 30 pages. Copies limited, no more than 1 to a customer.

EXPERIMENTS AND OBSERVATIONS ON THE GASTRIC JUICE AND THE PHYSIOLOGY OF DIGESTION, William Beaumont. A gunshot wound which left a man with a 2½ inch hole through his abdomen into his stomach (1822) enabled Beaumont to perform the remarkable experiments set down here. The first comprehensive, thorough study of motions and processes of the stomach, "his work remains a model of patient, persevering investigation. . . . Beaumont is the pioneer physiologist of this country." (Sir William Osler, in his introduction.) 4 illustrations. xi + 280pp. 5⅜ x 8. S527 Paperbound **$1.50**

AN INTRODUCTION TO THE STUDY OF EXPERIMENTAL MEDICINE, Claude Bernard. 90-year-old classic of medical science, only major work of Bernard available in English, records his efforts to transform physiology into exact science. Principles of scientific research illustrated by specific case histories from his work; roles of chance, error, preliminary false conclusions, in leading eventually to scientific truth; use of hypothesis. Much of modern application of mathematics to biology rests on the foundation set down here. New foreword by Professor I. B. Cohen, Harvard Univ. xxv + 266pp. 5⅜ x 8. T400 Paperbound **$1.50**

A WAY OF LIFE, AND OTHER SELECTED WRITINGS, Sir William Osler, Physician and humanist, Osler discourses brilliantly in thought provoking essays and on the history of medicine. He discusses Thomas Browne, Gui Patin, Robert Burton, Michael Servetus, William Beaumont, Laënnec. Includes such favorite writings as the title essay, "The Old Humanities and the New Science," "Creators, Transmitters, and Transmuters," "Books and Men," "The Student Life," and five more of his best discussions of philosophy, religion and literature. 5 photographs. Introduction by G. L. Keynes, M.D., F.R.C.S. Index. xx + 278pp. 5⅜ x 8. T488 Paperbound **$1.50**

LANGUAGE AND TRAVEL AIDS FOR SCIENTISTS

Trubner foreign language manuals

These unusual books are members of the famous Trubner series of colloquial manuals. They have been written to provide adults with a sound colloquial knowledge of a foreign language, and are suited for either class use or self-study. Each book is a complete course in itself, with progressive, easy to follow lessons. Phonetics, grammar, and syntax are covered, while hundreds of phrases and idioms, reading texts, exercises, and vocabulary are included. These books are unusual in being neither skimpy nor overdetailed in grammatical matters, and in presenting up-to-date, colloquial, and practical phrase material. Bilingual presentation is stressed, to make thorough self-study easier for the reader.

COLLOQUIAL HINDUSTANI, A. H. Harley, formerly Nizam's Reader in Urdu, U. of London. 30 pages on phonetics and scripts (devanagari & Arabic-Persian) are followed by 29 lessons, including material on English and Arabic-Persian influences. Key to all exercises. Vocabulary. 5 x 7½. 147pp. Clothbound **$1.75**

COLLOQUIAL GERMAN, P. F. Doring. Intensive thorough coverage of grammar in easily-followed form. Excellent for brush-up, with hundreds of colloquial phrases. 34 pages of bilingual texts. 224pp. 5 x 7½. Clothbound **$1.75**

COLLOQUIAL ARABIC. DeLacy O'Leary. Foremost Islamic scholar covers language of Egypt, Syria, Palestine, & Northern Arabia. Extremely clear coverage of complex Arabic verbs & noun plurals; also cultural aspects of language. Vocabulary. xviii + 192pp. 5 x 7½.
Clothbound **$1.75**

COLLOQUIAL PERSIAN, L. P. Elwell-Sutton. Best introduction to modern Persian, with 90 page grammatical section followed by conversations, 35 page vocabulary. 139pp. Clothbound **$1.75**

COLLOQUIAL SPANISH, W. R. Patterson. Castilian grammar and colloquial language, loaded with bilingual phrases and colloquialisms. Excellent for review or self-study. 164pp. 5 x 7½.
Clothbound **$1.75**

COLLOQUIAL RUMANIAN, G. Nandris, Professor of University of London. Extremely thorough coverage of phonetics, grammar, syntax; also included 70 page reader, and 70 page vocabulary. Probably the best grammar for this increasingly important language. 340pp. 5 x 7½.
Clothbound **$2.50**

COLLOQUIAL FRENCH, W. R. Patterson. 16th revised edition of this extremely popular manual. Grammar explained with model clarity, and hundreds of useful expressions and phrases; exercises, reading texts, etc. Appendixes of new useful words and phrases. 223pp. 5 x 7½.
Clothbound **$1.75**

COLLOQUIAL CZECH, J. Schwarz, former headmaster of Lingua Institute, Prague. Full easily followed coverage of grammar, hundreds of immediately useable phrases, texts. Perhaps the best Czech grammar in print. "An absolutely successful textbook," JOURNAL OF CZECHO-SLOVAK FORCES IN GREAT BRITAIN. 252pp. 5 x 7½. Clothbound **$3.00**

COLLOQUIAL ITALIAN, A. L. Hayward. Excellent self-study course in grammar, vocabulary, idioms, and reading. Easy progressive lessons will give a good working knowledge of Italian in the shortest possible time. 5 x 7½.
Clothbound **$1.75**

AN ENGLISH-FRENCH-GERMAN-SPANISH WORD FREQUENCY DICTIONARY, H. S. Eaton. An indispensable language study aid, this is a semantic frequency list of the 6000 most frequently used words in 4 languages—24,000 words in all. The lists, based on concepts rather than words alone, and containing all modern, exact, and idomatic vocabulary, are arranged side by side to form a unique 4-language dictionary. A simple key indicates the importance of the individual words within each language. Over 200 pages of separate indexes for each language enable you to locate individual words at a glance. Formerly "Semantic Frequency List." 2 Appendixes. xxi + 441pp. 6 x 9. T738 Paperbound **$2.45**

NEW RUSSIAN-ENGLISH AND ENGLISH-RUSSIAN DICTIONARY, M. A. O'Brien. Unusually comprehensive guide to reading, speaking, writing of Russian for both advanced and beginning students. Over 70,000 entries provided in new orthography, with full information on accentuation, grammatical classification. Shades of meaning, idiomatic uses, colloquialisms; tables of irregular verbs for both languages. Individual entries indicate stems, transitiveness, perfective and imperfective aspects, conjugation, regular and irregular sound changes, shift of accent, etc. Includes pronunciation instruction. Used at Harvard, Yale, Cornell, etc. 738pp. 4¼ x 6½. T208 Paperbound **$2.00**

PHRASE AND SENTENCE DICTIONARY OF SPOKEN RUSSIAN. English-Russian, Russian-English. Based on phrases and complete sentences, rather than isolated words; recognized as one of the best methods of learning the idiomatic speech of a country. Over 11,500 entries, indexed by single words, with more than 32,000 English and Russian sentences and phrases, in immediately useable form. Probably the largest list ever published. Shows accent changes in conjugation and declension; irregular forms listed in both alphabetical place and under main form of word. 15,000 word introduction covering Russian sounds, writing, grammer, syntax. 15 page appendix of geographical names, money, important signs, given names, foods, special Soviet terms, etc. Travellers, businessmen, students, government employees have found this their best source for Russian expressions. Originally published as U.S. Government Technical Manual TM 30-944. iv + 573pp. 5⅝ x 8⅜. T496 Paperbound **$2.75**

PHRASE AND SENTENCE DICTIONARY OF SPOKEN SPANISH, Spanish-English, English-Spanish. Compiled from spoken Spanish, emphasizing idiom and colloquial usage in both Castilian and Latin-American. More than 16,000 entries containing over 25,000 idioms—the largest list of idiomatic constructions ever published. Complete sentences given, indexed under single words—language in immediately useable form, for travellers, businessmen, students, etc. 25 page introduction provides rapid survey of sounds, grammar, syntax, with full consideration of irregular verbs. Especially apt in modern treatment of phrases and structure. 17 page glossary gives translations of geographical names, money values, numbers, national holidays, important street signs, useful expressions of high frequency, plus unique 7 page glossary of Spanish and Spanish-American foods and dishes. Originally published as U.S. Government Technical Manual TM 30-900. iv + 513pp. 5⅜ x 8. T495 Paperbound **$1.75**

MONEY CONVERTER AND TIPPING GUIDE FOR EUROPEAN TRAVEL, Charles Vomacka. A convenient purse-size handbook crammed with information about currency regulations and tipping for every European country. Newly added sections cover Israel, Turkey, Czechoslovakia, Rumania, Egypt, Russia, Poland. Telephone, cablegram, postal rates; duty-free imports, passports, visas, health certificates; foreign clothing sizes; weather tables. What and when to tip in every conceivable travel situation. 6th year of publication. 128pp. 5½ x 5¼. Sturdy paper binding.
T260 Paperbound **60¢**